BTEC Nationals

COMPUTING

Geoffrey Knott BA, AIB, Cert Ed
Nick Waites BSc, MSc, Cert Ed

Brancepeth Computer Publications

2000

©Geoffrey Knott and Nick Waites 2000

ISBN 0-9538848-1-3

Cover Design by Nick Waites
Graphical illustrations by Nick Waites and Geoffrey Knott
Production and Editing by Geoffrey Knott

Published in Great Britain by

Brancepeth Computer Publications Limited
Brancepeth Castle
Durham
DH7 8DF

Tel: 0191 378 3363
Fax: 0191 378 2972
E-mail: enquiries@bcpublications.co.uk
Web site: www.bcpublications.co.uk

British Cataloguing-in-Publications Data

A catalogue record for this book is available from the British Library

Printed in Great Britain by Athenaeum Press, Gateshead

Foreword by Douglas Kay

Qualification Leader for ICT, Edexcel Foundation

Before joining Edexcel I taught and managed IT and Computing courses in FE for 10 years, and in that capacity I became very familiar with the work of Geoffrey Knott and Nick Waites. I used their book, Computer Studies for BTEC, as my course text during that time, and now, in my capacity as Edexcel's developer of IT and Computing qualifications, I am delighted to be able to write this foreword to their latest publication. The authors' first textbook, "Computer Studies for BTEC" was published in 1987 and was followed by three further editions, the 4th in 1998. During that period it became the favoured text for the course of that title and this book is a worthy successor.

During their 14 year writing partnership, Geoffrey Knott and Nick Waites have concentrated on producing Computing and ICT texts for courses which formed the basis of their combined 45 years of teaching experience. It is difficult for one author to adequately cover all the subject matter involved in Computing and ICT courses and it is a major strength of their writing partnership that each author brings to it complementary skills, knowledge and experience.

If you are a student studying for one of the BTEC National qualifications in Computing you will find that this book comprehensively covers Edexcel's requirements for a course text. If, on the other hand, you are a lecturer teaching on one of the BTEC Nationals in Computing courses, you can with confidence recommend this book to your students.

Edexcel does not lightly give their endorsement to textbooks for their courses, but we had no hesitation in doing so for this excellent publication. I am sure that you will be as delighted with it as we are.

To Carolyn and Anne with love

The Authors

Geoffrey Knott and Nick Waites have long experience in Computing and IT education and have been producing highly successful course text books for well over a decade. They are authors of Computer Studies, AS/A2 Information and Communication Technology, Advanced VCE Information and Communication Technology, GNVQ Advanced Information Technology, GNVQ Intermediate Information Technology, Information Processing, Computing, Small Business Computer Systems, Information Technology Skills - A Student Guide, GCSE Information Systems and co-authors of Business GNVQ Advanced and Core Skills for GNVQ.

Other publications by the same authors:

Published by Brancepeth Computer Publications Ltd (Tel 0191 3783363):

Books

- ❑ Advanced VCE Information and Communication Technology ISBN 0-9538848-0-5

Internet

- ❑ ICT Resource Bank. This electronic resource comprises a large database of detailed information and other support materials on ICT, accessible by password through our Web site, plus printable Course Support Booklets (provided on CD-ROM). The ICT Resource Bank is available to institutions for an annual subscription.

For more information on all of these publications visit the BCP website at

www.bcpublications.co.uk

e-mail:

enquiries@bcpublications.co.uk

Published by Business Education Publishers Ltd (Tel 0191 5252400) :

Books

- ❑ GCE AS/A2 Information and Communications Technology
- ❑ Computing (A level)
- ❑ Information Processing
- ❑ GCSE Information Systems

Contents

Unit 1

Language and communications

Unit 2

Computational methods

Unit 3

Computer systems

Unit 4

Introduction to software development

Unit 5

Business information systems

Unit 6

Communications technology

Unit 1

Language and communications

Chapters

- 📖 1. Written and graphical communication
- 📖 2. Oral communication
- 📖 3. Study skills

Unit 1 Outcomes and assessment criteria

Outcomes	Assessment criteria
	To achieve each outcome a student must demonstrate the ability to:
1. Take part in **discussions**.	• make contributions that are relevant to the subject and purpose • make contributions that are suited to the situation and audience • make contributions to help the discussion progress • generate ways for others to become involved.
2. Produce **written** and **graphical material** to meet a range of end user needs.	• select and use a appropriate form and style of writing that is appropriate • organise information which is accurate and relevant to the subject • ensure the text is legible, the meaning is clear and spelling, grammar and punctuation are accurate.
3. Make a **presentation**.	• prepare a presentation to suit a given purpose • match language and style to suit the subject, formality of the situation and the needs of the audience • use techniques to interest audience including images and varying visual aids.
4. Respond to **written** materials.	• select and read materials for specific information • use appropriate reference material to help clarify the understanding of a subject • extract information and summarise it, compare accounts and recognise opinion and or possible bias.
5. Undertake and evaluate **relevant research**.	• prepare a plan to collect information • identify and collect the information • present and evaluate the information.

Chapter1

Written and graphical communication

When you are preparing a document, you need to keep in mind:

- ☐ its purpose. What is the document meant to communicate?
- ☐ the reader. Who is meant to read and understand its contents?

To ensure that the documents you produce are readable, you will need to:

- ☐ pay careful attention to spelling;
- ☐ ensure that your sentences convey the meanings you intend;
- ☐ use a language style which is appropriate to the subject and the reader;
- ☐ use document layouts which present the information clearly and effectively.

To produce an effective document, you must have a clear understanding of the information you are trying to communicate and be familiar with the requirements of your readers. For example, this text book would be unlikely to be useful to you if we, the authors, had little knowledge of our subject, or the contents of the BTEC Nationals course.

Spelling, grammar and meaning

Careful attention to spelling and good use of grammar are also important for clear communication. For example, you can probably work out the intended meaning of "The hows is neer the toun horl", but you can't be absolutely sure.

The aim of grammar is to ensure that the words of a sentence are arranged to convey a single meaning. Apart from giving a very bad impression to the reader, poor use of grammar can obscure meaning or convey a completely different, and unintended, message. Consider the following note provided by a parent to explain his child's absence from school.

"Albert has to stay at home today because he has diarrhoea through some bad fish."

We know what he means, but the sentence construction gives a completely different and peculiar message. A clearer explanation might have been: "As a result of eating some bad fish, Albert has diarrhoea and is unable to attend school." For a business, such careless use of language in communications with customers not only damages its image of professionalism, but may also result in serious financial loss or contractual misunderstanding. Consider the following statements made by the Sales Manager of Global Supplies Limited to a customer.

"The goods we sold to you were supplied by Acme Systems. We believe that the goods are a disgrace to the company and that you should be able to sue for damages."

The Sales Manager intends to say that the goods are a disgrace to Acme Systems and that the customer should be able to sue that company for damages. However, the statements could suggest an admission that the poor quality goods disgrace Global Supplies and that they are prepared to be sued.

Writing style

This book is written in a style which makes the content easier to read, that is, one with relatively short sentences and a friendly tone. We also avoid the unnecessary use of 'difficult' vocabulary and provide numerous examples to illustrate ideas. On the other hand, the book has a serious purpose and an over-friendly, perhaps 'jokey' style, would simply be patronising and sometimes less common vocabulary can be used to express ideas more briefly. For example, the words "intercede" or "mediate"can be used instead of the phrase "to plead in favour of". As a general rule don't use 'big' words simply to impress, especially if you are not sure what they mean. The Thesaurus tool (see later) in a word processor will suggest alternative vocabulary and you should use it with extreme care.

Some documents are not trying to communicate ideas or concepts and require simple statements of fact, without explanation. For example, the Table of Contents in this book simply lists chapter titles and main headings, together with the relevant page numbers. Similarly, you would expect notice of an important staff meeting to briefly identify basic information, such as the subject of the meeting, for example, 'New car parking arrangements', its location, date and time. However, a notice advertising a newly released film would include slogans such as, "A real weepy", or "You'll never sleep again.", to encourage people to go and see it.

Personal writing style

A memorandum example

Although writing is a skill and rules of grammar and spelling are vitally important, it is also a highly creative process and if practised sufficiently can be as clear a part of your personality as the way you speak. Those who need to use sign language can bring their own personalities to they way in which they use their hands and facial expressions to express simple or complex information, feelings and emotions. Admittedly, some documents such as invoices do not call for personal style, but most do. Even a brief memorandum asking people to attend a meeting can aggravate, annoy, or cause resentment if it is badly phrased.

Consider the following contrasting examples and judge what your response might be to each.

Memorandum

To: All Accounts staff

From: Mrs. V. Uptight, Accounts Department Manager

Subject: Upgrade of accounting software   **Date:** 14 June 2000

There will be a meeting at 5.30 p.m. tomorrow and all Accounts staff must attend. There is a lot to discuss and the meeting will take around two hours. Come and see me if you feel that you have an excuse for not attending.

<u>**Memorandum**</u>

To: All Accounts staff

From: Iris Pectu, Accounts Department Manager

Subject: Meeting 5.30 p.m. 15 June - Upgrade of accounting software   **Date:** 14 June 2000

I realise that this meeting is being called at very short notice, but the delay in the delivery of the software means that we have even less time than planned to complete the change to the new system. To ensure that the changeover to the new accounting software runs smoothly and does not disrupt services to our customers (and the vitally important task of receiving their invoice payments!), we need to discuss a number of different operating procedures. I cannot over-emphasise the importance of this meeting, so if you think that you may be unable to attend, please talk to me today and we will try to get the information to you some other way.

Unfortunately, the meeting is likely to take around 2 hours so I have arranged for sandwiches and coffee to keep us going.

Neither memo is likely to be welcome, but the first is abrupt, inconsiderate and does not even explain why the meeting is so important. It suggests little 'team spirit' and the dictatorial style of the memo probably reflects the Head of Department's management style. The memo would almost certainly cause resentment and if its tone is typical will not ensure that the operational changes to the accounting system go smoothly. The second memo appeals to the loyalty of staff and makes a real effort to explain the reasons for the meeting and the short notice given. The last two sentences demonstrate a care for the staff as individuals and a willingness to treat them as colleagues. Although the memos say a great deal about contrasting management styles, which is not relevant here, personal writing style is difficult to force and will, as with other forms of communication, reflect your own personality. Mrs. V Uptight would probably have great difficulty in writing the second memo.

Of course, you need to apply your personal style appropriately, to a number of different documents types and target readers. The following section provides examples of formal and informal styles for a range of document types.

Choosing a style and form of presentation

Although presentational techniques such as page layout and font styles are dealt with later in this chapter the following examples illustrate the use of style and presentation to meet different communication needs, such as attracting attention, writing to impress and gathering information through questionnaires.

Attracting attention in advertisements

Example 1: Hair care products

Study the two example advertisements in Figures 1.1 and 1.2. They are for similar types of product but each is aimed at a very different audience. To be effective, advertisements must capture your attention, but the methods used will depend largely on the age, lifestyle and personal values of their intended readers.

The advertisement for RIGID hair gel in Figure 1.1 is short and to the point, and uses a 'no-nonsense' writing style designed to emphasise the gel's ability to keep your hair in one place. The opening question "Used to being in control?" is not a complete sentence, but is perfectly acceptable in the context of a 'punchy' advertisement. This question form of headline is often used in advertisements because it is an effective way of grabbing your attention. Simple phrases are often used in newspaper headlines, such as "Man bites dog" - put in this way it could be open to misinterpretation. (Does the man bite the dog repeatedly?) The sentence "Yesterday, a man bit a dog." would be clearer but would lack

"Used to being in control?"

Now you can control your hair with **RIGID**, the high-performance gel from the Macho hair care range.

Call 0845 11110000 for more information and a free 5ml sample

Figure 1.1

the same impact. Further impact in the RIGID advertisement is achieved both with the graphic of the 'lantern-jawed' man, to highlight the 'strength' element and the bold and stark (*sans-serif*) font used for the word 'RIGID'. A sans-serif font lacks the short strokes at the ends of individual letters; the Arial font is of this type. The body text in this book is Times New Roman, which is a *serif* font.

The advertisement in Figure 1.2 for shampoo also uses a graphical image and capitalises the font to highlight the name of the product. However, the font is serif, in italics and is not in bold type, which is suited to the gentle tone of the message. Considerable detail is given about the product, and its highlighted (by underscoring) benefits for the environment are obviously aimed at a particular category of reader.

The advertisement uses well constructed and flowing sentences which assume the information is important to

Natura Hair www.naturahair.co.uk

We understand that you care about your health and the environment, so we developed a shampoo that protects the environment and looks after your hair, NATURALLY.

INDULGENTE

only uses natural products which are not harmful to the environment. Indulgente is kind to your hair and washes without destroying the natural oils that give your hair vitality.

Call our hair consultancy team on **0345 888999** for more information on how you can look after your hair and care for our planet. 2% of our profits go to the Global Nature Foundation www.globalnature.org.

Figure 1.2

the reader in deciding whether or not to buy the shampoo. The reader's attention is probably drawn by the image and the word 'Natura' in the company's name. The Italian word 'Indulgente' hints at a slightly luxurious element in the product, despite its ecological soundness.

Neither of these advertisements require technical or other detail, but some products, such as computers and financial services cannot be sold by simple slogans. Before making a purchase, potential buyers will want to know, for example, the capabilities, features and quality of the product being advertised. The next examples illustrate this point.

Example 2: Advertisements for computers and financial services

The first advertisement in Figure 1.3 gives the precise technical information which is needed to make an informed choice.

Writing style is of minimal importance as the information comprises a simple list of technical features. To attract attention to what would otherwise be a fairly boring image of a computer system, it uses a jet aircraft which helps to reinforce the impression of speed and perhaps, rather less credibly, the real-life quality of the graphics. The price is enclosed in an exploding star to indicate that the system is a real bargain. No time is spent on explanation, partly because it would require considerable space to do so for every technical feature and the seller is assuming that most readers of this particular advert will be familiar with the terminology.

Figure 1.3

Financial services legislation requires that certain information, such as the interest rate (using a standard method of calculation called the APR), must be included in advertisements for loan facilities. Advertisements for investments are also heavily controlled concerning the claims which can be made on the projected value of an investment, say, after 10 years. Figure 1.4 shows some typical features of an investment advertisement. The style is more restrained, friendly but not over-familiar and emphasises security with a castle logo and a family picture. The amount of £9,365 in large, bold type is clearly designed to attract attention. The asterisk next to the amount is very important as it points to the fact that it relates to a past investment, which is no guarantee of what would be received in 5 years if the same amount were again invested. Apart from the statement, invariably in very small print, at the bottom of the advertisement, financial services legislation requires numerous other statements which qualify what is claimed in the main text.

Safe as Houses

How secure is your future?

If you are aged between 23 and 65 and have £2500 or more to invest for 5 years you could gain rich rewards with a Safe As Houses Investment Bond.

If you had invested £5,000 in 1995, it would now be worth

£9,365*

Contact us on 0800 11 00 22 for further information.

* Past performance is not a guarantee of future returns, as these depend on bonuses yet to be earned.

Figure 1.4

Summarising information

Summarising refers to the process of preparing a shorter or condensed version of a body of information. To summarise information effectively, you must:

- ❑ thoroughly understand the information;

- ❑ select the main themes and major facts. You must not add to the content or alter any factual content;

- ❑ write the summary clearly and concisely (which is the whole point of a summary). The summary should 'flow' and read as a whole, not as a collection of disconnected sentences. A wide vocabulary will obviously help.

Minutes

Summarising is an important skill in many aspects of work. For example, the discussions at a formal meeting are recorded in the *minutes*, which then have to be agreed at the next meeting as a true record of what took place. Some minutes are referred to as Action Minutes and detail tasks to be completed and the names of the persons responsible for carrying them out, so it is important that minutes are accurately recorded and corrected if found to be in error. Consider the problems that may be caused if Mr. X was incorrectly quoted as admitting that he had failed to contact an important customer and lost valuable business as a result. The problem would be worse if he was not at the next meeting to put matters right. Minute taking is not an easy skill, especially if the meeting is not well managed and several people try to speak at the same time. The minutes secretary must be able to distinguish the important from the unimportant and learn to ignore flippant, indiscrete or irrelevant comments which are clearly not meant to be recorded. An example minutes document is given below (it relates to the Parish Council Agenda in the next section).

AMBRIDGE PARISH COUNCIL

MINUTES

OF THE MEETING of the PARISH COUNCIL held on MONDAY 19 JUNE 2000 at 7.30 p.m.

PRESENT	Councillors Smith, Brown, Ginelli, Jones (in the Chair), Patel and Kenelly.
	An apology for absence was received from Cllr Redman.
MINUTES	The Minutes of the meeting held on 19 May were agreed.
FINANCE	Agreed payment of fees to Cullen and Brown, solicitors of £1,654.50 for work done on Compulsory Purchase Order and £356 to Borchester County Council for installation of new lamp in Main Street.
PLANNING APPLICATIONS	Agreed no objection to extension at 13 Hayseed Cottages and that Cllr Patel look into the matter of the outhouse which has been constructed at the rear of Buttercup Way. It appears that planning permission has not been sought.
CORRESPONDENCE	Noted County Council report on government housing needs and the County Structure Plan. To be viewed by all members before next meeting.
TRAFFIC AND SAFETY	A365 - Cllr Ginelli had written to Inspector Plumridge concerning the increased traffic hazard and the danger to local residents. He will also write to the County Council arguing our case for a 30mph speed limit through Ambridge
AOB	None
NEXT MEETING	18 July 2000

At each meeting, the second item on the Agenda refers to the minutes of the previous meeting. Examples of other occasions when information needs to be summarised are given below.

❑   A member of staff attends a one-day conference on new VAT regulations and then has to pass on what he or she learned to the Financial Director.

❑   After numerous complaints to sales staff about the non-delivery of an order, a customer rings the Sales Manager, who then asks the Sales supervisor for a summary of the events since the first complaint was made.

Giving notice and details of meetings

Agendas

The quality and effectiveness of a meeting tends to be improved if the chairperson takes proper control and prevents members from speaking over one another. The meeting is also likely to be more productive if all members have proper notice of what is to be discussed and this is done through the agenda. If there are reports to be considered, these should be submitted for distribution to members before the meeting, rather than 'tabled'(presented at the meeting itself); this enables members to read them in advance and so, hopefully, be more able to make informed comment at the meeting. An example agenda follows.

AMBRIDGE PARISH COUNCIL

A MEETING of the **PARISH COUNCIL** will be held in the Village Hall, Ambridge on **MONDAY 26 JUNE 2000** at **7.30 p.m**

AGENDA

1. Apologies for absence.
2. Minutes of the meeting held on 19 May 2000 (copy attached).
3. Matters arising.
4. Finance.
5. Planning applications.
6. Correspondence.
7. Traffic and safety reports.
8. Any other business.
9. Date of next meeting.

Albert Benbow, Clerk to the Parish Council,   18 June 2000

Item 2, 'Minutes of the last meeting ...', is the point at which members must agree that the minutes are an accurate record or what was discussed and agreed at the last meeting. If there are any corrections, these are made and the Chairperson signs them as a correct record. Item 3, 'Matters Arising' relates to the discussion of items in the meetings of the last meeting which may need further discussion.

Public meeting notices

The above agenda includes the notice details of the meeting, but for public meetings it is impractical to issue agendas and there is often only one topic. The format of such notices is largely up to the producer, but it must include all information that people need in order to attend, that is the location, date and time. For people travelling some distance, directions will also be valuable. Obviously, the subject of the event or meeting is crucial.

Writing to impress

When applying for a job or a place at university, for example, your letter of application and *curriculum vitae* (CV) are usually the only means by which the employers or admissions tutors can initially judge your suitability for selection. If you fail to impress at this stage, you may well not be asked to proceed to the next stage of application, which is normally an interview. If this happened, you might say to yourself, "If only they had had the chance to meet me and talk to me, they would have seen that I was perfect for the job/course." Letters of application and cv's, even interviews, are very imperfect tools for selecting people, but for most organisations they are often the only practical way of doing so. As with most things, practice will improve your letter writing skills.

Preparing a cv is a little more straightforward, as the contents and layout are fairly standard, but you will need to think very carefully about the content. It is likely that you will have to modify your cv, not only as your experience, achievements and qualifications increase, but also to suit the requirements of different applications. If you are applying for a post as a sports club trainer, you would emphasise your athletic achievements, whereas an application for a position as a computer technician would tend to place these achievements in the 'Outside interests/activities' section of the cv.

A curriculum vitae (CV)

A CV is a brief account of a person's career and personal development. It normally accompanies letters of job application, but the content may need to be incorporated in a special application form, if one is provided for the purpose. A CV is also useful in support of a general letter of enquiry about job availability in a particular organisation. A typical CV is likely to include the following:

1. personal details;

2. education;

3. qualifications;

4. work experience;

5. interests, hobbies;

6. supplementary information.

Here is an example of a CV.

Curriculum Vitae

Name: Shahin Hussain

Age: 19   Date of Birth:18.4.81
Marital Status: Single
Nationality: British
Home Address: 12 Neville View, Ambridge, BC1 4LS
Telephone Number: 0141 654321
E-mail: shahin@talk21.com

Education

1992 - 1997　　Wood Lane Comprehensive School, Felpersham. Captain of
school cricket team 1996-1997

1997 - 1999　　Borchester College of Further Education, Felpersham.
Secretary of Students Union Management Committee and
member of Borchester College Soccer Team.

Qualifications

1997	GCSE Information Technology Grade A *
	GCSE English Grade B
	GCSE Mathematics Grade B
	GCSE History Grade C
	GCSE Art Grade C
	GCSE Geography Grade D
	(All with Welsh Joint Education Committee)

1998   Royal College of Music Piano Grade 7

1999   GNVQ Advanced Information Technology (Pass with Merit):

Information Technology Systems; Systems Analysis; Using Information Technology; Software; Organisations and Information Technology; Database Development; Communications and Networking; Information Technology Projects and Teamwork; Programming; Multimedia Systems.

Work Experience

1998   Work experience placement for 4 weeks as part of college course, with Kitchen Systems Ltd, Ambridge Road, Borchester, involved in IT support work in IT Services Department.

1999   Work experience placement for 5 weeks as part of college course, with National Farmers Union, Felpersham Road, Borchester, involved in database development work in Farming Services Department.

1999- to date   Assistant Network Engineer with Kitchen Systems Ltd, Ambridge Road, Borchester. (Present salary £9,800 p.a.)

Interests

I have a keen interest in all outdoor sports, particularly cricket. I am captain of the Ambridge Cricket Club's first team which plays in the Borchester League. I also play the piano for my own pleasure.

General Information

Career opportunities with my present employer are limited and I am seeking to develop my career in network engineering. I am taking a 1 week course next month (as part of my holiday entitlement) on a Novell Network Engineering course on 4 July 2000.
I have to give 2 weeks notice to terminate my present job.

Referees

The following persons will act as referees:

Mr Roger Pearson, Human Resources Manager, National Farmers Union, Felpersham Road, Borchester, Tel: 0141 364789

Mrs Anne McDonald, Course Leader, Advanced VCE in ICT, Borchester College of Further Education, Felpersham, Tel: 0141 349821

Letters of application

Such letters are essentially formal, although as explained earlier, provided that your personal writing style makes a positive contribution to the tone of the letter, then let it come through. However, although e-mail communication is leading to greater informality in communication, it has to be assumed that the recipient of a job application expects to see a formal letter.

The first example, given below, is properly constructed, presented and written in an appropriate style. (The numbering is simply to cross reference with the comments which follow the letter.)

Shahin's letter contains the following points:

(i)   The name, status and address of the recipient.

(ii)   The company reference, to enable the recipient to identify the matter to which the letter relates.

(iii)   The salutation. If the name of the recipient is not known, you would have to use 'Dear Sir/Madam and use the close 'Yours faithfully'. It is now usual to use the slightly less formal, 'Yours sincerely' when addressing people by name. There may be circumstances, however, when you judge it safer to use 'Yours faithfully'.

(iv)   A formal application statement to identify the post and where he heard about it.

(v)   Reference to any enclosures, in this case his CV.

(vi)   A brief account of his educational qualifications and work experience, even though this information is provided in more detail in the CV. Although the CV is important, the letter will be read first and should make sufficient impact to encourage further consideration of your application. The statement of confidence, provided it is justified, will help to do this.

(vii)   A closing paragraph which indicates a willingness to attend for interview and thereby a keen desire to be considered for the post..

---

12 Neville View
Ambridge
Borchester
BC1 4LS

28 June 2000

(i)   Mrs. M. Marconi
Human Resources Manager
Ambridge Bathrooms Ltd
32-34 Downham Road
Felpersham
Borchester, BC2 3LD

(ii)   Your ref: MM/NE1

(iii)   Dear Mrs Marconi,

(iv)   I wish to apply for the post of Assistant Network Administrator which was recently advertised in the Borchester Chronicle.

(v)   I have enclosed my curriculum vitae in support of my application.

(vi)   My present post is Network Support Technician at Kitchen Systems Ltd in Felpersham, where I have worked since completing my GNVQ Advanced Information Technology course at Borchester College in June 1999. I believe that my experience and the further qualification I hope to gain next month as a Novell Accredited Network Administrator would enable me to take on the duties you require with confidence and skill. Your advertisement indicates that you use the Novell network operating system, which is also that used by Kitchen Systems Ltd.

(vii)   I have to give two weeks notice to terminate my present job and can arrange to be available for interview at any time convenient to you.

Yours sincerely,

Shahin Hussain

Contrast the previous letter with following application for a Web Designer position.

---

12 Neville View
Ambridge
Borchester

Dear Madam,

I saw the advert of the job about Web Design in the Borchester Chronicle and I think that I would be good at it. I done a course on computers and the Internet at college and really liked it. I am 19 now and got 5 GCSE at school. I nearly passed the course at college. I would have passed but the tutor had it in for me. I don't really like working with peeple, so I thought the a computer job would be ideal. If you want to contact me you can get me on my mobile (0788 478590), but my top-up card might run out soon. Better still by e-mail at rodgerthedodger@supermail.com. If you want you can look at my personal website on www.rogerspalace.super.net, but I am still working on it and some of the links don't work.

Yours sincerley,

Roger Hutchinson

As you will notice, there are a number of major flaws in the letter:

❑   The name and address and reference of the recipient are missing and the letter is undated.

❑   The job is not clearly identified. The company may be advertising for several staff to work in the area of Internet and Web support.

❑   Roger refers to his GCSE's, but does not provide grades. The information about the course is obviously not helpful and the statements concerning his relationships with people and the course tutor suggest that he would not be able to work as part of a team.

❑   The contact information is not likely to inspire confidence and the use of silly names for his e-mail and web site address are clearly inappropriate as illustrations of his work.

❑ There are spelling mistakes and grammatical errors and the style is more appropriate for an e-mail to his friends.

Gathering information through questionnaires

A questionnaire is used to conduct a survey on an area of interest or research. It is a means of gathering information, and it consists of a number of questions that are to be answered by a single person. Sometimes the questions are of a personal nature, to do with people's opinions on various things such as the quality of television programmes, or the effectiveness of the government; at other times a questionnaire is used to gather factual information on such things as what banks people use, how often they visit their bank and for what main purposes, or what household products they generally purchase. Sometimes questionnaires will be posted to individuals (the *respondents*) who will complete and return them within a certain time span; on other occasions a questionnaire will be used by an interviewer to ask individuals questions directly.

Questionnaire design

There are a number of distinct stages in designing a questionnaire:

1. Identify the population.

    The *population* is the type of person to which the survey applies. It could be small, such as the members of a football team, or it could be all the students in a certain college. If the population is large, then it will generally be necessary to reduce the number of people involved. The usual method of doing this is to take a sample, that is, a proportion of the population selected according to some scheme. There are many methods of sampling, some designed to allow statistical analysis to be performed, others for convenience. In fact, one of the simplest methods, if the results of the survey are intended to give only a rough idea about something, is called convenience sampling, in which, as the name suggests, the interviewer uses the questionnaire on any suitable person who happens to be available. It is definitely not a reliable method, but it has the advantage of being quick and easy to use.

2. Design the layout of the questionnaire. Things to think about here are:

    (i)   For interviewer administered questionnaires, using a front sheet to record the interviewer, the date and time, the length of the interview, and any other relevant information.

    (ii) A statement of the purpose of the survey.

    (iii) The number of questions. Too many will be both time consuming and tedious for the respondent as well as an interviewer.

    (iv) The order of the questions. Generally start with broad, easy to answer, impersonal questions before going on to less interesting questions and then sensitive, personal and open-ended questions.

3. Design the format for the answers. The following pages show some examples of different questions and answers.

Example 1

1. **Please indicate your opinion of the importance of being able to use the college's computers for word processing assignments:**

CIRCLE ONE	
No opinion	1
Not desirable	2
Fairly desirable	3
Very desirable	4

This limits responses to defined categories and, by assigning a different number to each response, makes it easier to analyse the final survey results. It is best to limit the number of categories in this type of question to between three to seven, because people often find it difficult to discriminate between the categories when there are too many.

Example 2

The following method may be used to filter out people to whom a question does not apply, to reduce the number of questions to be answered.

2. **Have you ever made use of the college's computers?**

RING	
Yes	1
No	2

If Yes: What types of software have you used?

Wordprocessor	3
Spreadsheet	4
Desktop publishing	5
Graphics	6
Other (specify)....................	7

Example 3

An alternative is to indicate which question to answer next, depending on the answer to the current question:

3. **Have you ever made use of the college's computers?**

RING ONE		
Yes	1	GO TO Q10
No	2	GO TO Q15

Example 4

Sometimes open-ended questions are appropriate:

4.   What do you most like about your course?

....

....

This type of question increases the amount of work required in the analysis phase of the survey because the answers must somehow be categorised and allocated a suitable code after the questionnaires have been administered. It is generally advisable to limit the number of this type of question and rely mainly on forced response questions like the other examples given earlier.

Example 5

Another possibility for responses is to provide a numeric scale to indicate how well or how badly something is rated:

5.   How relevant was the course you took to your current employment?

	Highly relevant				Irrelevant
CIRCLE ONE	1	2	3	4	5

The phrasing of the questions is very important. Here are a few things to avoid:

Double questions: Do you own a computer and do you use it just for playing games?

Vague questions: What do you think of the computer services section?

What sort of computers do you think the college should have?

Leading questions: Why did you enjoy your course so much?

Coding the questions

If a computer is to be used for analysing the completed questionnaires, it is important that each response to each question is given a unique code. This must be done at the design stage and incorporated into the questionnaire in order to reduce the amount of work required in the analysis stage of the survey. The code could simply be the question number followed by the response for a question. For instance, in Example 5, if the *Highly relevant box* (1) had been ringed, the code would simply be 51 representing question 5, response 1. Of course coding may not be necessary at all if the analysis of the questionnaires is to be done manually.

Questionnaire presentation

Apart from expressing questions clearly and unambiguously, the questionnaire needs to be clearly presented to encourage simple and accurate completion. Consider the medical questionnaire shown in Figure 1.5 and then compare it with the improved version in Figure 1.6. The layout in Figure 1.5 is cluttered and is likely to lead to mistakes in its completion, Notice particularly that the list at the bottom of the form leaves little room to circle individual items.

The form in Figure 1.6 is uncluttered, pleasing in appearance and the use of tick boxes should encourage accurate completion. Note also that some of the questions in Figure 1.5 are rather vague and have been re-phrased.

MEDICAL HISTORY

Name _____

_____   Age ____

Address

Tel. no. _____   Post code _____

Do you smoke? _____

If YES, about how many do you smoke per day? _____

Is there any history of heart disease in your family? _____

Is there any history of bronchial problems in your family? _____

Is there any history of diabetes in your family? _____

Please circle if you have had any of the following

Measles
Mumps
Chicken Pox
Scarlet fever
Shingles
Black Plague

Figure 1.5. *A poorly designed and presented questionnaire*

MEDICAL HISTORY

Please use BLOCK CAPITALS

SECTION 1 : Personal details

First name(s)   Last name

Mr/Mrs/Miss/Ms

Address   Date of Birth

/ /

Tel. no.

SECTION 2 : Current health

Do you smoke cigarettes?   Do any of your parents or
                          Tick   grandparents have any of
                                  the following?
                     NO   Tick
         less than 10 per day   Heart problems
            10-20 per day   Bronchial problems
         more than 20 per day   Diabetes

SECTION 3 : Past illnesses

Have you ever had any
of the following?
                          Tick   Tick
              Measles   Scarlet fever
               Mumps   Shingles
           Chicken pox   Black plague

Figure 1.6. *A well-designed and presented questionnaire*

Presenting facts

Tabular and graphical presentation

Facts and figures are often presented in table form which reflects the structure of the information and makes it easier to interpret. The example on the next page (Table 1.1) shows how Borsetshire County Council use a table presentation to set out details of their planned budget and inform council tax payers of how their money is to be spent.

	Borsetshire County Council Budget				1999-2000
	2000-2001				
	Gross Expenditure	Government Grant for Specific Services	Charges for Services	Net Expenditure	Net Expenditure
	£m	£m	£m	£m	£m
Education	210.1	10.2	16.2	183.7	145.2
Fire	12.3	1.2	0.5	10.6	8.1
Highways	22.3	5.6	5.2	11.5	9.5
Police	36.5	18.1	8.6	9.8	7.2
Social Services	42.1	8.1	4.4	29.6	22.3
Other Services	15.1	3.1	2.2	9.8	6.7
Contingencies	20.8	3.2	2.8	14.8	12.4
Total Expenditure	359.2	49.5	39.9	269.8	211.4
Less: Government Block Grant				134.5	112.3
Use of Balances				1.3	3.8
To be raised from Council Tax				134.0	95.3

Table 1.1. *A budget set out in table form*

The table presentation provides tax payers with detailed information, which is important for some people, but others may prefer to see be presented with, for example a pie chart (Figure 1.7) to show the distribution of spending or a bar chart (Figure 1.8) to compare the amounts of planned spending on the various services, with the spending figures for the previous year.

Figure 1.7. *Pie chart showing distribution of budget*

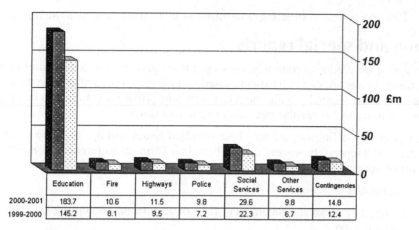

Borsetshire CC - Net Expenditure 2000-2001 and 1999-2000

	Education	Fire	Highways	Police	Social Services	Other Services	Contingencies
2000-2001	183.7	10.6	11.5	9.8	29.6	9.8	14.8
1999-2000	145.2	8.1	9.5	7.2	22.3	6.7	12.4

Figure 1.8. *Bar chart comparing planned expenditure with that of previous year*

Reports

Although reports may be delivered verbally, they are usually written. A report is a document which examines a particular topic or group of topics to: communicate information; report findings; make suggestions or put forward ideas.

Usually, a report will conclude by making recommendations for action. Reports can be classified according to whether they are routine, such as an Annual Company Report to Shareholders, or special, such as a Royal Commission to investigate the problem of child poverty. Reports do not have to be concerned with such major subjects and can be quite short, for example, in the case of a sports club treasurer's report on the club's financial position and the ways in which it can be improved. Reports can also be classified as formal or informal, although both must be structured.

Formal and informal reports

Formal reports are more heavily structured and generally longer than informal reports. The greater the level of detail in a report, the greater the need for structure. Representing a work of research, argument and recommendation, report writing is a significant test of anyone's communication skills. Because every report identifies its author and may be circulated to colleagues and superiors, it can be highly influential in making or breaking a person's reputation in an organisation. A highly structured report may contain the following sections:

(i) Title page.

(ii) Contents page.

(iii) Summary of recommendations.

(iv) Introduction and Terms of Reference (the objectives of the report).

(v) The information on which the report is based.

(vi) Conclusions.

(vii) Recommendations.

(viii) Appendices.

(ix) Reference section (references to information sources on which the report relies).

Routine and special reports

Reports which are produced routinely, for example, to give annual sales figures or report balance of trade figures are generally standardised and ideal for production by computer systems Routine reports are normally built into a business's information systems, to be output on demand or automatically at regular intervals or specified times.

Special reports, by definition, are not about standard issues and the structure tends to be less standardised. All reports, however, must be based on Terms of Reference or objectives. A special report be sequenced as follows:

(i) Terms of Reference.

(ii) A logically presented statement of facts or arguments concerning the subject of the investigation.

(iii) Findings. These identify possible solutions to the problem, giving the benefits and drawbacks or each solution.

(iv) Reasoned recommendations.

Draft report

A 'draft report' is the report before it has been put in its final presentation form. At this stage, the author is concerned with getting the content right, rather than obtaining a highly polished report. Its conclusions may also not be completely finalised and may be altered following further consultation and feedback from those who have commissioned the report. The term 'draft' can be used to refer to any document which is not yet in its final form.

Communicating by e-mail

E-mail etiquette (netiquette)

The word 'etiquette' refers to rules of correct behaviour in society or amongst members of a profession. These rules are not about being 'stuffy' but about observing courtesies which communicate respect and consideration for others. Of course, as society changes so do the rules of etiquette and today many people are happy to be addressed without titles or formality. This is not a problem in face-to-face communication because gestures, body language, facial expression and eye contact can all be used to communicate respect, consideration and friendliness without the constraints of more formal forms of address. Even on the telephone, tone of voice can be used to express feelings and emotions which are difficult to put directly into words. When writing to a stranger, you may have no way of knowing how they wish to be addressed or how they will respond to your usual style of writing, which may convey friendliness or cold formality. Either may be appropriate or inappropriate depending on the recipient of your document. Preparing a document for delivery by 'snail mail', that is, conventional post, takes preparation and effort and provides plenty of time for redrafting or even a decision not to send it at all. If the document is contentious in any way, such as a letter of resignation, or a complaint then the adage "sleep on it" is good advice; a difficult situation often appears very different the next day. E-mail is electronic and once a message is transmitted it may be in the recipient's mailbox seconds later. The first 'netiquette' rule of e-mail is "Think before you send." Some other important rules are:

☐ Check your e-mail regularly to ensure that you respond quickly to messages. Of course this applies to normal letter communications as well.

☐ If you can't reply immediately, send a quick acknowledgement.

☐ If you don't use encryption, be careful about what you say. A building society has been sued for libellous comments e-mailed by one of its employees. Laws on copyright, personal privacy, libel, pornography and incitement of racial hatred also apply to electronic communication.

☐ Use your words carefully, especially if you are angry or irritated. As explained earlier, e-mail does not provide the opportunities for body language or voice intonation to 'fine-tune' what you say. If you write something in jest, for example, "You are bone idle, you haven't replied to my e-mail", it is wise to use a 'smiley' (see later) to indicate that you are only joking.

☐ Keep your messages fairly brief. If you need to communicate a large amount of information send it as an attachment.

E-mail writing style

E-mail communications are encouraging informality, but you should always try to use wording and style which communicate respect. Because the medium is so quick, many e-mail users become very careless about spelling and grammar, which is probably acceptable between friends but is still unwise in business communication. Abbreviations are common, for example, BTW for "By the way", FAQ for "Frequently asked question", FWIW meaning "For what it's worth" and IMO for "In my opinion".

Smileys

These are ASCII or plain text characters formed into facial expressions to convey a variety of emotions. Suppose that you sent the following message:

"She has gone on holiday."

You might mean

"SHE has gone on holiday" (said with bitterness")

"She HAS gone on holiday" (confirming something that had been in doubt)

" She has gone on HOLIDAY" (said incredulously)

Even with capital letters, each of these could indicate different emotions from those suggested. Here are some examples of smileys which may help to more accurately express the emphasis in what you want to say. To get the effect you need to turn your head to view them sideways. (They look best in the Courier New font.)

```
:-)     Happy face - don't take what I said too seriously.
;-)     The smile with a wink implies sarcasm or irony.
:-(     The frown means that you don't like what was said to you.
8^0     The open mouth and wide eyes suggests that you are shocked.
```

Proofing documents

Some of the most commonly used proofing signs are shown in Figure 1.9.

Leave unchanged		Change to bold type
Insert and item in the text		Change to bold italic type
Delete		Start new paragraph
Delete and close up		Run on (no new paragraph)

Figure 1.9. *Standard proofing symbols*

To produce readable and presentable documents you need to develop the skill of *proofing* or searching for errors. Generally, except for very short documents, it is very difficult to carry out all proofing on screen and you will probably need to print a draft copy to read. With hard copy, you can use a ruler to guide your eye as you scan each line. If someone else is to carry out the corrections, it is helpful to use standard correction signs which are recognised and used by those involved in writing and publishing. Proofing requires concentration and systematic searching for several types of error which commonly occur. They are detailed below, together with examples.

Spelling

You may have little trouble with spelling, but most people have a 'blind spot' with certain words and some common errors are listed below.

Correct spelling	Common misspelling
sep*a*rate	separate
station*e*ry	stationary (if referring to paper)
station*a*ry	stationery (if you mean stopped/not moving)
sincer*e*ly	sincerly
lia*i*son	liason
person*n*el	personel
revers*i*ble	reversable
com*m*ittee	committee

Apart from checking for misspellings, you should try to be consistent where a word has more than one acceptable spelling. Frequently, for example, you will find that the letter '*s*' can sometimes be used in place of '*z*'. The Oxford English Dictionary will give you the word 'organization', but you will frequently see it spelt as 'organisation'. Similar examples include, 'specialize' or 'specialise', 'emphasize' or 'emphasise'. These are only examples and not demonstration of a rule. For example, 'advertise' is correct, 'advertize' is wrong and 'advize' is *not* an alternative to 'advise'.

Typographical or keying errors

Categories of typographical errors include words or individual characters out of order (*transposed*), missing or surplus words or characters and inappropriate or inconsistent use of lower case and capital letters. Look carefully at the two sentences which follow and you should be able to identify at least one example of each category of typographical error.

"Apart from being late, he was also poorly dressed."

"apart form being late, HE was was aslo dressd poorly ."

Punctuation errors

You need to look for incorrect and missing punctuation. Some rules, such as the use of a full stop at the end of a sentence, are absolute. Rules on the use of, for example, commas are less clear. Generally, they are used to improve the readability of a document and are often a matter of personal judgement. For example, the sentence

"Apart from being late he was also poorly dressed."

would not be incorrect but would be more readable if a comma was used as follows.

"Apart from being late, he was also poorly dressed."

Spacing errors

This relates to the incorrect omission of space or the inclusion of surplus space between words, sentences, lines or paragraphs. Generally, you should leave a single space between words and between a full stop and the beginning of the next sentence. You should also leave a blank line between paragraphs. (Alternatively, you can format the paragraph style to include additional space after each carriage return). Your word processor may provide the option to display characters which are normally *hidden*. These include spaces, tabs and carriage returns, and can make proofing for spacing errors easier. Figure 1.10 shows some hidden characters, with a space represented by a • and a carriage return by a ¶.

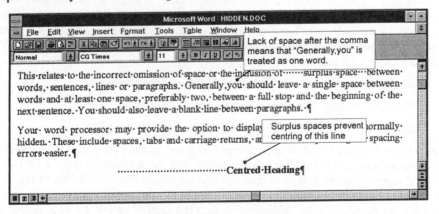

Figure 1.10. *Spacing errors*

Two possible consequences of erroneous spacing can be identified in the Figure.

☐ 'Centred Heading' is off centre because the preceding spaces are taken as characters and included as part of the heading.

❑   The lack of a space after a comma means that the word before and after it, and the comma itself, are taken as one word; this would mean, for example, that the word processor's spell checker would highlight 'Generally,you', in Figure 1.10, as a misspelling. To correct it you would have to insert the required space.

Spellchecker

All word processors and many other packages include a *spell checking* facility. You may find that, for example, it throws up words like 'organization' as being incorrectly spelled and indicates that only 'organisation' is correct. This does not mean that you cannot use the 'z' form. It simply means that the spellchecker's rules have not allowed for it. Spell checkers will identify as misspelled any word that does not appear in its *dictionary* (stored on disk). Thus, you may find that proper names, such as 'Wilkinson', or abbreviations like 'VCE', as well as many specialist technical terms, are highlighted as being incorrect. Most spell checkers allow you to add words to the dictionary, so that they are not identified as misspellings. If you misspell a word and it happens to be the correct spelling for another word, then the computer will not detect it. For example, 'stationery' and 'stationary' are both correctly spelled but have entirely different meanings. Such errors can only be found by careful proofing.

Thesaurus

Apart from a built-in spell checker, your word processor may also have a *Thesaurus*, which allows you to check the meanings of words and suggests alternatives. This facility should be used with great care, to avoid the use of unusual words which may obscure what you are trying to say. Further, it should only be used to jog your memory for an alternative word. If you use a word with which you are not familiar, you may discover that the word has a similar, but not identical, meaning to the original. For example, the meaning of the following sentence is quite clear.

"She was studious and passed all her examinations."

If you checked the Thesaurus for the word 'studious', it may throw up the suggestions such as, assiduous, diligent, industrious, determined, hard-working, busy, contemplative, intent and tireless. The adjectives do not necessarily relate to the activity of studying. To keep the meaning similar, you could change both adjectives to adverbs and keep the verb 'to study'. Possible alternatives of this form are shown below.

"She studied industriously and passed all her examinations."

"She studied diligently and passed all her examinations."

"She studied assiduously and passed all her examinations."

Even with these forms, the meaning is changed slightly. In the original, it is inferred that she was studious by nature, whereas the others suggest that she was studious for a limited period. The original is probably the easiest to read and best expresses the intended meaning. However, provided you clearly understand the meanings of the words suggested by the Thesaurus and that they are not simply 'wordy' alternatives, then the facility can make your language more varied and lively.

Grammar checker

The grammar checking process is usually an additional option within the spellchecker facility and can be useful for picking up some of the more obvious errors, which could also be picked up by careful proofing. These errors include, for example:

- ❏   using two full stops at the end of sentence;
- ❏   using a lower case letter at the start of a sentence;
- ❏   repeating the same word in succession.

Generally, however, the grammar checker should be used with extreme care as it will often make suggestions which may conform to the rules of grammar but if adopted would make complete nonsense of what you are trying to say. The grammar tool is only useful for identifying possible errors and you need to be confident in your use of grammar in order to determine whether an error actually exists. After the grammar checker has completed scanning a document it can be set to display readability statistics, as shown in Figure 1.11.

The 20% 'Passive sentences' figure relates to the use of sentences such as:

> An example is shown in the next Figure.

To use the 'active voice', which many word processors encourage, you would have to say:

> The next Figure shows an example.

Readability Statistics	? X
Counts	
Words	1715
Characters	9292
Paragraphs	48
Sentences	88
Averages	
Sentences per Paragraph	2.3
Words per Sentence	18.6
Characters per Word	5.3
Readability	
Passive Sentences	20%
Flesch Reading Ease	37.5
Flesch-Kincaid Grade Level	12.0
	OK

Figure 1.11. *Readability statistics*

Either is acceptable and which you use is a matter of personal preference but using the active voice can improve readability. Sometimes, the active voice is completely inappropriate, and you need to know when to ignore the grammar checker's warning against the passive voice. For example, the sentence

> You calculate the area of a rectangle by multiplying the width by the length.

is in the active voice but if I don't wish to address the reader directly, I would write

> The area of a rectangle is calculated by multiplying the length by the width.

Each of the US readability measures (Flesch Reading Ease and Flesch-Kincaid) is based on the average number of syllables per word and words per sentence. Readability also has to do with choice of words and the ways in which sentences are constructed, but the measures do provide a crude guide to readability. Again you need to use your own judgement in assessing readability and only shorten sentences or use words with fewer syllables if it will not destroy the flow and style of your writing. As explained earlier in this chapter, you need to tailor your style to suit the reader. For example, you would not expect to achieve the same readability score for a document aimed at university professors as you would for one aimed at young children.

Exercises

1. Using illustrative examples, suggest two reasons why correct spelling is important.
2. What is meant by proofing and why is it an important process?
3. a. Briefly describe the operation of a spell checker.
   b. With the aid of suitable examples, explain the limitations of a spell checker for proofing purposes.
4. Identify **three** types of document when a personal writing style may be important and **three** types of document when it would not be relevant.
5. Distinguish between a *serif* and *sans-serif* font, giving an example of each.
6. What rules concerning content should you bear in mind when summarising a document.
7. What is the purpose of meeting minutes.
8. What standard items would you expect to see on an agenda?
9. List the sections would you expect to see in a curriculum vitae to support a job application.
10. Suggest items of information you would expect to see in a job advertisement.
11. List the main components of a formal letter.
12. a. Give three examples of information gathering which would be suited to the use of questionnaires.
    b. Give an example of a question which can be answered using an opinion scale.
    c. Give an example of a leading question.
13. Distinguish between a bar chart and a pie chart and give an example of numerical information for which each would be appropriate.
14. List the main headings you would expect to find in a formal report.
15. What is a *draft* document?
16. Give two examples of e-mail etiquette.
17. What is a smiley?
18. a. When would you use a Thesaurus?
    b. When may a Thesaurus be of little use?
19. With the use of examples, distinguish between the 'passive voice' and the 'active voice'.
20. Suggest why a word processor's grammar checker cannot be wholly relied upon for correct grammar.

Chapter 2

Oral communication

Presentations

A presentation is only one of a number of ways which can be used to provide information for an audience, and as with other methods it has its own strengths and weaknesses. Printed material, such as textbooks, handouts, leaflets and pamphlets, and electronic systems, such as websites and CD-ROM resources, provide cost-effective ways of delivering information to mass audiences. However, the effectiveness of a textbook is usually improved if the reader has the opportunity to ask questions and receive clarification from a teacher. A major benefit of a presentation is that it involves 'live' contact between presenter and audience. Of course, some presentations may allow for little interaction between presenter and audience and if its subject comprises the presentation of purely factual information, there may be little need for any. In such an event, it is reasonable to suggest that a printed report would have served just as well and avoided the need for audience and presenter to meet at all.

Commercial organisations are likely to make presentations for a variety of reasons and to a variety of audiences. For example, when a manufacturer launches a new product, this may warrant several different presentations, each one tailored to a particular audience. For example, one presentation can inform sales staff of the product's main selling points, another can advise maintenance staff of the product's maintenance requirements and another can promote the product to potential distributors. Although all the presentations are dealing with the same subject, the details, delivery method and style are likely to be different for each. To be effective, a presentation's content needs to be relevant and of interest to its audience and the presenter must develop a number of presentation skills,. such as speaking clearly and responding effectively to audience feedback. Making a presentation is rather like giving a performance on stage and presenters, like stage actors, often make use of 'props' to support delivery of the message. Commonly used props for presentations include slides for display using an overhead projector (OHP) and computer displays developed with presentation software such as Microsoft PowerPoint. Flip charts and marker pens are useful tools for recording audience questions and feedback.

Structure and sequence

A presentation should have a clear structure with an *introduction*, followed by the *main body* of material, with a *conclusion* or summary of points at the end.

The introduction informs your audience of the general subject, perhaps using a main title and sub-title; it should also identify the presenter. If you simply launch into the detail of the subject, for example, with a slide announcing that customer complaints reached record levels in 1999, the audience may well be confused and fail to establish the point of the presentation until several more slides have been viewed. In any case, it is usual to give an oral introduction to the purpose and subject of your presentation, hopefully establishing a rapport with your audience at the same time.

Visual aids

Overhead projector slides and computer slide shows are there to reinforce the content of your presentation, to establish key points and provide a framework for your commentary. It is likely that your spoken commentary will expand on bullet points and include questioning and requests for audience feedback. An example of a structured presentation follows. The presentation includes sample introduction, body and closing slides, presenter script and key points for improving the quality of your own presentations.

Example presentation

This short presentation deals with the topic of e-commerce and is targeted at a group of SME (small to medium enterprise) proprietors and managers. The title slide identifies the topic, a theme and the presenter.

Title slide and introduction

Once the audience is seated, the presenter can introduce himself/herself and the purpose of the presentation. The presenter should be facing the audience and in a position which does not obscure the slides. With the title slide displayed, the presenter may begin by saying:

> E-commerce for small businesses
> *"Size need not be important."*
>
> Peter Lansing
> Electronic Futures Limited

"Hello and welcome. My name is Peter Lansing. I am e-commerce consultant for Electronic Futures Limited and run my own on-line business selling helicopter spares. Our company specialises in providing a competitive consultancy service for SMEs such as yourselves. The presentation I am about to make will show you how the Internet and e-commerce can give your business access to global markets, reduce your costs and increase your competitiveness. E-commerce allows you to compete with larger businesses. Remember, size need not be important".

☞ **Set the scene, give your audience a focus and a reason for staying awake**. This means stating the subject of the presentation and its relevance for the audience. It is helpful to establish a theme for the entire presentation. In this example, the catch phrase "Size need not be important" is meant to achieve this aim. It emphasises that e-commerce allows small enterprises the same commercial opportunities as large businesses.

☞ **Establish your credentials and give your audience confidence in what they are about to hear.** Peter Lansing points out his company's association with SMEs and the real benefits that e-commerce can bring. He also gives his own credentials (he is experienced in business) and thereby his qualifications for advising people on the subject of e-commerce. Even if you are not an expert on the subject of your presentation, you need to ensure that you have researched it well and present a confident image to your audience. If you appear hesitant, your audience will have little confidence in what you have to say. This is particularly important when your presentation is part of an interview process.

Body slide 1

The first slide in the main body of the presentation begins with a question and then lists key points relating to it. The presenter script may be as follows.

"Stated simply, e-commerce is <u>conducting business transactions over electronic networks</u>. E-commerce is fundamentally changing the way we do business. E-commerce can improve the efficiency of all stages of the business process, from design and manufacture to retailing and distribution.

The major catalyst for the expansion of international electronic retailing is the Internet. Its users, the number of which is rapidly increasing, can communicate with the Web sites of countless organisations all over the world, and it is through these World Wide Web sites that companies can provide 'virtual stores', with product catalogues, 'virtual shopping baskets' and secure credit card payment systems."

> **What is e-commerce?**
>
> ◎ Business transactions that are conducted over electronic networks.
>
> ◎ E-commerce is fundamentally changing the way we do business.
>
> ◎ Internet stores provide virtual shopping baskets and secure credit card payment systems.

☞ **Keep slide titles and key points short and uncomplicated.** Slide images are vitally important because your audience will remember what they see much more readily than what they hear, no matter how interesting the topic or your voice.

☞ **Use slide titles and key points as a guide for your talk.** Don't simply read what is on the slide; your listeners will soon start to fidget and mutter that you might as well have printed it out for them to read. The above example script appears to be quite lengthy, but would last less than a minute. So, you need to 'flesh out' the slide bullet points, but don't swamp your listeners with too much detail.

Closing slide

At this point, the presenter should review the key points which are of primary interest to the audience. However effective your presentation, they will not remember all of what you have said and the final slide should be used to provide impact points which they will remember. If they need to check on details later, this can be handled at the end in a question and answer session.

> **Business benefits**
>
> ◎ A shop window to the world
>
> ◎ Direct contact with customers
>
> ◎ Access to new markets
>
> ◎ Lower costs

☞ **The end of your presentation should be designed for impact,** so avoid detail and emphasise the key points. If you are using a computer to support your presentation, then slides can easily include graphics to increase impact, as the alternative closing slide example in Figure 2.1 shows.

Figure 2.1. *Closing slide with graphics*

Using slide presentation software

A computer slide presentation, for example with PowerPoint, needs to be carefully designed to take into account its content and the target audience. It is helpful to consider the following questions and guidelines.

1.   Is the user going to browse through and control the flow of the presentation or will the show be controlled by a presenter with spoken commentary? The answer to this question will affect the content of slides - if there is spoken commentary, supplementary information can be provided without cluttering up the slide with too much information.

2.   Is the information provided in the presentation regarded as important or of real interest to the audience? Careful use of animation and, where possible, sound can provide impact and prevent the audience from slipping into a deep sleep. On the other hand, fancy effects can distract the audience from the content of a message.

3.   Images should be carefully chosen to suit the subject and the target audience. Cartoon images can add a little humour, but may distract from a serious message. On the other hand effective use of cartoon images can 'lighten' the presentation of what is otherwise a serious subject.

4.   Text font styles and sizes should be consistent and appropriate to the presentation. A wild array of several font styles will simply make the text more difficult to read.

5.   Don't pack too much information onto one slide and keep the font size large enough for the audience to read, taking into account the distance that they will be from the screen.

6.   Good use of colour is more difficult for some, but provided colours are not too garish and text fonts contrast sufficiently with the background to make text legible, then the effect should never be too objectionable.

7.   Timing of slide changes and animations within slides is also important if the user is not controlling its progress. You will need to check time delays to give the audience time to absorb the message on each slide. Excessive delays between slide changes are likely to be irritating.

Personal style

Even if you are making a formal presentation, your own personality is bound to come through and it is generally a bad idea to fake it, at least too much. Some presenters have personalities which are highly suited to the task, with a keen sense of wit and an ability to appear enthusiastic, even on the dullest of subjects. They can also quickly establish a relaxed and friendly rapport with an audience. Of course, extroverts may need to exert some restraint in more formal situations, such as interviews. Most people are not blessed with these gifts and have to work a great deal harder to deliver effective presentations. You can be confident and appear so without being an extrovert, but no matter what your personality, careful preparation and a thorough grasp of the subject are vital to a competent performance. Preparation, together with carefully designed slide support, will help you to gain confidence, but speaking to an audience is a skill which can only be improved with practice.

Using your voice effectively

Without microphone support, you will need to make your voice project to everyone in the audience, not just the people in the front row. The first thing to make people 'switch off' is an inability to hear what the presenter is saying and most people are reluctant to say, "Can you speak up? I can't hear you."

Enunciation and articulation

Although you should avoid shouting, you will need to raise the volume and clearly enunciate. This means speaking clearly, emphasising the consonants, particularly the letters B P T D K and G and separating words. An example of fading or dropping of consonants is the pronunciation of Sco-land instead of Scotland or 'wha' instead of 'what'. In normal conversation most of us slur our speech to some extent, sometimes merging words into one another and fading out consonants. It is worth practising speaking your script beforehand and checking with friends whether they can clearly hear what you are saying, even at the far end of the room. Of course, it is possible to overdo the volume and enunciation, such that the audience may become more fascinated by the unnatural form of speaking than they are by the content of the presentation. Just place a little more emphasis on consonants and if you do have a tendency to gabble, it should help to slow you down.

Inflexion

Inflexion, or varying the pitch of your voice, is important for emphasis and to maintain interest. Listening to monotone speech **is** monotonous and will quickly lead to boredom and loss of interest. Some people put inflexion into their speech quite naturally but others who normally speak in a monotone can find it difficult to use inflexion naturally. Forcing your voice to go up and down may sound rather strange, but some gentle raising of pitch to emphasise particular words can be effective. For example, in the following sentence, speaking the underlined word at a very slightly higher pitch would create greater impact than maintenance of a monotone throughout.

The company underlined(doubled) its profits in one year.

Rehearsing the presentation

Rehearsal is vital for your confidence and the success of your presentation. You should try to give the whole presentation in advance, preferably in the location planned for the real presentation and using some friends or colleagues as audience. Hopefully, they will give you constructive advice if it needs improvement. By rehearsing, you will ensure that you are confident in using the equipment, such as an overhead projector, that your slides are clear and legible even from the back row of the audience, that the sequence and organisation of your material is as it should be, and that you have a thorough knowledge of your subject. This latter point is particularly important if you expect to answer questions from the audience. Rehearsal will also give you the opportunity to test the suitability of your appearance and body language.

Appearance and body language

You should be dressed in a way which suits the audience, which may be formal or informal, but you should dress with care and appropriately. You need to feel comfortable, confident and project a professional image to your audience. Your body language is very important and the following list of guidelines may be helpful.

1.   Stand straight and don't hunch your shoulders.

2.   Keep your feet slightly apart. This will steady you and help to calm your nerves.

3.   Look at your audience, not over them. Making brief eye contact with individuals shows that you are interested in their response and allows you to judge their response.

4.   Change your position occasionally, but give your audience a reasonably consistent range on which to focus. Walking backwards and forwards will distract your audience from the subject of your presentation.

5.   Avoid jangling keys or other nervous movements, but do use suitable gestures for emphasis. Expansive gestures such as briefly holding your hands wide apart in front of you when asking, "Are there any questions on that point?", for example, can make the audience feel involved. However, making stabbing gestures with your finger can appear aggressive.

6.   If you need to glance behind you to check the computer screen or the overhead display, stop talking and wait till you are facing the audience before you start speaking again. Talking with your back to the audience can appear rude and will probably mean that some people do not hear what you say.

Managing the presentation

If you are using an OHP:

1.   Before the presentation, make sure that the bulb is working and that you know how to switch it on. Make sure that the cable is out of harm's way and that you, or any member of the audience, will not trip over it.

2.   Ensure that all members of the audience will be able to see the display.

3.   Get used to putting the slides the correct way up and positioning them.

4.   Check that the slides focus properly on the display board and that the content is large enough to be legible.

5.   It is useful to use a pencil or wand to indicate a particular point on the display. Practise pointing at the slide film on the OHP, rather than at the projected image and ensure that the wand is long enough to prevent your hand from obscuring part of the image.

6.   Make sure that your slides are in the correct order and that you have somewhere to discard each one as the presentation proceeds.

7.   During the presentation, switch the OHP off when you are not using it for lengthy periods. The cooling fan can be quite noisy.

If you are using a computer-generated presentation, the ideal solution is to use an overhead display which will project the computer image onto a display board. When using an OHP you would stand, but for computer-generated displays, you need to be seated. If such equipment is not available, it is helpful if you have one screen to view and control the presentation and the audience has another. If there is only one screen audience numbers should be limited to five or six and you will have to sit to one side to avoid obscuring the screen.

Keeping the audience interested

Variety helps to keep an audience interested. Without it, boredom will quickly set in. So, vary the pace of the presentation. If you come to a part which requires greater emphasis or is more difficult to explain, slow the pace a little. Another section may simple list a number of fairly simple points which require little explanation and the pace can be quickened.

Business benefits

◎ A shop window to the world

◎ Direct contact with customers

◎ Access to new markets

◎ Lower costs

If you know that your audience has some knowledge or experience of the subject, ask them for comments to further illustrate a particular bullet point. For example, the second bullet point in the adjacent slide could allow the presenter to ask:

"Do you know what proportion of your customers have access to e-mail? How many of you use e-mail at present?"

The first question might obtain no response, but the second will probably result in the raising of hands. Questioning in this way is a bit of a 'fishing expedition' and you hope that someone will 'bite' and provoke a short discussion. Of, course, if time for the presentation is limited, or the audience is large (discussion requires some feeling of closeness and intimacy), you may have to avoid such breaks in continuity.

Be enthusiastic. If you look bored, the feeling will quickly transfer to your audience.

Make sure that your materials are well organised and that if there is some distraction, such as someone walking into the room, you can deal with the interruption and continue confidently from where you left off. Interruptions or distractions can destroy a presentation, but if you respond with good humour, they can act as 'ice breakers' and make both you and the audience feel more relaxed.

Closing questions and handouts

Oral presentations, even with visual aids, can lead to 'information overload' and you may need to provide handouts. If you plan to give handouts at the end of the presentation, tell your audience at the outset or they may spend the entire time trying to take notes and failing to listen to your commentary. It can be helpful to give your audience paper copies of the slides, to help them keep track of the presentation, but it is generally a bad idea to provide detailed notes during the presentation. Some people will spend time reading those instead of listening to you; more detailed handouts can be issued afterwards. The presentation needs to add something to the information which appears in the handout. Hopefully, this something will include your personality, extra examples, additional explanation, humorous comments, emphasis of key points and the opportunity for audience members to ask questions. Otherwise, the presentation could have been substituted by a handout.

It is usual to allow the audience to ask questions afterwards, so it is important that you understand everything you have said in your presentation. You may be able to answer some questions immediately, or it may be necessary for you to re-display a slide and quickly review one aspect of the presentation. If someone asks you a question which is outside the range of your topic, be honest and don't pretend that you know the answer. If you think that you can find the answer later, say something like, "I'm sorry, I don't know the answer to that question but I will try and find out and get back to you." A question may be completely outside the range of your presentation and it is perfectly acceptable to say, politely, that you can't answer it. It is important that you control the questioning and ensure that any individual does not prolong the session, particularly with questions which are not of general interest. You can always offer to answer such questions as others are leaving.

Interview skills

Whether you are applying for a place at college or university, or for a job, good interview skills are vital for your chances of success. It is important that you prepare for a job interview by:

☐ finding out all you can about the employer. You will want to know the size of the organisation, its product or service range, its branch network (if any) and where you might be located. If the organisation has a Web site, this can be an effective way of obtaining information, but you may also be able to obtain company brochures or consult the local Chamber of Commerce. The more research you have done the more the employer will be impressed.

☐ finding out details about the advertised post. There should be a job description, salary structure and so on in the advertisement. You may be unsure whether or not you really want the job so it is important to have questions to ask the employer in more detail, such as career structure, training etc.

☐ clearly identifying your own ambitions and career interests. It is as well to practise expressing these clearly. This may be quite a lengthy process but you need to try and anticipate what you responses would be to typical questions such as "What qualities do you think you can bring to this job?"

☐ identifying your own strengths and weaknesses in relation to the advertised post. If you have a significant weakness, for example, a lack of familiarity with a particular piece of software, try to identify a strength which will reduce the significance of the weakness. For example, you may have a high level of skill with other software and are able to pick up new skills very rapidly.

Good preparation should enable you to answer questions confidently and in a conversational manner. Interview formats vary and may include the requirement for a presentation. They also vary in formality and structure. A typical 30 minute interview would include 2 to 3 minutes 'warm up' with general pleasantries, 15 minutes questions from the interviewer(s), 5 to 10 minutes for your questions and 2 minutes for concluding comments. During the interview, it is desirable to:

1.   show knowledge and interest in the employer's business;

2.   show friendliness, confidence, enthusiasm, calm and quiet assertiveness;

3.   have and be able to express clear career goals and particular interests;

4.   maintain appropriate levels of eye contact;

5.   use a tone of voice which projects the qualities in 2;

6.   be relaxed and take an interest in what is being said;

7.   be well groomed and have a neat, professional appearance;

8.   have a clear grasp of your own skills and experience and their relationship to work in general and to the advertised post. Even if you don't have work experience, it is

helpful if you can point to activities in which you have taken responsibility. For example, you may have had some organisational responsibility in a sports club.

Answering questions

It is impossible to anticipate all the question which you may be asked, but you can prepare for some typical ones. It is not a good idea to memorise prepared answers because they will probably sound that way and it is better that you maintain a conversational tone and at least give the impression that you are responding naturally. Try to be honest, but use your discretion. For example, when asked, "How did you choose your college course?", the truth may be that you chose it to be with your friends but later found that the course was what you wanted to do. Rather than saying, "It's what I have wanted to do since I was 10", it would be better to say that you were unsure when you first joined the course but after a few weeks you realised that you had made the right choice. It's probably best to leave out any reference to your initial desire to be with your friends, but you could elaborate by saying that you found that you had many friends on the course and that this added to your enjoyment.

Don't ramble and try not to repeat yourself. Use examples to illustrate your answers - this adds interest - but be succinct and stick to the question. Always keep the requirements of the advertised post in mind. Hopefully, your interviewer will be friendly and the atmosphere relaxed, but don't take this as a signal to lay back in your chair and make careless conversation.

Common interview pitfalls

Here are some avoidable mistakes which may lead to rejection of a candidate: poor knowledge and preparation; lack of enthusiasm; little or no eye contact; arrogance, 'showing off' and insincerity; vague answers.

Discussions

"The earth is not flat." Although this was a subject of scientific discussion several hundred years ago, we now know that the earth is round and is, therefore not something to be argued about. For a subject to be discussed, it must be possible for people to have different opinions about it. Effective discussion requires the expression of opinions which are supported by arguments. A debate is a particularly formal type of discussion where a *motion* is put before the 'house' (the group participating in the debate) and following the presentation of arguments for and against the motion, the 'house' votes to accept or reject it. For example, a motion may state, "This house believes that the national speed limit should be reduced to 50 mph." A proposer and seconder present arguments to support the motion and another proposer and seconder argue to reject it. The discussion may then be thrown open to the 'floor' (the other people taking part in the debate) before a vote is taken to accept or reject the motion. This is the basis for deciding on new laws in the House of Commons and the quality of the debate is determined by the effectiveness of the speakers and the quality of the arguments and facts they present to support their opinions. An important part of debate is listening to the opinions and arguments of others. Of course, discussions can also take place in a much less formal way and the following paragraphs provide suggestions for making them effective.

The point of discussion is to come to a conclusion on some issue or to decide on a particular course of action, weighing the arguments for and against each option. Generally, the participants in a discussion are aware of rules that they will adopt, such as a majority vote or, consensus (general agreement). Majority voting is commonly used by committees, boards of directors and other groups charged with the responsibility of managing organisations. Majority voting may also be used by completely informal groups such as friends trying to decide which club they are going to or the destination for a holiday. In formal situations, it is less important to "keep everybody happy" and decisions will often be made with which not everyone agrees. The group of friends discussing where to go on holiday will obviously be very concerned about one another's feelings and will attempt to come to an agreement with which all are content. The success of any agreement is more likely if all the participants feel that they have had an opportunity to put their points of view and that the others listened and took them into account before coming to a conclusion. If this does not happen, some members may be left feeling resentful and become 'awkward' or even try to make trouble when other decisions are to be made. In the case of discussions between friends or work colleagues, such feelings can lead to the breakup of the group or loss of 'team spirit' and for committees or boards of directors, less effective management of the organisation.

Speaking and listening

Effective discussion, indeed communication in general, requires skill on the part of the speaker and the listener. Ideally, a speaker should:

- ☐ have a wide vocabulary and choose words which the listener will understand;

- ☐ pronounce words correctly;

- ☐ speak fluently and without too much hesitation;

- ☐ speak at a speed which suits the listener, not so slowly as to cause irritation and not so quickly as to cause the listener to lose much of what is being said;

- ☐ use inflexion or intonation in the voice to give variety of expression. Speaking without any variation in tone can be boring for the listener, but it also makes it difficult for the listener to interpret the true meaning of what the speaker is saying. For example, the sentence "I think that people should drive their cars less." spoken in a monotone would suggest, possibly incorrectly, that the speaker is unconvinced about it. With intonation, perhaps with the final word "less" being spoken at a higher pitch and slightly louder, would indicate a strong opinion on the subject.

- ☐ keep some eye contact with the listener, to judge their response to what is being said and to give the listener opportunity to intervene. However, maintaining permanent eye contact can be intrusive or threatening and can cause the other party embarrassment.

A listener should:

- ☐ concentrate on what the speaker is saying;

- ☐ respond with comments as necessary and interject if it is helpful to the flow of the discussion. By maintaining some eye contact, the speaker is able to see when the listener wishes to interject and can respond accordingly. In a lively discussion, there can be a tendency for a speaker to 'hog' the conversation or for a listener (who is not really listening) to continually interrupt and 'get their oar in'. Such tendencies should be avoided if proper discussion is to take place.

- ☐ respond non-verbally to what is being said, for example, nodding to signify understanding or approval, or smiling to provide encouragement.

Managing discussions

Discussion requires that all participants are given the opportunity to present their views, argue their case and comment on the views of others. For a discussion between two individuals, this requirement can be met quite easily, but where several people are involved, there is often a need for a chairperson. The job of the chairperson is to manage the discussion and determine that only one person speaks at a time. The chairperson should also try to channel discussion towards a conclusion and may well summarise views periodically to find points of agreement and identify points which need further discussion. Suppose, for example, a sports club committee holds a meeting to decide on whether to increase membership subscriptions and by how much. At a particular point, the chairperson may say, "We seem to be moving towards a view that we should increase the subscription. I'll ask each one of you for your final comments and then we will put it to the vote." At this point, less confident people are given a clear opportunity to express the opposing view. Sometimes stronger personalities will dominate general discussion, and a good chairperson will ensure that before a vote is taken, each person is invited to speak.

Generating ideas

Discussion is a productive way of generating and refining ideas. When an idea comes to us, we can think about it, turn it over in our minds and consider the potential benefits and pitfalls. Before we use the idea, we will often want to discuss it with others. Apart from gaining the benefit of other views on the idea, the process often leads us to re-examine the idea and perhaps reject it or see new possibilities which improve it. It is likely that every great inventor, having conceived an initial idea, has spent some time developing it through discussion with at least one other person.

Brainstorming

Brainstorming can be an effective in generating new ideas or suggestions. Ideas are accepted without discussion and typically, written directly onto a flip chart or board so that everyone can see. The pool of ideas can then be examined, unworkable ideas rejected and those with potential discussed further.

Team building

A team has common objectives, for example, the development of a new software package, or the building of a new swimming pool for a local community. Each member needs to know and understand the team's objectives, his or her own role and the roles of others in achieving them. Discussion at regular meetings is an essential part of a team's progress towards the achievement of its objectives. Progress needs to be monitored and individual members need opportunities to report on their own work and identify and resolve difficulties. Building a team involves the development of:

- ❑ ways of working to improve efficiency and productivity;
- ❑ co-operative and supportive relationships;
- ❑ mutual respect for each others' strengths;
- ❑ recognition of one's own weaknesses and the need to use the strength of others;
- ❑ the team's adaptability to changes in circumstances, such as a cut in its operating budget.

Achieving consensus through negotiation

Making decisions by consensus is desirable, but not always achievable, at least in the sense of absolute and unreserved agreement. Consensus can only be obtained when each member of a group has clearly expressed his or her views and disagreements, listened to and understood those of the others, and presented any alternatives they wish to be discussed. When, through discussion and negotiation a decision, which everyone understands, is reached then we can say a consensus decision has been made.

Negotiation can take many different forms, from the confrontational to the co-operative. Negotiation generally means compromise, that is, a willingness between parties to modify their own requirements to come to a common agreement. The most successful negotiations are those which leave all parties content and without feelings of resentment. If one party feels that he or she has been forced into an unwilling acceptance of an 'agreement', it is more likely that the agreement will be broken. Successful labour relations between employers and employees are based on good negotiating skills. Some general pointers towards good negotiation are given below:

- ☐ Each party should be clear about the objectives and wishes of the others.

- ☐ Identify areas of particular difficulty and resistance to any compromise. Attempt to find areas of agreement first and then work on the areas of resistance.

- ☐ Keep personalities out of the discussion. In other words, try not to allow personal likes and dislikes of others to obstruct negotiations.

- ☐ Avoid using threats and giving in to anger and frustration. If your counterpart gives in to such emotion, remain calm and patient and try to return attention to the areas of agreement and mutual benefit.

- ☐ Pay attention to you own body language and that of the other negotiators.

- ☐ Before making a proposal try to anticipate the possible responses. As in chess, it is important to think a few moves ahead.

- ☐ Emphasise the positive qualities in your own proposals and the benefits for your counterpart, but also admit the benefits for yourself.

Body language

Being able to read the body language of others and use body language yourself are very important communication skills. Of course, body language is something we use without thinking much of the time, but self-awareness is important if you don't want the wrong signals to be given out.

Although too deliberate use of body language will probably be recognised as such, it is helpful to be aware of some simple codes which you can use and recognise. By way of illustration, participants in business negotiations would probably use and recognise the following example body language codes (the meanings of postures and gestures vary with different cultures and those described below relate to the Western culture).

Posture	Meaning
Seated, leaning forward, feet flat on floor, hands open on knees	Acceptance
Seated, leaning forward, pointing or fists clenched	Aggressive rejection
Seated, legs slightly apart, feet under chair and leaning forward	Eager acceptance
Slumped in chair, gazing into space, doodling	Boredom
Standing with arms behind back, legs slightly apart and smiling	Attentive
Stroking chin, looking up and to the right	Evaluating and thinking of response

Exercises

1. Suppose that you are required to make a presentation to a group of 15 school students who are considering following the BTEC Nationals course next year.
   (a) List the items of equipment and support materials which you may require, briefly identifying the purpose of each item.
   (b) Suggest a title for the presentation, a short and memorable 'catch phrase' for the title slide.
   (c) Write a suitable opening script, which includes your personal introduction, a statement of the purpose of the presentation and your credentials.
   (d) Rehearse the script with a member of your group and modify it until you are both satisfied that it uses an appropriate style for the audience.
   (e) Word process (use the Outline feature if the package has one) an outline structure for the presentation. Make sure that the structure and sequence are quite clear.
   (f) Suggest 3 methods you may use to try and maintain the interest of your audience.
   (g) Identify any problems you can envisage with the physical arrangements for the presentation. Assume that you are to make the presentation in your usual class room or laboratory.
   (h) Distinguish between articulation and inflexion and explain why each would be important for the success of your presentation.

2. Suppose that you have applied for a job with a local Internet Services company and have been asked to attend for interview.
   (a) Suggest two ways in which you can prepare for the interview, briefly suggesting why each is important.
   (b) Identify 4 aspects of your behaviour (be reasonable) during the interview which are likely to:
      (i) improve your chances of success;
      (ii) damage your chances of success.

3. Suppose that you are a member of a team which is responsible for the production of a your employer's company web site. A team meeting has been called to identify ways in which the web site could be used to improve marketing and customer support services. The meeting will include a 'brainstorming' session to help in this task.
   (a) What is meant by 'brainstorming' and what is it meant to achieve?

(b) Consider your own personality and in particular, your confidence to take part in discussions generally. Suggest two ways in which your confidence in making a contribution may be:

(i) increased;

(ii) reduced.

Chapter 3

Study skills

The effectiveness of your study can be improved by careful attention to:

- ❑ planning;
- ❑ time management;
- ❑ efficient searching of information sources, both conventional and electronic;
- ❑ discriminatory use of information sources;
- ❑ the layout and presentation of your work, both in note form and as formatted documents.

There are also different methods of reading which can make the tasks of information gathering and learning easier. Note taking is an important skill for recording key pieces of information which you identify in a research text. Summarising is essential if you are to extract more detail and obtain a true interpretation of the text. It therefore requires more careful examination of a text than simple note taking.

Planning and time management

Planning requires that you identify the tasks you are required to complete, draw up a schedule which shows when each has to be completed and then analyse each one to determine its work requirements. Apart from scheduled tasks, you will obviously have to take account of the time taken up by lectures, workshops, meal and coffee breaks, travel, sleep, social activities and so on. If we suppose that all the tasks are to be completed by the same date, it will be necessary to analyse each one to determine its inputs. These will include, for example, research from texts in the library (you need to be available when its open), research from the Web (unless you have your own computer, check when you can have access), consultation with your tutor to check on progress (this will tie you to a particular time), investigation of the facilities provided by a software package, expanding on notes or summaries and word processing final documents. Here are some simple do's and don'ts.

- ❑ Not everyday follows the same pattern, so you will need to get used to a different plan for each day. If you know that you have a complete afternoon free on a Thursday, make sure that you are prepared to work on a task which requires a longer, uninterrupted effort.
- ❑ Some people can think more clearly in the mornings than the afternoons, so try to fit tasks which require careful thought and concentration into the times which suit you.
- ❑ Make good use of your time and don't let the work pile up.
- ❑ Try to understand concepts the first time that they are presented to you. Further review of the concepts will then further establish your understanding. Don't daydream in lectures and rely on reading the handout or textbook to learn later.

Research

Although there are many sources of information (the Internet is examined later), the text book is still the most important. When you are researching a topic, you will probably consult the library indexes, perhaps by entering key words into a computerised search system, or by consulting the manual subject indexes. Although browsing the shelves is useful once the general location has been found, you should always aim to narrow your search as quickly as possible.

It is best to research a topic from a variety of sources, although you will probably concentrate on one as your primary source, consulting others to obtain additional information, to verify the accuracy of stated facts and evaluate the worth of stated opinions. This is important even in subjects such as computing which are regarded as mainly factual.

If the results of your researches are to be worthwhile, then you will need to evaluate the information you find and be discriminating in selecting or rejecting it.

You should reject information which:

- is not relevant;
- is beyond the scope of your task;
- includes detail which you do not understand;
- repeats what is already there;
- is simply 'padding'.

Effective and efficient reading

There are different reading techniques to suit different purposes and text sources. For example, 'skimming' is useful for quickly finding a key word or phrase in a document, but useless for learning about a new and difficult topic. When undertaking research, you will need to examine a range of sources, first making a quick check to see if each is likely to be useful and then examining those selected in more detail. Suppose that you have picked up a book because its title seemed to fit with the topic your are researching. There are a number of stages (in a typical top-down approach) you can go through to determine whether it may actually be useful.

1. Check how the book is organised, its general content, author (who may be familiar to you from other texts you have read) and publication date (an old text may be suitable for basic concepts but hopeless for current technologies).

2. The Preface may give you an overall idea of the aims of the book and the target readers.

3. The Table of Contents and Index are obvious ways of checking for your required topic.

4. If you find a suitable page reference, go to it and judge whether the level of detail is what you want and whether you find it readable.

Some tasks require careful, word-by-word reading, but there are techniques which can be used to increase the rate at which you can absorb the information you need.

Speed reading

There are two main approaches to speed reading. With *expanded* reading, you use your peripheral vision to take in 2, 4 or even 6 words in at a glance. You may well do this to a limited extent already when the text is familiar or you don't need to take in every word - often referred to as "getting the gist of it". Speed reading trainers state the practical limit using this technique is around 700 words a minute.

To read dynamically, you need to be trained to use your peripheral vision both horizontally and vertically, effectively viewing sections of a page at a time and absorbing up 20 or more words at a glance. Reading speeds of between 1500 and 10,000 words per minute are achievable. Although most people are not going to take the trouble to obtain formal training, it can be useful to practice using your horizontal peripheral vision and gain an appreciable increase in reading speed. Of course, the purpose of reading is to take in information, so there is no point in using skimming or expanded reading if you are not achieving that purpose. It is worth trying to improve your reading speed, but you need to choose a method which suits the material you are studying. Reading requires concentration, so remember to pace yourself, taking a break or carrying on with a different task when necessary.

Assignments

1.1. Documents and writing style

Following the merger of Silicon Software with Omega Business Systems, the first board meeting of the new company, Silicon Business Software Limited, resulted in a number of important changes being implemented. One of the changes is to establish a Human Resources department. Previously, neither company had operated corporate personnel systems, but had left personnel matters to indvidual departments. You have been transferred to this new department, where your job involves you working as a senior assistant to the Human Resources Manager, Ann Robinson. After your initial meeting with Mrs Robinson, at which a variety of issues were discussed, you received the following internal memorandum.

Memorandum

To: Senior Personnel Assistant

From: Human Resources Manager

Re: Establishment of corporate materials

Date: 14 June 2000

I have given thought to our conversation on the need for standardised letters and forms to meet the functions of the new department. I am satisfied that we cannot standardise job advertisements, but want you to provide me with drafts of the following:

Forms:

   a job application form that all job applicants would have to complete (I would want it to contain sufficient information to enable me to use it as an employee record form).

   a staff appraisal form to record job performance.

Letters to fulfil the following tasks:

   invite applicants for job interviews;

   inform an applicant that he/she is not being called for interview;

   inform an interviewee that he/she is not being offered the job;

   offer the job to the successful interviewee;

   issua formal warning to an employee who is guilty of misconduct, stating that dismissal will result from a repetition of the conduct complained of;

   issue a dismissal;

   inform an employee that he/she is being made redundant;

I am aware that this is a substantial task but would ask you to complete it as a matter of urgency.

Tasks

1.   Draft the forms and letters requested in the memorandum, using a content, tone and style appropriate to each of them.
2.   Write a memorandum to the Human Resources Manager indicating that you expect the

work to take considerable time to complete.

3. Obtain examples of some of the above documents, letters and forms used by public and private sector organisations in your area. Compare these in order to produce a dossier containing an example of each document, letter or form which combines the examples of best practice in each.

1.2. Meeting documents

Draw up and word process an agenda for a meeting to discuss an issue relating to your course. For example, you will probably appoint one or more of your fellow students as representatives to attend Course Team meetings and will need to inform them of matters which you wish to pass on to Tutors. You should appoint a chairperson and minutes secretary (this job can be taken by a different person for each meeting). The minutes should be word processed by the minutes secretary after each meeting and be distributed to the rest of the group before the next meeting. As minute taking is a difficult skill, you will need to record the main points only and the name of the person who made each contribution. At the next meeting, the minutes of the previous meeting will be checked for accuracy before being signed by the chairperson.

1.3. Questionnaires

This assignment concerns the design and use of a questionnaire to do a survey on some area of interest.

1. Design a questionnaire to survey opinion on an area of interest to you. Think carefully about the aims of the survey, the size of the survey and how the results ae to be analysed, because these factors will greatly influence the design of the questions an how they are to be coded.

2. Apply the questionnaire to a suitable population or sample of a large population.

3. Calculate the percentages of response to each question and present the calculations in tabular form for easy reference.

4. Calculate any other useful statistics, such as means, medians or modes.

5. Produce appropriate statistical charts to illustrate the results of the survey.

6. Write a report describing the results of your survey and explain the reasoning behind your conclusions.

1.4. Presentation

As a member of the ICT support team employed by a recruitment agency, you have been asked to give a presentation to recruitment and administrative staff on ONE of the following topics.

1. Viruses, their types, their effects and the measures which can be taken to protect the company's systems against attack.

2. Hacking, the motives of hackers and the measures which HFC Ltd can take to protect their systems.

3. The Internet and the opportunities and dangers it presents for the future of the company.

Research and discussion

Assignment 6.2 in at the end of Unit 6 provides opportunities for extensive research, discussion and team building.

Unit 2

Computational methods

Chapters

Unit 2 Outcomes and assessment criteria

Outcomes	Assessment criteria To achieve each outcome a student must demonstrate the ability to:
1. Demonstrate and ability to **quantify data and handle numeric data** in a variety of forms.	• perform arithmetic on indices, fractions and decimals • carry out percentage calculations – % of, % increase decrease, calculation of original value given final value and % change • use indices and standard form to represent data • represent numeric data in binary, octal and hexadecimal form and perform simple arithmetic on such data.
2. Solve a range of problems using **algebraic techniques**.	• evaluate algebraic expressions • create algebraic expressions • change the subject of a formula.
3. Be introduced to and demonstrate an understanding of basic set theory. Acquire skills in the use of **logic circuits and truth tables**.	• use simple logic gates to represent logic circuits • create and test logic circuits using truth tables • simplify compound logic statements • solve simple set theory problems using venn diagrams.
4. Use a range of **graphical techniques** to represent and manipulate data.	• graph simple linear functions • calculate the slope/gradient of straight line graphs • solve simultaneous equations manually and graphically • perform simple matrix arithmetic • solve simultaneous equations using matrices • use vector geometry • transform polygons using simple matrix transformations • plot and solve quadratic equations graphically and by calculation.
5. Demonstrate confidence in the use of **basic statistical techniques to analyse data**.	• calculate the mean, mode and median for different types of frequency distribution • graph statistical data using bar charts, line graphs, histograms and pie charts • plot and understand the significance of a normal distributions • calculate the standard deviation of a number of sets of similar data and make comparisons.

Chapter 4

Arithmetic operations

The four fundamental processes of arithmetic are addition (+), subtraction (–), multiplication (×) and division (÷) , and these are termed arithmetic operations. Arithmetic operations are performed on numbers which may be presented and described in different forms. Some of the most common representations for numbers are described below.

❑ Integers are whole numbers, such as 1, 2, 332, 6, 25;

❑ Decimal fractions (or just decimals), where the fractional part of the number is separated from the whole part by a decimal point as in 1. 237, 2.2, 13.986;

❑ Common fractions (or vulgar fractions) are numbers like ½, $^6/_8$, $^3/_5$, $^9/_{10}$ each representing a part of a whole number;

❑ Directed (or Signed) numbers are preceded by a (+) or a (–) sign to indicate a positive quantity or a negative quantity respectively: +13, –21.5, –1$^1/_2$. The + sign is usually omitted for positive numbers;

The following sections in this chapter will examine the ways in which arithmetic operations are performed on numbers represented in these various forms.

Addition and subtraction

Integers and decimal fractions

When two or more numbers are added together, the result is called the sum of the numbers; the difference of two numbers results when one is subtracted from the other. A list of numbers to be added are written one above the other with every digit in its correct column. For example, 1234 + 567 + 82 + 307 is written as shown alongside. The sum of the numbers is 2190.

```
  1234
   567
    82
+  307
------
  2190
```

The addition is performed by first adding the digits in the units column, followed by the tens column and so on.

To find the difference of two numbers, again the numbers are written with the digits in each number aligned correctly. Starting at the units column, each pair of digits is subtracted. Thus the subtraction 397 - 245 is written as shown on the right.

```
  397
- 245
-----
  152
```

The difference of the numbers is 152.

When the numbers are decimals, the decimal points in the numbers must be aligned before they are added or subtracted. For example, to find 234.56 – 21.2 is written:

$$
\begin{array}{r}
234.56 \\
-\quad 21.20 \\
\hline
213.36
\end{array}
$$

Common fractions

The process of adding or subtracting common fractions is rather more complicated than for integers or decimals. For example, suppose that we wished to add ⅛ (one eighth) to ¾ (three quarters). We must ensure that before we add the numerators (the figures above the dividing lines), the denominators (the figures below the dividing lines) are the same. In this instance, we convert ¾ to eighths by multiplying both the numerator and the denominator by 2:

$$\frac{3\times2}{4\times2}=\frac{6}{8}$$

Now we can add the numerators to obtain

$$\frac{1}{8}+\frac{3}{4}=\frac{1}{8}+\frac{6}{8}=\frac{1+6}{8}=\frac{7}{8}$$

Another slightly more difficult problem occurs when the denominators of the fractions do not include a common factor as in, for example ²⁄₇ and ⅓, Here we must find a denominator which is divisible by both 7 and 3. The smallest such denominator is 21, hence

$$\frac{2}{7}+\frac{1}{3}=\frac{(2\times3)}{(7\times3)}+\frac{(1\times7)}{(3\times7)}=\frac{6}{21}+\frac{7}{21}=\frac{6+7}{21}=\frac{13}{21}$$

In the case of ¼ and ⅚, the common denominator would be 12, to give

$$\frac{1}{4}+\frac{5}{6}=\frac{(1\times3)}{(4\times3)}+\frac{(5\times2)}{(6\times2)}=\frac{3}{12}+\frac{10}{12}=\frac{13}{12}=1\tfrac{1}{12}$$

Multiplication and division

Integers and Decimal Fractions

The product of two numbers results when they are multiplied together. For example, the product of 432 and 102 would be calculated as shown alongside.

The multiplication does not take place in one step. Instead the process is broken down into a series of simpler procedures. Starting with the rightmost digit of the multiplier, the mul-

$$
\begin{array}{r}
432 \\
\times\quad 102 \\
\hline
864 \\
0000 \\
+\quad 43200 \\
\hline
44064 \\
\end{array}
$$

432	multiplicand
102	multiplier
864 (2 x 432)	first partial product
0000 (0 x 432)	second partial product
43200 (100 x 432)	third partial product 44064
44064	complete product

tiplicand is multiplied by each digit of the multiplier. Each multiplication results in a partial product. Successive partial products are written one place further to the left than the previous one to allow for the magnitude of the multiplying digit. Note that multiplication by 0 gives 0000 for the second partial product, and normally this would not be written down. The final product is the sum of the partial products.

If the signs of two numbers to be multiplied are the same, then the answer will always be positive; if the signs are different, the answer will be a negative value. Thus,

$$5 \times 3 = 15$$
$$-5 \times 3 = -15$$
$$5 \times -3 = -15$$
$$-5 \times -3 = 15$$

The same rules apply to the division of integers and decimals, and to the multiplication and division of common fractions.

A problem in division, such as $195 \div 15$, is usually tackled as follows:

$195 \div 150$	$=$	1 remainder 45	... (1)
	$=$	150×1	... (2)
	$=$	$195 - 150$	... (3)
$45 \div 15$	$=$	3 remainder 0	... (4)
	$=$	$45 - 45$	

$$
\begin{array}{r}
13 \\
15\,\overline{)\,195} \\
-150 \\
\hline
15 \quad 45 \\
-45 \\
\hline
0
\end{array}
$$

195 is called the dividend, 15 is the divisor and the result, 13, is called the quotient. The process involves the following steps:

1. The leftmost digit of the divisor is aligned with the leftmost digit of the dividend. Thus the divisor in this case is being treated as if it were a factor of ten greater, that is, 150.

2. Comparison of the dividend, 195, with the divisor, 150 gives the first quotient digit of 1, representing ten 15's.

3. The previous two steps have established that there are at least ten 15's in 195. The process is now repeated with the remainder after 150 has been subtracted from the dividend. This remainder is 45.

4. Since there are exactly three 15's in 45, and there are no more digits of the dividend to consider, the final quotient has been determined.

Common Fractions

A common fraction represents a proportion of something, such as one third, $\frac{1}{3}$ or three quarters, $\frac{3}{4}$. When fractions are multiplied, as in $\frac{1}{3} \times \frac{3}{4}$, we are finding a proportion of a fraction, in this case one third of three quarters. The process of finding the answer to this simply involves multiplying both the numerator and denominator:

$$\frac{1}{3}\times\frac{3}{4}=\frac{1\times3}{3\times4}=\frac{3}{12}=\frac{1}{4}$$

Notice that in the second step, both numerator and denominator contain the factor 3, so this may be cancelled out; if the numerator and denominator are both multiplied by the same number (a common factor) you can in effect ignore it. Here is another example:

$$\frac{3}{5}\times\frac{2}{3}=\frac{3\times2}{5\times3}=\frac{6}{15}=\frac{2}{5}$$

For a problem such as $2\,\frac{1}{2}\times1\,\frac{1}{3}$, it is necessary first to convert the integer parts of the numbers to the appropriate fractions:

$$2\,\frac{1}{2}=\frac{2\times2}{2}+\frac{1}{2}=\frac{5}{2}$$

and

$$1\,\frac{1}{3}=\frac{1\times3}{3}+\frac{1}{3}=\frac{4}{3}$$

Hence,

$$2\,\frac{1}{2}\times1\,\frac{1}{3}=\frac{5}{2}\times\frac{4}{3}=\frac{20}{6}=\frac{10}{3}=3\,\frac{1}{3}$$

Dividing one fraction by another, as in $\frac{1}{4}\div\frac{1}{2}$, involves multiplying by the reciprocal of the second fraction. The reciprocal is found by inverting the fraction. Thus, the reciprocal of $\frac{2}{7}$ is $\frac{7}{2}$ and the reciprocal of $\frac{1}{2}$ is $\frac{2}{1}\,(=2)$.

So,

$$\frac{1}{4}\div\frac{1}{2}=\frac{1}{4}\times\frac{2}{1}=\frac{2}{4}=\frac{1}{2}$$

Percentages

A percentage may be considered to be a common fraction with a denominator of 100, and the %, (per cent), symbol literally means per hundred. Percentages may also be represented as decimal fractions. Thus

$$5\%=\frac{5}{100}=0.05$$

$$175\%=\frac{175}{100}=0.175$$

Frequently performed calculations involving fractions and percentages are illustrated below.

1. Converting a percentage to a decimal fraction.

Divide the percentage value by 100: $15\%=\dfrac{15}{100}=0.15$

2. Writing a decimal fraction as a percentage.

      Multiply the decimal fraction by 100: $0.25 = (0.25 \times 100)\% = 25\%$

3. Writing a common fraction as a percentage.

      Multiply the common fraction by 100: $\frac{3}{5} = \left(\frac{3}{5} \times 100\right)\% = 60\%$

4. Finding a percentage of an amount.

      Multiply the amount by the percentage expressed as a common fraction.

      Thus, 10% of £5.30 is $£5.30 \times \frac{10}{100} = £0.53$, or 53p.

Problems involving percentages

Percentages are used in many situations in everyday life. A selection of applications is now briefly discussed along with typical calculations that are performed in each one.

Commission

Certain kinds of employees, especially salespersons, are paid commission. Often, they receive a basic amount, and the commission they earn is added to this to make up their total pay.

Example 1:

A salesman receives a basic salary of £500 per month plus a commission of 6% on all sales he makes during the month. If, during last month, he sold £6000 worth of goods, what was his salary for the month?

$$\text{Salary} = £500 + 6\% \text{ of } £6000$$

$$= £500 + \tfrac{6}{100} \times £6000$$

$$= £500 + £360$$

$$= £860$$

Price rises and price cuts

The term *inflation* is often used on television and in the newspapers. We might hear, for example, that last month the rate of inflation was 3%; this means that prices rose by 3%.

Example 2:

Inflation is set to rise by 2.5% next month. If I spent £200 on groceries this month, how much can I expect to pay for my groceries next month?

To find the rise in cost of my groceries all I need to do is to calculate 2.5% of £200.

$$\text{Rise in Cost} = 2.5\% \text{ of } £200$$

$$= \frac{2.5}{100} \times £200$$

$$= £5$$

My groceries will cost £200 + £5; that is, £205.

Example 3:

The original price (i.e. the marked price) of a jacket was given as £65 and it was offered in a sale where everything was to be sold at 30% off the marked price. How much did the jacket cost in the sale?

$$\text{Reduction in price} \quad = \quad 30\% \text{ of } £65$$

$$= \quad \frac{30}{100} \times £65$$

$$= \quad £19.50$$

The jacket cost £65 − £19.50 in the sale; that is, £45.50.

Value Added Tax (VAT)

VAT is a tax on certain goods and services. When an item that is purchased is liable to VAT, the person making the purchase must pay a tax on top of the price of the item. At present, this tax is 17.5% of the price of the item.

Example 4:

An item liable to VAT costs £23.75; what is its actual cost to the consumer?

$$\text{VAT} \quad = \quad 17.5\% \text{ of } £23.75$$

$$= \quad \frac{175}{100} \times £23.75$$

$$= \quad £4.16 \text{ (to the nearest penny)}$$

$$\text{Total cost} \quad = \quad £23.75 + £4.16; \text{ that is, } £27.91.$$

Example 5:

A vase cost £69.95 including VAT. What was its cost before the VAT was added?

The point to note here is that the figure of £69.95 must be 117.5 % (that is, 100% + 17.5% VAT) of the original, pre-VAT cost. Expressed as a fraction,

$$117.5\% \quad = \quad \frac{1175}{100}$$

$$\text{Therefore, the original cost} \quad = \quad \frac{100}{1175} \times £69.95$$

$$= \quad £59.53$$

Profit and loss

The profit is the difference between the cost of buying an item and the cost of selling it again. That is,

Profit = Selling Price − Cost Price

If, however, the cost price is greater than the selling price, then a loss is made. That is,

Loss = Cost Price − Selling Price

The percentage profit (or loss) is often quoted and this can be calculated by using the formula

% Profit (or Loss) = Profit (or Loss) ÷ Cost Price × 100%

Example 6:

A retailer buys in shirts at a cost of £15 each and sells them to the consumer at a price of £8.99 each. How much profit is made on each shirt and what percentage profit does the retailer make on each shirt?

Profit	=	£18.99 − £15	=	£3.99

$$\text{Percentage Profit} = \frac{£3.99}{£15} \times 100\%$$

$$= 0.266 \times 100\%$$

$$= 26.6\%$$

Ratio and proportion

Ratio and proportion are other names for fractions. For example, if there are 7 men and 10 women working in a certain office, then the ratio of men to women is $\frac{7}{10}$ or 7 : 10. Since there are a total of 17 people in the office, the proportion of men is $\frac{7}{17}$ and the proportion of women is $\frac{10}{17}$. These fractional proportions also may be represented as percentages by multiplying them by 100 as described earlier.

Problems involving ratio and proportion

Example 1:

A person has £350 a month to spend on groceries and clothes. If she spent £295 on groceries this month, what proportion was spent on clothes?

Amount spent on clothes   =   £350 − £295   = £55

Proportion spent on clothes   =   £55 ÷ £350 $= \dfrac{55}{350}$

Cancelling numerator and denominator by 5 gives $\dfrac{11}{70}$

Expressed as a percentage, the proportion   = $\dfrac{11}{70} \times 100\%$ = 15.7%

Example 2:

Three children aged 8, 10 and 12 years inherit money from their uncle. Their inheritance is £2400 and it is to be shared out in proportion to their ages. How much does each child get?

Their inheritances are in the proportion   8 : 10 : 12

This can be simplified by dividing each proportion by 2 to give 4 : 5 : 6

The total number of shares is 4 + 5 + 6 = 15

Therefore, the value of one share   =   £2400 ÷ 15 = £160

Thus,

the child aged 8 gets $4 \times$ £160 = £640

the child aged 10 gets $5 \times$ £l60 = £800 and

the child aged 12 gets $6 \times$ £l60 = £960.

Check the result: the total inheritance £640 + £800 + £960 = £2400.

Approximate solutions (estimation)

When doing calculations, whether by hand or using a calculator or computer, it is always a good idea to roughly check an answer to determine whether it is about what you would expect.

For example, suppose that you had to calculate $\frac{3}{7}$ of 50. You could easily see that $\frac{1}{7}$ of 50 is about 7 (because $7 \times 7 = 49$). So $\frac{3}{7}$ of 50 should be about 21. The correct answer is 21.429 to three decimal places, so your rough check confirms that the answer is in the right area.

Here is a more complicated problem, but we can approach it step by step in a similar way to the last example:

Calculate $\quad \dfrac{564}{43 \times 6} \times 125$

We could start by approximating 43×6 to about 260 (because $6 \times 40 = 240$) and then notice that $125 \div 260$ is about $\frac{1}{2}$. $564 \div 2$ is about 280. So we would expect an answer in this region, and it is because the answer is actually 273.256 to three decimal places. The trick is to make the numbers easy to handle by rounding them up or down to more convenient figures. As another example, we might approximate

$$\frac{12.5 \times 9.3}{12 \times 3.8} \qquad \text{to} \qquad \frac{10 \times 10}{1 \times 4}$$

which becomes about $100 \div 4 = 25$. The actual answer is 25.493 to three decimal places. If the problem is dealt with in stages, you can often calculate a rough answer in your head. In the last example, for instance, the stages would be

(i) 12.5×9.3 is about 10×10

(ii) 10×10 is 100

(iii) 1.2×3.8 is about $1 \times 4 = 4$

(iv) $100 \div 4$ is 25.

✍️Exercises

Addition, subtraction, multiplication and division

These exercises provide practice in basic number skills involving addition, subtraction, multiplication and division of integers, decimal fractions and common fractions.

1. Add and subtract the following pairs of numbers manually. When you have finished, check your answers using a calculator or spreadsheet. For subtraction, the second number should be subtracted from the first number.

   (a) 123, 56　　(b) 200, 179　　(c) 1000, 725　　(d) 123.5, 52.4

   (e) 12.5, 4.25　(f) 010, 3.56　　(g) 1.538, 0.729　(h) 12, 1 7

   (i) 2, -2　　　(j) -3, 4　　　(k) -4, -5 (1) 2.55, 7.95

2. Multiply and divide the following pairs of numbers manually. Check your answers with a calculator or spreadsheet. For division, the first number should be divided by the second number.

   (a) 56, 8　　　(b) 21, 7　　　(c) 125, 25　　d) 35, 16

   (e) 1000, 125　(f) 104, 56　　(g) 7.7, 1.1　　(h) 12.5, 2.5

   (i) -6, -3　　(j) 24, -3　　(k) -100, 25　　(1) -3.6, 0.9

   (m) 90, 120　　(n) 55, -110

3. Add these fractions, cancelling down where necessary to give answers in their lowest terms:

   (a) $\frac{1}{2}+\frac{1}{4}$　　(b) $\frac{1}{3}+\frac{1}{6}$　　(c) $\frac{2}{5}+\frac{3}{10}$　　(d) $\frac{2}{3}+\frac{1}{4}$

   (e) $\frac{5}{12}+\frac{1}{2}$　　(f) $\frac{1}{2}+\frac{1}{3}$　　(g) $\frac{1}{7}+\frac{6}{7}$　　(h) $\frac{1}{2}+\frac{3}{7}$

   (i) $1\frac{2}{3}+\frac{3}{4}$　　(j) $2\frac{1}{2}+1\frac{3}{5}$　　(k) $\frac{3}{4}+3\frac{7}{10}$

4. Subtract these fractions, giving answers in their lowest terms:

   (a) $\frac{3}{4}-\frac{1}{2}$　　(b) $\frac{3}{4}-\frac{3}{8}$　　(c) $\frac{2}{5}-\frac{1}{10}$　　(d) $\frac{7}{10}-\frac{1}{4}$

   (e) $\frac{5}{6}-\frac{1}{4}$　　(f) $\frac{1}{3}-\frac{1}{7}$　　(g) $\frac{6}{7}-\frac{1}{3}$　　(h) $\frac{19}{50}-\frac{3}{25}$

   (i) $1\frac{1}{2}-\frac{2}{3}$　　(j) $2\frac{3}{4}-1\frac{1}{6}$　　(k) $2\frac{3}{5}-1\frac{9}{10}$

5. Multiply these fractions, giving answers in their lowest terms:

   (a) $\frac{1}{2}\times\frac{1}{4}$　　(b) $\frac{3}{8}\times\frac{4}{5}$　　(c) $\frac{10}{13}\times\frac{13}{20}$　　(d) $\frac{2}{9}\times\frac{3}{4}$

   (e) $\frac{3}{7}\times\frac{7}{8}$　　(f) $\frac{1}{9}\times\frac{3}{5}$　　(g) $\frac{11}{13}\times\frac{26}{33}$　　(h) $\frac{2}{5}\times\frac{1}{34}$

   (i) $1\frac{2}{3}\times3\frac{1}{2}$　　(j) $9\frac{1}{2}\times3$　　(k) $\frac{2}{7}\times3\frac{1}{2}$　　(1) $\frac{5}{9}\times36$

6. Divide these fractions, giving answers in their lowest terms:

   (a) $\frac{1}{4}\div\frac{1}{2}$　　(b) $\frac{3}{8}\div\frac{3}{4}$　　(c) $\frac{1}{2}\div\frac{1}{4}$　　(d) $\frac{3}{20}\div\frac{9}{10}$

(e) $\frac{4}{5} \div \frac{5}{6}$ (f) $\frac{2}{7} \div \frac{13}{14}$ (g) $1 \div \frac{1}{4}$ (h) $3 \div \frac{1}{3}$

(I) $4\frac{1}{3} \div 6\frac{1}{2}$ (j) $\frac{9}{10} \div 3$ (k) $2\frac{2}{3} \div 5\frac{5}{6}$

Percentages

The following exercises are designed to improve your efficiency in calculations involving percentages.

1. Convert the following percentages to decimal fractions:
    (a) 20%   (b) 25%   (c) 12.5%   (d) 75%   (e) 5%
    (f) $33\frac{1}{3}$%   (g) 40%   (h) 45%   (i) 38%   (j) 29.5%
    (k) 37.5%   (l) 3.5%

2. Convert the following decimal fractions to percentages:
    (a) 0.35   (b) 0.95   (c) 0.1   (d) 0.025   (e) 0.375

3. Write the following fractions as percentages. Where appropriate, round off answers to two places of decimals:
    (a) $\frac{4}{5}$ (b) $\frac{9}{10}$ (c) $\frac{1}{4}$ (d) $\frac{3}{8}$ (e) $\frac{5}{7}$
    (f) $\frac{2}{3}$ (g) $\frac{1}{50}$ (h) $\frac{5}{6}$ (i) $\frac{1}{12}$ (j) $\frac{7}{8}$
    (k) $\frac{8}{9}$ (l) $\frac{12}{13}$

4. Calculate the following percentages and give your answers to the nearest penny:
    (a) 10% of £20   (b) 20% of £15   (c) 5% of £120
    (d) 15% of £10   (e) 25% of £4.60   (f) 12.5% of £80
    (g) 34% of £250   (h) 2.5% of £44   (i) 75% of £1000

The following exercises provide practice in solving problems involving percentages. Check your answers using a spreadsheet.

5. I wish to buy two tyres from a garage. The pre-VAT price marked on each tyre is £25.50. How much VAT will I pay, and how much will the tyres cost in total?

6. A meal for two at a restaurant cost £32.50. The restaurant adds a service charge of 10% to the bill. How much will the meal cost?

7. A retailer is offering 25% discount off the marked price of all stock. A pair of trousers is on display for £22.50. How much will they cost?

8. An art dealer buys a painting for £2090 and sells it for £3200. What is his profit and his percentage profit?

9. If the dealer in the previous question sold the painting for only £1995, what would be his percentage loss?

10. I bought goods from a DIY store and the cost was £101.66 including VAT. How much VAT was added to my bill?

11. A salesman is paid a basic monthly salary of £450 and receives 9% commission on the price of all sales he makes. If in a certain month he sells goods worth £8500, what would his pay be for that month?

12. The same salesman in the previous question has the choice of a new contract which will pay him 20% commission on the price of the total sales he makes above £5000 per month. Should he accept the new contract or stick to his existing one?

Ratio and proportion

These exercises provide practice in the use of ratio and proportion.

When giving answers as ratios, always write the ratios in their simplest terms (by cancelling where appropriate):

1. A book costs £4 and a folder cost £1.20. Write this as a ratio. Hint: Convert the amounts to pence and then cancel them down.

2. What proportion of £5 is £1.50? Give your answer as a fraction and as a percentage.

3. A small business has three bank accounts, called Account A, Account B and Account C. Account A has £2400 in it, Account B has £1800 in it and Account C has £900 in it. Express these amounts as a ratio.

4. Joan and Ann have £1275 in their joint bank account. The money in this account is to be drawn out and shared between them in the ratio of 3 : 2. How much money does each one receive?

5. Three brothers, Saj, Peter and Sanjay, invest money in a shop. The amounts they invest are, respectively, £1200, £2000 and £1500. The total profits to date, from the shop, amount to the sum of £5600. If they each receive a share of the profits in proportion to their investments, how much will each receive?

Estimation

These exercises involve estimation of the results of calculations.

1. Estimate the answer to each of the following calculations and then use a spreadsheet to see what the exact answer should be. Create a spreadsheet and enter the calculation as text in the first column, then your estimate in the second column, and finally the calculation as a formula in the third column.

    (a) 11.6×29.5 (b) 104×35 (c) $20 \times 19 \times 21$ (d) 2.5×12.2

    (e) $198 \div 21$ (f) $1000 \div 19.8$ (g) $(112.5 \times 79 \times 66) \div (39.2 \times 9.9)$

2. Take each of your pairs of answers from the task above and for each pair use the spreadsheet to:

    (a) Find the difference between the exact result and the estimated result. This produces the error.

    (b) Calculate the percentage error of the calculation, that is, use the formula

    percentage error = (error ÷ exact answer) × 100%

    (c) Comment on the accuracy of your estimation.

Chapter 5

Number systems and binary arithmetic

Although the denary, or decimal, numbering system, being so familiar is the one most human beings use, it is not at all suitable for computers. The denary system developed as a result of our having ten fingers which we could use for counting, but computers, being based on electronic components having only two states rather than ten, use the *binary numbering system* for storing information and for performing calculations. However, the rules for counting in binary and for binary arithmetic are no more complicated than those that we use for denary counting and arithmetic. In fact the binary numbering system has some important advantages over the denary system for computer processing.

In this chapter we will explore the basis of numbering systems in general, but we will concentrate on the binary system and explain some of the principles of binary arithmetic relevant to the study of computers.

The base of a number system

First consider the denary system. There are ten symbols, 0, 1, 2, 3, 4, 5, 6, 7, 8 and 9; the *base* or *radix* of a number system is identified by the number of different symbols it uses. Thus, the denary number system has a radix or base of 10. To identify a number, for example 123, as a denary number, it can be written as 123_{10}.

Place value

Each symbol can be given a weight or place (or positional) value, according to its position within any given number. In the denary system, each place value is a power of ten. Remember that the base of the denary number system is ten. Thus, for denary integers each place value is ten raised to a power. Starting from the least significant digit on the right, there are units (10^0), tens (10^1), hundreds (10^2), thousands (10^3) and so on.

10^3	10^2	10^1	10^0
thousands	hundreds	tens	units
1	2	6	3

Table 5.1. *Place values example* 1263_{10}

The idea of place value can be illustrated with examples of integer (whole) numbers. Table 5.1 shows that 1263_{10} can be expressed as one thousand, plus two hundreds, plus six tens and three units, or $1 \times 1000 + 2 \times 100 + 6 \times 10 + 3 \times 1 = 1263_{10}$.

Similarly, Table 5.2 shows that 487_{10} is the same as zero thousands, plus four hundreds, plus eight tens and seven units, or $0 \times 1000 + 4 \times 100 + 8 \times 10 + 7 \times 1 = 487_{10}$. Note that any number ($n$) raised to the power of zero (n^0) is equal to 1. This can be seen from Tables 5.1 and 5.2 and from the

10^3	10^2	10^1	10^0
thousands	hundreds	tens	units
0	4	8	7

Table 5.2. *Place values example 487_{10}*

place value tables shown later, for each of the binary, octal and hexadecimal number systems. The *fractional* component of a number is also determined by position, except that the power is negative, as shown in Table 5.3.

	10^{-1}	10^{-2}	10^{-3}
decimal point	tenths	hundredths	thousandths
.	6	2	5

Table 5.3. *Place values example $0 \cdot 625_{10}$*

Table 5.3 shows that $0 \cdot 625_{10}$, can be seen as:

$$6 \times \tfrac{1}{10} + 2 \times \tfrac{1}{100} + 5 \times \tfrac{1}{1000} = {}^{625}\!/_{1000} = {}^{5}\!/_{8}$$

Binary system

The binary system uses only two symbols, 0 and 1. Each digit in a binary number is known as a binary digit or *bit*. An example binary number is 11001_2, which is equivalent to 25_{10}. The binary system has a base of 2, so each place value is a power of two. The next two tables each show a range of integer place values and an example binary number. Table 5.4 demonstrates that the binary number 11101_2 is equivalent to denary $1 \times 16 + 1 \times 8 + 1 \times 4 + 0 \times 2 + 1 \times 1$ or 29_{10}. Table 5.5 shows that the binary number 01100111_2 is equivalent to $0 \times 128 + 1 \times 64 + 1 \times 32 + 0 \times 16 + 0 \times 8 + 1 \times 4 + 1 \times 2 + 1 \times 1 = 103_{10}$.

2^4	2^3	2^2	2^1	2^0
16	8	4	2	1
1	1	1	0	1

Table 5.4. *11101_2 or 29_{10}*

2^7	2^6	2^5	2^4	2^3	2^2	2^1	2^0
128	64	32	16	8	4	2	1
0	1	1	0	0	1	1	1

Table 5.5. *01100111_2 or 103_{10}*

Binary *fractions* can also be represented and an example is shown in Table 5.6.

	2^{-1}	2^{-2}	2^{-3}	2^{-4}
binary point	half	quarter	eighth	sixteenth
.	0	1	1	1

Table 5.6. *Fraction 0.0111_2*

We can see from this that $0 \cdot 0111_2$ is equivalent to $0 \times \tfrac{1}{2} + 1 \times \tfrac{1}{4} + 1 \times \tfrac{1}{8} + 1 \times \tfrac{1}{16} = {}^{7}\!/_{16}$

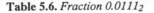

Table 5.7 shows the binary equivalents of 0 to 9 in the denary system.

base$_{10}$	base$_2$	base$_{10}$	base$_2$
0	0000	5	0101
1	0101	6	0110
2	0010	7	0111
3	0011	8	1000
4	0100	9	1001

Table 5.7. *Denary symbols and their binary equivalents*

Using the place values for the binary system shown in Tables 5.4 and 5.5, it can be seen how each of the denary numbers in Table 5.7 equates with its binary representation.

Octal and hexadecimal numbers

These number systems are often used as a shorthand method for representing binary numbers. As can be seen from the binary numbers in the earlier tables, they are very confusing to the eye and it is sometimes difficult, even with small groupings, to distinguish one pattern from another.

Where it is necessary for the computer's binary codes to be written or read by programmers, for example, it is invariably more convenient to use alternative coding methods. Octal and hexa-decimal (*hex*) notations are used in preference to denary because they are more readily converted to or from binary. It must be emphasised that computers can only handle binary forms of coding. Therefore octal and hexadecimal codes must be converted to binary before they can be handled by the computer.

Octal coding

The octal number system has a base of 8, using 0, 1, 2, 3, 4, 5, 6 and 7 as its symbols. Each place value is a power of eight; some of the place values are shown in Table 5.9.

8^4	8^3	8^2	8^1	8^0	8^{-1}	8^{-2}	8^{-3}
4096	512	64	8	1	$\frac{1}{8}$	$\frac{1}{64}$	$\frac{1}{512}$

Table 5.9. *Some octal place values*

Octal coding uses three bits at a time, allowing 8 or 2^3 (see Table 5.10) different patterns of bits.

Binary	0 0 0	0 0 1	0 1 0	0 1 1	1 0 0	1 0 1	1 1 0	1 1 1
Octal	0	1	2	3	4	5	6	7

Table 5.10. *Octal symbols and binary equivalents*

To represent any given value, a binary number can be split into groups of 3 bits, starting from the right-hand side, as the two 16-bit examples in Table 5.11 show.

0111001101100110_2	0	111	001	101	100	110
Octal code	0	7	1	5	4	6
1101010100010111_2	1	101	010	100	101	011
Octal code	1	5	2	4	5	3

Table 5.11. *Octal coding symbols*

Because the 16 bits will not divide exactly into groups of 3, the left-most or *most significant bit* (MSB) can only take the values 0_8 or 1_8.

Hexadecimal coding

The hexadecimal number system has a base of 16, and uses the following symbols: 0, 1, 2, 3, 4, 5, 6, 7, 8, 9, A, B, C, D, E and F. The six letters, A to F, are used instead of the denary numbers 10, 11, 12, 13, 14 and 15, respectively. This brings the number of hexadecimal symbols to sixteen. Some place values, each being a power of 16, are shown in Table 5.12.

16^3	16^2	16^1	16^0	16^{-1}	16^{-2}	16^{-3}
4096	256	16	1	$\frac{1}{16}$	$\frac{1}{256}$	$\frac{1}{4096}$

Table 5.12. *Hexadecimal place values*

A group of 4 bits provides 16 unique binary patterns, the number required to represent all 16 symbols of the hexadecimal (hex) number system. The symbols and their binary equivalents are given in Table 5.13.

Binary	0000	0001	0010	0011	0100	0101	0110	0111
Hex	0	1	2	3	4	5	6	7
Binary	1000	1001	1010	1011	1100	1101	1110	1111
Hex	8	9	A	B	C	D	E	F

Table 5.13. *Hexadecimal symbols and binary equivalents*

Therefore, a binary number can be coded by grouping the bits into groups of four and using the appropriate hexadecimal symbol for each group, as the examples in Table 5.14 show.

1100001111110110_2	1100	0011	1111	0110
Hexadecimal code	C	3	F	6
0101011010111101_2	0101	0110	1011	1101
Hexadecimal code	5	6	B	D

Table 5.14. *Hexadecimal coding examples*

In practice, hexadecimal is used in preference to octal code because computers organise their internal memory in 8-bit groupings (*bytes*) or multiples of bytes. These groupings conveniently divide into 4-bit *nibbles* which can be coded in the shorthand of hexadecimal. A knowledge of hexadecimal is essential for the interpretation of computer manufacturers' manuals, which use the coding system extensively to specify memory and backing storage features. Programmers using low level languages , such as assembly code, also need to be familiar with this number system.

Number base conversion methods

Conversion of binary numbers into their hexadecimal and octal equivalents is described in the preceding section. The following section provides methods and examples of conversion from:

- ❑ denary to binary;
- ❑ denary to octal;
- ❑ denary to hexadecimal.

Denary to binary

Method 1 - using conversion tables

Table 5.15 contains a range of place values for integer conversion; Table 5.16 can be used for fractions.

2^{14}	2^{13}	2^{12}	2^{11}	2^{10}	2^9	2^8	2^7	2^6	2^5	2^4	2^3	2^2	2^1	2^0
16384	8192	4096	2048	1024	512	256	128	64	32	16	8	4	2	1

Table 5.15. *Denary to binary conversion table - integers*

2^{-1}	2^{-2}	2^{-3}	2^{-4}	2^{-5}	2^{-6}	2^{-7}	2^{-8}	2^{-9}
½	$\frac{1}{4}$	$\frac{1}{8}$	$\frac{1}{16}$	$\frac{1}{32}$	$\frac{1}{64}$	$\frac{1}{128}$	$\frac{1}{256}$	$\frac{1}{512}$

Table 5.16. *Denary to binary conversion table - fractions*

To convert a denary number to binary requires the identification of those place values which, when added together, will equal the denary number. By reference to the appropriate table, a binary 1 is placed in each position, where the value is required and a binary 0 is recorded in each of those remaining. Starting with the largest value in the table, which is less than, or equal to the denary number, successive values to the right are selected and accumulated until the sum is obtained; a binary 1 is placed in each such position. Table 5.17 provides an integer example.

2^{14}	2^{13}	2^{12}	2^{11}	2^{10}	2^9	2^8	2^7	2^6	2^5	2^4	2^3	2^2	2^1	2^0
16384	8192	4096	2048	1024	512	256	128	64	32	16	8	4	2	1
		1	0	1	0	0	1	1	0	0	1	1	1	0

Table 5.17. *Integer 5326₁₀ converted to 1010011001110₂*

Obviously, any value which will result in the required sum being exceeded is skipped, a binary 0 being placed in the relevant position. The place values containing a binary 1 can be summed and the result checked as follows.

$1\times4096 + 0\times2048 + 1\times1024 + 0\times512 + 0\times256 + 1\times128 + 1\times64 + 0\times32 + 0\times16 + 1\times8 + 1\times4 + 1\times2 + 0\times1 = 5326_{10}$

Similarly, Table 5.18, shows a denary fraction converted to binary.

binary point	2^{-1}	2^{-2}	2^{-3}	2^{-4}	2^{-5}
	½	$1/4$	$1/8$	$1/16$	$1/32$
•	0	1	1	1	0

Table 5.18. *Fraction $7/16$ converted to •01110_2*

Again, the binary 1 place values can be totalled and the result confirmed, as follows.
$$0 \times \frac{1}{2} + 1 \times \frac{1}{4} + 1 \times \frac{1}{8} + 1 \times \frac{1}{16} + 0 \times \frac{1}{32} = \frac{7}{16}$$

Method 2 - successive division by the base

Integers

This technique requires that the denary number is successively *divided by 2*, the base of the binary system, until the result of a division is zero. If a division leaves a *remainder* of denary 1, a binary 1 is placed in the next available position in the binary number being formed; if there is a denary 0 remainder, a binary 0 is entered.

Table 5.19 illustrates the process. Note that the binary number should be read, beginning with the most significant bit (MSB), from the bottom of the table, to the least significant bit (LSB). The binary number is written as follows:

1273_{10} = 10011111001_2, the last binary 1, at the bottom of Table 5.19, being the most significant bit (MSB).

denary	divided by	equals	remainder	binary	
1273	2	636	1	1	LSB
636	2	318	0	0	
318	2	159	0	0	
159	2	79	1	1	
79	2	39	1	1	
39	2	19	1	1	
19	2	9	1	1	
9	2	4	1	1	
4	2	2	0	0	
2	2	1	0	0	
1	2	0	1	1	MSB

Table 5.19. *Integer 1273_{10} to 10011111001_2*

Real number conversion

Tables 5.20 and 5.21 show how a *real* (having a fractional component) denary number is converted; the integer and fractional parts must be dealt with separately and differently.

The *integer* part of 34.375_{10} is converted as shown in Table 5.20, by successive division (as in the previous example in Table 5.19). The *fractional* part is converted by a process of successive *multiplication*, as shown in Table 5.21; this table shows that, if a multiplication results in a 1 appearing before the decimal point, the 1 is placed in the next available place to the right of the binary point; otherwise, 0 is placed there. Note that the binary fraction is read from the top of the table, identified by MSB. The process is complete when a product of denary 1 is obtained (much of the time, an exact figure will not be achieved and the process is continued until the desired accuracy is reached). Looking at Tables 5.20 and 5.21 together, the result can be seen to be as follows: 34.375_{10} = 100010.011_2.

Conversion with limited precision

Sometimes, a decimal fraction cannot be converted to its precise binary equivalent (as achieved in Tables 5.20 and 5.21).

Table 5.22 shows the conversion of denary 0.425 to its binary equivalent, but with some loss of precision. The level of precision is determined by the number of place values allocated for the storage of the binary fraction; more places would allow a greater degree of precision.

Table 5.22 shows that, in this example, absolute precision cannot be achieved (the Product column will continue with the pattern shown and denary 1 will never be reached) and that, using the precision limit in the Table, 0.425_{10} is approximately equal to 0.011011001_2.

denary	divided by	equals	remainder	binary	
34	2	17	0	0	LSB
17	2	8	1	1	
8	2	4	0	0	
4	2	2	0	0	
2	2	1	0	0	
1	2	0	1	1	MSB

Table 5.20. *Conversion of 34_{10} (integer part of 34.375_{10})*

denary	multiplied by	equals	binary	
0.375	2	0.75	0	MSB
0.75	2	1.5	1	
0.5	2	1.0	1	LSB

Table 5.21. *Conversion of 0.375 (fractional part of 34.375_{10})*

denary	multiplied by	equals	binary	
0.425	2	0.85	0	MSB
0.85	2	1.7	1	
0.7	2	1.4	1	
0.4	2	0.8	0	
0.8	2	1.6	1	
0.6	2	1.2	1	
0.2	2	0.4	0	
0.4	2	0.8	0	
0.8	2	1.6	1	LSB
0.6	2	1.2	1	etc

Table 5.22. *Denary to binary conversion with loss of precision*

Referring to the place values in Table 5.16, it can be seen that the binary fraction is, in fact, equal to the following expression.

$$0 \times \frac{1}{2} + 1 \times \frac{1}{4} + 1 \times \frac{1}{8} + 0 \times \frac{1}{16} + 1 \times \frac{1}{32} + 1 \times \frac{1}{64} + 0 \times \frac{1}{128} + 0 \times \frac{1}{256} + 1 \times \frac{1}{512}$$

$$= \frac{217}{512}$$

$$= 0 \cdot 423828125$$

The difference is $0.425_{10} - 0.423828125_{10}$ or 0.0011721875_{10}. A greater degree of precision (although not absolute) could be obtained by continuing the process shown in Table 5.22 and using more significant digits.

Denary to octal

Method 2 (successive division by the base), described in the denary to binary section, is also used here, in each case using the relevant base of 8. Table 5.23 shows an example of denary to octal conversion. LSD and MSD stand for least significant *digit* and most significant *digit*.

That $1273_{10} = 2371_8$, is proved, with the following expression (and by reference to the place values shown in Table 5.24).

$$2371_8 = 2 \times 512 + 3 \times 64 + 7 \times 8 + 1 \times 1 = 1273_{10}.$$

denary	divided by	equals	remainder	octal	
1273	8	159	1	1	LSD
159	8	19	7	7	
19	8	2	3	3	
2	8	0	2	2	MSD

Table 5.23. *Integer 1273_{10} converted to octal 2371_8*

8^3	8^2	8^1	8^0
512	64	8	1
2	3	7	1

Table 5.24. *Integer 2371_8 and place values*

Denary to hexadecimal

Method 2 (successive division by the base), described in the denary to binary and denary to octal sections, is also used here, in this case using the relevant base of 16. Table 5.25 shows an example of denary to hexadecimal conversion. Remember that the symbol 'F' is equivalent to denary 15.

denary	divided by	equals	remainder	hex	
1273	16	79	9	9	LSD
79	16	4	15	F	
4	16	0	4	4	MSD

Table 5.25. *Integer 1273_{10} to $4F9_{16}$*

That $4F9_{16} = 1273_{10}$ can be proved by the following expression (the relevant place values appear in Table 5.26).

$$4F9_{16} = 4 \times 256 + 15(F) \times 16 + 9 \times 1 = 1273_{10}.$$

16^2	16^1	16^0
256	16	1
4	F	9

Table 5.26. *Integer $4F9_{16}$ and place values*

Binary arithmetic

Armed with an understanding of numbering systems and in particular the binary system, we will now examine how the simple arithmetic operations of addition and subtraction can be performed using binary numbers.

Binary addition

In order to understand how binary addition works it is a good idea to review the method for the addition of two whole numbers in the more familiar decimal system. Suppose that we wish to add the numbers 27 and 19. This is how such additions are normally performed:

1. Arrange the numbers so that so that digits with corresponding positional values are aligned:

$$\begin{array}{r} 2\quad7 \\ +1\quad9 \\ \hline \end{array}$$

2. Starting at the rightmost digits, add the first pair of digits, producing their sum. If this sum is equal to or greater than ten, thus producing a carry of 1, add this 1 into the addition of the next pair of digits to the left:

$$\begin{array}{r} 2\quad7 \\ +1_1\quad9 \\ \hline \text{carry }1\ 6 \end{array}$$

3. Continue doing this until there are no more additions to perform:

$$\begin{array}{r} 2\quad7 \\ +1_1\quad9 \\ \hline 4\quad6 \end{array}$$

The principles involved in decimal addition are equally appropriate to the addition of two binary numbers, but in this case a carry is produced whenever an addition produces a sum greater than or equal to two rather than ten. Using the same example as for decimal addition, we are dealing with the binary numbers 11001 (that is, 27) and 10011 (that is, 19). To add these, we go through the same steps as for the two decimal equivalents:

$$\begin{array}{r} 1\ 1\ 0\ 0\ 1 \\ +\ 1\ 0\ 0\ 1\ 1 \\ \hline \end{array}$$

1. Arrange the numbers so that so that digits with corresponding positional values are aligned:

2. Starting at the rightmost digits, add the first pair of digits, producing their sum. If this sum is equal to or greater than **two**, thus producing a carry of 1, add this 1 into the addition of the next pair of digits to the left:

$$\begin{array}{r} 1\ 1\ 0\ 0\ 1 \\ +\ 1\ 0\ 0\ 1_1\ 1 \\ \hline \text{carry }1\ 0 \end{array}$$

3. Continue doing this until there are no more additions to perform:

$$
\begin{array}{ccccc}
\begin{array}{r} 1\,1\,0\,0\,1 \\ +\,1\,0\,0_1\!1\,1 \\ \hline 1\,0\,1\,1\,0\,0 \end{array} &
\begin{array}{r} 1\,1\,0\,0\,1 \\ +\,1\,0\,0_1\!1\,1 \\ \hline 0\,1\,1\,0\,0 \end{array} &
\begin{array}{r} 1\,1\,0\,0\,1 \\ +\,1\,0\,0_1\!1\,1 \\ \hline 1\,1\,0\,0 \end{array} &
\begin{array}{r} 1\,1\,0\,0\,1 \\ +\,1\,0\,0_1\!1\,1 \\ \hline 1\,0\,0 \end{array} &
\begin{array}{r} 1\,1\,0\,0\,1 \\ +\,1\,0\,0_1\!1\,1 \\ \hline 0\,0 \end{array}
\end{array}
$$

Rules of binary arithmetic

Table 5.27 summarises the rules of binary addition and includes two further examples.

addition rules	carry	example sum	example sum
$0 + 0 = 0$		$\begin{array}{r}011010\\ +\ 110100 \\ \hline 1001110\end{array}$	$\begin{array}{r}101100\\ +000010 \\ \hline 101110\end{array}$
$0 + 1 = 1$			
$1 + 0 = 1$			
$1 + 1 = 0$	1		

Table 5.27. *Binary addition rules and examples*

Signed numbers

A number stored without indication as to whether it is positive or negative, but simply as having a given magnitude (25_{10}, 129_{10}, for example,) is known as an *unsigned number*. To be of practical use, a computer must be able to store, manipulate and differentiate between positive and negative numbers (*signed numbers*). There are a number of different ways this can be done. The most common are:

❏   sign and magnitude;

❏   complementation.

Sign and magnitude

With this method, the MSB position is occupied by an explicit *sign bit*; binary 0 and binary 1 are used to indicate, respectively, a positive and a negative number. The remainder of the binary word holds the *absolute* (independent of the sign) *magnitude* of the number. The examples in Table 5.28 illustrate this method, using a 16-bit word.

	MSB															LSB
$+0_{10}$	0	0	0	0	0	0	0	0	0	0	0	0	0	0	0	0
$+33_{10}$	0	0	0	0	0	0	0	0	0	0	1	0	0	0	0	1
-33_{10}	1	0	0	0	0	0	0	0	0	0	1	0	0	0	0	1
$+85_{10}$	0	0	0	0	0	0	0	0	0	1	0	1	0	1	0	1
-85_{10}	1	0	0	0	0	0	0	0	0	1	0	1	0	1	0	1
bit	15	14	13	12	11	10	9	8	7	6	5	4	3	2	1	0
	sign	<					m a g n i t u d e									>

Table 5.28. *Sign and magnitude format*

Note from the top row in Table 5.28, that the number zero uses a positive sign (0).

Two's complement numbers

A computer can carry out *addition*, using *two's complement* notation. *Subtraction* can also be effected, through addition (by first negating the number to be subtracted). A two's complement number has an *implicit sign bit*. In other words, it has a place value which contributes to the magnitude of the number, as well as indicating its sign (positive or negative). Table 5.29 shows two 8-bit examples. The positive number examples (+33 and +85) contain a binary 0 in the sign bit position, so the place value of -128 does not contribute to the magnitude of the numbers.

	MSB	place values						LSB
	-128_{10}	64_{10}	32_{10}	16_{10}	8_{10}	4_{10}	2_{10}	1_{10}
$+33_{10}$	0	0	1	0	0	0	0	1
-33_{10}	1	1	0	1	1	1	1	1
$+85_{10}$	0	1	0	1	0	1	0	1
-85_{10}	1	0	1	0	1	0	1	1
bit	7	6	5	4	3	2	1	0

Table 5.29. *Examples of two's complement, positive and negative numbers*

The negative number examples (-33 and -85) contain a binary 1 in the sign bit position, so its place value of -128 forms part of each number's value. The negative value is calculated by adding the negative place value of the sign bit to the positive values of the remaining bits, which contain a binary 1.

These points can be illustrated with the following analysis of the numbers.

$$+33_{10} = 00100001_2 = 0 + 0 + 32 + 0 + 0 + 0 + 0 + 1$$

$$-33_{10} = 11011111_2 = -128 + 64 + 0 + 16 + 8 + 4 + 2 + 1$$

$$+85_{10} = 01010101_2 = 0 + 64 + 0 + 16 + 0 + 4 + 0 + 1$$

$$-85_{10} = 10101011_2 = -128 + 0 + 32 + 0 + 8 + 0 + 2 + 1$$

Subtraction, using two's complement numbers uses the following method. The second number (the *subtrahend*) is negated and is added to the first (the *minuend*). This is equivalent to expressing in denary, for example,

$$(+55) - (+25) \text{ as } (+55) + (-25).$$

Conversion of binary to two's complement

The two's complement of a binary number is obtained through the following stages:

Stage 1

The number is converted to its *one's complement* representation by inverting the values of all the bits in the number. In other words all ones are flipped to zeroes and all zeroes are flipped to ones. The examples in Table 5.30 illustrate the one's complements of some binary numbers.

	Example (i) $+13_{10}$	Example (ii) $+36_{10}$	Example (iii) $+76_{10}$
binary number	0 0 0 0 1 1 0 1	0 0 1 0 0 1 0 0	0 1 0 0 1 1 0 0
one's complement	1 1 1 1 0 0 1 0	1 1 0 1 1 0 1 1	1 0 1 1 0 0 1 1

Table 5.30. *One's complement of binary numbers*

Stage 2

The one's complement of the binary numbers in Table 5.30 can then be converted to *two's complement* by adding 1, as shown in Table 5.31.

	Example (i) $+13_{10}$	Example (ii) $+36_{10}$	Example (iii) $+76_{10}$
one's complement	1 1 1 1 0 0 1 0	1 1 0 1 1 0 1 1	1 0 1 1 0 0 1 1
+	1	1	1
two's complement	1 1 1 1 0 0 1 1	1 1 0 1 1 1 0 0	1 0 1 1 0 1 0 0

Table 5.31. *Converting from one's to two's complement*

The two's complement numbers in each example now represent the following denary values.

$$\text{two's complement of } 13_{10} \text{ is } -128 + 64 + 32 + 16 + 0 + 0 + 2 + 1 = -13_{10}$$

$$\text{two's complement of } 36_{10} \text{ is } -128 + 64 + 0 + 16 + 8 + 4 + 0 + 0 = -36_{10}$$

$$\text{two's complement of } 76_{10} \text{ is } -128 + 0 + 32 + 16 + 0 + 4 + 0 + 0 = -76_{10}$$

Integer arithmetic using two's complement

Binary subtraction

Subtraction can be carried out by negating the second number (the *subtrahend*), in this case by conversion to two's complement form and adding it to the first number (the *minuend*). The ease with which binary numbers can be switched from positive to negative and vice-versa, by complementation, makes subtraction by addition suitable for computers.

Consider the examples in Tables 5.32 and 5.33, assuming a 6-bit word length.

minuend	0 1 1 1 0 1		$+29_{10}$
subtrahend	0 0 0 1 1 1		$+7_{10}$
one's complement of subtrahend	1 1 1 0 0 0		
	1	+	
two's complement of subtrahend	1 1 1 0 0 1	=	-7_{10}
minuend	0 1 1 1 0 1	+	$+29_{10}$
result	1 0 1 0 1 1 0	=	
ignore carry (c)	0 1 0 1 1 0		$+22_{10}$

Table 5.32. *Two's complement arithmetic $29_{10} - (+)7_{10} = 22_{10}$*

The result in Table 5.32 (the carry is ignored) can be proved as follows.

$$010110_2 = 0_{10} + 16_{10} + 0_{10} + 4_{10} + 2_{10} + 0_{10} = 22_{10}.$$

Now consider the example in Table 5.33, where the minuend is smaller than the subtrahend, resulting in a negative answer.

minuend	0 0 0 1 1 1		$+7_{10}$
subtrahend	0 0 1 0 0 1	−	$+9_{10}$
one's complement of subtrahend	1 1 0 1 1 0		
	1	+	
two's complement of subtrahend	1 1 0 1 1 1	=	-9_{10}
minuend	0 0 0 1 1 1	+	$+7_{10}$
result	1 1 1 1 1 0	=	-2_{10}

Table 5.33. *Two's complement arithmetic example $+7_{10} - (+9_{10}) = -2_{10}$*

The result in Table 5.33 can be proved as follows.

$$111110_2 = -32_{10} + 16_{10} + 8_{10} + 4_{10} + 2_{10} + 0_{10} = -2_{10}$$

✍️Exercises

1. Calculate the *denary* equivalents of the following binary numbers:
     (i)   11001110
     (ii)   10101011
     (iii) 01001100
     (iv)   11110000
     (v)   00001111

2. Using the conversion tables provided in this chapter, write down the *octal* and *hexadecimal* equivalents of the binary numbers in Exercise 1.

3. Why is hexadecimal notation used in preference to other number bases, as a shorthand for binary code?

4. Convert the following denary integers to binary, octal and hexadecimal:
     (i) 12   (ii) 15   (iii) 57   (iv) 172

5. Convert the following decimal fractions to 8-bit binary fractions:
     (i) 0.5   (ii) 0.25   (iii) 0.625   (iv) 0.7   (v) 0.963

6. Convert the following negative numbers to 8-bit 2's complement binary numbers:
     (i) -5   (ii) -12   (iii) -84   (iv) -8   (v) -128 (vi) -1

7. Convert the pairs of number in the following list to binary. Then, using 2's complement repesentation for negative numbers, add and subtract each pair using 8-bit binary numbers:
     (i) 17, 3   (ii) 37, 19   (iii) 85, 75   (iv) 13, 21   (v) -16, 27
     (vi) -16, 27   (vii) -73, 82   (viii) -18, -55
     Check your answers by converting them to denary.

Chapter 6

Graphs

This chapter deals with a range of graphical techniques for representing and manipulating numerical data. We start by describing Cartesian equations and Cartesian graphs before investigating the construction and uses of various types of graphs.

Cartesian graphs

An equation of the form $y = 3x + 2$ is called a Cartesian equation, and a graph of the equation is called a Cartesian graph. The *dependent* variable, y (the value of y depends on x), is said to be a *function* of the *independent* variable, x, or $y = f(x)$. When y is used as the vertical scale of a graph, and x is used for the horizontal scale, every point on the resulting grid can be represented by a pair of values, (x,y), called the Cartesian coordinates of the point. Cartesian coordinates are also referred to as *rectangular coordinates*. Henceforth, they will be referred to as just coordinates. The point at which the two axes meet is called the *origin* and has coordinates (0,0). Figure 6.1 shows the coordinates of a number of points on a graph.

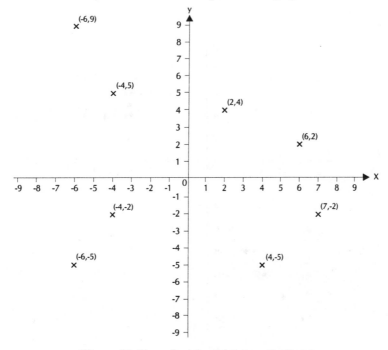

Figure 6.1. *Examples of rectangular coordinates*

In each case, the coordinates have been derived by counting the number of units the point is horizontally displaced from the origin for the x-ordinate, and the displacement vertically for the y-ordinate. The x-ordinate is negative for points to the left of the origin and the y-ordinate is negative for points below the origin.

Graphs of linear functions

A function of the form $y = mx + c$, where m and c are constants (values which do not change), is called a *linear* function of x, since it defines a straight line with *slope* or *gradient*, m, and *intercept*, c. Table 6.1 shows a number of coordinates on the line when $m = 2$ and $c = -4$.

x	−5	−4	−3	−2	−1	0	1	2	3	4	5
$y = 2x - 4$	−14	−12	−10	−8	−6	−4	−2	0	2	4	6

Table 6.1. *Co-ordinates for y = 2x – 4*

Figure 6.2 shows the corresponding graph of the straight line. Notice that the line intersects the y-axis at the point $y = -4$; this is called the intercept and is the value of c.

Though eleven points are given in the table above, in fact only two are absolutely necessary in order to draw the graph. However, it is best to use three points as a check that no mistake has been made in calculating the points.

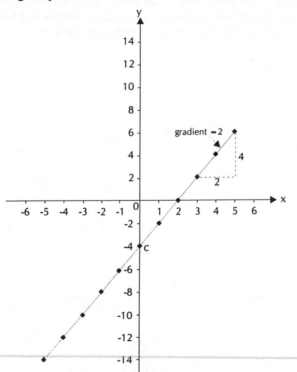

Figure 6.2. *Graph of y = 2x - 4*

Determination of the equation of a straight line

Given that a line can be drawn knowing only two coordinates on the line, it should be possible to find the equation of the line from these two coordinates.

First it is necessary to define what is meant by the slope or gradient of a line. Given two points on the line, the gradient is the ratio between the change in y to the change in x. So for the points (3,2) and (5,6) the gradient is given by

$$gradient = \frac{change\ in\ y}{change\ in\ x} = \frac{6-2}{5-3} = \frac{4}{2} = 2$$

In order to define a line, it is necessary to determine its gradient and intercept. Suppose it is required to find the equation of a line between the points (0,2) and (4,14). This is the type of problem which programs for graphic design must solve frequently. First the gradient of the line is determined:

$$gradient = \frac{14-2}{4-0} = 3$$

The equation of the line is therefore

$$y = 3x + c$$

Now the value of c, the intercept, is determined by substituting one pair of coordinates into the equation:

$$14 = 3(4) + c, \ or \ 2 = 3(0) + c$$

Therefore $c = 2$.

The equation of the line is

$$y = 3x + 2$$

Graphs of quadratic functions

Functions of the form

$$f(x) = x^2 - 2 \ or \ f(x) = x^2 - 3x + 2$$

are called *quadratic* functions and when plotted as graphs they produce curves called *parabolas*. In general, functions involving powers of the independent variable of greater than one are called *non-linear* functions. The quadratic functions

$$y = x^2 - 3x + 2, \ y = x^2 - 2x + 1 \ \text{and} \ y = x^2 + x + 1$$

are shown in Figure 6.3. The points where the curves cross the x-axis are called solutions or *roots* of the equations $x^2 - 3x + 2 = 0, x^2 - 2x + 1 = 0$ and $x^2 + x + 1 = 0$, respectively.

Notice that the graphs show three different possibilities for the number of roots of a quadratic equation:

(i)   Two different roots where the curve crosses the x-axis.

(ii)   A double root where the curve just touches the x-axis.

(iii) No roots because the curve never crosses the x-axis.

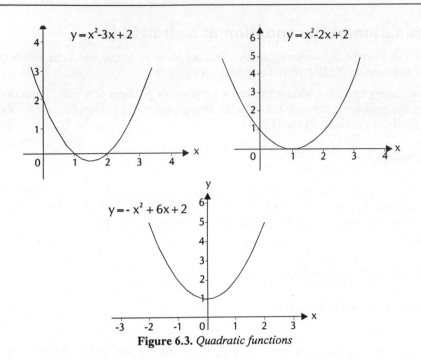

Figure 6.3. *Quadratic functions*

Another point to note is that if the coefficient of the x^2 term is negative then the curve will have a single maximum point and if the coefficient of the x^2 term is positive the curve will have a single minimum point. These two cases are illustrated in the Figure 6.4.

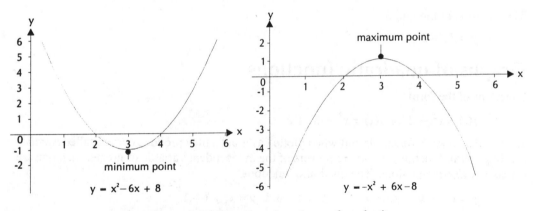

Figure 6.4. *Minimum and maximum of quadratic*

Drawing quadratics

A quadratic function has the general form

$$y = ax^2 + bx + c$$

The values that the coefficients a, b and c have determine the form of the quadratic curve. The effect of the sign of the coefficient, a, has been noted already; more useful observations for drawing quadratics are listed below and are illustrated in Figure 6.5.

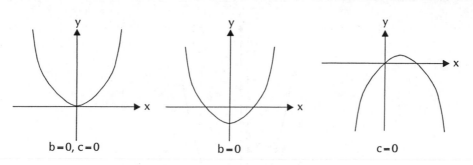

Figure 6.5. *Graphs of various quadratic functions*

(i)   When $b=0$ and $c=0$, the curve is symmetrical about the y-axis and the roots of the function are both at the origin.

(ii)   When $b=0$, the curve is symmetrical about the y-axis, and the roots, if they exist, symmetrically straddle the origin.

(iii) When $c=0$, the curve passes through the origin.

To sketch the graph of a quadratic, use the observations above in conjunction with a table of at least six evenly spaced coordinates on the curve. The range of these coordinates should be such that it covers the roots of the function and the maximum or minimum point. The locations of these points may be identified as follows:

(a)   Roots occur where the y values change sign for consecutive values of x.

(b)   A maximum point occurs where, for consecutive increasing values of x, the magnitude of the y values change from increasing to decreasing.

(c)   A minimum point occurs where the y values change from decreasing to increasing.

Table 6.2 shows the coordinates for the function $y = 2x^2 - x - 6$

x	−4	−3	−2	−1	0	1	2	3	4
y	30	25	4	−3	−6	−5	0	9	22
			A	B	C	D	E		

Table 6.2. *Coordinates for $y = 2x^2 - x - 6$*

The coordinates show that there is a root between points A and B (y changes sign), and that there is a minimum value between points C and D (y goes from decreasing to increasing). The second root is at point E.

The graph is shown in Figure 6.6.

Figure 6.6. *Graph of* $y = 2x^2 - x - 6$

✎Exercises

Straight line graphs

1. Draw graphs of the following equations:
   (i) $y = x + 3$ (ii) $y = 2x - 2$ (iii) $y = 3 - 2x$
   (iv) $y = 3x - 1$ (v) $y = x/2$ (vi) $y = -3 \cdot 5x - 4 \cdot 4$
2. Write down the slope and the intercept of each of the graphs in Q 1.
3. On the same axes draw the graphs of the lines

$$y = 3x + 1 \quad \text{and} \quad y = 5 - x$$

   Write down the co-ordinates of the point of intersection.
4. (i)   On graph paper plot the points given by the co-ordinates (2, 1) and (4, 5). Join the
         points with a straight line. What is the equation of this line?
   (ii) Repeat for the points (0,7) and (1,2).

Conversion graphs and tables

1. Draw a graph of the equation $y = 1 \cdot 5x$ for values of x ranging from 0 to 10. The slope of
   the line $(1 \cdot 5)$ can be interpreted as a conversion factor for converting pounds to dollars.
   In this case we could write the equation as *dollars* $= 1 \cdot 5$ *pounds*. This allows us to use the
   graph to convert between pounds and dollars.
   Convert the following amounts from pounds to dollars:
   (i) 5   (ii) 7   (iii) 10   (iv) $0 \cdot 5$ (v) $5 \cdot 5$
   Convert the following amounts from dollars to pounds:
   (i) 8   (ii) 6   (iii) 14   (iv) 13   (v) 11.5
2. Devise a method for converting larger amounts of pound/dollars, say for amounts up to
   £100.

3. There are 2·2 pounds (lbs) to the kilogram (kg). Draw the conversion graph of pounds/kilograms. Choose axes to allow values up to 20lbs to be converted into kilograms.

4. Sometimes it is preferable to use a conversion table rather than a graph. Construct a table that shows the total cost of goods assuming a VAT rate of 17·5%. The equation that links the cost to the total cost is

   TotalCost = 1.175×Cost

   Construct the table as shown alongside.

   Use the table to find the total price of the following amounts:

   (i) £7   (ii) £12   (iii) £38   (iv) £157

   How could you also allow for amounts less than £1?

5. What are the advantages and disadvantages of using a table rather than a graph for conversion purposes?

Quadratic equations

1. The following table shows selected values for the quadratic equation

   $$y = 0·5x^2 - x - 12$$

x	-5·0	-4·0	-3·0	-2.0	-1·0	0·0	1·0	2·0	3·0	4·0	5·0	6·0	7·0
y	5·5	0·0	-4·5	-8·0	10·5	-12·0	-12·5	-12·0	-10·5	-8·0	-4·5	0·0	5·5

   (i)   Between what two pairs of values of x do the roots of the equation occur?

   (ii)   Does the curve have a maximum or a minimum point?

   (iii)   Between which two x values does the maximum or minimum point lie?

   (iv)   Draw the curve.

   Check your answers using a spreadsheet.

2. Repeat the exercises in 1. for the following tables and equations:

   (i) $y = 8 - 6·5x - 2x^2$

x	-6·0	-5·0	-4·0	-3·0	-2·0	-1·0	0·0	1·0	2·0
y	-25·0	-9·5	2·0	9·5	13·0	12·5	8·0	-0·5	-13·0

   (ii) $y = x^2 - 10x + 10$

x	-1·0	0·0	1·0	2·0	3·0	4·0	5·0	6·0	7·0	8·0	9·0	10·0
y	21·0	10·0	1·0	-6·0	-11·0	-14·0	-15·0	-14·0	-11·0	-6·0	1·0	10·0

   (iii) $y = x^2 - 6x + 9$

x	-1·0	0·0	1·0	2·0	3·0	4·0	5·0	6·0	7·0
y	16·0	9·0	4·0	1·0	0·0	1·0	4·0	9·0	16·0

Chapter 7

Algebra

Algebra is a form of mathematical language. Algebra was devised to allow mathematical ideas to be written down in a concise and clear way. For example, suppose we wished to express the idea of adding together any two numbers; without algebra we could only provide typical examples such as 3 + 4, 7 + 12, 10 + 10. To list all of the pairs of numbers which could be added together would obviously be impossible. Using algebra, the idea of adding two numbers together can be written simply as $a + b$. Here, the letters a and b are 'stand-ins' for numbers; a and b can be replaced by whichever numbers we choose. In mathematics, the correct name for a stand-in letter is *variable*. Thus, a and b are both variables.

Any letters can be used for variables, including letters from other alphabets, such as the Greek alphabet, which is popular with mathematicians. The letter x is often used in algebra to denote an unknown quantity or number which needs to be found. Algebra allows formulae to be written down and is often quoted as being the language of science and engineering. Without the idea of a formula, scientists would have to resort to writing down descriptive 'recipes' for their chemistry and physics experiments. Recipes are long-winded and limited compared to formulae. Algebra allows certain types of problems to be solved. For example, consider this easy problem, (which you can probably do in your head without using algebra). You need to discover an unknown number given the following facts:

If you take this number, double it and then add 10 to it the result will be 20.

Using algebra, the problem can be written down as follows.

The number to be found can be denoted by x; in other words, x is the variable representing the unknown number. Doubling this number is the same as multiplying it by 2, so we can write this as 2 times x (that is, $2 \times x$) or just $2x$. Adding 10 to this gives $2x + 10$, and because this value should result in 20, the complete problem can be written algebraically as

$2x + 10 = 20$

which says that $2x + 10$ is equal to 20.

(Note that, in algebra, when multiplication is used the multiplication sign is dropped. For example, $5x$ means 5 times x.)

By doing the above we have produced a mathematic sentence of the type referred to as an *algebraic equation* or, more usually, just *equation*. This equation can now be solved to give the result for the unknown value x. You can probably see that x *has* the value 5 because 2 times 5 comes to 10 and adding 10 to this produces the result 20, which was what was required by the problem.

Here is another problem which can be written as an algebraic equation:

A rectangle has a length which is three times its width and its perimeter is 32 metres.

Let the width be represented by w. Then, the length must be three times this width, that is $3w$. The perimeter is the total distance around the rectangle, in other words the perimeter is twice the length plus twice the width of the rectangle. The perimeter is therefore

$$2 \times 3w + 2 \times w$$

which simplifies to

$$6w + 2w$$

and which further simplifies to

$$8w$$

We are told that the perimeter is 32 metres long and so the equation is $8w = 32$

This means that the width w must be 4 metres ($8 \times 4 = 32$) and the length must be 12 metres ($3w = 12$).

More formal methods for solving equations are given in a later section.

Evaluating algebraic expressions

In the above section, $2x + 10$ is an example of an *algebraic expression*. An algebraic expression is just a collection of variables (such as x or a) and constants (such as 12 and 5) connected by arithmetic operators. The most common operators are the familiar $+$, $-$, $\times$ and $\div$. Other examples of simple algebraic expressions are:

$$3 + p, \quad 4x - 6, \quad 5a + 2b, \quad x + yz \quad \text{and} \quad (a + b)/2$$

To evaluate expressions like these means that values are given or assigned to the variables and then the overall value of the expression is calculated. For example, let us evaluate the expression $4x - 6$ given that x has the value 5 (i.e. x has been assigned the value 5). Replacing x by 5 produces the expression $4 \times 5 - 6$. So, 4×5 gives 20 and then subtracting 6 gives the result 14.

More formally, an algebraic expression consists of a number of *terms* separated by addition or subtraction operators, and each term contains a number of *factors* containing numbers and letters connected by multiplication and division operators. For example, the expression

$$a + bc - e/f + 16$$

has four terms, a, bc, e/f and 16.

The first term contains only the single factor, a; the second term contains factors b and c connected by a multiplication operator; the third term has factor e divided by factor f, the final term consists of the constant 16. Variables and constants are particular instances of factors. Indexed variables such as p^2 with constants as indices, also appear in algebraic expressions.

Operator precedence

When numbers are assigned to the variables in an algebraic expression, so that it might be evaluated, there are rules of arithmetic operator *precedence* which determine how the evaluation should proceed. For example, in the expression

$$x + yz$$

the multiplication of y and z must precede the addition operation. If the requirement was for the sum of x and y to be multiplied by z then the expression would be written

$$(x + y)z \quad \text{or} \quad z(x + y)$$

The brackets indicate that the addition operation is to precede the multiplication. The order of operator precedence is as follows:

1. Brackets.

2. Exponentiation (raising to a power) e.g. 3^2 (3 squared)

3. Multiplication and Division

4. Addition and Subtraction

To show how to use the above precedence rules, let us evaluate the expression

$$5 - \frac{(a + b)}{c^2}$$

given that $a = 7$, $b = 5$ and $c = 2$.

First, let us replace the variables a, b and c with their actual values. This gives

$$5 - \frac{(7 + 5)}{2^2}$$

Brackets must be evaluated first, so $7 + 5$ gives 12 and the expression becomes

$$5 - \frac{12}{2^2}$$

The temptation at this point would be to subtract the 12 from the 5 but division and exponentiation both have a higher precedence than subtraction. The exponentiation must be carried out next; 2^2 (2 squared, or 2 times 2) gives the result 4 and so the expression is now

$$5 - \frac{12}{4}$$

The division must now be carried out as it has a higher precedence than subtraction; $12 \div 4$ gives 3 and so the expression is reduced to

$$5 - 3$$

which produces the final result of 2.

Formulae

As mentioned earlier, formulae have an important role to play in many areas of life. A formula allows the relationship between two or more quantities to be expressed in a simple and concise form. There are many well-known formulae such as

$$\text{area of rectangle} = \text{length} \times \text{breadth}$$

In algebra this could be written more concisely as

$A = lb$ where A stands for area, l for length and b for breadth.

The first form is obviously more readable than the second. The above formula allows us to calculate the area of a rectangle given that we know the values of the length and the breadth of the rectangle. Putting known values into a formula in order to calculate some unknown value (in this case the area) is known as substituting into a formulae In other words, we substitute known values for the variables in the formula.

The following formula allows temperature, given in degrees Fahrenheit, to be converted into degrees Centigrade.

$$C = \frac{5}{9}(F - 32)$$

Given a Fahrenheit temperature of 95 degrees, we can substitute this value into the equation to give

$$C = \frac{5}{9}(95 - 32)$$

which reduces to

$$C = \frac{5}{9}(63)$$

which gives C = 35 (5 ninths of 63 is 35).

Subscripts in algebra

The Greek letter Σ (pronounced *sigma*) is frequently used in algebraic notation to represent the sum of a number of numbers. Thus the notation

$$\sum_{i=1}^{i=5} x_i$$

represents the sum of the five variables x_1, x_2, x_3, x_4, x_5.

In other words, it is the sum of any five numbers represented by these five variables. The integer *subscripts* attached to the variables indicate that the variables have some link with each other, but apart from that they are like any other variables. A variable with a subscript that is itself a variable, such as x_i represents a range of variables, as illustrated above. The number of variables so represented is determined by the consecutive integer values that can be taken by the subscript; these subscript values are 1 to 5 in the example above. Thus, for the numbers 12, 33, -7, -92, 21, the notation

$$\sum_{i=1}^{i=5} x_i$$

would represent 12 + 33 + (-7) + (-92) + 21, that is, -33, and the variables x_1, x_2, x_3, x_4, x_5 would have, in this case, the values 12, 33, -7, -92, 21 respectively. This notation will come in useful when we are dealing with statistics.

Factorising algebraic expressions

Factorising algebraic expressions involves finding *common factors* in the *terms* that comprise the expression. Terms are separated by + or - signs. For instance, in the expression $3a + 3b - c$, there are three terms: $3a$, $3b$ and c. Moreover, the terms $3a$ and $3b$ contain the common factor 3. So instead of writing $3a + 3b$ we can write $3(a + b)$ and the whole expression can be written $3(a + b) - c$. Notice that the original expression contains two multiplications (ie $3 \times a$ and $3 \times b$), one addition and one subtraction, whereas the factorised expression only requires one multiplication (ie $3 \times (a + b)$), one addition and one subtraction. This means that factorisation can save time and effort when algebraic expressions need to be evaluated by replacing the variables with actual numbers.

Sometimes a common factor can be a term containing a combination of constants and variables. For example, in the expression $6xy + 2x^2y - 4x^2y^2$, the common factor is $2xy$ which means that we can rewrite the expression as $2xy(3 + x - 2xy)$. You can check that this expression is correct by removing the brackets:

$$2xy(3 + x - 2xy) = 2xy \times 3 + 2xy \times x + 2xy \times 2xy = 6xy + 2x^2y + 4x^2y^2$$

In more complex expression, factorisation may be done in two stages. For instance, with the expression $a^2 + abc - 2ac - 2bc^2$ we can start by recognising that the first two terms have common factor a and the last two terms have common factor $-2c$. We can therefore rewrite the expression as $a(a + bc) - 2c(a + bc)$. Now the term $(a + bc)$ is a common factor and we can write $a(a + bc) - 2c(a + bc) = (a + bc)(a - 2c)$.

Factorisation of quadratic expressions

Quadratic expressions contain terms in which at least one variable is raised to the power 2. Here are some examples of quadratic functions:

$$a^2 - b^2, \ 9m^2 - 16n^2, a^2 + 2ab + b^2, 4a^2 - 6ab + 9b^2, 10x^2 - 19x - 15$$

These functions can all be factorised in special ways.

Difference of two squares

The first function, $a^2 - b^2$, is an example of the *difference between two squares*. This type of function has the factors $(a + b)(a - b)$. Again, this can be checked by removing the brackets:

$(a + b)(a - b)$

$= a \times a + a \times -b + b \times a + -b \times -b$

$= a^2 + ab - ab + b^2$

$= a^2 - b^2$

Similarly, the second function factorises to $9m^2 - 16n^2 = (3m - 4n)(3m + 4n)$

This can be of practical use in simplifying calculations. For example, suppose that we want to calculate $45^2 - 35^2$. Using the difference of two squares, we can rewrite this calculation $(45+35)(45-35) = 80 \times 10 = 800$.

Perfect squares

The function $a^2 + 2ab + b^2$ can be written as $a^2 + ab + ab + b^2$. We can then group the first two and the last two terms which have the common factors a and b respectively:

$$a^2 + ab + ab + b^2 = a(a+b) + b(a+b)$$
$$= (a+b)(a+b)$$
$$= (a+b)^2$$

Quadratic functions such as this, that have two identical factors, are called *perfect squares*.

The function $4a^2 - 6ab + 9b^2$ is also a perfect square:

$$4a^2 - 12ab + 9b^2 = 4a^2 - 6ab - 6ab + 9b^2$$
$$= 2a(2a - 3b) - 3b(2a - 3b)$$
$$= (2a - 3b)(2a - 3b)$$
$$= (2a - 3b)^2$$

Factorising quadratic functions of the form $ax^2 + bx + c$

With quadratic functions of the form $ax^2 + bx + c$, where a, b and c (the *coefficients* of the function) are integers, it may be possible to find two common factors by using the following approach. If we are looking for the factors of the quadratic $6x^2 + 11x + 3$, then

$$a = 6,\ b = 11 \text{ and } c = 3.$$

This means that since a is formed from the product of two integers, then these two integers can only be 6 and 1 or 3 and 2, and they must both have the same sign. Similarly, since c is also formed from the product of two integers, then these two integers can only be 3 and 1; they must also have the same signs because their product is positive (ie 3). Furthermore, when we multiply one of the factors of a by one of the factors of c and then add the products we must arrive at the value of b which is 11. All this sounds quite complicated, but if we work through possible combinations of factors in a logical manner, it becomes much clearer. First we take one pair of the factors of a, which is the x^2 coefficient, and try combining the two values with the factors of c as follows:

The diagram shows factors of a being combined with factors of c by multiplying and adding. The sum of the multiplied factors are compared with b, which is 11 in this case. Thus

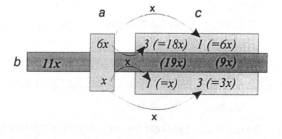

$$6x \times 3 + x \times 1 = 19x \text{ and}$$

$$6x \times 1 + x \times 3 = 9x$$

Neither of these give the required value of 11 for b, so we need to repeat with the other pair of factors for a as shown on the right. This time we see that

$$3x \times 3 + 2x \times 1 = 11x \text{ and}$$

$$3x \times 1 + 2x \times 3 = 9x$$

The value of b has been successfully obtained by combining the two pairs of factors (3, 2) and (3, 1). This tells us that the quadratic function factorises to *(3x+1)(2x+3)*. For a different quadratic function with perhaps more pairs of factors, you would need to methodically combine all the different pairs of a and c factors until the required value for b was obtained. Note, however,

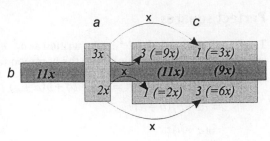

that it might not be possible to factorise a quadratic function at all, so don't be too dismayed if you can't find suitable factors.

Algebraic equations

Placing an equals sign between two algebraic expressions indicates that they have the same numeric value:

$$5x - 6 = 3 \qquad \text{and} \qquad 3y + 5 = y - 3$$

are both equations involving a single unknown variable. In each case the value or values of the variable for which the equation holds true may be determined by making the unknown the *subject* of the equation. This is achieved by applying a sequence of arithmetic operations to both sides of the equation until the variable alone is on the left hand side of the equals sign. For example, to solve the first equation, $5x - 6 = 3$, the following steps would be followed:

(i)   Add 6 to both sides: $5x = 3 + 6$

that is, $5x - 6 + 6 = 3 + 6$ and therefore $5x = 9$

(ii)   Divide both sides by 5:

$$\frac{5x}{5} = \frac{9}{5} \text{ and therefore } x = \frac{9}{5}$$

or, $x = 1.8$, which is the solution.

The solution to the second example might proceed as follows:

(i)   Subtract 5 from both sides: $3y = y - 3 - 5$

that is, $3y = y - 8$

(ii)   Subtract y from both sides: $3y - y = -8$

that is, $2y = -8$

(iii)   Divide both sides by 2: $y = -4$.

The following example illustrates a slightly more difficult equation:

Solve $3(p - 3) = p + 2$

(i)   Remove the brackets by multiplying each term inside the brackets by the term outside the brackets: $3p - 9 = p + 2$

(ii)   Add 9 to both sides: $3p = p + 11$

(iii)   Subtract p from both sides: $2p = 11$

(iv)   Divide both sides by 2: $p = 5.5$,   which is the solution.

Simultaneous equations

If an equation contains two variables (or two unknown values) then it cannot be solved on its own; another equation is needed. In other words, two equations are required to solve for two unknown values; similarly, three equations would be needed if three unknown values were required to be found. Equations like these are referred to as *simultaneous equations*. We will only concern ourselves with simultaneous equations containing two unknowns.

Here is a pair of simultaneous equations:

$$2x + y = 7 \qquad \text{and} \qquad 4x - y = 11$$

The two unknown values, x and y, need to be found. The method we will use first is called the elimination method; later we will see how simultaneous equations can be solved using graphs.

The elimination method requires one of the variables to be eliminated (hence its name) thereby leaving only one unknown to be found; once one unknown is found, the other can be easily determined. Here are the equations again:

$$2x + y = 7$$
$$4x - y = 11$$

and we can see that by adding these equations together the y variable will disappear because y added to $-y$ gives 0. Thus, adding the equations term by term gives

		$2x$	$+$	y	$=$	7
$+$		$4x$	$-$	y	$=$	11
$=$		$6x$	$+$	0	$=$	18
or just				$6x$	$=$	18

Dividing both sides by 6 produces the result $x = 3$.

We can now find y by substituting the value of x into either equation. Using the first equation $2x + y = 7$ and substituting the 3 for x gives

$$2 \times 3 + y = 7 \qquad \text{or}$$
$$6 + y = 7$$

The value of y is clearly 1; Thus the result is $x = 3$ and $y = 1$. Substitution of x by 3 and y by 1 into the original equations confirms that we have found the correct values. Now consider the simultaneous equations

$$4x + 3y = 18 \qquad \text{(equation 1)}$$
$$4x + y = 14 \qquad \text{(equation 2)}$$

This time, if we subtract equation 2 from equation 1, term by term, the variable x will disappear.

Therefore

		$4x$	$+$	$3y$	$=$	18
$-$		$4x$	$+$	y	$=$	14
$=$		0	$+$	$2y$	$=$	4
or just				$2y$	$=$	4

giving the result $y = 2$. Substituting this value of y into equation 2 (equation 1 could equally well have been used) gives

$$4x + 2 = 14$$

Therefore $4x = 12$ and so $x = 3$. The solution is therefore

$$x = 3, y = 2.$$

The simultaneous equations

$$3x + 4y = 18 \quad \text{(equation 1)}$$
$$4x - 3y = -1 \quad \text{(equation 2)}$$

pose an extra problem because neither adding them or subtracting them will eliminate one of the variables. We can get around this problem by multiplying each equation by a certain value so that the numbers (or coefficients) in front of x or y become equal and so can cancel each other out when we add or subtract them. Here, we will choose to eliminate the y variable by multiplying equation 1 by 3 and equation 2 by 4. Note that we must multiply every term in equation 1 by 3 and every term in equation 2 by 4 in order to maintain the balance of the equations. This produces

$$9x + 12y = 54$$
$$16x - 12y = -4$$

and by adding these together we get

$$25x = 50$$

and so $x = 2$. Substituting this value of x into equation 1 gives

$$3 \times 2 + 4y = 18 \text{ or}$$
$$6 + 4y = 18$$

which results in $y = 3$. Thus the solution is

$$x = 2, y = 3.$$

Using graphs to solve simultaneous equations

In this method, graphs of the two equations are drawn on the same set of axes and the co-ordinates of the point at which they cross (that is, the x and y values of their intersection) provide the required solution. Each equation will produce a straight line (or linear) graph.

For example, consider the equations

$$x + y = 6$$
$$2x - 3y = 2$$

In order to draw the graph of the equation $x + y = 6$ we require only three points because the graph will be a straight line. It is easy to determine any three points by realizing that x and y must add up to 6. We always look for easy results! If x is set to 0 then y must equal 6 and so we can plot the point $(0, 6)$ on the graph. Similarly, if y is set to 0 then x must equal 6 allowing us to plot the point $(6, 0)$ on the graph. A third point will help us draw the line more accurately, so let us choose x to be 3 so that y will also be 3. Thus the third point is $(3,3)$.

The graph of $2x - 3y = 2$ now needs to be drawn and this can be approached in the same way. By letting y be equal to 0 reduces the equation to $2x = 2$, and hence $x = 1$. This gives us the point (1, 0). By letting x be equal to 0 reduces the equation to $-3y = 2$ and hence $y = -\frac{2}{3}$. This gives us the point $(0, -\frac{2}{3})$. We need one more point; let us choose $y = 4$ making the equation $2x - 12 = 2$. This reduces to $2x = 14$ making $x = 7$ and giving the final point (7, 4). Note that any suitable value for y could be used.

The graphs of the equations are shown in Figure 7.1 and it can be seen that the co-ordinates of the point of intersection are $x = 4$ and $y = 2$. These are the solutions to the equations. (Substitute these values into each equation to check this for yourself).

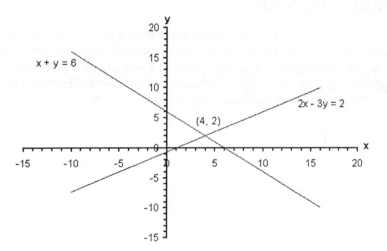

Figure 7.1. *Using a graph to solve simultaneous equations*

Problem-solving with simultaneous equations

A typical problem to be solved is as follows:

An electrical store charges a customer £100 for 4 reels of cable and 2 sockets; another customer is charged £110 for 3 reels of cable and 5 sockets. What are the individual prices of a reel of cable and a socket?

Let x pounds be the price of a reel of cable and y pounds be the price of a socket. Using the above information allows the following equations to be written down

$$4x + 2y = 100 \quad \text{(first equation)}$$
$$3x + 5y = 110 \quad \text{(second equation)}$$

To eliminate y we can multiply the first equation by 5 and the second equation by 2 and then subtract the resulting equations. This will give

	20x	+	10y	=	500
−	6x	+	10y	=	220
=			14x	=	280
or just			x	=	20

Substituting for x into the first equation gives

$$4 \times 20 + 2y \quad = \quad 100$$

or

$$80 + 2y \quad = \quad 100$$

which reduces to $2y = \quad 20$ and hence $y = 10$.

The solution is therefore that a reel of cable costs £20 and a socket costs £10.

Quadratic equations

Quadratic equations involving a single variable take the form $ax^2 + bx + c = 0$, where a, b and c are constants and x is the variable. There are two solutions, or *roots*, of such equations. These roots correspond to the places where the quadratic function $ax^2 + bx + c$ crosses the x-axis when it is plotted as a graph (see *Graphs of Quadratic Functions* in Chapter 6). Figure 7.2 illustrates the graphical solution of a quadratic equation.

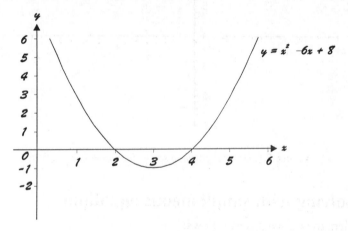

Figure 7.2. *Graph of a quadratic function*

The roots of the quadratic equation $x^2 - 6x + 8 = 0$ are at $x=2$ and $x=4$. Thus if we substitute each of these values into the left-hand side of the equation, it evaluates to zero in both cases:

$$2^2 - 6 \times 2 + 8 = 0$$

$$4^2 - 6 \times 4 + 8 = 0$$

Though graphs can be used to solve quadratic equations, their usefulness is limited by the accuracy with which they can be drawn and interpreted. The previous example had integer roots, but what if a slightly different quadratic equation had roots 3.613 and 8.099? It would probably be quite difficult to draw a graph that could be read with this degree of accuracy, and we might very easily estimate the roots inaccurately.

Fortunately there are two non-graphical methods that we can use to solve quadratic equations: factorisation and by use of a special formula.

Factorisation of quadratic functions

With certain quadratic functions, particularly where the coefficients a, b and c are integers, it is possible to represent them in factorised form. For instance, the function $2x^2 - 8x$ can be factorised as $2x(x - 4)$. Thus, the equation $2x^2 - 8x = 0$ can be written $2x(x - 4) = 0$ which tells us that the roots of the equation are $x=0$ and $x=4$, since either of these two values substituted into the left-hand side of the equation makes it evaluate to zero. Similarly, the quadratic equation $9x^2 - 16 = 0$ can be written $9x^2 = 16$ or $x^2 = \dfrac{16}{9}$, and therefore $x = \pm\sqrt{\dfrac{16}{9}} = \pm\dfrac{4}{3}$.

For the quadratic equation $2x^2 - x - 7 = 0$ we can factorise the left-hand side and write $(2x + 3)(x - 2) = 0$ which tells us that the equation is true when either $2x + 3 = 0$ or $x - 2 = 0$. In other words the roots of the equation are $x = -1.5$ and $x = 2$. Refer to the earlier section in this chapter on *Factorising Quadratic Functions* for more information on how to do this.

Using the formula for solving quadratic equations

The following formula can be used for finding the roots of quadratic equations of the form $ax^2 + bx + c = 0$:

$$x = \frac{-b \pm \sqrt{b^2 - 4ac}}{2a}$$

For example, to solve $3x^2 + 5x + 1 = 0$ we would calculate

$$x = \frac{-5 \pm \sqrt{5^2 - 4 \times 3 \times 1}}{2 \times 3}$$

$$= \frac{-5 \pm \sqrt{25 - 12}}{6}$$

$$= \frac{-5 \pm \sqrt{13}}{6}$$

$$= \frac{-5 \pm 3.601}{6}$$

This gives $x = -1.434$ and $x = -0.232$ as the roots of the quadratic equation $3x^2 + 5x + 1 = 0$ to 3 decimal places.

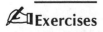 **Exercises**

Forming equations

These exercises are concerned with forming equations from information supplied. At this point you need not actually solve the equations you have formed (unless you want to); a later activity will provide practice at solving equations.

1. My brother is twice as old as I am and our ages added together come to 48. Write down the equation needed to calculate my age. (Let x represent my age).

2. The length of a rectangle is 4 cms longer than its width, and its perimeter is 40 cms. Write down the equation needed to calculate the width of the rectangle.

3. A company calculates wages as follows:

Each employee receives £20 plus an amount arrived at by multiplying the hours worked by a fixed hourly rate of £4.50.

Write down the equation (or formula) required to calculate an employee's wage.

Evaluation algebraic expressions

These exercises concern the evaluation of algebraic expressions. Pay careful attention to precedence.

1. (a) Evaluate $a + bc$ when $a = 5$, $b = 3$ and $c = 7$.

(b) Evaluate $\dfrac{(x+y)}{(x-y)}$ when $x = 8$ and $y = 4$.

(c) Evaluate $a + b^2$ when $a = 10$ and $b = 5$.

(d) Evaluate $e + \dfrac{f}{g} - h$ when $e = 10$, $f = 20$, $g = 5$ and $h = 7$.

(e) A student evaluated the expression $\dfrac{(30-12)}{(6+3)}$ and got the result 6.

What did he do wrong? What is the correct result?

These questions concern substitution into formulae.

2. The formula for a straight line on a graph is $y = mx + c$. Find the value of y when

(a) $m = 2$, $x = 3$ and $c = 4$

(b) $m = 4$, $x = 5$ and $c = 0.5$

3. Use the formula $C = \dfrac{5}{9}(F - 32)$ to convert the following Fahrenheit (F) temperatures to Centigrade (C):

(a) 50 degrees (b) 77 degrees (c) 41degrees.

4. The formula for the circumference (C) of a circle given the radius (r) is given by

$C = 2\pi r$, where π (called pi) can be taken as 3.14.

Calculate the circumference of a circle when the radius is

(a) 20cms   (b) 5.25cms   (c) 200metres

Solving equations

These exercises provide basic practice in solving equations.

Solve the following equations.

(a) $x + 4 = 6$ (b) $x - 7 = 14$ (c) $2x + 6 = 8$ (d) $3x - 1 = 11$

(e) $5p + 3p = 16$ (f) $3 - p = 2$ (g) $14 - 2p = 8$ (h) $3y = y + 6$

(i) $4p + 2 = 7p - 10$ (j) $2(x + 2) = 13 - x$ (k) $2p = 3(p - 2)$

(l) $10(x + 3) = 5x$

Simultaneous equations

1. This question is designed to help you develop the technique of elimination in order to solve simultaneous equations easily. Hints are provided in brackets beside some of the equations. Always check that your answers are correct by substituting your solutions for x and y into the original equations.

Solve the following

(a) $x + y = 7$ (add the equations)
    $x - y = 1$

(b) $2x + y = 8$ (subtract the equations)
    $x + y = 6$

(c) $3x - y = 2$
    $7x + y = 8$

(d) $3x - 2y = 9$
    $x + 2y = 15$

(e) $4x + 4y = 12$
    $2x + 4y = 10$

(f) $4x + 2y = 10$ (multiply this equation by 5)
    $3x + 5y = 11$ (multiply this equation by 2)

(g) $x + y = 20$ (multiply this equation by 3)
    $3x - 3y = 12$ (leave this equation as it is)

(h) $2x + 3y = 16$
    $7x - 2y = 31$

2. This question requires that you use the graphical method of solving simultaneous equations. Use a spreadsheet to draw the graphs.

Solve

(a) $x + y = 15$
    $5x - 2y = 5$

(b) $x - 2y = 1$
    $x + y = 4$

(c) $3x + 4y = 18$
    $2x + 3y = 13$

(d) $7x - 2y = 5$
    $4x + 2y = 6$

Problem-solving with simultaneous equations

These questions require that you formulate two simultaneous equations for each problem using the data that you are given. You must then solve those equations using either the elimination method or the graphical method; the choice is left up to you.

(a) The perimeter of a rectangle is 16 metres and the difference between the length and breadth of the rectangle is 2 metres. What are the dimensions of the rectangle?

(b) A holiday costs £1290 for 3 adults and 2 children; the same holiday costs £1180 for 2 adults and 4 children. Calculate the cost of the same holiday for 3 adults and 3 children.

(c) Two numbers need to be found such that 3 times the first number plus 2 times the second number come to a total of 29, and 4 times the first number plus 3 times the second number come to 40.

Chapter 8

Set theory and logic

Introduction

Data and instructions in a digital computer are represented by the binary numbering system discussed in an earlier chapter. Internal registers and internal memory of the computer must be able to 'remember' data and instructions as sequences of binary digits. The Arithmetic and Logic Unit (ALU) must be able to perform arithmetic on numbers held in this form, and the decoding circuitry of the Control Unit must be able to recognise and interpret program instructions represented by binary numbers. All of these functions, and many more, are performed by logic circuits.

Computer logic is based on a branch of mathematical logic called Boolean Algebra (named after the English mathematician George Boole) which allows the symbolic manipulation of logical variables in a manner very similar to the manipulation of 'unknowns' in an ordinary algebraic expression of the form

$$x.(y+z) \text{ or } x.y + x.z$$

Just as laws are needed for ordinary algebraic expressions, very similar fundamental laws exist for the manipulation of boolean expressions. These laws permit complex logical expressions, representing logic circuits, to be analysed or designed. This chapter introduces the foundations of Boolean Algebra and its relevance to computer circuitry. The chapter starts with an elementary introduction to set theory which is closely related to Boolean Algebra, logic and binary arithmetic. The subject of computer logic is developed further in Chapter 12.

Set theory

A *set* is a collection of objects called *elements*. A set is usually denoted by a capital letter and the elements of the set are enclosed by braces, ie { }, and separated by commas. For example, the set, D, of digits used to represent the denary numbering system is

$$D = \{0, 1, 2, 3, 4, 5, 6, 7, 8, 9\}$$

whereas the set, B, of binary digits is

$$B = \{0, 1\}$$

The symbol $\in$ is used to denote a single element of a set, so that $0 \in B$ is interpreted as "0 is an element of B" and $5 \in D$ means "5 is an element of D".

The size, that is number of elements in a set, is denoted by n(name of set). For instance, $n(D) = 10$ and $n(B) = 2$ because there are 10 elements in D and 2 elements in B.

B is said to be a *subset* of D because every element of B also belongs to D. In set notation this is written B ⊂ D. Because **B** has two elements, it has 2^2 subsets, namely {}, {0}, {1} and {0, 1}. The first subset in the list, {}, is called the *empty* or *null* set containing no elements at all, and the last subset in the list is called the *universal* set of B since it contains all of the elements of concern regarding the binary numbering system. D has 2^{10} (= 1024) subsets: {}, {0}, {1}, {2}, ... {0, 1}, {0, 2}, {0, 1, 2}, {0, 1, 3}, ... etc up to {0, 1, 2, 3, 4, 5, 6, 7, 8, 9}.

The whole set and the empty set are subsets of every set and are called *improper* subsets. All other subsets are called *proper* subsets. Thus, in general any set with n elements has $2^n - 2$ proper subsets. Thus our binary set B has two proper subsets, {0} and {1}.

The *complement* of a set, S, with respect to a universal set, T, consists of those elements of T that are not contained in S. Thus, for our universal set of denary digits, the complement of S = {0, 1, 2} is the set S' = {3, 4, 5, 6, 7, 8, 9} since S' contains those elements of the universal set (ie the digits 0-9) that are not contained in S. An apostrophe after the name of a set denotes the set's complement.

The *union* of two sets consists of those elements that are either in one of the sets or in both of the sets. Thus for the two sets A = {a, b, c} and B = {b, c, d, e} the union of the sets, denoted by

　　　AUB

is {a, b, c, d, e}.

The *intersection* of A and B, denoted by A∩B, is {b, c}, that is the elements that are in both A and B.

Venn diagrams

In Venn diagrams, the universal set is represented by a rectangle and subsets of the universal set are shown as circles. This graph-

Figure 8.1. *Union and intersection of sets*

ical notation allows set operations such as union, intersection and complementation to be illustrated clearly. For example, for two sets A and B, their union and intersection are illustrated in Figure 8.1.

Because set X is a subset of set Y, the Venn diagram shows X completely within Y as illustrated in Figure 8.2.

Venn diagrams can be used to illustrate the actual elements of the unions, intersections and complements of sets. For example, suppose that the universal set A is the set of positive value integers between 1 and 20, B is a subset of A comprising the odd numbers less than 10, and C is the subset of A comprising prime numbers. Then we can represent the union, intersection and complements of B and C by the Venn diagram shown in Figure 8.3. The figure shows that:

B = {1, 3, 5, 7, 9}, C = {1, 2, 3, 5, 7, 11, 13, 17, 19},

B∩C = {1, 3, 5, 7}, BUC = {1, 2, 3, 5, 7, 9, 11, 13, 15, 17, 19} and (B∩C)' = {2, 4, 6, 8, 10, 12, 14, 15, 16, 18, 20}

Figure 8.2. *X is a subset of Y*

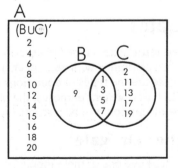

Figure 8.3. *Venn diagram*

Boolean variables

A boolean variable has one of two values representing the presence or absence of an electrical signal when dealing with computer circuitry. These values are normally represented by 1 (signal present) and 0 (signal absent). In terms of computer circuitry, a boolean variable represents a voltage on a line which may be an input to a logic circuit or an output from a logic circuit. For instance, a value of 1 might represent five volts and a value of 0, zero volts. Thus if p, q and r are all boolean variables, they are each able to represent a value of 1 or 0.

Boolean variables are used to represent binary signals in electronic circuits and, using boolean algebra which is a form of set algebra, boolean functions representing computer circuits can be analysed and manipulated. It turns out that basic computer components (ie gates) are based on the basic set operations union, intersection and complementation, so we can use boolean algebra to analyse and design combinations of electronic components required by computer circuitry.

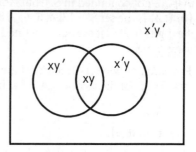

Figure 8.4. *Venn diagram for two boolean variables x and y*

In terms of Venn diagrams, we interpret boolean variables as having a value of 1 inside the circle and a value of 0 outside it. This allows the set operations union, intersection and complementation to be performed on boolean variables. The circles representing the boolean variables are arranged in such a way as to include all possible combinations of 1s and 0s. For example, the Venn diagram for two boolean variables x and y is shown in Figure 8.4. It is usual in computer-related boolean algebra to represent the union of two boolean variables with the '+' sign and call it 'OR', and the intersection as a '.' and call it 'AND'; complementation is usually shown using a bar over the variable. Thus, the Venn diagram representing the the boolean function $x.y + \bar{x}.y$ is shown in Figure 8.5. It is clear from this simple example that the expression simplifies to y which is represented by the rightmost circle, but for more complex boolean expressions it is unlikely that a simplified expression will be so clearly defined. For this reason, other simplification methods, discussed in later sections of this chapter, are generally preferred.

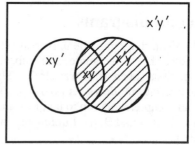

Figure 8.5. *Venn diagram for x.y + $\bar{x}.y$*

Gates

The term 'gate' is used to describe the members of a set of basic electronic components which, when combined with each other, are able to perform complex logical and arithmetic operations. These are the types of operations associated with the ALU (Arithmetic and Logic Unit) of the CPU. For present purposes, the physical construction of the gates is of no direct concern, and the discussion will be restricted to their functions only.

The 'Or' gate

Gates have one or more inputs but only a single output. The nature of the gate determines what the output should be given the current inputs. For example, the OR gate could be defined as in

Table 8.1. X and Y are Boolean variables capable at any time of having the value 1 or 0. Thus at any instant X could have a value of 0 and Y a value of 1, or X could have a value of 1 and Y could have a value of 1; there are four such combinations of the values of X and Y as shown in the table above. With an OR gate, when there is at least one 1 in the input variables, the output is 1. The third column of the table shows the output produced by each combination of the two inputs. The complete table is known as a *truth table* and completely defines the operation of the OR gate for every combination of inputs. As will be shown throughout this chapter, truth tables are extremely useful for describing logic circuits.

Inputs		Output
X	Y	X OR Y
0	0	0
0	1	1
1	0	1
1	1	1

Table 8.1. *Truth table for 'OR' gate*

Symbolically, the combination of X and Y using an OR gate is written

X   *OR*   Y or

X + Y (read as 'X or Y')

Both forms mean that X and Y are inputs to an OR gate. The second form is that required for Boolean Algebra and the '+' is known as the OR operator.

The symbol used when drawing an OR gate in a logic circuit is shown in Figure 8.6. It shows that

Figure 8.6. *OR gate symbol*

the output is 1 if the X OR Y input is 1.

Gates are the physical realisations of simple Boolean expressions. The design of logic circuits is performed symbolically using Boolean Algebra. A Boolean algebraic expression can then be converted very easily into a logic circuit consisting of a combination of gates.

The OR gate is only one of several which are used to produce logic circuits. The other gates of interest are AND, NOT, EOR, NAND and NOR. The first two, in conjunction with the OR gate, are of the most relevance in the current context since these three are directly related to the Boolean operators used in Boolean Algebra.

The 'And' gate

The AND gate is defined by the truth table in Table 8.2. It shows that

the output is 1 when the X input AND the Y input are 1s.

X	Y	X AND Y
0	0	0
0	1	0
1	0	0
1	1	1

Table 8.2. *Truth table for AND gate*

This time, the gate only produces an output of 1 when both inputs are 1s. The Boolean operator equivalent to the AND gate is the AND operator '.', and is written

X.Y (read as 'X and Y')

The symbol for the AND gate is shown in Figure 8.7.

Figure 8.7. *AND gate symbol*

The 'Not' gate

The third important gate is the NOT gate which has the truth table shown in Table 8.3. This gate only has a single input which is inverted at the output. A NOT gate is often called an 'inverter' for this reason and is usually written $\overline{X}$ in Boolean expressions. The symbol for a NOT gate is shown in Figure 8.8.

X	NOT X
0	1
1	0

Table 8.3. *Truth table for NOT gate*

$$X \longrightarrow\!\!\!\triangleright\!\circ\!\longrightarrow \overline{X}$$

Figure 8.8. *NOT gate symbol*

Example of a useful logic circuit

At this point it is worth considering an example of a widely used logic circuit to illustrate the relevance of this chapter. The circuit, which is called a *half adder*, performs the addition of two binary digits to give a sum term, S and a carry term, C, both being Boolean variables. The inputs to the circuit are X and Y representing the two binary digits to be added. The rules for binary addition are shown in Table 8.4 and the equivalent truth table is shown in Table 8.5.

0 + 0 = 0 carry 0 (00)
0 + 1 = 1 carry 0 (01)
1 + 0 = 1 carry 0 (01)
1 + 1 = 0 carry 1 (10)

Table 8.4. *Rules for binary addition*

X	Y	S	C
0	0	0	0
0	1	1	0
1	0	1	0
1	1	0	1

Table 8.5. *Truth table for binary addition*

The requirement is for a combination of AND/OR/NOT gates to give two separate outputs for (S)um and (C)arry given any two binary digits represented by X and Y. The circuit is shown in Figure 8.4 (notice that the various gates have the same X and Y inputs) and the equivalent Boolean expressions for S and C are

$$S = X.\overline{Y} + \overline{X}.Y$$

$$C = X.Y$$

Figure 8.9. *Half adder circuit*

To prove that the circuit actually works a truth table (Table 8.6) is constructed showing the output from every component in the circuit from stage to stage, given the inputs to that stage.

Thus if X=0 and Y=0, $\overline{Y}$=1 and using the truth table for the AND gate, $X.\overline{Y} = 0.1 = 0$ and $\overline{X}.Y = 1.0 = 0$. The rightmost OR gate in the diagram has inputs $X.\overline{Y}$ and $\overline{X}.Y$, that is, 0 and 0, and using the truth table for the OR gate, it can be seen that this results in an output of 0 for S. Similarly, if X=0 and Y=0, the truth table for the AND gate shows that X.Y=0, that is C=0 for this combination of inputs.

X	Y	X̄	Ȳ	X.Ȳ	X̄.Y	X.Ȳ + X̄.Y (S)	X.Y (C)
0	0	1	1	0	0	0	0
0	1	1	0	0	1	1	0
1	0	0	1	1	0	1	0
1	1	0	0	0	0	0	1

Table 8.6. *Truth table for half adder circuit*

Following this type of argument for the remaining rows in the truth table, it can be seen that the circuit produces exactly the right output for each combination of inputs to perform binary addition on the input bits. Thus a combination of a few elementary components has produced a most important circuit. A truth table allowed the operation of the circuit to be confirmed. Later it will be shown how the Boolean expressions representing the circuit can be derived directly from the first truth table defining the required operation of the circuit.

Deriving Boolean expressions from truth tables

Suppose that it is required to produce a suitable logic circuit from the following circuit specification.

A circuit has two binary inputs, X and Y. The output from the circuit is 1 when the two inputs are the same; otherwise the output is 0.

X	Y	OUTPUT
0	0	1
0	1	0
1	0	0
1	1	1

The first step is to produce a truth table to define the circuit fully and this is shown in Table 8.7. Each possible combination of X and Y has been listed. Where X and Y are the same, OUTPUT has been assigned a value of 1; where X and Y are different, OUTPUT has been assigned a value of 0.

Table 8.7. *Truth table for specified circuit*

The next step is to define, for each entry in the OUTPUT column having a value of 1, a Boolean expression involving X and Y which uniquely defines that value. So for the first row in the table, where X=0 and Y=0, the expression X̄.Ȳ has a value of 1; for any other combination of X and Y it has a value of 0. The expression therefore satisfies the requirement of uniquely defining this combination of values. The expression X.Y has a value of 1 only when X=1 and Y=1, otherwise it has a value of 0, and so it uniquely defines the last row in the truth table. Together the expressions X̄.Ȳ and X.Y will produce an output of 1 when X=0 and Y=0 or when X=1 and Y=1. Hence

X	Y	X̄	Ȳ	X̄.Ȳ	X.Y	X̄.Ȳ+X.Y
0	0	1	1	1	0	1
0	1	1	0	0	0	0
1	0	0	1	0	0	0
1	1	0	0	0	1	1

Table 8.8

$$\text{OUTPUT} = \bar{X}.\bar{Y} + X.Y$$

The truth table in Table 8.8 confirms this result and the circuit is shown in Figure 8.10.

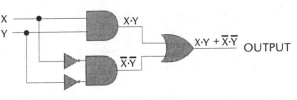

Figure 8.10.

The process of converting a truth table to a Boolean expression is summarised as follows:

(a) Consider only the rows of the truth table for which the output is to be 1.

(b) Take each of these rows in turn and write alongside the row an expression containing the input variables connected by the AND operator. If the value of an input variable is 0 then it will appear inverted in the expression.

(c) Combine these expressions using the OR operator.

To provide another illustration of the process suppose that three binary signals A, B and C, are required to represent a number in the range 0 to 4. The variable A represents the most significant digit of the binary number ABC, B is the next significant digit, and C is the least significant digit. A circuit is required to detect an illegal combination (that is the numbers 5 to 7) by producing an output of 1. The truth table is shown in Table 8.9. Therefore

OUTPUT = $A.\bar{B}.C + A.B.\bar{C} + A.B.C$

and the required circuit is shown in Figure 8.11. As an exercise, use a truth table to prove that the Boolean expression above does indeed produce the required outputs.

A	B	C		OUTPUT	
0	0	0	(0)	0	
0	0	1	(1)	0	
0	1	0	(2)	0	
0	1	1	(3)	0	
1	0	0	(4)	0	
1	0	1	(5)	1	$A.\bar{B}.C$
1	1	0	(6)	1	$A.B.\bar{C}$
1	1	1	(7)	1	$A.B.C$

Table 8.9

Figure 8.11.

Minimisation of Boolean functions

Though the circuit above does perform as specified, it is very inefficient; it uses more gates than are absolutely necessary to produce the required outputs. In fact rather than six gates, only two are necessary because, as the truth table in Table 8.10 shows,

$A.\bar{B}.C + A.B.\bar{C} + A.B.C = A.(B + C)$

A	B	C	$\bar{B}$	$\bar{C}$	$A.\bar{B}.C$	$A.B.\bar{C}$	$A.B.C$	$(A.\bar{B}.C + A.B.\bar{C} + A.B.C)$	$(B+C)$	$A.(B+C)$
0	0	0	1	1	0	0	0	0	0	0
0	0	1	1	0	0	0	0	0	1	0
0	1	0	0	1	0	0	0	0	1	0
0	1	1	0	0	0	0	0	0	1	0
1	0	0	1	1	0	0	0	0	0	0
1	0	1	1	0	1	0	0	1	1	1
1	1	0	0	1	0	1	0	1	1	1
1	1	1	0	0	0	0	1	1	1	1

Table 8.10.

The circuit for the simplified expression is shown in Figure 8.12.

Figure 8.12.

The laws of Boolean algebra enable boolean expressions such as that in the example above to be transformed and simplified. The process of simplifying or *minimising* boolean functions is an important step in the design of computer circuits; in general, the simpler the function, the more economical it is to produce the equivalent circuit. This was certainly true when computer circuits were constructed from discrete components (i.e. gates). However, with the development of integrated circuit technology and Very Large Scale Integration (VLSI) the importance of individual components in the overall cost of a circuit became much less significant. The emphasis shifted to finding methods of finding the best combination of logic gates to perform a given set of functions on a single chip. Computer circuit designers now address the problem of finding the best combination of gates to perform a given set of functions rather than trying to find the smallest number of gates for a particular function. However, whatever the aim, it is still necessary to be able to manipulate boolean expressions and this requires a knowledge of the *Laws of Boolean Algebra*.

Laws of Boolean Algebra

The most useful of these laws are as follows:

1.   Commutative Laws.

     (a)   X+Y=Y+X; (b) X.Y=Y.X

2.   Associative Laws.

     (a)   X+(Y+Z) = (X+Y)+Z; (b) X.(Y.Z) = (X.Y).Z

3.   Distributive Laws.

     (a)   X.(Y+Z) = X.Y + X.Z; (b) X + Y.Z = (X+Y).(X+Z)

4.   De Morgan's Laws.

     (a) $\overline{(X + Y)} = \overline{X}.\overline{Y}$; (b) $\overline{(X.Y)} = \overline{X} + \overline{Y}$

5.   Laws of Absorption.

     (a)   X + X.Y = X; (b) X.(X + Y) = X

6.   Laws of Tautology.

     (a)   X + X = X; (b) X.X = X

7.   Law of Complementation.

$$\overline{\overline{X}} = X$$

Other useful identities:

8.   (a) $X + \overline{X} = 1$; (b) $X.\overline{X} = 0$

9.   (a) X + 1 = 1; (b) X.1 = X

10.   (a) X + 0 = X; (b) X.0 = 0

Notice that with each of the laws, there is a connection between (a) and (b). Given one of these rules, the other may be derived by replacing the '+' operator with the '.' operator or vice-versa. Thus if it is known that $X + X.Y = X$, then the 'dual' of the rule, that $X.(X+Y)=X$, is also true. All identities in Boolean Algebra have this useful *Property of Duality* which states that

> *If a given statement holds in boolean algebra, then so does the formula obtained by interchanging '.' and +, and the elements 0 and 1 throughout the formula.*

To illustrate the use of these laws in the simplification of Boolean expressions, consider the expression derived earlier:

$$A.\overline{B}.C + A.B.\overline{C} + A.B.C$$

Simplification of this expression could proceed as follows:

(i) $\quad A.\overline{B}.C + A.B.\overline{C} + A.B.C = A.\overline{B}.C + (A.B.\overline{C} + A.B.C)$

Rule 1 allows us to deal with terms in any order.

(ii) Considering the bracketed pair of terms,

$A.B.\overline{C} + A.B.C = A.B.(\overline{C} + C)$ by rule 3(a)

Here A.B is treated as if it were a single variable, and the expression is therefore of the form

$X.\overline{C} + X.C = X.(\overline{C} + C)$ where X represents A.B

(iii) Rule 8(a) shows that $\overline{C} + C = 1$, so that

$A.B.(\overline{C} + C) = A.B.1$

and by rule 8(d),

$A.B.1 = A.B$

(iv) Hence,

$A.\overline{B}.C + (A.B.\overline{C} + A.B.C) = A.\overline{B}.C + A.B$

(v) Again using rule 3(a),

$A.\overline{B}.C + A.B = A.(\overline{B}.C + B)$

This is of the form

$X.Y + X.Z = X.(Y + Z)$

(vi) Now consider the term $\overline{B}.C + B$.

Using rule 1(a), this can be rewritten $B + \overline{B}.C$, and now using rule 3(b),

$B + \overline{B}.C = (B + \overline{B}).(B + C)$

As in step (iii), $(B + \overline{B}) = 1$ and $1.(B+C) = (B+C)$.

Hence $B + \overline{B}.C = (B + C)$ and therefore

$A.(B + \overline{B}.C) = A.(B+C)$

Thus the original expression has been considerably simplified and confirms the identity stated earlier.

Fortunately, the process of simplifying expressions involving AND terms separated by OR operators can be performed in a much simpler way using the Karnaugh Map method. This method, as well as being quicker and less prone to error, is also more likely to result in the best simplification possible, particularly where four variables are involved. In certain cases, however, a knowledge of the laws of Boolean Algebra are required. Examples of such instances will be provided later.

Karnaugh maps

A Karnaugh map consists of a two-dimensional grid which is used to represent a Boolean expression in such a way that it can be simplified with great ease. For example, consider the expression

$$\overline{X}.Y + X.\overline{Y} + X.Y$$

This expression involves two Boolean variables, X and Y. The number of different terms possible with two variable is four, and therefore the Karnaugh map for expressions involving two variables is a 2×2 grid, as shown in Figure 8.13.

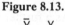

	$\overline{Y}$	Y
$\overline{X}$	(a)	(b)
X	(c)	(d)

Figure 8.13.

Each cell in the grid may be regarded as having a co-ordinate formed from a combination of X and Y. Thus the cell labelled (a) has the co-ordinate $\overline{X}.\overline{Y}$, (b) has the co-ordinate $\overline{X}.Y$, (c) has the co-ordinate $X.\overline{Y}$, and (d) has the co-ordinate $X.Y$. When entered onto the map, the expression quoted above translates to the map in Figure 8.14.

	$\overline{Y}$	Y
$\overline{X}$	0	1
X	1	1

Figure 8.14.

Each '1' on the map indicates the presence of the term corresponding to its cell co-ordinate in the expression, and each '0' indicates its absence.

Using a further example, the expression $\overline{X}.Y + \overline{X}.\overline{Y}$ translates to the map shown in Figure 8.15.

	$\overline{Y}$	Y
$\overline{X}$	1	1
X	0	0

Having drawn the appropriate Karnaugh map, the next stage is to attempt to identify a simplified expression. The procedure is as follows:

Figure 8.15.

(i)   Identify all pairs of adjacent '1's on the map (horizontally and vertically).

(ii) Draw loops around each pair.

(iii) Attempt to include every '1' on the map in at least one loop; it is allowable to have the same '1' in two different loops.

(iv) The aim is to include each '1' in at least one loop, but using as few loops as possible.

Thus the expression $\overline{X}.Y + X.\overline{Y} + X.Y$ is mapped as shown in Figure 8.16.

(v)   Take each loop in turn and write down the term represented: the loop labelled (a) in Figure 8.16 spans both X and $\overline{X}$, but Y remains constant. The loop is therefore given the value Y. In the loop labelled (b), both Y co-ordinates are covered but X remains constant. This loop has the value X.

Figure 8.16.

(vi) The loop values are ORed together. In the example, the expression is therefore equivalent to $X + Y$.

Karnaugh maps take advantage of a small number of the laws of Boolean Algebra. The Distributive Law allows terms with common variables to be grouped together:

$$X.\overline{Y} + X.Y = X.(\overline{Y} + Y) \text{ (see rule 3(a))}$$

Another law, 8(a), gives the identity $\overline{Y} + Y = 1$.

And finally, law 8(d) says that $X.1 = X$.

The Karnaugh map allows this sequence of applications of laws to be performed in a single step:

the loop (b) representing $X.\overline{Y} + X.Y$ becomes X.

'1's may be included in more than one loop because of the Law of Tautology (Tautology is saying the same thing twice). Thus $X + X = X$, and conversely, $X = X + X$. In other words, any term in an expression may be duplicated as many times as desired without affecting the value of the expression. So, given the expression

$$\overline{X}.Y + X.\overline{Y} + X.Y,$$

the term X.Y may be duplicated to give the equivalent expression

$$\overline{X}.Y + X.Y + X.\overline{Y} + X.Y,$$

where loop (a) is $\overline{X}.Y + X.Y$, and loop (b) is $X.\overline{Y} + X.Y$.

As a further example, the expression

$$\overline{X}.\overline{Y} + \overline{X}.Y + X.Y$$

gives the map in Figure 8.17 and the equivalent expression is

$$\overline{X} + Y$$

Figure 8.17.

Karnaugh maps for three variables

Expressions containing three variables can contain up to eight terms. The 3-variable map is drawn as shown in Figure 8.18.

This time a co-ordinate pair comprises an X variable and a YZ term.

Figure 8.18.

For example, the cell (a) represents the term $\overline{X}.\overline{Y}.Z$, and (b) represents X.Y.Z.

The map in Figure 8.19 represents the expression $X.\overline{Y}.Z + X.Y.\overline{Z} + X.Y.Z$.

In loop (a), X and Z are common factors, but Y changes

Figure 8.19.

($\overline{Y}.Z + Y.Z$). The loop has the value X.Z. In loop (b), X and Y are constant but Z changes ($Y.Z + Y.\overline{Z}$). Thus (b) has value X.Y. The expression therefore simplifies to

$$X.Y + X.Z$$

and a further application of law 3(a) gives the final solution

$$X.\overline{Y}.Z + X.Y.\overline{Z} + X.Y.Z = X.(Y + Z)$$

With a 3-variable map, as well as looping pairs of '1's, it is necessary to look for groups of four '1's. For example, the map shown in Figure 8.20 could represent the expression

$$X.Y.Z + \overline{X}.\overline{Y}.Z + \overline{X}.Y.Z + X.\overline{Y}.Z$$

Figure 8.20.

The single loop spans the X co-ordinate completely, and so X can be removed from the simplified expression. In the YZ terms spanned, Y changes and Z is constant. The simplified expression is merely Z.

Two further examples of groups of four are shown in Figures 8.21 and 8.22.

Figure 8.21.

Figure 8.22.

In Figure 8.23 the group of four is formed from opposite sides of the grid. Figures 8.24 to 8.27 provide some further examples with combinations of different types of loops illustrated.

Note that the largest groups are identified first, and then sufficient smaller groups so that every '1' is in at least one loop.

Figure 8.23.

Figure 8.24.

Figure 8.25.

Figure 8.26.

Figure 8.27.

Karnaugh maps for four variables

With four variables there can be up to sixteen different terms involved, and the 4-variable map is a 4×4 grid, as shown in Figure 8.28.

It is necessary to look for groupings of 8, 4 and 2 with the 4-variable map. Figures 8.29 to 8.32 illustrate a number of possible groupings, including some that occur on the edges of the maps and which are sometimes difficult to recognise. Again, to determine the term equivalent to the loop, look for the variables that remain common to the co-ordinates of the loop's range horizontally and vertically.

Figure 8.28.

Figure 8.29. **Figure 8.30.**

Figure 8.31. **Figure 8.32.**

Exercises

Sets

1. Calculate the number of proper subsets and list the proper subsets of the following sets:
   (i)   R = {red, white, blue}
   (ii) J = {Alan, Roy, Angela, Mike}
   (iii) X = {1, 2, 3, 4, 5}

2. If A is the set of letters of the alphabet, and C is the subset of consonants,
   (i)   What letters are in the set C' ?
   (ii) In set notation write "C is a subset of A".
   (iii) Write expressions for the union and intersection of C and C'. What sets do the union and intersection of C and C' represent?

3. Harry is studying GCSE English, maths, science, history, art, French, graphics and R.E. Mary is studying GCSE English, maths, history, geography, French, Spanish, psychology, economics, R.E. and sociology. If H is the set of Harry's GCSE subjects and M is the set of Mary's GCSE subjects, write down the following sets:
   (i)   H∪M
   (ii) H∩M
   How many proper subsets of H and M are there?

4. Draw a Venn diagram for question 3.

Truth tables

5. Prove that the following identities are true using truth tables:
   (i)   X.(Y+Z) = X.Y + X.Z

(ii) $X+Y.Z = (X+Y).(X+Z)$

(iii) $\overline{(X+Y)} = \overline{X} .\overline{Y}$

(iv) $\overline{(X.Y)} = \overline{X} + \overline{Y}$

(v) $X + X.Y = X$

(vi) $X.(X+Y) = X$

(vii) $\overline{A}.\overline{B} + A.B = (A.\overline{B} + \overline{A}.B)$

(viii) $A.\overline{B}.C + A.\overline{B}.\overline{C} + A.B.C + \overline{A}.\overline{B}.\overline{C} = A.(\overline{B}+C) + \overline{(B+C)}$

Karnaugh maps

6. Simplify the expressions represented by the following Karnaugh maps:

(i)

	$\overline{Y}.\overline{Z}$	$\overline{Y}.Z$	$Y.Z$	$Y.\overline{Z}$
$\overline{X}$	0	1	1	0
X	1	1	1	0

(ii)

	$\overline{Y}.\overline{Z}$	$\overline{Y}.Z$	$Y.Z$	$Y.\overline{Z}$
$\overline{X}$	1	1	0	1
X	1	1	1	0

(iii)

	$\overline{Y}.\overline{Z}$	$\overline{Y}.Z$	$Y.Z$	$Y.\overline{Z}$
$\overline{X}$	1	0	1	1
X	1	0	0	0

(iv)

	$\overline{Y}.\overline{Z}$	$\overline{Y}.Z$	$Y.Z$	$Y.\overline{Z}$
$\overline{X}$	1	1	1	1
X	0	0	1	1

(v)

	$\overline{Y}.\overline{Z}$	$\overline{Y}.Z$	$Y.Z$	$Y.\overline{Z}$
$\overline{X}$	1	0	1	1
X	1	0	0	0

(vi)

	$\overline{Y}.\overline{Z}$	$\overline{Y}.Z$	$Y.Z$	$Y.\overline{Z}$
$\overline{X}$	1	0	0	1
X	1	1	1	1

(vii)

	$\overline{Y}.\overline{Z}$	$\overline{Y}.Z$	$Y.Z$	$Y.\overline{Z}$
$\overline{W}.\overline{X}$	1	1	0	1
$\overline{W}.X$	0	1	0	0
$W.X$	0	1	1	0
$W.\overline{X}$	1	1	1	1

(viii)

	$\overline{Y}.\overline{Z}$	$\overline{Y}.Z$	$Y.Z$	$Y.\overline{Z}$
$\overline{W}.\overline{X}$	1	0	0	1
$\overline{W}.X$	1	1	1	1
$W.X$	0	1	1	1
$W.\overline{X}$	1	1	0	1

(ix)

	$\overline{Y}.\overline{Z}$	$\overline{Y}.Z$	$Y.Z$	$Y.\overline{Z}$
$\overline{W}.\overline{X}$	1	0	1	1
$\overline{W}.X$	0	0	1	1
$W.X$	1	0	0	0
$W.\overline{X}$	1	0	0	0

(x)

	$\overline{Y}.\overline{Z}$	$\overline{Y}.Z$	$Y.Z$	$Y.\overline{Z}$
$\overline{W}.\overline{X}$	0	0	1	0
$\overline{W}.X$	1	1	1	1
$W.X$	1	0	1	1
$W.\overline{X}$	0	0	1	0

Chapter 9

Arrays and matrices

Matrices allow numerical information to be presented in a compact form. In addition, matrix algebra allows matrices to be manipulated in various useful ways so that they can be used in a wide range of applications. In this chapter we concenrate on the use of matrices in computer graphics. However, to introduce matrices we first look at tabular data in the form of *arrays*.

The idea of an *array* of data is an important concept in computer programming and, as a foundation for further study of that subject, we will introduce the mathemetical notation used to define arrays and show how they can be used to process tabular data. This investigation of one and two-dimensional arrays will then lead on to the concept of *vectors* and *matrices*.

Arrays

A data structure comprising a list of data items, such as numbers, is called an *array*. Algebraically, an array is usually defined as follows:

$$L_i \qquad i = 1, .. N$$

The array has the name, L, in this instance and the i subscript takes values from 1 to N, where N is an integer representing the number of values in the array. Thus, for the six values 3, 4, 2, 0, 1, 9 $N=6$ and

$$L_1 = 3; \; L_2 = 4; \; L_3 = 2; \; L_4 = 0; \; L_5 = 1; \; L_6 = 9$$

This is called a one-dimensional array because it is a simple list of numbers in which any particular number can be referenced by a single subscript.

One-dimensional arrays

A one-dimensional array could be used to represent a list of student marks in a number of subjects, prices of a number of articles, heights of children, or in fact any collection of numbers which can be conveniently grouped together. For this reason, arrays are frequently used to represent data which are to be analysed statistically.

Arrays used in computer languages represent a set of consecutive memory locations. Array notation allows this area of memory to be referred to by a single variable. In a Pascal program, for instance, the declaration

```
ListNums   :array[1..20] of integer;
```

reserves 20 storage locations (or areas of memory capable of storing a single number) which are collectively know as `ListNums`. A subscript in brackets is used to specify which one of these 20 is being referenced at any time. Thus the notationre `ListNums[5]` refers to the fifth element of the array, `ListNums`, in memory. In programs, a variable used for the subscript greatly facilitates processing operations on arrays. For example, in order to add 20 numbers held in the array, ListNums, in memory, the following Pascal code could be used:

```
for i:= 1 to 20 do S:= S + ListNums[i];
```

Here S is being used to accumulate the contents of the array elements and would initially be set to zero. The for statement sets the subscript i to an initial value of 1, and every time the statement following do is executed, increments i by 1 and again executes the statement; S:= S + ListNums[i] adds the specified array element to the running total, S, and stores the result back to S.

The sequence of processing is therefore

```
S = 0 + ListNums[1]

S = ListNums[1] + ListNums[2]

S = (ListNums[1] + ListNums[2]) + ListNums[3]

S = (ListNums[1] + ListNums[2] + ListNums[3]) + ListNums[4]
```

and so on until ListNums[20] is finally referenced.

If arrays were not implemented in the language then the addition would be effected by writing

```
S := Num1 + Num2 + Num3 + Num4 + .... + Num20
```

where each number now has its own individual variable name and the numbers must be treated as individuals. This is obviously very unwieldy, and unworkable for large numbers (say 100 or more) of values.

Other languages such as BASIC, C and COBOL have similar facilities for allowing the use of arrays.

Two-dimensional arrays

A table of information is an example of a two-dimensional array. A particular item in a table is referenced by its row and position within the row (or column). For example, Table 9.1 details features of four manufacturers of removable media.

Media	Syquest	Olympus	Panasonic	Iomega
Price (£)	105	229	229	359
Price (£) per disk	17	7	20	15
Capacity (Mb)	230	230	650	1,000
Buffer size (k)	32	256	512	256
Seek time (ms)	13.5	27	92	12

Table 9.1. *Two-dimensional 5 × 4 array*

The Mb capacity figure (230) for the Olympus requires two 'co-ordinates': the row for capacity and the column for Olympus. If the table contained only a single column for one manufacturer then it would be an example of a one-dimensional array. Thus a two-dimensional array may be viewed as a set of one-dimensional arrays.

In array notation, the table could be represented by a single variable, M, with two subscripts, i (for the rows) and j (for the columns):

$$M_{i,j} \quad i = 1,...,5$$
$$j = 1,...,4$$

The array is of size 5 by 4 (written 5 × 4), the size of arrays being defined as *row × column*. Thus, in Table 9.1

$$M_{2,1} = 17, \quad M_{4,1} = 32, \quad M_{5,4} = 12$$

High level programming languages which allow one-dimensional arrays will almost invariably cater for two-dimensional arrays too. Again using Pascal as an example, the same two-dimensional array could be declared before use with the declaration

```
M    :array[1..5, 1..4] of integer;
```

which allocates storage space sufficient for the 20 elements (5 × 4) of array, M. Program statements which make reference to this array must use two subscripts to refer to a particular element. Thus M[3,2] makes reference to the second element in the third row.

Performing calculations on arrays

Suppose that a certain computer program for producing graphics on a monitor stores information about simple geometrical shapes in tabular form. Each point of a figure to be drawn is stored in a table of x-y co-ordinates. These co-ordinates give the position of each vertex (i.e. corner) of the figure. For example, the rectangle in Figure 9.1 might be stored as detailed in Table 9.2.

Point	x	y
1	100	0
2	100	200
3	0	200
4	0	0

Table 9.2. *Co-ordinates for drawing rectangle*

A positive value indicates cursor movement right for x and up for y; negative values mean move left for x and down for y. By performing various calculations on the co-ordinates, the original rectangle in Figure 9.1 can be transformed in a number of different ways.

The following examples assume that the original rectangle's co-ordinate values are stored in the two-dimensional array, A, of dimension 4 × 2, shown in Table 9.3.

The transformed co-ordinates will be stored in the array B, also 4 × 2. Each of the transformation illustrations shows the original rectangle filled grey, for comparison.

j i	1	2
1	100	0
2	100	200
3	0	200
4	0	0

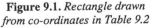

Table 9.3. *Co-ordinates of rectangle stored in array A*

Figure 9.1. *Rectangle drawn from co-ordinates in Table 9.2*

Scaling

In this transformation, Figure 9.2 retains the original shape but is drawn either larger or smaller depending on a *scaling factor*. The new co-ordinate values are calculated by multiplying each by a constant scaling factor. For example, to double the dimensions of the figure, each co-ordinate value in array A (Table 9.3) would be multiplied by a scaling factor of 2,

$$B_{i,j} = 2 \times A_{i,j}$$

$$i = 1,..4$$

$$j = 1, 2$$

and storing the resulting co-ordinates in array B (Table 9.4). Multiplication by a value smaller than 1 would reduce the size of the rectangle.

j	1	2
i		
1	200	0
2	200	400
3	0	400
4	0	0

Table 9.4. *Array B with scaling factor of 2*

Figure 9.2. *Original rectangle scaled by a factor of 2*

Reflection about the y-axis

As Figure 9.3 shows, when the rectangle is reflected about the y-axis the size and shape of the figure remain exactly the same but it is a mirror image of the original.

This transformation is effected by multiplying each x-ordinate by −1 as follows.

$$B_{i,1} = (-1) \times A_{i,1} \quad i = 1,..4$$

Array B then contains the values shown in Table 9.5.

j	1	2
i		
1	−100	0
2	−100	200
3	0	200
4	0	0

Table 9.5. *Co-ordinate values for reflection about y-axis*

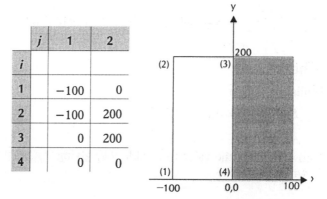

Figure 9.3. *Original rectangle reflected about the y-axis*

Reflection about the x-axis

This has a similar effect to a reflection about the y-axis, and is produced by multiplying each y-ordinate by −1:

$$B_{i,2} = (-1) \times A_{i,2} \quad i = 1,..4$$

The x-ordinate is left as it is:

$$B_{i,1} = A_{i,1} \quad i = 1,..4$$

x-shear

Here the x-ordinate is formed from the sum of the x and y values, and the y value is unmodified:

$$B_{i,1} = A_{i,1} + A_{i,2} \quad i = 1,..4$$

$$B_{i,2} = A_{i,2} \quad\quad i = 1,..4$$

The results are in Table 9.5. The transformation distorts the shape, as shown in Figure 9.4.

j	1	2
i		
1	100	0
2	300	200
3	200	200
4	0	0

Table 9.5. *Co-ordinate values for x-shear*

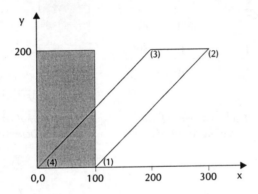

Figure 9.4. *x-shear on original rectangle*

j	1	2
i		
1	100	100
2	100	300
3	200	0
4	0	0

Table 9.6. *Co-ordinate values for y-shear*

y-shear

Similar to x-shear :

$$B_{i,2} = A_{i,1} + A_{i,2} \quad i = 1,..4$$

$$B_{i,1} = A_{i,1} \quad\quad i = 1,..4$$

B now contains the values in Table 9.6, giving the shape shown in Figure 9.5.

Figure 9.5. *Y-shear on original rectangle*

Matrix algebra

By applying simple rules we can add subtract and multiply two matrices. These fundamental matrix operations are used in many branches of mathematics and they are particularly useful in certain computer processing tasks. Later in this section we will investigate the use of matrices in computer graphics animation, but to begin with we will look at the basic matrix notation and arithmetic operations required to understand this application.

Matrix notation

The size of a matrix is defined by the number of rows and columns of elements that it contains. For instance, a 3×2 matrix, such as matrix A below, has 3 rows and 2 columns:

$$A = \begin{pmatrix} 3 & 1 \\ -5 & 6 \\ 0 & -2 \end{pmatrix}$$

The first row of A is $(3, 1)$ and the second column of A is $\begin{pmatrix} 1 \\ 6 \\ -2 \end{pmatrix}$.

Her are two more examples of matrices:

$$B = \begin{pmatrix} 3 & 1 & 5 \\ 5 & 2 & 4 \\ 9 & 1 & 7 \end{pmatrix} \text{ is a } 3 \times 3 \text{ matrix}; \quad C = \begin{pmatrix} 1 & 0 & 2 & 4 & 7 \\ 0 & 9 & 3 & 1 & 6 \end{pmatrix} \text{ is a } 2 \times 5 \text{ matrix}.$$

Note that a 2×5 matrix is not the same as a 5×2 matrix: two matrices have the same size only if they have exactly the same number of rows and columns.

Some special matrices

A *square* matrix has the same number of rows as columns. Thus 2×2, 3×3 and 4×4 matrices are all square matrices.

The *unit* matrix is a square matrix that has 1s in the left-to-right diagonal and zeros in all the other elements. Thus the matrices $\begin{pmatrix} 1 & 0 \\ 0 & 1 \end{pmatrix}$ and $\begin{pmatrix} 1 & 0 & 0 \\ 0 & 1 & 0 \\ 0 & 0 & 1 \end{pmatrix}$ are both unit matrices.

The *inverse* of a square matrix M is denoted by M^{-1}, and is such that the product of a matrix and its inverse is equal to the corresponding unit matrix. Thus for a 2×2 matrix, M,

$$MM^{-1} = \begin{pmatrix} 1 & 0 \\ 0 & 1 \end{pmatrix}$$

Matrix addition and subtraction

Addition and subtraction of two matrices is perfromed by adding or subtracting the corresponding elements of the two matrices. This means that both matrices must be the same size. Thus, if

$$A = \begin{pmatrix} 3 & 1 \\ -5 & 6 \\ 0 & -2 \end{pmatrix} \text{ and } B = \begin{pmatrix} 6 & 2 \\ 7 & -3 \\ 1 & 5 \end{pmatrix} \text{ then}$$

$$A + B = \begin{pmatrix} 3 & 1 \\ -5 & 6 \\ 0 & -2 \end{pmatrix} + \begin{pmatrix} 6 & 2 \\ 7 & -3 \\ 1 & 5 \end{pmatrix} = \begin{pmatrix} 9 & 3 \\ 2 & 3 \\ 1 & 3 \end{pmatrix}$$

and 　　$$A - B = \begin{pmatrix} 3 & 1 \\ -5 & 6 \\ 0 & -2 \end{pmatrix} - \begin{pmatrix} 6 & 2 \\ 7 & -3 \\ 1 & 5 \end{pmatrix} = \begin{pmatrix} -3 & -1 \\ -12 & 9 \\ -1 & -7 \end{pmatrix}$$

Matrix multiplication

The simplest form of matrix multiplication is when a matrix is multiplied by a single number.
So if matrix $C = \begin{pmatrix} 1 & 0 & 2 & 4 & 7 \\ 0 & 9 & 3 & 1 & 6 \end{pmatrix}$, then $3C = \begin{pmatrix} 3 & 0 & 6 & 12 & 21 \\ 0 & 27 & 9 & 3 & 18 \end{pmatrix}$. This applies to multiplication by any type of number, no matter whether it is integer, negative or fractional.

Multiplication of two matrices is more complicated. Firstly, the two matrices to be multiplied must be such that the number of columns of the first matrix must equal the number of rows of the second matrix. Thus it is possible to multiply a 3×2 matrix by a 2×5 matrix, but it is not possible to multiply a 2×3 matrix by a 5×5 matrix. A simple way to remember this condition is to write the sizes of the two matrices next to each other. The inner two numbers (the value 2 in this case) must be equal: (3×2) (2×5).

If this condition is true, then the two matrices to be multiplied are said to be *compatible*, and only compatible matrices can be multiplied. This means that matrix multiplication cannot be reversed, that is, if P is a 4×2 matrix and Q is a 2×3 matrix, then we can calculate P×Q but not Q×P.

The size of the resulting matrix when a 3×2 matrix is multiplied by a 2×5 matrix is a 3×5 matrix. In other words, the size of the resulting matrix has the same number of rows as the first matrix and the same number of columns as the second matrix.

The process of multiplying two matrices is as follows. Suppose we use subscripts to represent the elements of two compatible matrices A and B that are to be multiplied to produce the matrix product, C. That is $C = A \times B$ or

$$\begin{pmatrix} c_{11} & c_{12} \\ c_{21} & c_{22} \end{pmatrix} = \begin{pmatrix} a_{11} & a_{12} & a_{13} \\ a_{21} & a_{22} & a_{23} \end{pmatrix} \times \begin{pmatrix} b_{11} & b_{12} \\ b_{21} & b_{22} \\ b_{31} & b_{32} \end{pmatrix}.$$

Then the element in the *first row* and the *first column* of C is the product of the *first row of A* and the *first column of B*:

$$c_{11} = (a_{11} \quad a_{12} \quad a_{13}) \times \begin{pmatrix} b_{11} \\ b_{21} \\ b_{31} \end{pmatrix} = a_{11}b_{11} + a_{12}b_{21} + a_{13}b_{31}$$

The element in the *second row* and the *first column* of C is the product of the *second row of A* and the *first column of B*:

$$c_{21} = (a_{21} \quad a_{22} \quad a_{23}) \times \begin{pmatrix} b_{11} \\ b_{21} \\ b_{31} \end{pmatrix} = a_{21}b_{11} + a_{22}b_{21} + a_{23}b_{31}$$

The element in the *first row* and the *second column* of C is the product of the *first row of A* and the *second column of B*:

$$c_{12} = (a_{11} \quad a_{12} \quad a_{13}) \times \begin{pmatrix} b_{12} \\ b_{22} \\ b_{32} \end{pmatrix} = a_{11}b_{12} + a_{12}b_{22} + a_{13}b_{32}$$

The element in the *second row* and the *second column* of C is the product of the *second row of A* and the *second column of B*:

$$c_{22} = (a_{21} \quad a_{22} \quad a_{23}) \times \begin{pmatrix} b_{12} \\ b_{22} \\ b_{32} \end{pmatrix} = a_{21}b_{12} + a_{22}b_{22} + a_{23}b_{32}$$

Suppose that $A = \begin{pmatrix} 3 & 2 & 6 \\ 1 & 9 & 5 \end{pmatrix}$ and $B = \begin{pmatrix} 2 & 6 \\ 3 & 7 \\ 1 & 2 \end{pmatrix}$.

Then $C = \begin{pmatrix} 3 & 2 & 6 \\ 1 & 9 & 5 \end{pmatrix} \times \begin{pmatrix} 2 & 6 \\ 3 & 7 \\ 1 & 2 \end{pmatrix} = \begin{pmatrix} 3\times2+2\times3+6\times1 & 3\times6+2\times7+6\times2 \\ 1\times2+9\times3+5\times1 & 1\times6+9\times7+5\times2 \end{pmatrix}$

$$= \begin{pmatrix} 6+6+6 & 18+14+12 \\ 2+27+5 & 6+63+10 \end{pmatrix} = \begin{pmatrix} 18 & 44 \\ 34 & 79 \end{pmatrix}$$

Two by two matrices

In this section we will consider some special properties of 2×2 matrices and how they can be used to solve simultaneous linear equations.

Determinant

The *determinant* of a square matrix is a single number associated with the matrix, and for a 2×2 matrix $\begin{pmatrix} a & c \\ b & d \end{pmatrix}$ it has the value given by $ad - bc$. So, for the matrix $M = \begin{pmatrix} 3 & 4 \\ 2 & 7 \end{pmatrix}$, $det\, M$, or $|M| = 3\times7 - 2\times4 = 13$.

Inverse

The *inverse* of a 2×2 matrix such as $P = \begin{pmatrix} a & c \\ b & d \end{pmatrix}$ is calculated as follows:

1. Swap a and d
2. Change the signs of b and c
3. Divide by the determinant.

Thus the inverse of P is given by $\quad P^{-1} = \dfrac{1}{ad - bc} \begin{pmatrix} d & -c \\ -b & a \end{pmatrix}$

For example, for matrix $M = \begin{pmatrix} 3 & 4 \\ 2 & 7 \end{pmatrix}$, its determinant is 13 (see above) and its inverse is therefore given by

$$M^{-1} = \frac{1}{13} \begin{pmatrix} 7 & -4 \\ -2 & 3 \end{pmatrix} = \begin{pmatrix} \frac{7}{13} & -\frac{4}{13} \\ -\frac{2}{13} & \frac{3}{13} \end{pmatrix}.$$

Matrix equations

The inverse of a matrix can be used to solve matrix equations of the form $AX=B$, where A, X and B are matrices. If A and B are known, then, by multiplying both sides of the equation by A^{-1}, we have $AA^{-1}X = A^{-1}B$. We know that AA^{-1} is equal to the unit matrix, and multiplying a matrix by the unit matrix has no effect, so $AA^{-1}X = X$ and therefore $X = A^{-1}B$. For example, suppose we want to solve the matrix equation $AX=B$ when $A = \begin{pmatrix} 6 & 1 \\ 2 & 2 \end{pmatrix}$ and $B = \begin{pmatrix} 2 \\ 10 \end{pmatrix}$. First we calculate

$$A^{-1} = \frac{1}{12-2} \begin{pmatrix} 2 & -1 \\ -2 & 6 \end{pmatrix} = \frac{1}{10} \begin{pmatrix} 2 & -1 \\ -2 & 6 \end{pmatrix}$$

Then

$$X = \frac{1}{10} \begin{pmatrix} 2 & -1 \\ -2 & 6 \end{pmatrix} \begin{pmatrix} 2 \\ 10 \end{pmatrix} = \frac{1}{10} \begin{pmatrix} -6 \\ 56 \end{pmatrix} = \begin{pmatrix} -0.6 \\ 5.6 \end{pmatrix}$$

Solving simultaneous linear equations with matrices

Matrix equations can be used to solve simultaneous linear equations of the form

$$ax + by = l$$
$$cx + dy = m$$

by representing the equations as a matrix equation in the form

$$\begin{pmatrix} a & b \\ c & d \end{pmatrix} \begin{pmatrix} x \\ y \end{pmatrix} = \begin{pmatrix} l \\ m \end{pmatrix}$$

As we saw in the previous section, this equation can be solved for x and y by calculating

$$\begin{pmatrix} x \\ y \end{pmatrix} = \begin{pmatrix} a & b \\ c & d \end{pmatrix}^{-1} \begin{pmatrix} l \\ m \end{pmatrix}$$

For example, suppose that we wish to find the solution of the simultaneous equations

$$3x + 2y = 13,\ 3x - 4y = 1.$$

We first write the corresponding matrix equation: $\begin{pmatrix} x \\ y \end{pmatrix} = \begin{pmatrix} 3 & 2 \\ 3 & -4 \end{pmatrix}^{-1} \begin{pmatrix} 13 \\ 1 \end{pmatrix}$

Next we need to calculate $\begin{pmatrix} 3 & 2 \\ 3 & -4 \end{pmatrix}^{-1} = \dfrac{1}{-18} \begin{pmatrix} -4 & -2 \\ -3 & 3 \end{pmatrix}.$

Then

$$\begin{pmatrix} x \\ y \end{pmatrix} = \frac{1}{-18} \begin{pmatrix} -4 & -2 \\ -3 & 3 \end{pmatrix} \begin{pmatrix} 13 \\ 1 \end{pmatrix} = \frac{1}{-18} \begin{pmatrix} -54 \\ -36 \end{pmatrix} = \begin{pmatrix} 3 \\ 2 \end{pmatrix}$$

Thus the solution is $x = 3,\ y = 2.$

Using matrices for geometrical transformations

The examples earlier in this chapter illustrating simple 2-dimensional transformations using arrays can be very conveniently generalised by using matrices. A matrix is somewhat like a 2-dimensional array and a coordinate pair, representing the vertex of a 2-dimensional geometrical shape, is a special 1-dimensional form of a matrix called a *vector*. Transformations on geometrical shapes can be performed by multiplying each vertex vector by a 2 × 2 matrix to give a set of transformed vertices. The new vertices then represent the transformed shape. By changing the matrix values different transformations can be effected. Multiplying a vertex vector by a 2 × 2 matrix can be represented by the following notation:

$$(xt, yt) = (x, y) \begin{pmatrix} a & c \\ b & d \end{pmatrix}$$

This states that the point (x, y) transforms to the point (xt, yt) when multiplied by the transform matrix $\begin{pmatrix} a & c \\ b & d \end{pmatrix}$. The matrix operation shown above produces the following equations for xt and yt, the transformed coordinates of the point (x, y):

$$xt = ax + by$$

$$yt = cx + dy$$

The choice of a, b, c and d determines the particular transformation to be performed on the point. An application of this process is to perform transformations on sets of vertices representing shapes using standard transformation matrices such as those discussed earlier (ie scaling, reflecting and shearing). A shape can be transformed by applying the appropriate transformation matrix to each of its vertices. These vertices form an $n \times 2$ matrix, wher n represents the number of vertices in the shape, so applying a particular transformation involves multiplying the vertex matrix by the appropriate transformation matrix. An example is provided in the next section.

2-D transformation matrices

Table 9.7 shows a number of examples of transformation matrices for two-dimensional shapes.

Transform Type	Tranformation Matrix	Comments
Scaling	$\begin{pmatrix} s_x & 0 \\ 0 & s_y \end{pmatrix}$	s_x is the x scaling factor and s_y is the y scaling factor. $s_x = s_y$ for uniform scaling
Reflection about the x-axis	$\begin{pmatrix} 1 & 0 \\ 0 & -1 \end{pmatrix}$	
Reflection about the y-axis	$\begin{pmatrix} -1 & 0 \\ 0 & 1 \end{pmatrix}$	
x shear	$\begin{pmatrix} 1 & 0 \\ 0 & s_x \end{pmatrix}$	s_x is the x-shear factor
y shear	$\begin{pmatrix} 1 & s_y \\ 0 & 1 \end{pmatrix}$	s_y is the y-shear value
Clockwise rotation about the origin	$\begin{pmatrix} \cos\theta & -\sin\theta \\ \sin\theta & \cos\theta \end{pmatrix}$	θ is the angle of rotation
Anticlockwise rotation about the origin	$\begin{pmatrix} \cos\theta & \sin\theta \\ -\sin\theta & \cos\theta \end{pmatrix}$	θ is the angle of rotation

Table 9.7. *Some transformation matrices*

As an example of how to use these matrices, we will apply some transformations to the shape shown in Figure 9.6.

The coordinates of the shape, starting from the vertex at the origin and moving clockwise can be represented by the 4×2 matrix $v = \begin{pmatrix} 0 & 0 \\ 15 & 3 \\ 10 & 0 \\ 15 & -3 \end{pmatrix}$.

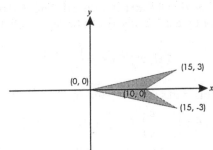

Figure 9.6. *Shape to be transformed*

If we wish to produce a new matrix, s, representing the original figure rotated 30° anticlockwise, then we calculate

$$s = \begin{pmatrix} 0 & 0 \\ 15 & 3 \\ 10 & 0 \\ 15 & -3 \end{pmatrix} \times \begin{pmatrix} \cos 30° & \sin 30° \\ -\sin 30° & \cos 30° \end{pmatrix} = \begin{pmatrix} 0 & 0 \\ 15 & 3 \\ 10 & 0 \\ 15 & -3 \end{pmatrix} \times \begin{pmatrix} 0.866 & 0.5 \\ -0.5 & 0.866 \end{pmatrix} = \begin{pmatrix} 0 & 0 \\ 11.5 & 10.1 \\ 8.7 & 5 \\ 14.5 & 4.9 \end{pmatrix}.$$

Figure 9.7 shows the rotated shape. We can use this procedure for any type of transformation simply by choosing the appropriate values for the transformation matrix. This convenient procedure is ideal for implementation on a computer to produce animation effects. For example, to make a shape appear to rotate continuously we repeatedly calculate the rotation transform in a loop that increases the value of the angle of rotation. The required algorithm is outlined below:

1.   Draw the shape for $\theta = 0°$

2.   Increment θ, say by 5°.

Figure 9.7. *Shape rotated by 30 deg.*

3.   Calculate the new coordinates of the shape by multiplying the vertex matrix by the rotation matrix.

5.   Erase the current shape.

6.   Draw the shape using the new coordinates

7.   Repeat from step 2.

Repeatedly drawing, erasing and redrawing a shape in a different position gives the illusion of movement.

In-place transformations

Up to now our transformations have been made relative to the origin. For example, reflection about the x-axis involves reflecting about the horizontal line that passes through the origin; reflection about the y-axis involves reflecting about the vertical line that passes through the origin; scaling applies scaling factors to the distance of points from the origin. However, suppose that we wish to reflect the shape shown in Figure 9.8 about the vertical plane indicated by the dotted line rather than about the origin.

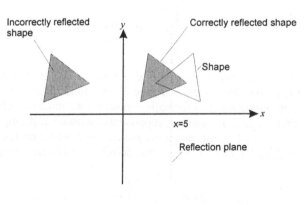

Figure 9.8. *Reflection about specified plane*

If we just apply our y-reflection transformation matrix, the shape would appear in the wrong place as indicated in Figure 9.8. The solution is first to move the shape so that its reflection plane coincides with the origin, then apply the transformation matrix, and finally move the new shape back to where it should be. In this example it simply means that we subtract 5 from the x-coordinates of every vertex, apply the transformation and then add 5 to the new x-coordinates. This process is illustrated in Figure 9.9.

This process of moving the shape to the origin, performing the transformation and then moving the shape back again is necessary for all transformations that are required in-place rather than relative to the origin.

Figure 9.9. *Procedure for reflecting about a given plane*

Using matrix multiplication to move a shape.

Moving a shape from one position to another is termed *translation*. To translate a point (x_0, y_0) a distance T_x along the x-axis and T_y along the y-axis, to form a new point (x_1, y_2) we simply calculate $x_1 = x_0 + T_x$ and $y_1 = y_0 + T_y$. For example, to move the point (3, 5) a distance $T_x = 1$ and $T_y = 2$, we simply calculate the new point (3+1, 5+2) = (4, 7). In terms of moving a complete shape with a number of vertices, we simply add the displacement values (ie T_x and T_y) to each vertex.

It turns out that translation can also be performed by using matrix multiplication if we use *homogeneous* transformation matrices. These are 3×3 matrices that have the following general form:

$$T = \begin{pmatrix} a & c & 0 \\ b & d & 0 \\ T_x & T_y & 1 \end{pmatrix}$$

The elements *a, b, c* and *d* are the now familiar constants used in our previous 2×2 tranformation matrices. T_x and T_y represent the *x* and *y* displacements required. In order to use homogeneous transformation matrices we must modify our vertex vector to be *(x, y, 1)* rather than *(x, y)*. For example, suppose that without applying any transformation, we want to move a point (6, 2) 3 units along the x-axis. Then we set $a=1$, $b=0$, $c=0$ and $d=1$ (this applies a uniform scaling factor of 1, which has no effect) and calculate the new point using

$$(6 \quad 2 \quad 1) \times \begin{pmatrix} 1 & 0 & 0 \\ 0 & 1 & 0 \\ 3 & 0 & 1 \end{pmatrix} = (6+0+3 \quad 0+2+0 \quad 0+0+1)$$

$$= (9 \quad 2 \quad 1)$$

This might seem like a complicated way to perform a simple task, but using homogeneous matrices has a two major advantages:

1.   A shape can be transformed or translated to a different position using a single matrix multiplication.

2.   Because exactly the same process can be used for both transforming and translating shapes, it simplifies the creation of computer programs to perform animation effects.

As a final example of using matrices to perform two-dimensional transformations, we will examine in detail the calculations required to rotate a square in-place about its mid point, as illustrated in Figure 9.10.

Figure 9.10. *Rotating a square in-place about its centre*

The vertex matrix of the square, each vertex having the form (x, y, 1) is $\begin{pmatrix} 2 & 1 & 1 \\ 4 & 1 & 1 \\ 4 & 3 & 1 \\ 2 & 3 & 1 \end{pmatrix}$. The coordinates of the centre of the square are (3, 2). To move the square's centre to the origin we use the homogeneous translation matrix

$$\begin{pmatrix} 1 & 0 & 0 \\ 0 & 1 & 0 \\ -3 & -2 & 1 \end{pmatrix}$$

Thus, the calculation for the translated coordinates is given by

$$\begin{pmatrix} 2 & 1 & 1 \\ 4 & 1 & 1 \\ 4 & 3 & 1 \\ 2 & 3 & 1 \end{pmatrix} \times \begin{pmatrix} 1 & 0 & 0 \\ 0 & 1 & 0 \\ -3 & -2 & 1 \end{pmatrix} = \begin{pmatrix} -1 & -1 & 1 \\ 1 & -1 & 1 \\ 1 & 1 & 1 \\ -1 & 1 & 1 \end{pmatrix}$$

This matrix represents the coordinates of the square with its centre at the origin.

To rotate the square clockwise 45° about its centre (now the origin) we use the matrix

$$\begin{pmatrix} \cos 45° & -\sin 45° & 0 \\ \sin 45° & \cos 45° & 0 \\ 0 & 0 & 1 \end{pmatrix} = \begin{pmatrix} 0.707 & -0.707 & 0 \\ 0.707 & 0.707 & 0 \\ 0 & 0 & 1 \end{pmatrix}$$

Thus the rotation calculation becomes

$$\begin{pmatrix} -1 & -1 & 1 \\ 1 & -1 & 1 \\ 1 & 1 & 1 \\ -1 & 1 & 1 \end{pmatrix} \times \begin{pmatrix} 0.707 & -0.707 & 0 \\ 0.707 & 0.707 & 0 \\ 0 & 0 & 1 \end{pmatrix} = \begin{pmatrix} -1.414 & 0 & 1 \\ 0 & -1.414 & 1 \\ 1.414 & 0 & 1 \\ 0 & 1.414 & 1 \end{pmatrix}$$

This matrix contains the coordinates of the square rotated by 45° about its centre at the origin.

Finally we return the rotated square back to its original position by multiplying the vertex matrix by another translation matrix:

$$\begin{pmatrix} -1.414 & 0 & 1 \\ 0 & -1.414 & 1 \\ 1.414 & 0 & 1 \\ 0 & 1.414 & 1 \end{pmatrix} \times \begin{pmatrix} 1 & 0 & 0 \\ 0 & 1 & 0 \\ 3 & 2 & 1 \end{pmatrix} = \begin{pmatrix} 1586 & 2 & 1 \\ 3 & 0.586 & 1 \\ 4.414 & 2 & 1 \\ 3 & 3.414 & 1 \end{pmatrix}$$

The final 4×3 matrix contains the new coordinates of the square rotated about its centre.

Exercises

Two-dimensional arrays

1. With reference to the following two dimensional array, T, answer the questions below:

	j				
i	0	1	2	3	4
0	10	13	6	−2	0
1	33	17	−21	16	39
2	45	−9	40	39	22
3	49	71	12	88	−45

(i) What are the values of the following elements of T?

$T_{3,4}$ $T_{0,1}$ $T_{2,1}$ $T_{1,3}$

(ii) What elements of T contain the following values?

−9   12   45   6   33   0

Performing calculations on arrays

2. The following table represents the x-y coordinates of a simple geometrical figure.

x	0	1	3	1	0	−1	0	−1
y	3	1	0	−1	−3	−1	−3	1

(i) Plot the figure on graph paper.

(ii) Apply the following scaling factors to the figure and plot the new shape:

2   5   ·5   3·5

(iii) Perform an x-shear and y-shear on the original figure and plot the new shapes.

Matrices

1. Find the sum and the difference of the following pairs of matrices:

    (i) $\begin{pmatrix} 2 & 3 \\ 5 & 6 \end{pmatrix}, \begin{pmatrix} 5 & -3 \\ 1 & 8 \end{pmatrix}$ (ii) $\begin{pmatrix} 7 & 2 \\ 1 & 6 \\ -9 & 2 \\ 5 & 8 \end{pmatrix}, \begin{pmatrix} 0 & 1 \\ 2 & 3 \\ 4 & 7 \\ -5 & -3 \end{pmatrix}$ (iii) $\begin{pmatrix} 5 & 8 & 1 \\ -9 & -2 & 0 \end{pmatrix}, \begin{pmatrix} -6 & 7 & 2 \\ -4 & 9 & 6 \end{pmatrix}$

2. The sizes of a number of matrices are given below. List all combinations of pairs of matrices that are *compatible* for multiplication purposes.

    A=2 x 2;B=3 x 2;C=2 x 4;D=5 x 3; E=2 x 1

3. If the matrices in question 2 are defined as follows, perform all the possible matrix multiplications:

    $A = \begin{pmatrix} 2 & 3 \\ 5 & 6 \end{pmatrix}, B = \begin{pmatrix} 7 & 2 \\ -3 & 0 \\ 1 & 4 \end{pmatrix}, C = \begin{pmatrix} 7 & 1 & -3 & 0 \\ -2 & -7 & 2 & 9 \end{pmatrix}, D = \begin{pmatrix} 6 & 7 & 1 \\ -9 & 5 & 0 \\ -1 & 6 & 3 \\ 8 & 2 & 4 \\ 5 & -5 & 2 \end{pmatrix}, E = \begin{pmatrix} 4 \\ 3 \end{pmatrix}$

4. Calculate the determinant of A (see Q.3).

5. Solve the matrix equations:

    (i) AX=E;(ii) AX=C

6. Design a simple geometrical shape and, using coordinate transformation matrices, apply and draw the results of the transformations below. Use spreadsheet matrix functions to perform the calculations.

    (i)   Reflection about the x-axis (ii) Reflection about the y-axis

    (iii) Reflection about the vertical plane located at x=3

    (iv) Scaling by a factor of 5

    (v)   Scaling by a factor of 0.4 in place (relative to the centre of the figure).

    (vi) Y-shear using a y shear factor of 3

    (vii) Clockwise rotation through 30 deg about the origin

    (viii)Anticlockwise rotation through 60 deg about the centre of the figure.

Chapter 10

Statistics

Types of statistics

The term *statistics* refers to the processing of numerical data in order to make it more comprehensible. The figures derived from statistical analysis are also known as 'statistics'. The word 'statistics' derives from 'state', since it was governments that first recognised the urgent need for coherent information relating to population densities, distribution of wealth, political trends, and so on. Broadly speaking, the subject can be divided into two areas:

❑ *descriptive* statistics. These deal with methods of describing large amounts of data. Such data is summarised in a wide variety of different forms: as single numbers representing central values or measures of dispersion; as tables of figures; as pictorial representations; as graphs. Whatever the method employed, its function is to make a mass of figures easier to understand by organising it in a way which emphasises any trends within the figures.

❑ *analytical* statistics. These deal with methods enabling conclusions to be drawn from the data.

This chapter will consider only descriptive statistics since analytical statistics generally involves mathematical techniques beyond the scope of this book. Statistics are quoted in all manners of ways in everyday life:

"Megadent can reduce tooth decay by up to 30%"

"Smoking causes 200 deaths per day"

"Profits rose by 50% last year"

"The average salary of teachers is £19563·79"

The student of statistics must be able to consider statements such as those above critically by asking such questions as:

"What is the source of this information?"

"What (if anything) is being left unsaid?"

"How has the data been obtained?"

"What evidence is there for making this statement?"

"Is it intended to be misleading?"

"What does it actually mean?"

This chapter provides a framework for producing and evaluating simple statistical quantities, so that they can be viewed intelligently and produced without ambiguity.

Pictorial representations

Suppose that a certain college is divided into four faculties and it is necessary to show pictorially the relative number of students in each faculty for particular academic years. Table 10.1 shows the figures to be used.

Faculty	Number of students			
	1997	1998	1999	2000
Business Studies	889	913	1076	1253
Humanities	501	626	715	836
Science	416	481	263	352
Technology	387	412	448	479
Total	2193	2432	2502	2920

Table 10.1. *Student numbers from 1997 to 2000, arranged by faculty*

This data could be represented diagrammatically in a number of forms:

- ❏ pictogram;
- ❏ pie chart;
- ❏ bar chart;
- ❏ graph.

Spreadsheet, word processing and graphics packages are available to take the hard work out of producing the last three types of diagrams. For example, Microsoft's Excel will produce a wide variety of pictorial representations of data entered in the form shown in Table 10.1.

Pictograms

This form of presentation involves the use of pictures to represent a set of figures. For example, the student numbers in the four faculties for 1992 could be shown as Figure 10.1.

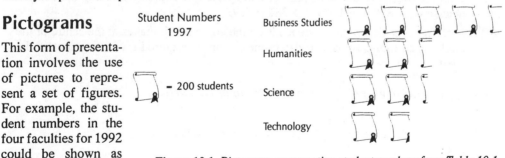

Figure 10.1. *Pictogram representing student numbers from Table 10.1*

Here the same picture, representing a number of students, is shown repeatedly; the values of the figure for each faculty is indicated by the number of pictures shown.

An alternative method, illustrated in Figure 10.2, is sometimes employed to represent a number by the size of the picture used. This second type of representation, however, can easily be very misleading. If the height of the picture is made approximately proportional to the quantity being represented, then the width

Growth in Business Studies
Student Numbers

Figure 10.1. *Using picture size to represent number of students*

of the picture will probably be increased by a corresponding amount to make it look right. However, this produces an increase in area and gives a false impression to the eye. For example, if the figure being represented doubles, then the area will look disproportionately large. Even if great care is taken in making the area of the pictures relatively accurate representations of the quantities, it is still quite difficult to interpret such diagrams, and they are best avoided altogether. Pictograms which are drawn well and which are not misleading can be very effective in presenting data in a non-technical way. The pictures immediately arrest the attention of the observer and at the same time impart the required information.

Pie charts

A pie chart is a circle divided into segments, looking rather like a pie or cake cut into slices - hence its name. The area of each segment is proportional to the size of the figure represented, and the complete 'pie' represents the overall total of all the component parts. It is therefore a convenient way of illustrating the sizes of component quantities in relation to each other and to the overall total. The student numbers for 1997 could be shown in pie chart form as illustrated by Figure 10.3. The following instructions explain how a pie chart can be constructed manually if a suitable computer is not available:

Student numbers for 1997 (total 2193)

Figure 10.3. *Pie chart for student numbers in 1997*

(i)   Find the overall figure to be represented by the full circle by totalling the component figures: 889 + 501 + 416 + 387 = 2193.

(ii) Since the area of a segment depends on the angle that it makes at the centre of the circle, each figure is used to determine the angle required for its segment of the chart:

889 requires an angle of $\dfrac{889}{2193} \times 360 = 146°$ *approximately.*

501 requires an angle of $\dfrac{501}{2193} \times 360 = 82°$ *approximately.*

416 requires an angle of $\dfrac{416}{2193} \times 360 = 68°$ *approximately.*

387 requires an angle of $\dfrac{387}{2193} \times 360 = 64°$ *approximately.*

Total = 360°

(iii) Draw a circle and use a protractor to divide the circle into the appropriately sized segments.

(iv) Indicate the percentage contribution that each segment makes to the whole 'pie', label each sector and give the whole diagram a title.

(v)   Where appropriate, state the source of the data.

Bar charts

A basic bar chart, such as that shown in Figure 10.4 for 1997 student numbers, consists of a series of bars with lengths proportional to the quantities they represent. The scale of the vertical axis in the diagram is in units of number of students and the horizontal axis is labelled with the names of the four faculties.

There are numerous variations of the basic bar chart, the commonest of which is the *multiple bar chart* shown in Figure 10.5. Here, the figures for two years are represented side by side for each faculty.

Bar charts are very useful for depicting a series of changes in the figures of interest. They are generally preferable to pictograms because they are easier to construct and they can represent data more accurately. Multiple bar charts are not recommended for more than four sets of figures. More than this number of adjacent components detracts from the clarity and usefulness of the diagram.

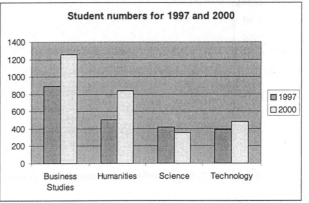

Figure 10.4. *Bar chart of student numbers for 1997 by Faculty*

Figure 10.5. *Bar chart comparing student numbers in 1997 and 2000*

Line charts

Again referring to the student numbers given earlier, suppose it was required to compare the way that student numbers changed over the four years, for the faculties of Business Studies and Science. One possible way to do this would be to use a multiple bar chart with the horizontal axis labelled with the four years 1997-2000. Two adjacent bars could be used for the faculty figures for each year and the diagram would look much the same as in Figure 10.5. However, the figures could be illustrated in a more striking manner by means of a line chart such as that shown in Figure 10.6.

The lines joining the points marked with the square and triangle symbols help to emphasise trends, so that it is quite easy to see that Business Studies student numbers are increasing whereas those of Science are declining. It should be noted, however, with this particular type of diagram, that using the connecting lines to interpolate intermediate values is not possible: the horizontal scale does not represent a continuous quantity with meaningful values between those marked. Note the following precautions when drawing line charts and graphs in general:

(i)   The choice of horizontal scale can greatly affect the visual impression that is given. Though the two graphs in Figure 10.7 represent the same data, by compressing the horizontal scale in the right hand graph the profit trend appears more dramatic. The

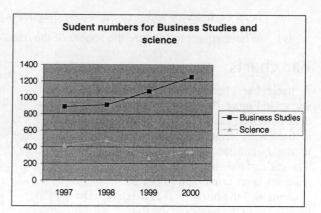

Figure 10.6. *Line graph emphasising trends in student numbers for Business Studies and Science*

left hand graph conveys an accurate impression of the data whereas the right hand graph distorts it.

Figure 10.7. *Compression of horizontal scale resulting in distortion of graphed figures*

(ii)   The vertical scale should always start at zero, again to avoid giving the wrong impression. In the left-hand graph in Figure 10.8, the vertical scale starts at a point close to the range covered by the figures, and the resulting graph further dramatises the data.

Figure 10.8. *Distortion through restricted data range and compression of horizontal scale*

When the vertical scale covers only the range that the data spans and the horizontal scale is compressed, the data becomes totally distorted, as illustrated in the right-hand graph in Figure 10.8.

It is difficult to believe that all four graphs in Figures 10.7 and 10.8 are based on exactly the same data.

(iii) Quote the source of the data so that the actual figures used can be checked if required.

Frequency distributions

Table 10.2 shows the mileages recorded by a number of refuse disposal vehicles in one week.

Mileages recorded by refuse disposal vehicles											
482	502	466	408	486	440	470	447	413	451	410	430
469	438	452	459	455	473	423	436	412	403	493	436
471	498	450	421	482	440	442	474	407	448	444	485
505	515	500	462	460	476	472	454	451	438	457	446
453	453	508	475	418	465	450	447	477	436	464	453
415	511	430	457	490	447	433	416	419	460	428	434
420	443	456	432	425	497	459	449	439	509	483	502
424	421	413	441	458	438	444	445	435	468	430	442
455	452	479	481	468	435	462	478	463	498	494	489
495	407	462	432	424	451	426	433	474	431	471	488

Table 10.2. *Unsorted, raw data*

A casual examination of this set of figures is unlikely to reveal anything other than the fact that most of the figures are in the 400's with an occasional one in the 500's. From a table in this form it would be very difficult to determine any patterns present in the data. For instance, are the numbers evenly distributed, or is there a certain small range containing a preponderance of figures compared to other similar ranges?

The statistical techniques considered in this part of the chapter allow raw data such as that in the above table to be summarised and presented in a form which facilitates identification of trends and allows the significance of the figures to be grasped. It should be noted, however, that as the crude data is converted into more convenient forms of representation, the fine details within the data begin to be lost.

Ungrouped frequency distributions

A first step in the analysis of the data in the table could be to sort the figures into ascending order of magnitude and at the same time to note the number of times any figures are repeated. Table 10.3 has been produced in this manner and it is termed an *ungrouped frequency distribution*. The table consists of a list of every unique mileage with its *frequency* of occurrence, that is, the number of times it occurred in Table 10.2.

mileage	freq	mileage	freq	mileage	freq	mileage	freq
403	1	434	1	456	1	479	1
407	2	435	2	457	2	481	1
408	1	436	3	458	1	482	2
410	1	438	3	459	2	483	1
412	1	439	1	460	2	485	1
413	2	440	2	462	3	486	1
415	1	441	1	463	1	488	1
416	1	442	2	464	1	489	1
418	1	443	1	465	1	490	1
419	1	444	2	466	1	493	1
420	1	445	1	468	2	494	1
421	2	446	1	469	1	495	1
423	1	447	3	470	1	497	1
424	2	448	1	471	2	498	2
425	1	449	1	472	1	500	1
426	1	450	2	473	1	502	2
428	1	451	3	474	2	505	1
430	3	452	2	475	1	508	1
431	1	453	3	476	1	509	1
432	2	454	1	477	1	511	1
433	2	455	2	478	1	515	1

Table 10.3. *Ungrouped frequency distribution*

Notice that the sum of the frequencies is equal to the number of items in the original table, that is,

$$\sum f = 120$$

Grouped frequency distribution

Though the data has now been organised, there are still too many numbers for the mind to be able to grasp the information hidden within them. Therefore the next step is to simplify the presentation of the data even further.

At this stage, in the production of a *grouped frequency distribution*, the crude data is replaced by a set of groups which split the mileages into a number of small ranges called *classes*. Table 10.4 is an example of a grouped frequency distribution based on the ungrouped frequency distribution shown earlier in Table 10.3.

The overall range of mileages, 403 to 515, has been split

Mileages	Frequency
400 to under 420	12
420 to under 440	27
440 to under 460	34
460 to under 480	24
480 to under 500	15
500 to under 520	8
Total	120

Table 10.4. *Grouped frequency distribution*

into six classes each covering an equal sub-range of the total range of values. Notice that the class limits, that is the boundary values of the classes, do not overlap, nor are there any gaps between them; these are important characteristics of grouped frequency distributions.

The effect of grouping data in this way is to allow patterns to be detected more easily. For instance, it is now clear that most of the figures cluster in and around the '440 to under 460' class. The cost of being able to extract this piece of information is loss of the exact details of the raw data; a grouped frequency distribution summarises the crude data. Thus any further information deduced or calculated from this grouped frequency distribution can only be approximate.

Choice of classes

The construction of a grouped frequency distribution will always involve making decisions regarding the number and size of classes to be used. Though these choices will depend on individual circumstances to a large extent, the following guidelines should be noted:

(i)   Class intervals should be equal wherever possible.

(ii)   Restrict the number of classes to between ten and twenty; too many or too few classes will obscure information.

(iii) Classes should be chosen such that occurrences within the intervals are mainly grouped about the mid-point of the classes in order that calculations based on the distribution can be made as accurately as possible. Examination of the ungrouped frequency distribution should highlight any tendencies of figures to cluster at regular intervals over the range of values considered.

(iv)   Class intervals of 5, 10 or multiples of 10 are easier to work with than intervals such as 7 or 11 (manually, that is: it is not a problem when using a computer package for statistical analysis).

Cumulative frequency distributions

Table 10.5 on the next page contains an additional two columns to the data in Table 10.4.

The entries in the column labelled 'Cumulative Frequency' have been calculated by keeping a running total of the frequencies given in the adjacent column. As expected, the final entry shows that the sum of all the frequencies is 120. The final column shows the same accumulated figures as percentages of the total number of figures.

Mileages	Frequency	Cumulative frequency	Cumulative percentage
400 to under 420	12	12	10·0
420 to under 440	27	39	32·5
440 to under 460	34	73	60·8
460 to under 480	24	97	80·8
480 to under 500	15	112	93·3
500 to under 520	8	120	100·0
Total	120		

Table 10.5. *'Less than' cumulative frequency distribution*

This new table allows further observations to be made regarding the data being examined. For example, the table now shows that 80·8% of the vehicles travelled less than 480 miles; 6·7% (100 − 93·3) of the vehicles travelled more than 500 miles; 20% (80·8 − 60·8) of the vehicles travelled between 440 and 480 miles.

Because the figures have been accumulated from the lowest class to the highest, Table 10.5 is called a 'less than' cumulative frequency distribution.

Table 10.6 shows a 'more than' cumulative frequency distribution in which the frequencies have been accumulated in reverse order.

Mileages	Frequency	Cumulative frequency	Cumulative percentage
400 to under 420	12	120	100·0
420 to under 440	27	108	90·0
440 to under 460	34	81	67·5
460 to under 480	24	47	39·2
480 to under 500	15	23	19·2
500 to under 520	8	8	6·7
Total	120		

Table 10.6. *'More than' cumulative frequency distribution*

Hence, Table 10.6 shows directly that 90% of the vehicles travelled more than 420 miles and 6·7% travelled more than 500 miles. Simple calculations also allow 'less than' figures to be derived, just as 'more than' figures can be calculated from the 'less than' cumulative frequency distribution.

Histograms

When the data in a grouped frequency distribution is presented diagrammatically, the resulting representation is called a *histogram*. The class groupings are used to label the horizontal axis, and the frequency (either as an actual figure or as a percentage of the total number of figures) is used for the vertical axis. Figure 10.9 shows the grouped frequency distribution.

Figure 10.9. *Histogram of grouped frequency distribution*

A histogram essentially consists of vertically aligned rectangles in which:

(i)   the widths represent the class intervals;

(ii)   the heights represent the frequencies.

The area of a rectangle in a histogram is directly proportional to the quantity that it represents. This is the distinction between a histogram and a bar chart which looks somewhat similar. Where a histogram has unequal class intervals, as illustrated in the Figure 10.10, great care must be taken to ensure that the areas under the rectangles are still proportioned correctly.

Notice that the first class, representing 39 occurrences, being twice as wide as the other class intervals, is drawn half height. The dotted line shows the result of drawing it incorrectly: the diagram would be seriously in error.

Figure 10.10. *Histogram with unequal class intervals*

Ogives

Ogive is the name given to the graph obtained when a cumulative frequency distribution is represented diagrammatically. Another name commonly used for an ogive is a *cumulative frequency curve*. Figure 10.11 shows one 'less than' cumulative frequency distribution as a 'less than' ogive.

Note that ogives start at zero on the vertical scale and end at the outside class limit of the last class. The vertical axis on the right of the diagram gives the cumulative frequency as a percentage, so that either scale may be used. The graph may be used in the same way as Table 10.5, on which it is based. Thus, approximately 50% of the mileages are less than 452 miles. This is an approximate figure because the 50% point does not correspond exactly with a class boundary; it is not clear whether the mileages in the interval 440 to under 460 are evenly distributed over the interval.

Figure 10.11. *'Less than' ogive*

Ogives may also be of the 'more than' variety when they are based on the corresponding cumulative frequency distribution. An ogive curve provides a useful and efficient method of determining *percentiles*. Percentiles are points in the distribution below which a given percentage of the total lies. A percentile divides a set of observations into two groups. For example, using a 'less than' ogive, 25% of the mileages are below the 25 percentile (that is below 434 miles approximately). Commonly used percentiles are known as *quartiles*:

❏ the 25th percentile is the first quartile;

❏ the 50th percentile is the second quartile (also known as the *median*);

❏ the 75th percentile is the third quartile.

Percentiles are a very useful way of expressing such statistics as "50% of the individual wealth of the U.K. is in the hands of 5% of the population".

Measures of location

Measures of location, or measures of central value, are average values. The most common types of averages are

(i) The *arithmetic mean* (or just *mean*).

(ii) The *median*.

(iii) The *mode*.

Each one of these measures attempts to represent a collection of figures with one single figure, though in fact each really is only representative of one aspect of the figures. They all may be determined exactly from ungrouped data, or approximately from grouped data. The following sections summarise the methods of calculation and the significance of each average. In the following pages reference will be made to the data in the ungrouped frequency distribution shown in Table 10.7.

House number	1	2	3	4	5	6	7	8	9	10	11	12	13	14	15	16	17	18	19
Number of children	0	0	0	0	0	0	1	1	1	1	2	2	2	2	3	3	4	5	6

Table 10.7. *Children in Mean Street*

The following notation will be used:

$\sum$ = sum of

$\bar{x}$ = mean value

x_i = single value

n = number of values

f = frequency

Mean

Calculation of the mean

(a) Ungrouped data:

(i) add together all the values;

(ii) divide by the number of values.

The mathematical notation for the calculation is

$$\bar{x} = \frac{\sum x_i}{n} \qquad i = 1, ..., n$$

Using the values in Table 10.7, this gives

$$\bar{x} = \frac{33}{19} = 1 \cdot 74 \text{ approx}$$

(b)　Grouped frequency distribution

    (i)　multiply each class mid point by the class frequency;

    (ii)　add these values together;

    (iii)　divide by the sum of the frequencies.

The mathematical notation for the calculation is

$$\bar{x} = \frac{\sum (f \times ClassMid)}{\sum f}$$

Using the values in Table 10.7 this gives

$$\bar{x} = \frac{12 \times 410 + 27 \times 430 + 34 \times 450 + 24 \times 470 + 15 \times 490 + 8 \times 510}{120}$$

$$\bar{x} = 454 \cdot 5$$

Significance of the mean

The arithmetic mean indicates what value each item would have if the total of all values were shared out equally. To discover the result which would follow from an equal distribution of something (consumption of beer per head, say) the mean is the most suitable measure.

Features of the mean

The mean:

❑　makes use of every value in the distribution;

❑　can be distorted by extreme values;

❑　can be used for further mathematical processing;

❑　may result in an impossible figure (1·74 children);

❑　best known of all the averages.

Median

Calculation of the median

(a)　Ungrouped data

    (i)　arrange the data into ascending order of magnitude;

(ii)   locate the middle term - this is the median. (If there are an even number of numbers and there is no middle term then the nearest to the mid-point on either side will do)

The median item in the Mean Street example is the 10th one and the value of the median is therefore 1. In the mileages example, from Table 10.3 the middle item is the 60th and the median value is 452 miles.

(b)   Grouped frequency distribution

(i)   produce the equivalent ogive;

(ii)   read off the value of the 2nd quartile - this gives the median value. (See the 'less than' ogive in Figure 10.11)

Significance of the median

The median is merely the value of the middle term when the data is arranged into ascending order of magnitude. Consequently there will be as many terms above it as below it. If a person interested in a job with a firm wanted some idea of the salary to expect, he or she might use the median salary as a guide.

Features of the median

The median:

❑   uses only one value in the distribution;

❑   cannot be used for further mathematical processing;

❑   it is always an actual value occurring in the distribution;

❑   it can be computed from incomplete data.

Mode

Calculation of the mode

The mode is usually derived from an ungrouped frequency distribution by determining the value which occurs most frequently. In Mean Street, the value occurring most frequently is 0 children. In Table 10.3, which shows an ungrouped frequency distribution, there are several modes: each mileage which occurs three times is a mode of the distribution of mileages.

Significance of the mode

As the mode is the value that occurs most frequently, it represents the typical item. It is this form of average that is implied by such expressions as 'the average person' or 'the average holiday'.

Features of the mode

The mode:

❑   is an actual value;

❑   cannot be used for further mathematical processing.

Dispersion

Quoting an average value, such as the mean, is an attempt to describe a distribution figure by a single representative number. Such averages, however, suffer from the disadvantage that they give no indication of the spread, or dispersion, of the figures represented. For example, the following two sets of numbers have identical means but the range of values is much greater in the first case than the second:

10 20 30 mean value = 20

18 20 22 mean value = 20

Figure 10.12 further illustrates how two distributions with the same mean value can have greatly different distributions.

It is therefore also desirable to be able to describe the dispersion of data in a distribution with just a single figure.

Figure 10.12. *Two widely differing distributions of the same mean value*

Four such measures will be described. They are:

(a)   the *range*;

(b)   the *interquartile range*;

(c)   the *mean deviation*;

(d)   the *standard deviation*.

Range

The *range* is merely the difference between the highest and the lowest values:

range = highest value − lowest value

The range of the distribution of mileages given in the ungrouped frequency distribution in Table 10.3 is given by:

range = 515 − 403 = 112 miles

Unfortunately the range, like the mean, is influenced by extreme values. If the majority of the figures in the distribution cluster around a certain value, but there are a small number having extreme values, then the range does not provide a very accurate measure of the dispersion of the majority of the distribution. For example, if in the ungrouped frequency distribution in Table 10.3, one of the mileages had been 112 miles, then the range would be 515 − 112 = 403 miles, more than three times the previous figure, even though only one figure had changed.

Interquartile range

The disadvantage with the range as a measure of dispersion, as identified above, can be overcome to some degree by ignoring the extreme high and low values so that the measure of dispersion is representative of the majority of the distribution. One method of doing this is to use the values at the lower limit of the 3rd quartile and the upper limit of the 1st quartile as the values from which the range is calculated.

These figures give the *interquartile range*. For example, with reference to the 'less than' ogive in Figure 10.12, these figures are as follows:

lower limit of 3rd quartile (75th percentile) = 476

upper limit of 1st quartile (25th percentile) = 434

interquartile range = 476 − 434 = 42 miles

Another measure of dispersion which is sometimes useful is the *semi-interquartile range* which is found by dividing the interquartile range by two. Another name for this latter measure of dispersion is the *quartile deviation*. The chief disadvantages of these measures of dispersion are that they still are unable to take into account any degree of clustering in the distribution, and they do not use all of the values in the distribution.

Mean deviation

Another method of measuring dispersion is to find the deviations of all the items from the average, ignore their signs, and find the arithmetic mean of their magnitude. This is known as the *mean deviation*. For example, to find the mean deviation of the following set of numbers,

27   33   36   37   39   39   40   44   50   55

the mean deviation can be calculated as follows.

(i) Sum of numbers	= 400
(ii) Mean value	$= \dfrac{400}{10} = 40$
(iii) Deviation from mean:	−13 −7 −4 −3 −1 −1 0 4 10 15
(iv) Sum of deviations (ignoring sign)	= 58
(v) Mean deviation	$= \dfrac{58}{10} = 5\cdot8$

The mean deviation of the numbers is $5\cdot8$.

Standard deviation

The Greek letter σ is universally adopted to represent standard deviation. The formula for standard deviation is as follows:

$$\text{Standard deviation } (\sigma) = \sqrt{\frac{\Sigma\left(x-\bar{x}\right)^2}{n}}$$

or, where the figures come from an ungrouped frequency distribution,

$$\sigma = \sqrt{\frac{\Sigma f\left(x-\bar{x}\right)^2}{\Sigma f}}$$

Setting out the calculation in the form of a table, and using the figures above for the mean deviation calculation, the calculation may be performed as shown on the right. Note that

x	$(x-\bar{x})$	$(x-\bar{x})^2$
27	−13	169
33	−7	49
36	−4	16
37	−3	9
39	−1	1
39	−1	1
40	0	0
44	4	16
50	10	100
55	15	225
$\Sigma x = 400$		$\Sigma(x-\bar{x})^2 = 586$

by squaring the difference between the mean and a value, the minus signs disappear.

$$\text{Standard deviation } (\sigma) = \sqrt{\frac{(x-\bar{x})^2}{n}} = \sqrt{\frac{586}{10}} = 7 \cdot 655.$$

To summarise, the steps involved in calculating the standard deviation of a distribution are as follows:

(i)   Calculate the arithmetic mean.

(ii)   Subtract the mean from each value.

(iii)   Square each value in (ii).

(iv) find the sum of all the values in (iii).

(v)   Divide by the number of numbers.

(vi)   Take the square root of the result of (v).

Where the standard deviation is to be calculated from an ungrouped frequency distribution, in step (ii) the result would be multiplied by the frequency of the value, and in step (v) the sum of the frequencies would be used as the divisor. Reference is frequently made to the *variance* of a distribution. This is the square of the standard deviation. In the previous example, the variance of the distribution is given by

$$\text{Variance} = (\text{standard deviation})^2 = 58 \cdot 6$$

and conversely,

$$\text{Standard deviation} = \sqrt{\text{variance}} = \sqrt{58 \cdot 6} = 7 \cdot 655$$

Comparison of measures of dispersion

Of the measures of dispersion considered in this section, the *standard deviation* is the most important, but also the most difficult to comprehend. Basically, the standard deviation provides a measure of the likelihood of any random value from the distribution being close to the arithmetic mean of the distribution. The greater the measure of deviation, the less likely it is that any value chosen at random will be the mean value. Its importance lies chiefly in the considerable use made of it in analytical statistics, and a familiarity with it is crucial to making progress in more advanced statistical techniques.

The *range* is very easy to calculate but is sensitive to extreme values, and it does not take into account all of the figures or give any indication of the clustering of data. It is not generally a very reliable or accurate measure of dispersion.

The *interquartile range* also has the disadvantage that only two values from the distribution are used in its calculation, but it is less affected by extreme values. It is useful when the distribution is evenly distributed except for a number of extreme values.

The *mean deviation* has the advantage of using all of the figures in the distribution and is a measure of how far, on average, the values in the distribution are dispersed from the mean value. Its chief disadvantage is that it is not particularly well suited to algebraic treatment.

If the distribution of values is fairly symmetrical about the mean, bell shaped and the number of items is large, (that is, it is more or less what is known as a *normal distribution* as shown in

Figure 10.13), then the following relations are approximately true:

$$\text{Quartile deviation} = \frac{2}{3} \text{ standard deviation,}$$

and

$$\text{Mean deviation} = \frac{4}{5} \text{ standard deviation.}$$

So, for approximately normal distributions (which are of great importance in analytical statistics), the quartile and mean deviations may be used to approximate the standard deviation.

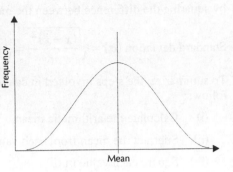

Figure 10.13. *Normal distribution*

Normal distribution

Imagine that you are holding a cupful of uncooked rice and you spill the rice onto the marked centre of a straight line drawn on a hard floor. Then you measure the distance of each grain of rice from the mark, counting distances on one side of the line as positive and distances to the other side as negative, as shown in Figure 10.14.

You would probably find that the majority of rice grains were within 10cm of the mark, a significant number had spread to between 10 and 20cm from the mark, a smaller number between 20 and 30cm, fewer over 30cm and so on. You may even get some grains that travel an unusually large distance from the mark. If you produced a histogram, such as that shown in Figure 10.15, showing the number of

Figure 10.14. *Distribution of rice grains dropped onto a hard surface*

grains of rice in intervals of, say 5cm, from the centre mark, you would have drawn a distribution closely resembling the Normal distribution which has a characteristic bell shape (shown superimposed on the histogram). Most of the measurements would cluster around the mean value (i.e. 0) where the bell humps in the middle. The spread, or dispersion, of the results would depend on the height from which the rice was dropped - increasing the height would increase the standard deviation of the figures because the grains would tend to travel further from the centre mark. However, the number

Figure 10.15. *Histogram of rice grain distribution*

of rice grains would reduce with increasing distance from the mean. Notice that your distance figures would not be discrete - you could have measurements of say 50.3 cm or 6.152 cm etc. The accuracy of the measurements would depend on your measuring instrument.

Characteristics of the Normal distribution

1. The importance of the normal distribution lies in its ability to model the distribution of a large number of different types of variables. Although many of these distributions are not precisely normal, they are close enough for practical purposes. For instance, if a large sample of women of height, say five feet five inches, were weighed, we might find their average weight to be about 57kg with a standard deviation of, say, 10kg. We might also observe that 68% of the measurements were between 47kg and 77kg, ie within one standard deviation of the mean, 95% between 37kg and 97kg, ie within two standard deviations of the mean, and almost 100% between 27kg and 87kg, ie within three standard deviations from the mean. This means that most of the observations would occur close to the mean and very few more than three standard deviations from the mean, ie weighing less than 37kg. or more than 87kg. This relationship between percentage of observations and standard deviations from the mean is a characteristic of the normal distribution and it occurs very frequently in practice. Figure 10.16 illustrates the relationship.

Figure 10.16. *Percentiles under the normal distribution*

2. It can be used as a good approximation to a wide range of practical and theoretical probability distributions.

3. It is often the basis of standard tests of statistical significance in analytical statistics.

4. The shape of the curve is determined by the mean and standard deviation of the variable being measured. The mean value determines the position of the curve on the horizontal axis, and the standard deviation determines the spread and height of the curve. As the standard deviation increases, the normal curve flattens and spreads out as illustrated in Figure 10.17.

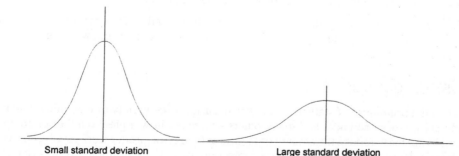

Figure 10.17. *Effect of the standard deviation on the shape of the normal curve*

5.   Irrespective of its shape, the area under the curve is always 1. This is because the curve represents a probability distribution, meaning that the sum of all the probabilities associated with the variable being measured must equal 1. If you look back to Figure 10.16, you will see that if you add all the percentages shown, the total is 100%, which is the equivalent to a probability value of 1.

6.   The distribution is symmetrical about the mean value of the variable being measured.

7.   In practice the normal distribution is used to find the probability of occurrence of the relevant variable being between two specified limits, rather than of a variable having a specific value. For instance, we might want to know the probability that a certain male taken at random is taller than 1.7 metres (which is about the average height for a man), or smaller than 1.5 metres assuming that the heights of men can be represented by a normal distribution. These quantities can easily be calculated because they are represented by areas under the normal curve, as shown in Figure 10.18. However, a single value of say *exactly* 1.6 metres does not have any area under the normal curve and therefore has a value of 0. This is because there are an infinite number of height values possible (height being a continuous variable), so each exact height has an infinitesimal probability of occurring.

Figure 10.18. *Areas under the normal curve representing probabilities of certain height measurements occurring*

Other examples of approximately normal distributions are:

❑   throwing a dart at a dartboard and measuring the height at which it lands;

❑   getting people to estimate a foot and then measuring the error in the estimate;

❑   measuring the IQ's of a randomly chosen set of adults;

In each case you would expect the measurements to cluster and be symmetrical about a mean value, with the chances of getting a result in a certain interval decreasing with the distance of the interval from the mean.

Statistics packages

Because of the usefulness of statistical analysis in such a wide variety of disciplines - in business, medicine, social sciences and many others - there are now a great number of computer programs available to reduce the amount of laborious (and error-prone) work involved in statistical analysis. Many of these packages are subject orientated (for example, SPSS - Statistical Package for Social Sciences) offering facilities relevant to the subject, while others are purely general purpose. Many statistics packages will generate diagrams such as pie charts and bar charts automatically.

Most well known spreadsheets contain functions to calculate means and standard deviations and also to produce statistical diagrams from data entered.

When using such packages, however, it is vital that the user is aware of the theory on which the package operates, particularly when the package is being used for analytical statistics. When considering the use or purchase of a program for statistical analysis, a vital factor is the quality and detail of the documentation provided; with good documentation the user can be confident about the interpretation of the statistical analysis undertaken.

Exercises

Graph and charts

1. The table shows the number of occasions members of a sports centre participated in martial arts activities for the years 1996 to 2000.

Activity	Number of participants				
	1996	1997	1998	1999	2000
Aikido	434	513	567	581	621
Judo	556	587	522	501	543
Karate	890	983	1012	1232	1520
Taekwondo	1472	1561	1273	1105	899
Tai Chi	322	562	669	823	1874

Enter the information in the table above into a spreadsheet and use to generate graphs to:

(i) Compare the attendances for the five activities in the year 2000.

(ii) Illustrate the growth of attendances for Tai Chi over the five years.

(iii) Compare the popularity of judo and karate over the five years.

(iv) Show how total attendances for all the activities compare for the years 1996 and 2000

Averages and frequency distributions

2. Calculate the mean of the numbers 3, 5, 2, 7, 8, 1, 9, 3, 5, 2, 6, 8, 2.

What is the modal value of these numbers?

What is the median value?

What average value could still be calculated if the first and the last numbers were missing?

3. The following table shows the number of visits to an alternative health clinic required by 20 patients to receive acupuncture treatment for back pain in order to obtain significant pain relief:

Calculate the mean, mode and median number of visits required. Which of these averages would be the most suitable to quote for people who wanted to have some idea of about how many treatments would generally be required for significant pain relief.

Patient	1	2	3	4	5	6	7	8	9	10	11	12	13	14	15	16	17	18	19	20
Visits	4	2	8	7	4	1	2	9	6	3	3	5	2	4	4	7	9	3	8	4

4. A survey of 960 motorists who used their cars to travel to work were asked to estimate how much money they spent on fule per week. The results of the survey are shown below.

Class interval (£)	Frequency
0 to under 5	6
5 to under 10	18
10 to under 15	44
15 to under 20	123
20 to under 25	176
25 to under 30	203
30 to under 35	188
35 to under 40	163
40 to under 45	37
45 to under 50	2

   (i)   Calculate the mean, mode and median fuel expenditure for the 960 motorists.
   (ii) Represent the table as a histogram.
   (iii) Draw greater than and less than ogives for the frequency distribution.
   (iv) What are the first second and third quartile values for the less than ogive?

Standard deviation

5. Explain the significance of the standard deviation. What is the connection between the mean and the standard deviation?

6. Calculate the standard deviation of the figures provided in question 2. Check your answer using a spreadsheet.

7. Estimate the standard deviation of the frequency distribution provided in question 4.

8. Describe the general characteristics of the Normal distribution. Suggest distributions occurring in everyday life that are likely to be approximately Normal. What effect do the mean and standard deviation have on the particular form of a Normal distribution?

Assignments

2.1. Boolean algebra and logic

Seven-segment displays are the familiar digital displays used in many domestic devices such as watches, calculators, stereos and cameras. Each character is composed form up to seven tiny LEDs organised in the shape of a number eight as shown in (a). The seven segments, labelled a to g in (b), can be activated separately so that characters are formed from appropriate combinations of characters. Part (c) shows the combinations of segments that are required in order to display the digits 0 to 9.

Tasks

1. Draw a truth table to specify the combination of inputs required to display each of the ten digits. The truth table will have the following form:

Inputs (BCD				Digit	Outputs						
A	B	C	D		a	b	c	d	e	f	g
0	0	0	0	0	1	1	1	1	1	1	0
0	0	0	1	1	0	1	1	0	0	0	0
				etc							
1	0	0	1	9	1	1	1	0	0	1	1

2. Derive expressions for each of the seven outputs.
3. Using Karnaugh maps simply each of the seven expressions.
4. Draw seven logic circuits, one for each segment, such that when four signals representing a binary coded decimal digit are applied to each circuit, the appropriate digit is displayed. Your logic circuit diagrams should use the correct symbols for AND, OR and NOT gates.

2.2 Denary to binary conversion

An algorithm for converting positive denary integers to binary is as follows:

If N is a positive denary integer to be converted to the binary digits $a_n\ a_{n-1}\ a_{n-2} .. a_1\ a_0$,

```
b₀ = N
i=0
while bᵢ <> 0
    if bᵢ is odd then aᵢ=1 else aᵢ=0
    bᵢ₊₁=(bᵢ-aᵢ)/2
    i=i+1
end while
```

For N=13, the algorithm would produce the binary digits $a_0=1$, $a_1=0$, $a_2=1$, $a_3=1$, that is, the binary number 1101 in reverse order.

1. Show step-by-step how the denary number 79 is converted into binary using this algorithm.

2. A number can be tested for being odd or even as follows:

   (i)   Divide the number by 2: 13/2 = 6.5

   (ii) Remove the fractional part: 6.5 becomes 6

   (iii) Multiply by 2: 6 × 2 = 12

   (iv) Compare this new number with the original number: in this case, because the two numbers are different, the original number must have been odd. If the two numbers were the same, the original number would have been even. (Prove this for yourself using the number 20 for example).

   The spreadsheet function *trunc* will truncate a number to an integer by removing the fractional part. Thus if you divide an integer by 2 and truncate it and then multiply the answer by 2, you can determine whether the original number was odd or even. The *int* function can be used in a similar way.

   Using the algorithm in question 1 and the information above, set up a spreadsheet to convert a denary number to binary.

3. Fractional denary numbers, such as 0.625 can be converted to an eight-bit binary fraction using the following algorithm, where X is the fraction to be converted:

   ```
   b₀ = X
   i = 0
   while i < 8
     if bᵢ × 2 ≥ 1 then aᵢ=1 else aᵢ =0
     bᵢ=bᵢ-aᵢ
     i=i+1
   end while
   ```

   Thus 0.625 becomes .10100000

   Use a spreadsheet to convert a denary fraction to a binary fraction.

2.3. Statistics

A dairy farmer has decided to analyse the milk yields of his cows for 1999. The figures are shown below.

Mth	Bessie	Maisie	Cowslip	Dandelion	Dolly	Ermintrude	Ruth	Bob	Gretchen	Polly
Jan	177	186	194	178	153	116	186	0	100	204
Feb	179	192	212	182	154	116	178	0	112	194
Mar	186	184	210	181	155	113	184	0	113	206
Apr	176	195	194	177	148	93	186	0	102	206
May	182	191	205	183	146	113	185	0	122	205
Jun	186	186	209	180	148	93	178	0	110	203
Jul	178	194	201	182	152	102	179	0	107	207
Aug	185	187	189	182	149	100	186	0	106	200
Sep	175	187	195	179	148	119	176	0	99	200
Oct	178	194	196	182	153	108	176	0	97	196
Nov	182	192	204	182	154	95	177	0	104	205
Dec	178	190	197	179	156	82	179	0	113	199

1. With the aid of a spreadsheet, calculate the following statistics (you can ignore the entry for Bob - he wasn't supposed to be milked):
   (i)   Overall range of milk yields.
   (ii)   Range of yields for each cow.
   (iii) Mean yields of each cow.
   (iv)   Modal yields of each cow.
   (v)   Median yields of each cow.
   (vi)   Mean yield for the whole herd in the best month and the worst month.

2. Of the above three average values for the mean yield of each cow, which one would you quote as being the **typical** milk yield? Which one would you use to estimate the income from the milk produced by a particular cow (ie by multiplying the average milk yield by the selling price per pint)? Justify your answers.

3. (i)   Produce a grouped frequency distribution for the milk yields for all the cows for 1999.
   (ii)   Draw a histogram using the frequency distribution.

4. Using appropriate spreadsheet charts,
   (i)   Illustrate the total monthly milk yields. (i.e. total milk yield for each month)
   (ii)   Compare the total monthly yields
   (iii) Show Polly's milk yields for 1999.
   (iv)   Compare the milk yields of Cowslip and Ermintrude.
   (vi)   Compare the mean yields of the cows.
   Justify the choice of each chart.

5. Calculate the means and standard deviations of Dandelion's and Gretchen's milk yields. What do these statistics for the two cows tell you?

Unit 3

Computer systems

Chapters

Unit 3 Outcomes and assessment criteria

Outcomes	Assessment criteria To achieve each outcome a student must demonstrate the ability to:
1. Understand **data representation, simple logic design and the fetch-execute cycle** of a model microprocessor.	• correctly convert values to/from various number systems, representation of values as floating point numbers, integer values, modern character codes, and simple bit patterns • show the relevance of different number systems to common generic applications • provide examples of possible errors due to inappropriate choice of data representation • demonstrate a correct understanding of the fetch-execute cycle of a model or idealised microprocessor.
2. Evaluate the parameters of **modern computer systems hardware.**	• select machine components or sub-systems appropriate to a given user requirement • specify a complete computer system to suit a given task and evaluate the performance of the selected system.
3. Write simple **low level programs.**	• write simple programs involving data transfer, basic arithmetic and sequence changing instructions • describe the operation of assemblers.
4. Install and use **modern operating systems.**	• correctly contrast the functions of different types of operating systems • install, use and administer a computer operating system.

Chapter 11

Basic concepts

A computer system consists of a collection of devices (the *hardware*) controlled by a computer program (the *software*). But what actually happens inside a computer to cause all these components to work together? How does a program control the hardware? How is data stored in the memory of a computer? This chapter provides the answers to these and other questions regarding the fundamental operation of a computer. However, a computer system is in a way like a jigsaw puzzle: the pieces of the puzzle are theoretical concepts embracing mathematics and physics, and they must be understood and fitted together in a certain way before the whole picture can be seen. So, to begin with, we will identify and describe a number of important ideas to provide a basis for understanding how they fit together to make a computer.

Binary numbers

If there is a single concept that can be said to be the basis of the operation of a modern digital computer, then it must be the *binary numbering system*. Incredible as it might seem, the operation of a computer is based entirely on the numbers 0 and 1. A computer "remembers" only the numbers 0 and 1; a computer does arithmetic using only the numbers 0 and 1; indeed, the notorious logical abilities of a computer rely solely on the numbers 0 and 1. This is the reason for the emphasis on binary numbers and binary arithmetic in Chapter 5, *Number Systems and Binary Arithmetic*.

So in terms of the operation of a computer what is the significance of all this? The point is that there are many simple ways that only two digits can be represented. For example, opposites such as big and small, positive and negative, up and down, or on and off can all be used. What all of these examples have in common is that they have two different states that can be used to represent the binary digits 0 and 1. In an electronic device such as a computer, the two states most commonly used are

- ❑   the presence of an electrical voltage (above a certain value, such as five volts); this is used to represent binary 1, and

- ❑   the absence (or near absence) of an electrical voltage, which represents binary 0.

If we can find some means of storing and reading these voltage states using some kind of electronic device, then we have the potential for making computer memory. Of course this device exists: it is constructed from *gates* which in turn use transistors. When a number of gates are linked together in a certain way they form a device called a *flip-flop,* which is able to "remember" a binary digit.

One type of flip-flop has a single input by which electrical signals are used to *set* the device to store a logic 1, or *reset* it to store a logic 0. Once a flip-flop has been set or reset, it stays that way until further signals change it; in other words, it "remembers" a binary digit - it stores a single *bit*. Figure 11.1 shows two flip-flops, one set to store a binary 1 and the other reset to store a binary 0.

Figure 11.1(a) shows a logic 1 signal applied to the *set* input in order to set the flip-flop to store a binary 1. In (b) a logic 0 signal is applied to the *reset* input to make the device store 0.

The memory size of a computer is frequently specified in terms of a number of *kilobytes* (K) or *megabytes* (M). A *byte* is a group of eight flip-flops regarded collectively as a unit of memory. So, rather than storing a single *bit* (that is, a single 1 or a single 0) in memory, a byte is usually the smallest amount of data that is stored. A kilobyte is approximately one thousand bytes (1024 bytes, actually) and a megabyte is approximately a thousand kilobytes (1024 x 1024 bytes). In order to store a byte of data in memory, the data needs to be presented to the eight flip-flops as a group of eight simultaneous signals; Figure 11.2 illustrates this.

Figure 11.1. *Binary digits stored using a flip-flop*

Figure 11.2. *Eight flip-flops used to store a byte of data*

Figure 11.2 shows a set of eight flip-flops organised to represent an eight bit binary number. The leftmost unit represents 2^7, or 128, and the rightmost unit represents 2^0, or 1. The whole eight-bit number therefore represents

$$0\times2^7 +1\times2^6 +1\times2^5 +0\times2^4 +0\times2^3 +0\times2^2 +1\times2^1 +0\times2^0$$
$$=0+64+32+0+0+0+2+0$$
$$=98$$

The largest number that we can store in this way, using a single byte of memory is

$$1\times2^7 +1\times2^6 +1\times2^5 +1\times2^4 +1\times2^3 +1\times2^2 +1\times2^1 +1\times2^0$$
$$=128+64+32+16+8+4+2+1$$
$$=255$$

However, we can store larger numbers by using several bytes and treat them as a single number. Moreover, by using numeric codes to represent alphabetic characters and other symbols such as punctuation marks, we are able to store text as well as numeric data. Table 11.1 shows part of a commonly used method for storing textual data; it is called the ASCII character set (American Standard Code for Information Interchange). Each letter in the table has its own unique code.

character	ASCII	character	ASCII	character	ASCII	character	ASCII
0	0110000	9	0111001	I	1001001	R	1010010
1	0110001	A	1000001	J	1001010	S	1010011
2	0110010	B	1000010	K	1001011	T	1010100
3	0110011	C	1000011	L	1001100	U	1010101
4	0110100	D	1000100	M	1001101	V	1010110
5	0110101	E	1000101	N	1001110	W	1010111
6	0110110	F	1000110	O	1001111	X	1011000
7	0110111	G	1000111	P	1010000	Y	1011001
8	0111000	H	1001000	Q	1010001	Z	1011010

Table 11.1. *Extract from ASCII character set*

Thus, if the binary code 1000010 shown in Figure 11.2 was being used to store a character rather than a number, it would represent the capital letter B.

So now we are able to store numeric data or text, depending on how we choose to regard the memory contents. Yet another possibility is to view the contents of memory as instructions forming a computer program. For example, a certain combination of bits might mean add two numbers; another combination might mean move a number from one part of memory to another, or transfer the contents of a memory location to an output device such as a printer, or read the keyboard and store the ASCII code of the key that has just been pressed. In this way it is possible to store instructions to perform a large number of simple tasks, and we can specify more complex tasks by grouping these simple operations into sequences forming computer programs.

What we need to consider now is how a set of instructions stored in the memory can be interpreted and performed one after another by the computer automatically. In other words, how can a computer program be executed? We have seen that logic gates can be combined in order to store binary data, and other combinations of gates can be used to perform switching operations to direct data to different parts of a computer system, depending on the a combination of bits in a memory location being used to store a program. Yet other combinations of gates can be used to perform arithmetic operations, and in fact gates are so important that we will spend some time looking at the characteristics of a number of different types in order to show how they may be applied inside a computer to perform some essential tasks such as executing a stored program.

Figure 11.3 on the next page summarises what we have discussed so far regarding computer memory devices.

Figure 11.3. *From transistors to computer memory*

Gates: the building blocks of computers

Gates are simple electronic devices that respond in a certain way to inputs in the form of electrical signals. These electrical signals represent either a binary 1 (called logic 1) when the signal voltage is high or a binary 0 (called logic 0) when the signal voltage is low. For example, one type of gate called an *OR gate* works like this: it has two or more inputs and a single output such that if at least one of the inputs is at logic 1 then the output is logic 1, otherwise the output is logic 0.

Figure 11.4 shows all the possible combinations of two inputs to an *OR* gate with their corresponding outputs.

Figure 11.4. *Operation of an OR gate*

Thus, when at least one of the pair of inputs is at logic 1, then the output is at logic 1: only when both inputs are zero is the output zero.

A gate with different input/output characteristics is the *AND* gate, shown in Figure 11.5.

Figure 11.5. *Operation of an AND gate*

The AND gate only produces an output of 1 when both inputs are 1. So, if at least one input is 0, the output is 0.

A third important type of gate is the *NOT* gate, sometimes called an *invertor*.

Figure 11.6 shows that the gate simply inverts the input, so that if the input is 1, the output is 0, and if the input is 0, the output is 1.

Figure 11.6. *Operation of the NOT gate*

Using gates to interpret stored instructions.

We saw earlier that computer instructions can be stored in memory just like any other type of data. How a set of program instructions can be automatically performed in sequence will be explained a little later, but for the moment let us assume that an instruction has been retrieved from memory and is ready to be interpreted and executed. Suppose also that the three most significant bits (that is, the three leftmost bits) of the instruction specify what action is to be performed.(Normally there will be more bits than three to specify an action, but the principle about to be explained would still apply). Because the pattern of these three bits uniquely identi-

fies the action to be performed, we could use a combination of gates such as that shown in Figure 11.7 to generate a signal to trigger the computer circuitry which performs the action. The outputs from the three flip-flops containing the code for the required operation are fed into a three-input *AND* gate with the middle input inverted using a *NOT* gate to make it logic 1. Thus, only if the code in these three bits is 101 will the inputs to the *AND* gate be all 1's, producing an output of logic 1 from the *AND* gate; only then will the appropriate circuitry be triggered to perform the

Figure 11.7. *Simple decoder for a three-bit instruction code*

operation. A logic circuit used in this way is called a *decoder*. The outputs from the three operation code flip-flops will be simultaneously fed into other decoders, each one dealing with a different operation code. Because each operation code will have its own unique decoding circuitry, only one decoder will produce a logic 1 output to trigger the required operation. Eight decoders would be required for our simple three-bit instruction code, one each for the codes 000, 001, 010, 011, 100, 101, 110 and 111.

We have yet to consider how the instructions stored in memory can be executed one after another automatically. This involves the *fetch-execute cycle* discussed in the next section.

Fetch-execute cycle

Every computer contains circuitry to perform a number of distinct tasks. On of these tasks, the overall co-ordination and control of the computer, is performed by the *Control Unit*. One of its functions is to transfer the contents of memory locations into a special storage location called the *Current Instruction Register* (CIR) which is like a very small, special-purpose section of memory, but it is located in the Control Unit itself. Another register, called the Program Counter (PC) tells the Control Unit which memory location to copy into the CIR. Once an instruction has been transferred into the CIR, the Control Unit triggers the decoding circuitry as described in the previous section. The PC is incremented to point to the next instruction to be loaded into the CIR, the appropriate operation is then performed, again under the direction of the Control Unit, and the next instruction is transferred into the CIR. This sequence of operations continues until one of the program instructions loaded into the CIR is a *Halt* instruction, which tells the Control Unit that the program is complete. In other words, once the Control Unit has started to execute the program, the program itself must contain an instruction to terminate the process.

The sequence of events just described is usually termed the *fetch-execute cycle*, in which each instruction in turn is *fetch*ed from memory and then *execute*d until a *Halt* instruction is encountered. Figure 11.8 summarises the way that a program is automatically executed.

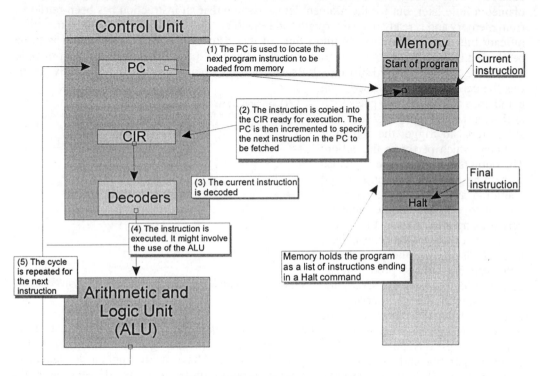

Figure 11.8. *The fetch-execute cycle*

Notice that the circuitry which is responsible for executing any arithmetic or logic operations required by the current instruction is called the Arithmetic and Logic Unit (ALU) and in the next section we will describe a little of what happens inside the ALU by showing how the addition of two 8-bit numbers might be performed using logic gates.

Using logic gates for binary addition

Computer arithmetic is described in some detail Chapter 5, *Number systems and Binary Arithmetic,* and in Chapter 8, *Set Theory and Logic*, we introduced the idea of logic gates and their use in binary addition. In this section we will revisit binary addition, emphasising the role of logic components in performing calculations.

The Table 11.2 summarises the result of adding two binary digits X and Y.

X	Y	Carry	Sum
0	0	0	0
0	1	0	1
1	0	0	1
1	1	1	0

Table 11.2. *Operation of a Half Adder*

When we add two single binary digits, we obtain one of the values 00, 01, 10 or 11 as shown in the table. The left digit can be regarded as a carry, though half the time it will be zero. If we regard the 1's and the 0's as binary signals, then an electronic unit which adds two binary digits requires two inputs X and Y, and two outputs, *Carry* and *Sum* as shown in Figure 11.9.

Figure 11.9. *Half Adder*

This device is usually called a *Half Adder*, but how can gates be used to construct it? To begin with, the table above shows that a single *AND* gate with two inputs X and Y would produce the column labelled *Carry*.

Figure 11.5 shows that this is true, so we can easily implement part of the *Half Adder* by just using one *AND* gate, as shown in Figure 11.10.

X→
Y→ AND → Carry

Figure 11.10. *Carry term of a Half Adder*

The *Sum* term of a *Half Adder* can be produced by the logic circuit shown in Figure 11.11.

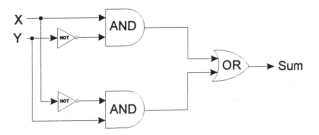

Figure 11.11. *Sum term of a Half Adder*

To help to understand how it works, look at Figure 11.12. It shows how the circuit uses all four possible combinations of the inputs X and Y.

Figure 11.12a shows how the X and Y inputs, both at logic 0, are affected as they go through the circuit. As required, the *Carry* and *Sum* outputs are both logic 0. In Figure 11.12b, X is at logic 0 and Y is logic 1; the carry output is still logic 0, but the sum output becomes 1 as required. As you would expect, when X is 1 and Y is 0 as in Figure 11.12c, the same *Sum* and *Carry* outputs occur. Finally, in Figure 11.12d, when both inputs are at logic 1, the *Carry* output is 1 and the *Sum* output is 0.

Figure 11.12. *Operation of the circuit for the Sum output of a Half Adder*

When we put the two logic circuits for the *Sum* and *Carry* outputs together in Figure 11.13, we obtain the complete circuit for a *Half Adder*.

Figure 11.13. *Complete logic circuit for a Half Adder*

However, this circuit is capable of only adding two bits; in binary addition, as we saw earlier, we need to cope with adding three bits: the bits in the two numbers plus a possible carry from the addition of the two bits to the right. In other words, we really need a *Full Adder*. Fortunately, once we have designed a Half Adder, it is simply a matter of combining two of them in the manner shown in Figure 11.14 in order to have a Full Adder.

As shown in Figure 11.14a, the two digits to be added are used as the inputs to the first *Half Adder*. The *Sum* output of *Half Adder 1* and the *Carry* output from the previous addition are used as the inputs to the second *Half Adder*. The *Sum* output from the second *Half Adder* is the final *Sum* output from the *Full Adder*, and the final *Carry* output is produced by *OR*ing the *Carry* outputs from both *Half Adders*. Figure 11.14b shows the *Full Adder* as a unit with three inputs and two outputs as required.

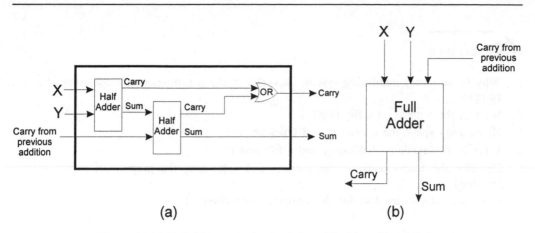

Figure 11.14. *Full Adder: a logic circuit for adding three binary digits*

Now, all that remains is to show how several *Full Adders* can be combined to enable two binary numbers, each consisting of a number of digits, to be added and the result stored. We will assume for simplicity that the two numbers to be added are a maximum of eight bits long and that they are already stored in two eight-bit registers. The resulting number will be transferred to another eight-bit register. The logic circuit is shown in Figure 11.15.

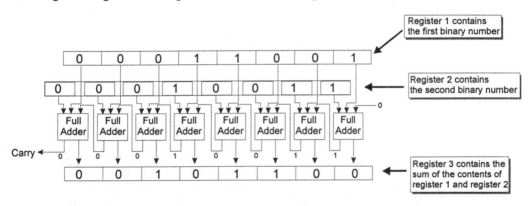

Figure 11.15. *Logic circuit for the addition of two eight-bit numbers*

Each pair of digits, together with the carry from the previous addition are added by one full adder, the sum digit being transferred to register 3 in the diagram. The carry bit from this addition is transferred to the next full adder to the left. This is called *parallel addition* because all of the bit pairs are added at the same time, that is, in parallel.

✍️Exercises

1. Why is the binary numbering system important to the construction and operation of a computer?
2. What is the purpose of a flip-flop?
3. Name and explain the operation of 3 types of gate.
4. What is the function a half-adder and a full adder?
5. Describe the fetch-execute cycle, naming and explaining the purpose of important registers.
6. How can gates be used to decode computer instructions?

Chapter 12

Computer logic

In Chapter 11, *Basic Concepts,* we introduced the idea of logic gates and showed how combinations of AND, OR and NOT gates are used in the construction of logic circuits for binary addition. In this chapter we look at the design of more complex logic circuits and introduce three more gates that are of practical importance in the construction of computer circuitry. We then show in detail how logic circuits can be designed to perform binary addition. The chapter concludes with an introduction to flip-flops and some of their uses. This chapter draws heavily on the information presented in Chapter 8, *Set Theory and Logic.*

The design of logic circuits

The complete process of designing a logic circuit may be summarised as follows:

(i)   Identify Boolean variables equivalent to the inputs to the circuit required.

(ii)   Identify the outputs from the circuit.

(iii)   Draw a truth table to define the output required for each possible combination of the input variables.

(iv)   Derive an expression from the truth table for the output in terms of the input variables.

(v)   Simplify this expression using a Karnaugh map.

(vi)   Examine the simplified expression for possible further simplifications using direct applications of the laws of Boolean Algebra.

(vii)   Draw the circuit using the appropriate gate symbols.

The following problem illustrates the process.

Four binary signals A, B, C, D represent a single Binary Coded Decimal (BCD) digit. A logic circuit is required to output logic 1 on the occurrence of an invalid combination of the signals, that is, when they represent a number in the range 10 to 15.

(i)   The inputs to the circuit are clearly defined and it is assumed that A is the most significant digit and D the least significant digit.

(ii)   The single output is to be 1 when the binary number represented by ABCD is in the range 10 to 15, that is, 1010 to 1111 in binary.

(iii)   The truth table (Table 12.1) has 16 entries, representing the numbers 0 to 15.

(iv)   The expression for the output is given by

$$\text{OUTPUT} = A.\overline{B}.C.\overline{D} + A.\overline{B}.C.D + A.B.\overline{C}.\overline{D} + A.B.\overline{C}.D + A.B.C.\overline{D} + A.B.C.D$$

A	B	C	D		OUTPUT	
0	0	0	0	(0)	0	
0	0	0	1	(1)	0	
0	0	1	0	(2)	0	
0	0	1	1	(3)	0	
0	1	0	0	(4)	0	
0	1	0	1	(5)	0	
0	1	1	0	(6)	0	
0	1	1	1	(7)	0	
1	0	0	0	(8)	0	
1	0	0	1	(9)	0	
1	0	1	0	(10)	1	$A.\bar{B}.C.\bar{D}$
1	0	1	1	(11)	1	$A.\bar{B}.C.D$
1	1	0	0	(12)	1	$A.B.\bar{C}.\bar{D}$
1	1	0	1	(13)	1	$A.B.\bar{C}.D$
1	1	1	0	(14)	1	$A.B.C.\bar{D}$
1	1	1	1	(15)	1	$A.B.C.D$

Table 12.1

(v) The Karnaugh map is shown in Figure 12.1.

(vi) Using the Distributive law the expression A.B + A.C may be written A.(B + C).

(vii) This expression translates to the logic diagram in Figure 12.2.

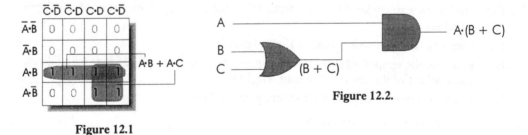

Figure 12.1

Figure 12.2.

More logic gates

The gates that have yet to be defined are the NOR(Not OR), NAND(Not AND) and XOR (eXclusive OR) gates.

The truth table for the NOR gate (Table 12.2) shows that its outputs are the inverse of those for the OR gate.

Algebraically, the NOR gate is written $(\overline{X+Y})$. Thus the gate appears to be formed from one OR gate and one NOT gate inverting the output from the OR gate. In practice, however, the OR gate outputs are generated from a single simple circuit and not by the combination of an OR gate followed by a NOT gate.

X	Y	X NOR Y
0	0	1
0	1	0
1	0	0
1	1	0

Table 12.2. *NOR gate truth table*

The symbol for the NOR gate is shown in Figure 12.3(a).

The truth table for the NAND gate (Table 12.3) shows that its outputs are the inverse of those for the AND gate.

X	Y	X NAND Y
0	0	1
0	1	1
1	0	1
1	1	0

Table 12.3. *Truth table for NAND gate*

In Boolean Algebra, the gate is written $(\overline{X.Y})$. The comments above regarding the construction of the NOR gate similarly apply here: the NAND gate is not constructed from an AND gate followed by a NOT gate, but consists of a single circuit no more complex than the other gates.

The symbol for the NAND gate is shown in Figure 12.3(b).

(a) NOR gate   (b) NAND gate

Figure 12.3. *Symbols used for NOR and NAND gates*

The importance of the NAND gate and NOR gate

The importance of these gates may be attributed to two factors:

(i)   each may be manufactured cheaply and easily;

(ii)   each can be used in the production of any circuit using AND/OR/NOT logical components. In other words, NOR gates and NAND gates can be used in the place of AND, OR or NOT gates.

These two properties mean that a logic circuit using, for instance, NOR gates only, can be produced more easily and cheaply than the same circuit using combinations of three different types of components (AND, OR and NOT gates). A unit using a number of the same component is much easier to manufacture than one using several different components. The logic diagrams in Figure 12.4, (a), (b) and (c), show how NOR gates may be used to represent the functions of NOT, AND and OR gates.

Figure 12.3. *NOR gates used to represent functions of NOT, AND and OR gates*

The logic diagrams in Figure 12.5, (a), (b) and (c), show how NAND gates may be used to represent the functions of NOT, AND and OR gates.

Figure 12.5. *NAND gates used to represent functions of NOT, AND and OR gates*

(As an exercise, write down Boolean expressions equivalent to the circuits shown above and prove their validity using truth tables).

It may appear from the diagrams shown above that circuits using NAND or NOR gates will generally require more gates than when using AND/OR NOT components. This may be true on occasions, but at other times fewer gates may be required. The number of gates required often may be reduced by transforming the Boolean expression into a more suitable form. For example, the following expression, when implemented directly using NOR gates, uses more gates than the expression requires using AND/OR/NOT logic:

$$X.\overline{Y} + \overline{X}.Y \text{ (2 AND gates, 2 NOT gates, 1 OR gate = 5 gates)}$$

However, it can be shown that the following identity is true:

$$X.\overline{Y} + \overline{X}.Y = \overline{\overline{(\overline{X}+\overline{Y})}+\overline{(X+Y)}}$$

which may not look very helpful but, in fact, shows that the original expression can be transformed into one much more suited to implementation by NOR gates. As Figure 12.6 shows, the circuit based on this transformed expression has only five NOR gates.

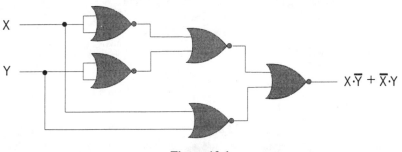

Figure 12.6.

The Exclusive OR gate

This is usually abbreviated to XOR or EOR. The truth table for the XOR gate is shown in Table 12.4.The exclusive OR gate is so named because, of its output values, the case where both inputs are logic 1 is excluded; in the OR gate these inputs produce an output of 1. In effect, the

XOR gate has an output of logic 1 when the inputs are different; when the inputs are the same, the output is logic 0.

Algebraically, the XOR gate is $X.\overline{Y} + \overline{X}.Y$ and the symbol that is frequently used is shown in Figure 12.7.

X
Y
$X.\overline{Y} + \overline{X}.Y$

Figure 12.7. *Symbol for XOR gate*

X	Y	X XOR Y
0	0	0
0	1	1
1	0	1
1	1	0

Table 12.4. *Truth table for XOR gate*

As an example of its use, suppose that it is required to generate an even parity bit for a four bit word ABCD. The truth table for this problem is shown in Table 12.5.

The expression for even parity is thus

Parity bit =

$A.\overline{B}.\overline{C}.D + \overline{A}.\overline{B}.C.\overline{D} + \overline{A}.B.\overline{C}.\overline{D} + \overline{A}.B.C.D$
$+ \ A.\overline{B}.\overline{C}.\overline{D} \ + \ A.\overline{B}.C.D \ + \ A.B.\overline{C}.D \ +$
$A.B.C.\overline{D}$

and the Karnaugh map representation is shown in Figure 12.6(a).

As the map shows, there is no way of simplifying the expression. However, if the terms are grouped together as follows, a pattern begins to emerge.

Parity bit =

$\overline{A}.\overline{B}.(\overline{C}.D + C.\overline{D}) + \overline{A}.B.(C.D + \overline{C}.\overline{D}) + A.\overline{B}.(\overline{C}.\overline{D} + C.D) + A.B.(\overline{C}.D + C.\overline{D})$

Rearranging the terms,

Parity bit =

$\overline{A}.\overline{B}.(\overline{C}.D + C.\overline{D}) + A.B.(\overline{C}.D + C.\overline{D}) + \overline{A}.B.(C.D + \overline{C}.\overline{D}) + A.\overline{B}.(C.D + \overline{C}.\overline{D})$

A	B	C	D	parity bit	
0	0	0	0	0	
0	0	0	1	1	$\overline{A}.\overline{B}.\overline{C}.D$
0	0	1	0	1	$\overline{A}.\overline{B}.C.\overline{D}$
0	0	1	1	0	
0	1	0	0	1	$\overline{A}.B.\overline{C}.\overline{D}$
0	1	0	1	0	
0	1	1	0	0	
0	1	1	1	1	$\overline{A}.B.C.D$
1	0	0	0	1	$A.\overline{B}.\overline{C}.\overline{D}$
1	0	0	1	0	
1	0	1	0	0	
1	0	1	1	1	$A.\overline{B}.C.D$
1	1	0	0	0	
1	1	0	1	1	$A.B.\overline{C}.D$
1	1	1	0	1	$A.B.C.\overline{D}$
1	1	1	1	0	

Table 12.5

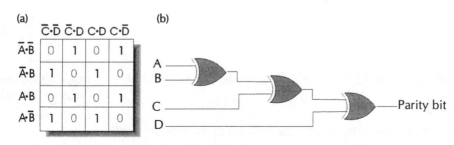

(a)

	$\overline{C}.\overline{D}$	$\overline{C}.D$	$C.D$	$C.\overline{D}$
$\overline{A}.\overline{B}$	0	1	0	1
$\overline{A}.B$	1	0	1	0
$A.B$	0	1	0	1
$A.\overline{B}$	1	0	1	0

(b)

A
B
C
D
Parity bit

Figure 12.6. *Karnaugh map and equivalent circuit*

Again, using the Distributive law, the first two and the last two terms can be grouped together to give:

$$\text{parity bit} = (\overline{A}.\overline{B} + A.B).(\overline{C}.D + C.\overline{D}) + (\overline{A}.B + A.\overline{B}).(\overline{C}.\overline{D} + C.D)$$

Notice that two of the terms in brackets are immediately recognisable as XOR functions. In addition it can be shown that

$$\overline{\overline{X}.Y + X.\overline{Y}} = \overline{X}.\overline{Y} + X.Y$$

Using this identity, the expression for parity becomes:

$$\text{parity bit} = \overline{(\overline{A}.B + A.\overline{B})}.(\overline{C}.D + C.\overline{D}) + (\overline{A}.B + A.\overline{B}).\overline{(\overline{C}.D + C.\overline{D})}$$

Now each bracketed term looks like an XOR gate and, treating each bracketed term as a unit, the complete expression has the form

$$\overline{X}.Y + X.\overline{Y}, \text{ where } X = (\overline{A}.B + A.\overline{B}) \text{ and } Y = (\overline{C}.D + C.\overline{D})$$

Thus the whole expression, and every term within it, represent XOR gates. The equivalent circuit is shown in Figure 12.6(b).

Designing logic circuits for binary addition

The logic circuits which perform the function of addition in the Arithmetic and Logic Unit of the Central Processing Unit are called *adders*. A unit which adds two binary digits is called a *half adder* and one which adds together three binary digits is called a *full adder*. In this section each of these units will be examined in detail, and it will be shown how such units are combined to add binary numbers.

Half adders

In Chapter 11, *Basic Concepts*, the construction of a half adder was explained in order to illustrate how electronic circuits can be used to perform arithmetic operations. Remember that the function of a half adder is to add two binary digits and produce as output a Sum term and Carry term. The operation of the half adder is defined by the truth table in Table 12.6.

X	Y	Sum		Carry	
0	0	0		0	
0	1	1	$\overline{X}.Y$	0	
1	0	1	$X.\overline{Y}$	0	
1	1	0		1	$X.Y$

Table 12.6.

Thus, the expressions for the Sum and Carry terms are given by:

$$\text{Sum} = \overline{X}.Y + X.\overline{Y}$$

$$\text{Carry} = X.Y$$

The symbol in Figure 12.7 will henceforth be used for a half adder.

Figure 12.7. *Symbol used for a Half Adder*

Full adders

Table 12.6 shows the truth table for the addition of three binary digits.

Considering the Sum term first, the expression derived from the truth table is

$$\text{Sum} = \overline{X}.\overline{Y}.Z + \overline{X}.Y.\overline{Z} + X.\overline{Y}.\overline{Z} + X.Y.Z$$

X	Y	Z	Sum		Carry	
0	0	0	0		0	
0	0	1	1	$\overline{X}.\overline{Y}.Z$	0	
0	1	0	1	$\overline{X}.Y.\overline{Z}$	0	
0	1	1	0		1	$\overline{X}.Y.Z$
1	0	0	1	$X.\overline{Y}.\overline{Z}$	0	
1	0	1	0		1	$X.\overline{Y}.Z$
1	1	0	0		1	$X.Y.\overline{Z}$
1	1	1	1	$X.Y.Z$	1	$X.Y.Z$

Table 12.6. *Truth table for addition of three binary digits*

Grouping together the first and third terms, and the middle two terms gives

$$\text{Sum} = \overline{Z}.(\overline{X}.Y + X.\overline{Y}) + Z.(\overline{X}.\overline{Y} + X.Y)$$

Using the identity

$$\overline{\overline{X}.Y + X.\overline{Y}} = \overline{X}.\overline{Y} + X.Y \quad \text{(this can easily be proved using a truth table)}$$

the Sum term can be written

$$\text{Sum} = \overline{Z}.\left(\overline{X}.Y + X.\overline{Y}\right) + Z.\left(\overline{\overline{X}.Y + X.\overline{Y}}\right)$$

which is of the form

$$\overline{Z}.S + Z.\overline{S} \quad \text{where } S = \overline{X}.Y + X.\overline{Y}$$

In other words, S is the sum term from a half adder with inputs X and Y, and Sum is one of the outputs from a half adder with inputs Z and S. The Sum term can now be produced using two half adders, as shown in Figure 12.8.

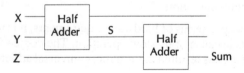

Figure 12.8. *Using two half adders to produce Sum term*

Returning to the Carry term, the expression derived from the truth table is

$$\text{Carry} = \overline{X}.Y.Z + X.\overline{Y}.Z + X.Y.\overline{Z} + X.Y.Z$$

Again gathering terms,

$$\text{Carry} = Z.(\overline{X}.Y + X.\overline{Y}) + X.Y.(\overline{Z} + Z)$$
$$= Z.(\overline{X}.Y + X.\overline{Y}) + X.Y \quad \text{since } \overline{Z} + Z = 1 \text{ and } X.Y.1 = X.Y$$

Substituting S for $\overline{X}.Y + X.\overline{Y}$ as before, the expression becomes

$$\text{Carry} = Z.S + X.Y$$

Both of these terms look like the carry term from a half adder: Z.S is the carry term from a half adder with inputs Z and S (the carry term from the second half adder in the diagram above); X.Y is the carry output from the first half adder in the diagram. The two carry outputs merely need to be ORed together, to give the final circuit in Figure 12.9.

Figure 12.9.

Adding binary numbers

So far, the circuits for addition have only been capable of adding two or three binary digits; more complex schemes are necessary in order to add two binary numbers each comprising several digits. Two approaches will be considered. The first adds numbers bit by bit, one pair of bits after another and is termed *serial addition*; the other accepts as inputs all pairs of bits in the two numbers simultaneously and is called *parallel addition*.

Serial addition

Suppose that the numbers to be added have a four-bit wordlength, and the two numbers A and B have digits a3, a2, a1, a0, and b3, b2, b1, b0 respectively. The circuit for a four-bit serial adder is shown in Figure 12.10.

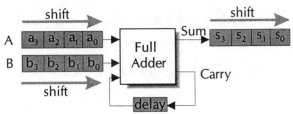

Figure 12.10. *Four-bit serial adder*

In this particular design, a single full adder is presented with pairs of bits from the two numbers in the sequence a0 b0 , a1 b1 , a2 b2 , a3 b3 . As each pair of bits is added, the sum term is transmitted to a shift register to hold the result, and the carry term is delayed so that it is added in to the next addition operation.

Though this method is cheap in terms of hardware requirements, it is not often (if at all) used in modern digital computers because of its slow operation. The degree to which hardware prices have dropped in recent years has resulted in the almost universal adoption of parallel addition.

Parallel addition

In parallel addition, a separate adder is used for the addition of each digit pair. Thus for the addition of two four-digit numbers, one half adder and three full adders would be used. In this type of circuit, all the digits are input simultaneously, with the carry term from each stage being connected directly to the input of the next stage. This is shown in Figure 12.11.

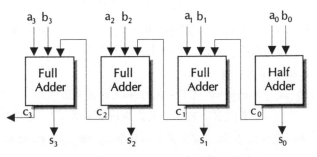

Figure 12.11. *Circuit for parallel addition*

Though faster than serial addition, one fault of the type of parallel adder shown above is the successive carry out to carry in connections which cause relatively long delays; more elaborate schemes are capable of overcoming this problem (at the expense of added circuitry).

The efficiency of the addition circuits is of particular importance in microprocessors where the functions of multiplication and division, as well as subtraction, often use these circuits. Most computers have special purpose circuitry for multiplication and division.

Flip-flops

One of the fundamental functions performed by digital computers is the storage of data in memory. The electronic component which is usually used for this purpose is called a *flip-flop*. Other names for the same device are *bistable*, *latch* and *toggle*, but flip-flop is the most commonly used name.

A flip-flop is capable of storing, in electrical form, a single binary digit. Thus, a collection of eight flip-flops can store a byte of data. As well as being used for memory, flip-flops form the basis of other useful CPU components, such as *shift registers* and *binary counters*.

Flip-flops are frequently constructed with gates, but using *sequential logic* rather than the *combinational logic* described in the previous part of this chapter. As we have seen, a combinational logic circuit produces an output which is entirely dependent on the current inputs; with sequential logic, because of the use of feedback, the output from a sequential logic circuit depends on its current state in addition to the current inputs. In other words, the output from a sequential logic circuit is partly determined by the previous inputs it received.

In this section we describe the operational characteristics of the simplest type of flip-flop, the *SR flip-flop*, before going on to show how it may be constructed using NAND gates. We then discuss the synchronous version of the SR flip-flop, the *clocked SR flip-flop* before showing how shift registers, binary counters and memory units may be fabricated using them.

Though there are a number of different types of flip-flops in common use, including JK, Master-Slave and D-type flip-flops, essentially they are all based on the SR flip-flop, and it is beyond the scope of this book to discuss the precise differences between them and why one type is preferred over another for certain types of application.

Operation of the SR flip-flop

The term flip-flop derives from its characteristic of being in one of two stable states at any instant, and hence the alternative name, *bistable*. These two states we conveniently designate 0 and 1. In state 1, the device is said to be *set*, and in state 0, *reset*, hence SR flip-flop. If the flip-flop is in state 1, it will remain in that state until an input causes it to change to state 0, in which state it will also remain until changed. Thus it remembers its current state until some signal causes it to change state. Figure 12.12 shows the symbol generally used for an unclocked SR flip-flop. The two outputs are labelled Q and $\bar{Q}$ because each is the complement of the other. The current state of the device is by convention that of the Q output.

Figure 12.12.
Unclocked SR flip-flop

The input lines, S and R, are used to control the state of the flip-flop. If a signal is applied to the S line, the flip-flop is set (ie Q=1); a signal on the R line resets it (ie Q=0). The absence of any signal leaves the state of the flip-flop unchanged. Applying a signal to both lines simultaneously is not allowed.

Table 12.7 illustrates these rules with a sequence of input signals and the resulting state of the flip-flop.

S	R	Q	Effect of input
1	0	1	set
0	0	1	remains in same state
0	0	1	remains in same state
0	1	0	reset
0	0	0	remains in same state
1	0	1	set
1	0	1	already set so no effect
0	1	0	reset
0	1	0	already set so no effect

Table 12.7. *The effect of input signals on the SR flip-flop*

Construction of the SR flip-flop

A simple form of an SR flip-flop may be implemented using two NAND gates connected as shown in Figure 12.13. The operation of this flip-flop is defined by Table12.8.

Figure 12.13. *Construction of SR flip-flop*

S	R	Q'
0	0	Q
0	1	0
1	0	0
1	1	not defined

Table 12.8. *Operation of SR flip-flop*

The current state of the circuit is denoted by Q and the resulting state, due to the two inputs, is Q'. We can verify the operation of the circuit by tracing each pair of inputs and comparing them with the outputs shown:

(i) $\overline{S}=1$, $\overline{R}=1$ and Q=1. This corresponds to the null input, self-sustaining state. The inputs to the lower NAND gate are both 1, producing an output, Q', of 0. This means that the inputs to the upper NAND gate are 1 and 0, producing an output of 1; no change in the outputs. If the current state is Q=0, the lower gate has inputs 0 and 1, producing an output of 1, and the upper gate now has both inputs at logic-1, producing an output of 0; again no change.

(ii) $\overline{S}=0$ and $\overline{R}=1$. This is the *set* condition. Because $\overline{S}=0$, the upper gate must output logic-1; the inputs to the lower gate both being 1, the output is 0.

(iii) $\overline{S}=1$ and $\overline{R}=0$. This is the *reset* condition. Because $\overline{R}=0$, the lower gate must output logic-1 this time, and the two logic-1 inputs to the top gate produce an output of 0.

(iv) $\overline{S}=0$ and $\overline{R}=0$. In this instance the output from the flip-flop cannot be determined; the resulting state will be unpredictable and will depend on such factors as temperature and component tolerances.

The clocked SR flip-flop

Figure 12.14 shows the symbol for a clocked SR flip-flop. It has an additional input designated *clock* or *enable*. The circuit for a clocked SR flip-flop is shown in Figure 12.15.

Figure 12.14. *Clocked SR flip-flop*

Figure 12.15. *Construction of Clocked SR flip-flop*

The extra input allows the operation of the flip-flop to be controlled by a timing signal which is used to synchronize the operation of the separate components of a circuit. Circuits controlled by a clock are called *synchronous* circuits; where a clock is not used the circuit is *asynchronous*.

Because of the added complexity of asynchronous circuits, most circuits are of the synchronous variety.

The effect of the additional gates in the circuit is to hold the S and R inputs at the null state ($\overline{S}=\overline{Q}=1$) until a clock pulse is applied to the first two gates, at which time set and reset signals are applied to the flip-flop. In effect, the clock pulse *enables* the flip-flop to assume a new state.

Shift registers

A four stage shift register is shown in the Figure 12.16.

Figure 12.16. *A four-stage shift register*

A sequence of signals representing a binary number is applied to the input. Each input is set up while the clock is at logic-0. When the clock pulse becomes logic-1, each flip-flop is enabled and assumes the value of the signal being applied to the S input. Therefore, the complete contents of the flip-flops are shifted along by one bit at every clock pulse. The current state of each flip-flop is available on the lines labelled O/P0 to O/P3. Table 12.9 illustrates the process with the binary sequence 1101, assuming that the initial contents of the shift register is 0000.

clock pulse	input	O/P0	O/P1	O/P2	O/P3
		0	0	0	0
1	1	1	0	0	0
2	0	0	1	0	0
3	1	1	0	1	0
4	1	1	1	0	1

Table 12.9. *Operation of a four-stage shift register*

Binary counters

A binary counter consists of a collection of flip-flops each of which is associated with a bit position in the binary representation of a number. If there are n flip-flops in a binary counter, the number of possible states is 2^n and the counting sequence is from 0 to 2^n-1. If the maximum value is exceeded, the counting sequence starts at 0 again. A simple form of a binary counter is based on an SR flip-flop connected to act as a *toggle circuit* shown in Figure 12.17.

Input

Figure 12.17. *Toggle*

Each pulse applied to the clock input inverts the output, Q, of the circuit; in effect, this is dividing the input frequency by two by performing alternate *set* and *reset* operations. Table 12.10 shows how the output changes after each logic-1 input, assuming that the current output is logic-0. Notice that logic-0 inputs have no effect on the output. A four-bit counter uses four toggle circuits connected in series. (See Figure 12.18)

The output from the first toggle circuit alternates between 0 and 1 as shown in the previous table. Each time a logic-1 is output from the first toggle component, the second one is enabled and its output inverts; each time the output from the second component is logic-1, the third one is enabled and its output inverts, and so on.

Therefore, the first component inverts after each logic-1 input, the second one inverts after two logic-1 inputs, the third after four and the fourth after eight. Table 5.23 shows how the outputs of each of the toggle circuits, A, B, C and D change for a sequence of logic-1 inputs. Thus, A represents the least significant bit of the 4-bit number and D the most significant bit. The counter thus counts up from 0 to 15 cyclically.

	input	output (Q)
		0
1	1	1
2	0	1
3	1	0
4	0	0
5	1	1
6	0	1
	etc	

Table 12.10. *Operation of a toggle*

Figure 12.18. *Four-bit binary counter*

Memory circuits

One of the fundamental characteristics of the digital computer is its ability to store data and programs in random-access memory. We have seen already that sequential circuits are capable of storing binary signals and that collections of such components may be used to store bytes or larger words of data. Large arrays of such circuits constitute the internal memory of a computer. Figure 12.19 shows one possible arrangement for a random-access memory unit. The *Address Lines*, typically 16 or 32 for a microcomputer, specify which particular memory word is to be accessed; a *Chip Enable* line (not shown) enables the chip if it is logic-1, or disables the chip if it is logic-0; when enabled, the chip may be written to, by making *Write=1* and read from, using Write=0.

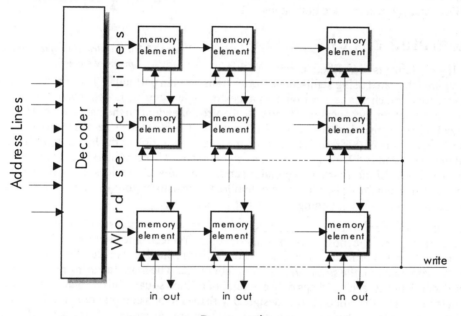

Figure 12.19. *Random access memory*

Each horizontal row of memory elements represents a word of memory which may be selected by an Address Decoder. So for an 8-bit word there will be a row of eight memory elements. When an address is input to the address decoder, it selects the corresponding word

For a 16-bit address, the decoder will select one line from 2^{16} possibilities. If a read operation is required, the word, corresponding to the states of the eight memory elements, will appear on the *Out* lines; a write operation will cause the eight memory elements to take on the binary values on the *In* lines.

The construction of the memory elements, each storing a single bit, is shown in Figure 12.20.

Each element comprises a flip-flop and a number of other gates to control the transfer of data between the flip-flop and the common internal data lines. Notice that the AND gates are used to control the passage of signals; only when all inputs to an AND gate are 1 will the output become 1. Each *word-select* line is used to enable all elements in a row for reading or writing, and each column has two internal data lines, one for reading - data-in - and one for writing - data-out. The data-out line takes the value of the element in the currently enabled word.

Thus, when *Word select=1* the Q output from the memory element is ORed with the data-out line. A word is written into a memory location by presenting the appropriate address to the decoder (which enables the word memory elements), the bit pattern of the word to the data-in lines and then setting *Write=1*. Two AND gates in each memory element allow its state to be changed to the value on the data-in line providing *Write* and *Word select* are both at logic-1.

Figure 12.20. *Construction of a single-bit memory element*

Integrated circuits

The logic elements described earlier in this chapter are fabricated using semi-conductors - transistors in particular. The speed of operation of transistors, which act as electronic switches in logic circuits, is dependent on their size; power consumption, heat generated and cost are also dependent on their size. Since size is such a critical factor, a great deal of research has been done to reduce the size of a transistor as far as possible. The result of this research has been the steady evolution of the Integrated Circuit (IC). Though invented in 1959, integrated circuits were first used in computers in the late 1960s. The PDP-11 was one of the first commercial machines to use such devices. At that time an integrated circuit contained less than one hundred transistors; today, microprocessors   are constructed from chips containing millions of transistors .

Electronic devices are constructed using combinations of components such as resistors, capacitors and transistors. The most common material of microelectronic circuits is silicon, the same type that is found in ordinary sand. The silicon is first refined and made into thin discs which form the base material, the *substrate*, for a number of ICs. The manufacturing process produces several identical ICs, each perhaps only a quarter of an inch square, on one wafer of silicon. The circuit to be set into the silicon is first designed with the aid of a computer to minimize the number of components   before being used to prepare a series of masks. After being photographically reduced to the actual chip size, the masks are used in a photographic process which sequentially isolates each chip from its immediate neighbours, defines the position of the components, modifies the structure of the substrate to give it the required semiconducting characteristics and interconnects the components using etched metallic films. Further stages are required to test the circuits, separate them and package them into the familiar 'bug' shape.

Table 12.11 is a rough guide to the five generations of ICs, in terms of chip complexity.

generation	no. of components
Small Scale Integration (SSI)	2 - 64
Medium Scale Integration (MSI)	64 - 2000
Large Scale Integration (LSI)	2000 - 64,000
Very Large Scale Integration (VLSI)	64,000 - 2,000,000
Ultra Large Scale Integration (ULSI)	2,000,000 - 100,000,000

Table 12.11. *Generations of integrated circuits (ICs)*

Since its invention in 1959, the IC has undergone rapid growth, its complexity following a progression known as Moores Law which states that the maximum number of components on a microprocessor chip doubles about every one and a half years. Of course there is a limit to how small an electronic component can be made, and therefore the maximum speed at which a microprocessor can be made to operate, so that eventually it will be impossible to make circuits smaller. However, just as the development of the transistor resulted from advances in theoretical physics, there is evidence that further advances will produce technological innovations that will again revolutionise the construction of computers.

Exercises

1. For each of the following, simplify the expression using a Karnaugh map and draw a circuit of the simplified expression:
    (i) $X.Y.\overline{Z} + X.Y.Z + X.\overline{Y}.Z$
    (ii) $A.B.C + A.\overline{B}.C + A.B.\overline{C} + \overline{A}.\overline{B}.C + \overline{A}.B.C$
    (iii) $A.B.C.D + A.B.\overline{C}.D + A.B.C.\overline{D} + \overline{A}.B.\overline{C}.D + \overline{A}.B.C.\overline{D} + A.\overline{B}.\overline{C}.\overline{D}$
    (iv) $\overline{W}.X + X.\overline{Y} + X.\overline{Y}.Z + \overline{W}.\overline{Y}.\overline{Z} + W.X.\overline{Y}.\overline{Z}$

2. Given two binary signals, X and Y, produce a truth table to define the difference of the two digits for every combination. There will be two outputs representing the difference and a 'borrow'. Hence, draw the circuit for a 'half subtractor'.

3. Produce a truth table which defines the 4-bit product when two numbers are multiplied together (the largest number produced will be $3 \times 3 = 9$, which requires 4 bits). Simplify each of the four outputs, using Karnaugh maps and produce a circuit for hardware multiplication of 2-bit numbers.

4. Design and circuit that will generate and odd parity bit for a 4-bit word ABCD (see section on the XOR gate).

5. Describe the operation of the SR flip-flop.

6. What determines whether a circuit is synchronous or asynchronous?

7. Name 3 types of computer circuits that use flip flops. Briefly describe their operation.

Chapter 13

Data representation

Data, in the context of this chapter, is a general term which covers any data or information which is capable of being handled by the computer's internal circuitry, or of being stored on backing storage media such as magnetic tape or disk. To be processed by computer, data must be in a form which the computer can handle; it must be *machine-sensible*.

Forms of coding

To be machine-sensible, data has to be in *binary* format. In Chapter 5, it is explained that the binary number system uses only two digits, 0 and 1. Both main memory and external storage media, such as magnetic disk and tape, use electrical/magnetic patterns representing the binary digits 0 and 1 to record and handle data and instructions.

Why binary? - bi-stable devices

Computer storage uses two-state or bi-stable devices to indicate the presence of a binary 0 or 1. The circuits inside a computer represent these two states by being either conducting or non-conducting, that is, current is either flowing or is not flowing through the circuit. A simple example of a bi-stable device is an electric light bulb. At any one time it must be in one of two states, on or off. Magnetic storage media use magnetic fields and the two possible polarities (north and south) are used as bi-stable devices to represent 0 and 1. To understand the benefits of using binary representation, consider the electronic requirements which would be necessary if the denary system were used. To record the ten denary symbols 0 to 9, a computer's circuitry would have to use and accommodate ten clearly defined physical electronic states. Extremely reliable components would be needed to avoid the machine confusing one physical state with another. With bi-stable devices, slight changes in performance do not prevent differentiation between the two physical states which represent 0 and 1.

Character and numeric codes

Much of the data processed by computer and stored on backing storage are represented by *character* codes. The codes used inside the computer are referred to as *internal* codes, whereas those used by various peripherals are termed *external* codes. Data transferred between peripheral devices and the processor may use a variety of binary character codes, but when processing data the processor will tend to use a particular internal code, which will vary with machines of different manufacture. Sometimes, an external character code may continue to be used for storage of data in main memory; alphabetic data remains in character code form during computer processing. On the other hand, numeric data, presented by a peripheral in character code form, is converted to one of a number of numeric codes for processing purposes. Code conversion may be executed within a peripheral, within the *interface* device between a peripheral and the processor, or within the processor itself. Characters may be grouped as follows:

- ❑ alphabetic (upper and lower case);
- ❑ numeric (0 to 9);
- ❑ special characters (apostrophe, comma, etc.);
- ❑ control characters and codes.

Control characters are used in data transmission, perhaps to indicate the start or end of a *block* of data; *control codes* can be used to affect the display of data on a VDU screen and include those which cause, for example, carriage return, delete, highlight or blinking. Control characters and control codes do not form part of the data which are to be usefully processed, but are needed for control. The range of characters which can be represented by a computer system is known as its *character set*. The ASCII (American Standard Code for Information Interchange) code uses seven binary digits (*bits*) to represent a full range of characters; an extract is shown in Table 11.1. in Chapter 11. Data passing between a peripheral and the computer is usually in character code, typically ASCII.

Parity checking of codes

The ASCII code is a 7-bit code. An additional bit, known as the *parity bit* (in the left-most or most significant bit position), is used to detect *single bit* errors which may occur during data transfer. Such errors may result from a peripheral fault or from corruption of data on storage media. The parity scheme used for detecting single bit errors is simple (the detection of multiple bit errors is more complex) . There are two types of parity, odd and even, though it is of little significance which is used. If odd parity is used, the parity bit is set to binary 1 or 0, such that there is an odd number of binary 1s in the group. Conversely, even parity requires that there is an even number of binary 1s in the group. Examples of these two forms of parity are provided in Table 13.1.

data - no parity	parity bit	data - odd parity	parity bit	data - even parity
1 0 0 1 0 1 0	0	1 0 0 1 0 1 0	1	1 0 0 1 0 1 0
0 1 0 1 1 0 1	1	0 1 0 1 1 0 1	0	0 1 0 1 1 0 1

Table 13.1. *Examples of data using odd and even parity*

If even parity is being used and main memory receives the grouping 10010100 then the presence of an odd number of binary 1s indicates an error in transmission. Provided that the number of bits corrupted is odd, all transmission errors will be detected. However, an even number of bits in error will not affect the parity condition and thus will not be revealed. Additional controls can be implemented to detect multiple bit errors; these controls make use of parity checks on blocks of characters; known *as block check characters* (BCC), they are used extensively in data transmission control.

Data storage in main memory

Character codes, such as the ASCII code, are primarily of use during data transfer between a peripheral and the main memory. They are also generally used to represent non-numeric data inside the computer. Numeric data are usually converted to one of a number of *numeric codes*, including binary coded decimal (BCD) and floating point formats (see later).

Binary coded decimal (BCD)

As the name suggests, BCD uses a binary code to represent each of the decimal symbols. It is a 4-bit code, using the natural binary weightings of 8, 4, 2 and 1 and is only used for the representation of numeric values. Each of the ten symbols used in the decimal system is coded with its 4-bit binary equivalent, as shown in Table 13.2.

denary	0	1	2	3	4	5	6	7	8	9
BCD	0000	0001	0010	0011	0100	0101	0110	0111	1000	1001

Table 13.2. BCD equivalents of denary symbols

In this way, any decimal number can be represented by coding each digit separately. An example BCD number is shown in Table 13.3.

denary	6	2	4
BCD	0110	0010	0100

Table 13.3. BCD representation of 624_{10}

BCD arithmetic

Floating point arithmetic (see *Floating-point Representation*) can introduce small inaccuracies which can be a problem in financial data processing applications. For example, an amount of $120 \cdot 50$ stored in floating point form may return a value of $120 \cdot 499999$; although the application of *rounding algorithms* (see later) can adjust the figure to the required number of significant figures, the rounding is being carried out on the binary representation, when it is the decimal form which should be rounded. For BCD numbers, each decimal character is separately coded, and more complex electronics are needed to carry out arithmetic on data in BCD form than are necessary for pure binary numbers. BCD numbers also take more memory space than pure binary numbers. For example, with a 16-bit word the maximum BCD number is 9999_{10}, while using binary it is 65535_{10}. Numbers with a fractional element (*real* numbers) are represented with an implied decimal point which can be located between any of the 4-bit groupings.

Internal parity checks

Most mini and mainframe computers use parity bits to detect and sometimes correct, data transfer errors within the computer, so the actual length of codes is extended to allow for this. Parity checking, built into the circuitry of the memory chips is a feature of many microcomputer systems. Memory chips can develop faults, so it is important that a user is made aware of parity errors (which may indicate the beginnings of major memory faults), before significant data loss occurs.

The structure of main memory

Main memory is divided into a number of cells or *locations*, each of which has a unique name or *address* and is capable of holding a unit or grouping of bits which may represent data or an instruction. Memory locations are normally addressed using whole numbers from zero upwards. The *size* of memory location used varies from one make of computer to another and is related to the coding methods employed and the number of bits it is designed to handle as a unit.

Memory words and bytes

A *memory word* is a given number of bits in memory, addressable as a unit. The addresses of memory locations run consecutively, starting with address 0 and running up to the largest address. Each location contains a word which can be retrieved by specification of its address. Similarly, an instruction to write to a location results in the storage of a word into the quoted address. For example, the word 01100110 may be stored in location address 15 and the word 11000110 in location address 16. A memory word may represent data or an instruction.

The memory's *word length* equates with the number of bits which can be stored in a location. Thus, memory which handles words of 16 bits is known as 16-bit memory, whilst that which makes use of 32-bit words is known as 32-bit memory. In practice, a machine may use words of different lengths for different operations.

Word length is one of the most important design characteristics of computers, in that it can be fundamental to the efficiency and speed of the computer. Generally, the larger and more powerful the computer, the greater the word length. Until recently, 32-bit and 64-bit words were largely used by mainframe and minicomputer systems exclusively. When first introduced, microcomputers were 4-bit or 8-bit machines, but advances in technology have made 32-bit and 64-bit microcomputers commonplace. Even if a machine normally handles words of 16 or 32 or 64 bits, reference sometimes needs to be made to a smaller unit, the *byte*, which is 8 bits. Programming in a low level language (Chapter 19) requires separate identification of bytes. Table 13.4 illustrates the formation of a 16-bit word, with byte subdivisions.

high order byte								low order byte							
MSB															LSB
bit 15	bit 14	bit 13	bit 12	bit 11	bit 10	bit 9	bit 8	bit 7	bit 6	bit 5	bit 4	bit 3	bit 2	bit 1	bit 0

Table 13.4. *High and low order bytes*

The leftmost bit in a word is referred to as the most significant bit (MSB) and the rightmost as the least significant bit (LSB). The most significant *byte* in a 16-bit word is identified as the *high order byte*, the least significant byte as the *low order byte*. A 32-bit word would be divided into byte-1 (the lowest order byte), byte-2, byte-3 and byte-4 (the highest order byte). A number of different memory structures have been used, based on different word lengths, which have sufficient flexibility to accommodate the requirements of both numeric and non-numeric data.

Number representation inside the computer

To be of practical use, a computer must be able to store, manipulate and differentiate between positive and negative numbers. There are a number of different ways this can be done. The most common are: sign and magnitude; complementation. These ideas are also discussed in Chapter 5, *Number systems and Binary Arithmetic*.

Sign and magnitude

With this method, the MSB position is occupied by an explicit *sign bit*; binary 0 and binary 1 are used to indicate, respectively, a positive and a negative number. The remainder of the binary word holds the *absolute* (independent of the sign) *magnitude* of the number.

The examples in Table 13.5 illustrate this method, using a 16-bit word. Note from the top row that the number zero uses a positive sign (0).

	MSB															LSB
+0$_{10}$	0	0	0	0	0	0	0	0	0	0	0	0	0	0	0	0
+33$_{10}$	0	0	0	0	0	0	0	0	0	0	1	0	0	0	0	1
−33$_{10}$	1	0	0	0	0	0	0	0	0	0	1	0	0	0	0	1
+85$_{10}$	0	0	0	0	0	0	0	0	0	1	0	1	0	1	0	1
−85$_{10}$	1	0	0	0	0	0	0	0	0	1	0	1	0	1	0	1
	bit-15	bit-14	bit-13	bit-12	bit-11	bit-10	bit-9	bit-8	bit-7	bit-6	bit-5	bit-4	bit-3	bit-2	bit-1	bit-0
	sign	<							m a g n i t u d e							>

Table 13.5. *Sign and magnitude format*

By switching the number 3 to its ten's complement (10 − 3 = 7), the calculation becomes 8 + 7 = 15, which with the carry of ten being ignored, gives the answer 5. There is no benefit in using ten's complement for subtraction because the process of complementation itself involves subtraction. However, this is not the case with binary complementation.

Two's complement numbers

Computers are able to perform both addition and subtraction by using two's complement arithmetic. The sign bit of a two's complement number forms part of the number and therefore contributes to its magnitude. In other words, it has a place value which contributes to the magnitude of the number, as well as indicating its sign (positive or negative). A two's complement number thus has an *implicit sign bit*. Table 13.8 shows four 8-bit examples. Note that the positive numbers (+33 and +85) contain a binary 0 in the sign position, so the place value of −128 does not contribute to the magnitude of the numbers. The negative numbers (−33 and −85) contain a binary 1 in the sign bit position, so its place value of −128 forms part of each number's value. The negative value is calculated by adding the negative place value of the sign bit to the positive values of the remaining bits, which contain a binary 1.These points can be illustrated with the following analysis of the numbers already shown in Table 13.6.

$+33_{10} = 00100001_2 = 0 + 0 + 32 + 0 + 0 + 0 + 0 + 1$

$-33_{10} = 11011111_2 = -128 + 64 + 0 + 16 + 8 + 4 + 2 + 1$

$+85_{10} = 01010101_2 = 0 + 64 + 0 + 16 + 0 + 4 + 0 + 1$

$-85_{10} = 10101011_2 = -128 + 0 + 32 + 0 + 8 + 0 + 2 + 1$

	MSB		place values				LSB	
	−128$_{10}$	64$_{10}$	32$_{10}$	16$_{10}$	8$_{10}$	4$_{10}$	2$_{10}$	1$_{10}$
+33$_{10}$	0	0	1	0	0	0	0	1
−33$_{10}$	1	1	0	1	1	1	1	1
+85$_{10}$	0	1	0	1	0	1	0	1
−85$_{10}$	1	0	1	0	1	0	1	1
	bit-7	bit-6	bit-5	bit-4	bit-3	bit-2	bit-1	bit-0

Table 13.6. *Two's complement, positive and negative numbers*

Subtraction, using two's complement numbers uses the following method. The second number (the *subtrahend*) is negated and is added to the first (the *minuend*). This is equivalent to expressing in denary, for example, $(+55) - (+25)$ as $(+55) + (-25)$.

Number range and arithmetic overflow

The *number range* for any given word is determined by the number of bits in the word and the fact that the MSB is needed to indicate the sign (unless, of course, the number is unsigned). This applies whatever method is used to indicate the sign of numbers. The number range which can be stored in any given word length can be readily calculated.

Thus, in an 8-bit word using *two's complement* (illustrated in Table 13.7), the maximum number which can be represented is either $+127$ $(2^{n-1} - 1)$ or -128 (-2^{n-1}), where $n = $ word length.

$01111111_2 =$	$0_{10} + 64_{10} + 32_{10} + 16_{10} + 8_{10} + 4_{10} + 2_{10} + 1_{10} = +127_{10}$
$10000000_2 =$	-128_{10}
	sign bit implicit (-128)

Table 13.7. *Two's complement number range in an 8-bit word*

For *sign and magnitude*, 8 bits give a range of $\pm 127_{10}$ $(\pm 2^{n-1} - 1)$, as shown in Table 13.8.

$01111111_2 =$	$+(64_{10} + 32_{10} + 16_{10} + 8_{10} + 4_{10} + 2_{10} + 1_{10}) = +127_{10}$
$11111111_2 =$	$-(64_{10} + 32_{10} + 16_{10} + 8_{10} + 4_{10} + 2_{10} + 1_{10}) = -127_{10}$
	sign bit explicit ($0 = +, 1 = -$)

Table 13.8. *Sign and magnitude number range in an 8-bit word*

Detection of overflow

If the result of an operation involving two numbers exceeds the maximum permitted by the word, then overflow occurs. For example, using 16-bit words and two's complement representation, overflow occurs if the result is outside of the range -32768_{10} (-2^{16-1}) to $+32767_{10}$ $(2^{16-1} - 1)$. Similarly, a 24-bit word permits a range of -8388608_{10} (-2^{24-1}) to 8388607_{10} $(2^{24-1} - 1)$.

Overflow needs to be detected by the computer so that an incorrect result is not overlooked. The hardware in the arithmetic logic unit (ALU) can detect an overflow condition by comparing the states of the *carry in* to, and the *carry out* from, the sign bit. If they are not equal, overflow has occurred and the answer is incorrect. Consider the two's complement examples in the next two tables, assuming an 8-bit word length. The sum in Table 13.9 shows a correct result, but the example in Table 13.10 appears to result in a negative sum (-96); this incorrect result is a consequence of overflow, indicated by the conflicting *carry in* and *carry out* states. Overflow will also occur when two *negative* numbers are added to produce a sum beyond the range of the word. An *overflow flag* (a single bit) in the *condition codes*, *status* or *flag register* is set as soon as an overflow occurs. Thus, following the execution of an arithmetic process, a low level programmer can include a single test on the overflow flag to determine whether or not incorrect results are due to arithmetic overflow. Other machines may use the flag to implement an *interrupt*, which interrupts the processor's operations, to suspend processing and display an error message.

	64_{10}	0 1 0 0 0 0 0 0	
+	4_{10}	0 0 0 0 0 1 0 0	
=	68_{10}	0 1 0 0 0 1 0 0	
carry		0 0	

Table 13.9. *Sum without overflow*

	96_{10}	0 1 1 0 0 0 0 0	
+	64_{10}	0 1 0 0 0 0 0 0	
=	-96_{10}	1 0 1 0 0 0 0 0	incorrect answer
carry		0 1	carries differ - overflow

Table 13.10. *Incorrect sum resulting from overflow*

The problem of limited number range and the need for accuracy can be overcome by the use of two or more words of memory to store a single number.

Real numbers

The first part of this section has concentrated on the storage and handling of *integers*. Although a programmer could choose to restrict numbers to integer format, all general-purpose computers must be able to deal with *real numbers*. Real numbers include all the integers and fractions of a number system, that is, all numbers above and below zero and including zero. Many computer applications require the use of numbers with a fractional element, that is, real numbers. Clearly, this can provide for a greater level of precision than is permitted by integer numbers, but at the cost of increased storage requirements. There are two basic methods of representing real numbers in computer storage: *fixed-point* and *floating-point* representation.

Fixed-point representation

Fixed-point numbers use what can be seen as a conventional format. The binary point is *assumed* to be immediately to the right of the integer part, which is where we would locate the decimal point if we were expressing real denary values. A programmer can require the binary point to be in any position within a memory word, according to the number of bits he or she wishes to assign to the integer and fractional parts. If more bits in a memory word are assigned to the fractional part, greater precision is possible; on the other hand fewer bits are then available for the integer part and this reduces the magnitude range. Conversely, increasing the proportion of a word given to the integer part increases the magnitude range, but reduces the possible level of precision. Table 13.11 illustrates fixed point format.

Table 13.11. *Fixed point format*

Of course, a programmer may equally assume a given memory word to be entirely integer, with no fractional part. The binary point is said to have an *assumed* position which gives meaning to a number. Using 8-bit words, the programmer may decide that the binary points for two numbers, labelled (i) and (ii), are located as shown in Table 13.12.

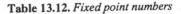

	integer part	fractional part
(i) 2.75_{10}	0 0 0 0 1 0 .	1 1$_2$
(ii) 28.25_{10}	0 1 1 1 0 0 .	0 1$_2$

Table 13.12. *Fixed point numbers*

If the programmer then relocates the binary points, the same binary groupings take on different values. Using the numbers from Table 13.12, the point for number (i) is shifted one place to the left, which *halves* its value; the point in number (ii) is shifted one place to the right, which *doubles* its value. The results of the shifts are shown in Table 13.13. Therefore, a programmer using fixed point numbers must keep track of the point position in order to know their value. This problem is of particular concern to the programmer using low level languages.

	integer part		fractional part
(i) 1.375_{10}	0 0 0 0 1	.	0 1 1_2
(ii) 56.5_{10}	0 1 1 1 0 0 0	.	1_2

Table 13.13. *Fixed point numbers after moving binary point*

If a programmer is using fixed point numbers, this simply means that the decisions on the degree of precision are made by the programmer. If no floating point facility is available, the programmer must use integer arithmetic (see earlier) and set the precision after each calculation. The practicalities of this are of concern to the low level programmer, but briefly, involve the *scaling* of numbers to remove any fractional part, carrying out integer arithmetic and then re-scaling the result to the required number of fractional places. Today, all computers provide a floating point number facility, but there was a time when a programmer had to represent all real numbers in fixed point form. As explained later, floating point numbers require a longer word length than 8 bits, which was the norm, for example, for the first generation of microcomputers.

Number range and precision of fixed point numbers

Continuing with the topic of fixed point numbers, consider a 16-bit word with the binary point assumed to be between the bit-4 and bit-5 positions; sign and magnitude format is being used, so the sign bit (shown in bold type) occupies the most significant bit position, which leaves 10 bits for the integral part and 5 bits for the fractional part of the number. The number range which can be represented is limited to that given in Table 13.14.

Positive 0_{10} to $+1023 \cdot 96875_{10}$	Negative 0_{10} to -1024_{10}
$0\,0\,0\,0\,0\,0\,0\,0\,0\,0\,0 \cdot 0\,0\,0\,0\,0_2$	$0\,0\,0\,0\,0\,0\,0\,0\,0\,0\,0 \cdot 0\,0\,0\,0\,0_2$
$0\,1\,1\,1\,1\,1\,1\,1\,1\,1\,1 \cdot 1\,1\,1\,1\,1_2$	$1\,0\,0\,0\,0\,0\,0\,0\,0\,0\,0 \cdot 0\,0\,0\,0\,0_2$
sign	sign

Table 13.14. *Example sign and magnitude range*

Precision is limited by the number of bits allocated to the fractional part of the number and no matter what word length is used, some loss of precision is occasionally inevitable.

Arithmetic overflow

Consider the multiplication of two denary values in Table 13.15, where only 1 place is available for the integer part and 3 places for the fractional part. The maximum positive value the location can hold is $9 \cdot 999_{10}$. Although such a location is large enough to hold each of the two numbers to be multiplied, the product $11 \cdot 057$ (after rounding to 3 decimal places) results in an arithmetic overflow error.

$1 \cdot 363_{10} \times 8 \cdot 112_{10} = 11 \cdot 057_{10}$	The 10s digit is lost

Table 13.15. *Multiplication resulting in overflow*

Given a particular word length for *fixed point* numbers, the allocation of more bits to the fractional part improves precision but at the cost of reduced number range. Conversely, the result of the above multiplication could be accommodated if 2 places are given to the integer part, but this would leave one less bit for the fractional element and consequently, reduced precision.

Arithmetic underflow

This condition occurs when a number (a fraction or a negative number) is too small to fit into a given length word. The denary example in Table 13.16 illustrates underflow which results from the smallness of a fraction.

$0 \cdot 125_{10} \times 0 \cdot 005_{10} = 0 \cdot 000625_{10}$	underflow error

Table 13.16. *Arithmetic underflow*

Provision is made for a maximum of 3 decimal places. Multiplication of the two decimal fractions gives a product which underflows, giving an erroneous result of zero.

Another example illustrates how a negative number can underflow and result in more serious error; given the provision of only two integer places, $-99_{10} \times 2_{10}$ gives a product of -198_{10}, which does not fit. The main drawback of fixed point form is the small range of numbers that can be represented. *Floating-point* number representation helps overcome this problem at the cost of slightly slower computation and some reduction in precision.

Floating-point representation

A *mantissa* and *exponent* (or *index*) can be used to represent a number. Denary numbers, written in *standard index* form, reveal a format similar to that used for the storage of binary floating point numbers. Examples of binary floating point and denary standard index numbers are given in Table 13.17. Note that the formats are not exactly the same.

binary	binary floating point			denary	denary standard index	
	mantissa	exponent			mantissa	exponent
101.0101_2	0.1010101_2	$\times 2^3$		$6{,}800{,}000_{10}$	6.8_{10}	$\times 10^6$
0.0011001_2	0.11001_2	$\times 2^{-2}$		0.0000564_{10}	5.64_{10}	$\times 10^{-5}$

Table 13.17. *Binary floating point and denary standard index examples*

In floating-point notation, the point is not fixed by the programmer. Instead it remains in a position at the left of the mantissa. Floating-point notation is based on the expression: $m \times r^e$, where *m* is positive or negative and *e* is positive or negative, *m* is the mantissa, *r* is the radix or base and *e* is the exponent (power). In binary, the radix is 2 (see Chapter 5).

Fixed-point numbers can be converted to floating-point numbers by a process of *normalisation*. As the first example (101.0101_2) in Table 13.18 shows, if the number is *greater than* 1_2 then the point floats to the left (actually achieved by shifting the mantissa to the right), to a position immediately before the most significant bit. This part becomes the mantissa (m). The point has moved 3 places to the left, the mantissa is now 0.1010101_2 and the exponent (*e*) is 3.

The second example (0.0011001_2) in Table 13.17 shows that, if the number is a *fraction* and a binary 1 does not immediately follow the point, then the point floats to the right (actually achieved by shifting the mantissa to the left) of any leading zeros, until the first non-zero bit is reached; the mantissa becomes 0.11001_2. The point has moved 2 places to the right, so the exponent (e) is -2. Two more examples are given in Tables 13.18 and 13.19.

fixed point	binary floating point	
	mantissa	exponent
1110.001_2	0.1110001_2	$\times 2^4$

fixed point	binary floating point	
	mantissa	exponent
0.000111_2	0.111000_2	$\times 2^{-3}$

Table 13.18. *Fixed point > binary 1 converted to floating point*

Table 13.19. *Fixed point < binary 1 converted to floating point*

In Table 13.18, the point moves four places to the left, so the exponent is 4; in Table 13.19, the fraction is normalised by moving the point three places to the right, so the exponent is -3.

The floating point format used in this text follows a number of rules.

❑ With normalised *positive* numbers the binary point must not be followed immediately by a binary 0. Only positive, floating point number examples have been provided so far.

❑ Conversely, normalised *negative* numbers require that the binary point is not followed immediately by a binary 1. The next section, on storage of floating point numbers, describes the format for negative numbers in more detail.

❑ Any normalised binary mantissa must be a fraction falling within the range $+0 \cdot 5$ to less than $+1$ for positive values and -1 to less than $-0 \cdot 5$ for negative values. The range of possible normalised mantissas, given a 4-bit allocation, is shown in Table 13.20.

positive mantissas	denary equivalent	negative mantissas	denary equivalent
$0 \cdot 100_2$	$+\frac{1}{2}$	$1 \cdot 000_2$	-1
$0 \cdot 101_2$	$+\frac{5}{8}$	$1 \cdot 001_2$	$-\frac{7}{8}$
$0 \cdot 110_2$	$+\frac{3}{4}$	$1 \cdot 010_2$	$-\frac{3}{4}$
$0 \cdot 111_2$	$+\frac{7}{8}$	$1 \cdot 011_2$	$-\frac{5}{8}$

Table 13.20. *Range of possible normalised, 4-bit mantissas, with zero exponent*

Storage of floating-point numbers

As already indicated, floating-point numbers are stored in two parts:

❑ The *mantissa*, the length of which is determined by the precision to which numbers are represented. Clearly, if fewer bits are allocated to the mantissa (which is always a left-justified fraction) then less precision is possible.

❑ The *exponent*, which is usually allocated one-third to one-half of the number of bits used for the mantissa.

Table 13.21 assumes the use of a 16-bit word for the storage of each floating-point number, in two's complement form, 12 bits being used for the mantissa and 4 bits for the exponent.

	sign	mantissa (fraction)										exponent (integer)			
bit	15	14	13	12	11	10	9	8	7	6	5	4	3	2	1	0

Table 13.21. *Example floating point format for a 16-bit word*

The binary point in the mantissa fraction is immediately to the right of the sign bit, which is 0 for a positive and 1 for a negative floating-point number (Table 13.22).

positive floating point form		negative floating point form	
12 bits	4 bits	12 bits	4 bits
0 · 1 * * * * * * * * * *	* * * *	1 · 0 * * * * * * * * * *	* * * * *
mantissa	exponent	mantissa	exponent

Table 13.22. *Positive and negative representation in floating point form*

In two's complement form, the most significant digit to the right of the binary point is 1 for a positive and 0 for a negative floating-point number. It should be noticed that the sign bit and the most significant non-sign bit differ in both cases. As explained earlier, any representation where they are the same indicates that the mantissa needs to be normalised. This may be necessary after any floating-point arithmetic operation.

Floating-point conversion

To obtain the denary equivalent of a number held in floating point form requires the mantissa to be multiplied by 2, raised to the *power* of e, which has the value stored in the exponent part of the number. For example, the floating point number in Table 13.23, which uses 8 bits for the mantissa and 4 bits for the exponent, converts to denary as follows.

8-bit mantissa		4-bit exponent
0.1 1 0 1 0 0 1	×	0 1 0 1 (2^5)

Table 13.23. *Floating point number*

$$0 \cdot 1101001_2 \times 2^5 = 11010 \cdot 01_2 \quad \text{(by moving the binary point 5 places to the right)}$$

$$= (16 + 8 + 2 + \tfrac{1}{4}) = 26\tfrac{1}{4}$$

So, the floating point number $0 \cdot 1101001_2 \times 2^5$ is equivalent to fixed point $11010 \cdot 01_2$.

If 4 bits are allocated to the exponent, e can have a value between +7 and −8 (assuming two's complement form). Alternatively, in a 16-bit machine, two words with a total of 32 bits may be used to store each floating-point number, the mantissa occupying 24 bits, and the exponent, 8 bits. In such a representation, the exponent e could have a value between +127 and −128 (assuming two's complement).

Exercises

1. Why do digital computers rely on the use of *binary code* in preference to, say, the denary system?

2. Distinguish between *control codes* and *control characters*.

3. (i)   A binary code, 0110110, is sent from one computer to another, but the code is received as 0010110. Show how the error could have been detected by the inclusion of an extra bit.

   (ii) The same binary code, 0110110, arrives at the receiver as 1000111. Assuming use of the technique identified in (i), why would this error not be detected?

4. Convert the denary number 8432 to *binary coded decimal* (BCD) format.

5. How many *bytes* are there in a 32-bit *memory word*?

6. If a computer uses a 16-bit word to represent integers, how would it represent the values 32, −32, 72, −72, 473 and −473 in:

   (i)   *sign and magnitude* format;

   (ii) *two's complement* format.

7. Assuming byte storage, why would the addition 75 + 96 result in *arithmetic overflow*?

7. What would be the denary equivalents of the two's complement *number range* for a 12-bit word?

9. A particular computer uses a 16-bit word to store floating-point numbers, allocating 10 bits to the mantissa and 6 bits to the exponent; both parts are stored in two's complement form. Positive numbers are normalised when the bit immediately to the right of the binary point has a value of 1. Negative numbers are normalised when the bit immediately to the right of the binary point has a value of 0.

   (i)   Calculate the denary values of:

   a.   0110100101000011;

   b.   1010010100100101;

   c.   0001010101001110.

   (ii) Write down the bit patterns for the following numbers, in normalised form:

   a. $+5 \cdot 4$;

   b. $-0 \cdot 625$

Chapter 14

Computer systems architecture

The term "Computer Systems Architecture" refers to the composition of computer systems and the mechanisms by which components communicate electronically with each other. A computer system is a collection of a large number of separate components. Many of these are electro-mechanical or electronic, that is physical, components collectively termed the *hardware*. The remaining components are the electronically stored *software* items that either control the hardware (computer programs) or are used by other pieces of software (data). A separate chapter is devoted to the subject of software. Computer systems such as desktop computers (PCs) are general-purpose machines, capable of performing a wide range of data processing tasks. Computer programs make this versatility possible by controlling the hardware in different ways. For instance, many modern computer games control the components of the computer system that allow animated graphics to be displayed on the visual display unit. On the other hand, a company payroll program controls those hardware components required for processing and printing numeric and text-based data. A knowledge of the characteristics of the many different forms of hardware and software components is essential to the task of understanding and specifying computer system configurations for specific purposes. In this chapter we provide a broad introduction to the many different forms of hardware that can be found in typical PC systems; subsequent chapters deal with some of these subjects in more detail. Throughout this and subsequent chapters in this Unit, particular emphasis is placed on hardware and software used in typical personal computer systems.

Computer system components

The term *hardware* is used to describe all the physical devices that form a computer system. Figure 14.1 shows a few familiar examples.

Although computer hardware catalogues list many examples of hardware devices, each one is likely to be concerned with a particular functional area from the following categories:

Figure 14.1. *Examples of computer hardware*

- input, output and backing storage devices, collectively known as *peripherals*;
- internal memory;
- motherboard and processor.

Input, output and backing storage

Figure 14.2 illustrates the functions of input, output and storage devices for communication with the central processing unit (CPU).

Figure 14.2. *How the CPU communicates with the outside world*

The job of each group of devices is as follows

- *Input* devices take data (text, graphics, sound and so on) from the outside world and convert it into the internal codes used inside the computer. Each device is designed to meet particular user requirements, so a microphone allows data entry through sound waves and a keyboard responds to keystrokes. Apart from working in a different way, they are designed to accept different kinds of data, so a microphone can accept speech input or be used to capture music. All input devices convert the data from the user's form into computer-sensible form.

- *Output* devices convert computer-sensible data into the forms users require. For example, a speaker converts data to sound and a screen produces a visual display. Of course, the data must be appropriate for the devices, so a music recording cannot be output to a display screen, although with appropriate software, the sound waves could be graphically displayed.

- *Backing storage* devices provide permanent storage for computer programs (software) and data files. A magnetic disk, for example, allows large amounts of data to be stored in magnetic form, so data is not lost from the disk when the computer is switched off. Programs are held on backing storage and are only loaded into the computer's memory when the user needs them. Data files, such as word processed documents or a company's payroll records are also held on backing storage and are called into memory as required by the program(s) in use.

Input, output and backing storage devices are known as *peripherals* because they are outside, or peripheral to, the central processing unit (CPU). Even though disk and CD-ROM drives are usually held inside the system unit casing, they are still classed as peripherals. The topics of input, output and storage devices are dealt with in more detail in Chapters 15 and 16.

Input/output ports

Obviously, all of these types of devices must be connected to and be able to communicate electronically with the Central Processing Unit. Input/output ports are the connection points for peripheral devices, such as the mouse, printer or modem (for communication with other remote computers via a communications network such as the public telephone system).

Serial port

Microcomputers usually have at least two serial ports, one for connecting a mouse and the other for a modem. Serial ports transfer data in a single stream (one binary digit after another) as Figure 14.3 illustrates.

Figure 14.3. *Serial mouse*

Parallel port

The parallel port, known as a Centronics interface, is used to connect a printer. The port can also be used to communicate with some externally attached disk drives. The data is trans-ferred as parallel groups of

Figure 14.4. *Computer sending data from a parallel port to a printer*

bits (each one representing a character), as shown in Figure 14.4. Another parallel port is normally specially reserved for connecting the display screen.

PC I/O connectors

Figure 14.5 shows the rear of a typical system unit casing with its various ports and connectors.

Figure 14.5. *Rear of system unit casing, showing ports and types of connectors*

One side of a connection is *male*, with pins and the other *female*, with holes to match the pin pattern.

Controllers and interfaces

Controllers

These are electronic devices that control the transfer of data between a computer and peripherals. For example, disk drives, display screens, keyboards, and printers all require controllers.

In personal computers, the controllers are often single chips. Motherboards incorporate all the necessary controllers for standard components, such as the display screen, keyboard, and floppy disk drives. Hard disk drives and CDROM drives that use the *PCI* bus have controllers built in; they communicate with the CPU via an *IDE* interface integrated within the motherboard. Some devices, including certain types of hard drives and optical storage devices, use *SCSI* interfaces that may need to be provided on expansion cards.

Controllers are designed to communicate with the computer's expansion bus (See **Buses**). Consequently extra controllers for additional devices must be compatible with a particular computer's expansion bus architecture.

IDE interfaces

The Intelligent/Integrated Drive Electronics (IDE) interface is specifically for mass storage devices, in which the controller is integrated into the mass storage device. Basic PCs usually provide IDE interfaces for up to four devices.

SCSI interfaces

Pronounced "scuzzy", SCSI (Small Computer System Interface) is a fast parallel interface standard used by PCs, Apple Macintosh computers, and many UNIX systems for attaching peripheral devices to computers. Many Apple Macintosh computers come with a SCSI port for attaching devices such as disk drives and printers. SCSI interfaces provide faster data transmission rates than standard serial and parallel ports and many devices can be linked to a single SCSI port.

SCSI devices can be attached to a PC by inserting a SCSI board in one of the expansion slots. Many high-end new PCs come with SCSI built in.

AGP interfaces

The abbreviation for Accelerated Graphics Port, *AGP* is a new interface specification developed by Intel Corporation. Based on PCI, AGP is designed especially for 3-D graphics. AGP has a number of important system requirements:

- ❏ The motherboard chipset must support AGP.
- ❏ The motherboard must be equipped with an AGP bus slot or must have an integrated AGP graphics system.
- ❏ The operating system must be Windows 95 (version 2.1), Windows 98 or Windows NT 4.0. Currently, many professional Macintoshes support AGP.

Internal Memory

RAM

A computer can only run a program when it is in memory or *RAM* (*Random Access Memory*).

Data needed by the program is also held in RAM. An important characteristic of RAM is that it is *volatile*. This means that the contents of the main memory can be destroyed, either by being overwritten as new data is entered for processing and new programs used, or when the machine is switched off. It is not practical to store data files and programs permanently in main memory because of its volatility.

Types of RAM

DRAM

Pronounced "dee-ram", DRAM stands for Dynamic Random Access Memory, the type of memory used in most personal computers. DRAM chips are available in several forms. Each is appropriate to particular types of applications. The most common forms of DRAM are:

❑ DIP (Dual In-line Package). The DIP-Style DRAM package was popular when it was common for memory to be installed directly on the computer's system board. DIPs are through-hole components, which means they install in holes extending into the surface of the printed circuit board. DIPs can be soldered in place or seated in sockets.

❑ SOJ (Small Outline J-lead), and TSOP (Thin, Small Outline Package). These are components which mount directly onto the surface of the printed circuit board. TSOP and SOJ gained in popularity with the advent of the SIMM. Of the two, the SOJ package is by far the most popular..

EDO DRAM

This abbreviation stands for Extended Data Output Dynamic Random Access Memory. Unlike conventional DRAM which can only access one block of data at a time, EDO RAM can start fetching the next block of memory at the same time that it sends the previous block to the CPU. This makes EDO RAM faster than conventional DRAM.

FPM RAM

An abbreviation for Fast Page Mode RAM, FPM RAM is a fast form of DRAM It is sometimes called Page Mode Memory and is generally slower than EDO DRAM. FPM RAM is being superceded by newer types of memory, such as SDRAM.

SDRAM

SDRAM stands for *Synchronous* DRAM, a new type of DRAM that can run at much higher clock speeds. SDRAM is capable of running at 133 MHz, about twice as fast as EDO DRAM. SDRAM is replacing EDO DRAM in many newer computers.

RDRAM

Short for Rambus DRAM, a type of memory developed by Rambus, Inc. Whereas the fastest current memory technologies used by PCs (SDRAM) can deliver data at a maximum speed of about 133 MHz, RDRAM transfers data at up to 600 MHz.

Types of Memory Modules

Modern motherboards have banks of special slots for memory modules. Currently there are two main forms of these modules:

❑ SIMMs (Single Inline Memory Modules) and, more recently,

❑ DIMMs (Dual Inline Memory Modules).

Each module is a board onto which are soldered a number of memory chips. DIMMs are very high density memory modules that have two banks of chips soldered to the circuit board. Because they require less space than SIMMs, they are likely to supercede SIMMs

Figure 14.6. *Example of a SIMM*

in the near future. Figure 14.6 shows an example of a SIMM containing nine memory chips. One of the chips is usually used for parity checking.

The table below summarises the major characteristics of SIMMs and DIMMs. As you can see, SDRAM DIMMS are much faster than EDO DRAM SIMMs (*ns* stands for nanosecond, one thousandth of a millionth of a second). Currently, megabyte for megabyte, DIMMs are also much cheaper than SIMMs.

Type	Capacity range (MB)	Approx. access speed (ns)	Type	Pins
SIMM	8 - 64	60	EDO RAM	72
DIMM	8 - 256	8	SDRAM	168

Most new motherboards accept only 168-pin DIMMs, but some also accept 72-pin SIMMs. Motherboard documentation will specify the type of RAM that it supports: typically FP DRAM or EDO DRAM for SIMMs, or EDO DRAM or SDRAM for DIMMs.

Cache memory

Cache Memory is a special high-speed memory designed to accelerate processing of memory instructions by the CPU. The CPU can access instructions and data located in cache memory much faster than instructions and data in main memory. For example, on a typical 100-megahertz system board, it takes the CPU as much as 180 nanoseconds to obtain information from main memory, compared to just 45 nanoseconds from cache memory. Therefore, the more instructions and data the CPU can access directly from cache memory, the faster the computer can run. Cache can be internal or external. Internal cache is built into the computer's CPU, and external cache is located outside the CPU.

ROM and flash memory

ROM is a type of memory designed to hold data more permanently than RAM. With most types of ROM, the data is built into the memory when it is manufactured and cannot be changed. For this reason it is *non-volatile*, so the contents are not lost when power is removed. ROM is used to hold the *BIOS* (Basic Input/Output System) and the *bootstrap loader*. Flash memory also retains its contents when power is removed, but unlike ROM, its contents can be changed by software. Most modern microcomputers use flash memory to allow the BIOS to be changed automatically when new hardware devices are added.

Central processing unit (CPU)

Also referred to as the *processor*, the CPU is the heart of the computer and has two part main parts:

Control unit

The control unit:

☐ fetches program instructions from memory and decodes and executes them, calling on the ALU (see below) when calculations or comparisons need to be carried out on data;

☐ controls the flow of data both within the CPU and to and from peripheral devices such as printers, disk drives and keyboards;

☐ ensures that devices operate according to program instructions, by sending electrical control signals to them as required.

Arithmetic/logic unit (ALU)

The ALU contains circuitry to carry out important tasks such as addition, subtraction, multiplication and division of numbers fetched from RAM or held in registers in the processor. It can also, for example, compare two numbers and discover whether or not they are equal and perform logical operations, such as AND, OR and NOT. The data-flow routes between various hardware components and the CPU are illustrated in Figure 14.7.

Figure 14.7. *The data flows between hardware devices*

Co-processors

In order to speed certain types of computations, a computer system might incorporate one or more co-processors. For example, a graphics accelerator card (see **Expansion Cards**) will usually include its own processor to deal with graphics computations independently of the main motherboard processor. Modern processors include a maths co-processor to deal with floating-point computations, though earlier PCs sometimes had a separate chip on the motherboard for this purpose.

Motherboard

The motherboard is the main circuit board inside a microcomputer's system casing. A number of major hardware components are plugged into it, including the CPU, the BIOS memory and RAM. It also has a number of *expansion slots*, into which plug-in circuit boards can be inserted. These are slots into which *expansion boards* or *cards* can be plugged, to add extra features to a system. Note the following points regarding motherboards:

☐ The motherboard has printed circuits (not shown) which provide the electrical connections between all the components plugged into it. One or more *buses* are built into the motherboard to provide fast connections between components. Buses are discussed in more detail in the next section.

❏ All replaceable components must be compatible with the motherboard. This often prevents certain upgrading of the machine. For example, one type of memory called EDO RAM uses 72 pins to contact with the motherboard, but SDRAM, which allows data to be accessed more quickly than EDO RAM, uses 128 pins and therefore a different sized socket. (Memory is discussed in more detail in **Types of RAM)**. In the same way, when a new processor becomes available, upgrading a machine from an older type will often mean replacing the motherboard.

❏ The processor chip plugs into a ZIF (Zero Insertion Force) socket; this allows the processor to be inserted or removed without damage.

❏ RAM chips are fixed to a small circuit board called a SIMM (Single In-line Memory Module). For example, a 64MB SIMM has 8 × 8MB memory chips attached to it. In the motherboard map, there are two memory *banks*, each with two slots, so 4 SIMMs could be attached. If 64MB SIMMs were used, this would allow the computer to have 256MB of RAM.

❏ Modern motherboards often incorporate interfaces and functions that required separate expansion boards in the past. For example, a motherboard may include two IDE interfaces for hard drives and CD ROM drives in addition to a floppy disk interface. Many motherboards now also include sound chips that also used to require a separate card in the past.

Expansion Cards

Figure 14.8 shows the appearance of a typical expansion card. Some of these circuit boards may be used for controlling peripheral devices, but there are many other boards available for a wide range of applications. Because each pin on an expansion slot is connected to the same pin on all the other expansion slots by a printed circuit, a board can be plugged in to any compatible slot. Expansion slots are connected to the system bus (it makes electrical contact), so when an expansion card is plugged in, it becomes part of the system. Here are some common examples of expansion cards:

Figure 14.8. *A plug-in expansion card*

❏ modem cards for connection to the Internet and for receiving and transmitting faxes;

❏ graphics cards (video adapters, graphics accelerators) for accelerating graphics-based applications such as games and for capturing video sequences from external sources such as VCRs and video cameras;

❏ TV cards to allow the computer to show TV programs on the monitor;

❏ network cards to allow several computers to be linked in a network;

❏ sound cards for capturing and playing high quality sound sequences;

❏ SCSI (Small Computer System Interface) card, a fast parallel interface standard for connecting peripheral devices. (see **Controllers and Interfaces**).

Two of these, video adapters and sound cards, are described in more detail below.

Video Adapters

A video adapter is a board that plugs into an expansion slot of a personal computer's motherboard to give it display capabilities when connected to a monitor. These display capabilities depend on both the electronics provided in the video adapter and the display monitor. For example, a monochrome monitor cannot display colours whatever the quality of the video adapter. Adapters usually provide two basic categories of video modes:

❑   text mode - a monitor can display only ASCII characters;

❑   graphics mode - a monitor can display any bit-mapped image.

So that large quantities of the computer's RAM is not used for storing display data, modern video adapters contain their own memory. The amount of memory determines maximum resolution and the number of colours that can be displayed. At lower resolutions a monitor can display more colours. Some accelerators use conventional DRAM, but others have video RAM (VRAM), which enables both the video circuitry and the processor to access the memory simultaneously. A typical graphics card might contain 4MB to 8MB of VRAM. In addition, most adapters have their own graphics coprocessor for performing graphics calculations. Such adapters are often called graphics accelerators. Because of the growth of multimedia software and games requiring high-resolution graphics, most computer manufacturers now include a graphics accelerator with their systems.

Sound cards

These are expansion boards that enable computers to capture, play and edit high quality sound. As mentioned earlier, a motherboard might incorporate sound capabilities, but if not a sound card will be necessary, particularly if the computer includes a CD-ROM. Sound cards include sockets for speakers to play sound files and a microphone for recording sound on disk. Bundled software allows sound files to be loaded, edited, stored and played. The majority of sound cards support the MIDI standard for representing music electronically, and most sound cards are compatible with the Sound Blaster card which has become the standard for PC sound.

Buses

Though all computers have the same basic functional components, the architectural details in some are far more complex than in others. A particular area of variation relates to the arrangement of the bus systems which permit communication between the various parts of the computer system. A number of features concerning buses can be identified:

❑   a bus is a group of parallel wires, one for each bit of a word, along which data can flow (as electrical signals);

❑   the *system* bus comprises a number of such communication channels, connecting a computer's processor and its associated components of memory and input/output(I/O) devices;

❑   a single bus may carry data for different functions at separate times or it may be dedicated to one function. A computer will usually have several buses, used for specific purposes, for example, the I/O bus or main memory-to-processor bus;

❑   some buses are *bi-directional*, that is data can flow in both directions;

❑   the *width* of a bus determines the length of word which can be handled at one time.

So, a processor which used a 16-bit bus, but required a 32-bit word to address memory, would combine two 16-bit words in two separate fetch operations.

Communication is required within a processor, to allow movement of data between its various registers, between the processor and memory and for I/O transfers. In a *single* bus system, both I/O and memory transfers share the same communication channel, whereas in a *two-bus* system, I/O and memory transfers are carried out independently; similarly, in small systems with few I/O devices, they usually share the same bus, but a larger system requires several I/O buses to ensure efficient operation.

Each of the separately identified functions of memory, register-to-register and I/O transfers (assuming that the I/O bus is shared by a number of devices), must have the use of:

☐ a *data bus*, for the transfer of data subject to processing or manipulation in the machine;

☐ an *address bus* which carries the address of, for example, a memory word to be read, or the output device to which a character is to be transmitted;

☐ a *control bus*, which as the name suggest, carries signals concerning the timing of various operations, such as memory write, memory read and I/O operations.

All signals on a bus follow strict timing sequences, so some operations take longer than others.

Bus architecture - a brief history

This concerns the internal structure of a computer, that is the way in which the various components are connected and communicate with one another. As technological advances improve the performance of certain components, so the architecture has to change to take advantage of these improvements.

Micro channel architecture (MCA)

MCA aimed to overcome the limitations of the old, Industry Standard Architecture (ISA), IBM AT (Advanced Technology) machines as well as a myriad of clones produced by IBM's competitors. IBM used MCA in their 32-bit PS/2 (Personal System 2) range.

System bus width and system performance

One of the many differences with the MCA approach concerns the width of the *system bus*. This bus is a communication link between the processor and system components and is an essential, but passive, part of system architecture. The active components, such as the processor, disk controller and other peripherals are the primary determinants of system performance. As long as the data transfer speed along the bus matches the requirements of these devices and does not create a bottleneck, the bus does not affect system performance. The MCA bus is 32 bits, compared with the AT's 16 bits, and the wider data path allows components within the system to be accessed twice as quickly. The MCA bus also uses bus-mastering controllers to handle data transfers more quickly. The wider bus is also compatible with the 32-bit external bus used on more recent processors. The bus can be controlled by separate *bus master* processors, relieving the main processor of this task.

MCA is also radically different from AT architecture in many other respects. For example, the expansion slots in the PS/2 range which allow the user to insert extra features, perhaps for networking or for extra memory, are physically different from those in the AT and PC machines and their expansion cards will not fit in the PS/2 machines. The problem for existing AT and PC users was that they could not buy new PS/2 machines and still make use of their existing expansion cards. This incompatibility also meant that few manufacturers produced MCA versions of their expansion cards. IBM and Apricot were the biggest proponents of the MCA standard, but it never became the standard architecture.

Extended industry standard architecture (EISA)

A consortium of IBM's competitors including Compaq, Zenith, NEC and Olivetti amongst others, established a new architecture (EISA - Extended Industry Standard Architecture) which aims to give the benefits of MCA and to retain compatibility with existing AT expansion cards. EISA also uses a 32-bit bus, thus providing the same data transfer benefits as MCA, particularly for hard disk controllers (a very important contributor to overall system performance). Both EISA and MCA machines were more expensive than the ISA-based microcomputers, and tended to be used where extra power was needed, as *file servers* in networked systems. Most small business users found that ISA machines were adequate for their needs, particularly as the use of *local bus* technology was further increasing their power.

Local bus

A local bus is a high speed data path connecting the processor with a peripheral. Local bus design is used, primarily, to speed communications with hard disk controllers and display adapters. The

Figure 14.9. *ISA bus*

need for local bus derives from the imbalance between the clock speed of a 32-bit processor (typically, in excess of 100MHz) and the ISA 16-bit system bus (operating at 8 MHz). The ISA system is illustrated in Figure 14.9.

This imbalance can result in the processor idling while waiting for data to be transferred from disk, or the display adapter waiting for screen data. The widespread use of Windows, a *graphical user interface* and software packages which make intensive use of the hard disk (such as databases) and screen graphics (computer-aided design), has highlighted the deficiencies of such imbalanced computer systems. A local bus provides a wider data path, currently 32 bits and an increased clock speed, typically 33MHz or more. The first local bus systems appeared in 1992, with manufacturers following a standard referred to as *VL-bus*, developed by VESA (Video Electronics Standards Association). Figure 14.10 illustrates the broad principle of a local bus system.

Figure 14.10. *Local bus*

In 1993, Intel backed the development of a new industry standard called *PCI*. The PCI standard encourages the development of computer systems which allow local bus connection to any high-speed peripheral. Apart from speeding communication with screen graphics controllers, PCI local bus can be used with, for example, hard disk, network and motion video controllers (up to 10 devices in total).

USB, short for Universal Serial Bus, is a new external bus standard that supports data transfer rates of 12 Mbps (12 million bits per second). A single USB port can be used to connect up to 127 peripheral devices, such as mice, modems, and keyboards. USB also supports *Plug-and-Play* installation and *hot plugging* (adding and removing devices while the computer is running and have the operating system automatically recognise the change - also called *hot swapping*). USB is expected to completely replace serial and parallel ports.

Exercises

1. What is meant by the term 'hardware'?
2. Name 3 types of device that are generally connected to a computer system. Give two examples of each type.
3. What two types of memory are commonly found in a computer? For each type, give an example of what it stores.
4. A CPU has two main components. Name and briefly explain the function of each part.
5. Explain the purpose of a port.
6. What is the name of the main circuit board inside a computer?
7. What is the function of a Controller?
8. Name three types of interfaces for peripherals and say for what types of peripherals each interface has been designed.
9. What do the following abbreviations mean?

    DRAM

    EDO RAM

    FPM RAM

    SDRAM

    RDRAM

    VRAM
10. Name two types of commonly used memory modules. Typically, what types of RAM are used in each case?
11. Explain the function of Cache memory.
12. What is *Flash Memory*?
13. Give two typical uses of Co-processors.
14. What are the main upgradable components of a motherboard?
15. Name 4 types of expansion cards.
16. Define a Bus. Name and describe the uses of three common PC buses.

Chapter 15

Input and output devices

Input and output devices allow users to communicate with the computer, in different ways, according to their requirements. For a given type of device, such as a printer, there are many different product specifications, each designed to meet a particular need. For example, when judging a printer specification, you need to consider its speed of output and the quality of the print it can produce. The first part of the chapter deals with input devices and the second with output devices. For each type of device there is

❑ a general description of the device and details of the main products of that type. For example, when examining printers, you need to be aware of differences between laser and inkjet products;

❑ where necessary, an explanation of technical terms found in product specifications and guidance on matching device specifications to users' needs.

Input devices

Input devices enable information to be entered into a computer for processing or storage on magnetic media. The computer can only process or store information if it is in an electronic, binary coded form, so input devices are needed to convert, for example, letters of the alphabet, digits in our number system, the sounds of the human voice or musical instruments, into the computer's code.

The most commonly used input device is the keyboard, which converts key presses into the computer's code. So, for example, pressing the 'A' key produces electrical signals which the computer uses to represent that letter. The computer uses a different code for each character on the keyboard. The ASCII (American Standard Code for Information Interchange) binary code is recognised by all computers. Similarly, a *scanner* allows typed or hand-written documents to be read into a computer and a microphone enables the entry of sounds, perhaps to give voice commands to the computer. Each input device needs its own software to make it work on a particular computer system.

Computer keyboards

A number of alternatives are available to suit different ways of working, different work conditions and special applications.

Standard keyboard

A typical standard computer keyboard is shown in Figure 15.1. The arrangement of keys on the main part of the keyboard is the same as for any typewriter. This QWERTY layout comes from mechanical typewriters and has little to do with the requirements of a computer keyboard. It has continued as the favoured design because many people are used to it and changing the layout of the keys would mean retraining for millions of keyboard users. The computer keyboard does have other keys, specifically designed for the computer. Function keys, for example, are programmable and are used by software pack-

Figure 15.1 A typical standard keyboard

ages to access particular options, such as Help menus. Some common examples of keyboard use are:

- ❑ entering text and numbers into the computer, perhaps using a word processor;

- ❑ entering keywords into a *search engine,* a type of program used to find information on the World Wide Web;

- ❑ controlling animated graphics characters in computer games;

- ❑ entering commands to an operating system such as MS-DOS.

Microsoft Natural keyboard

An alternative keyboard design has been developed by Microsoft. Its shape and main features are illustrated in Figure 15.2. The Natural keyboard splits the keys into two main areas and angles the keys slightly, allowing the user to keep a straighter, more comfortable wrist posture. The keyboard also slopes and provides palm support, which puts less strain on the wrists and allows the shoulders to relax. Repetitive strain injury (RSI) is a common complaint of keyboard users

Figure 15.2. *Microsoft Natural keyboard*

and a comfortable wrist posture helps to avoid it. The design was based on *ergonomic* research, which is the "study of efficiency of workers and working arrangements" (Oxford English Dictionary).

Membrane keyboard

This is a keyboard covered by a transparent, plastic cover, to protect the keys from dirt. Membrane keyboards are used in factories or other locations where the dirt from users' fingers or the surroundings may damage them. The membrane makes its difficult to type accurately and quickly, so these keyboards are not used in a normal office environment.

Concept keypads

In specialist applications, the standard keyboard is not always the most convenient method of input. In a factory, for example, a limited number of functions may be necessary for the operation of a computerised lathe. These functions can be set out on a touch-sensitive pad and clearly marked. This is possible because all inputs are anticipated and the range is small. The operator is saved the trouble of typing in the individual characters which form instructions.

Concept keypads are used in shops, restaurants and bars. For example, each key position on the pad can be assigned to a particular drink. Pressing a key automatically enters the charge for the specified drink. Concept keypads are also useful in education, particularly for the mentally and physically handicapped. Different overlays, which can set different areas of the keypad to different functions, allow its use for different educational programs. For example, if the responses required by a user are limited to 'yes' and 'no', the overlay is simply divided into two parts, one for each response. The cells have to be programmed to match the overlay in use. Figure 15.3 illustrates this idea.

Figure 15.3. *Educational concept keypad with sample overlay*

The grid shown on the keypad is divided into a grid of 16×8 (128) programmable cells and the example overlay shows that the grid is to be programmed into 4 areas. Each area occupies 32 cells ($128 \div 4$) and pressure on any of the cells in one area indicates that the user has selected a particular picture. This may result, for example, in the matching word being displayed on screen. Alternatively, the input may be the user's response to the word shown on screen.

Choosing a keyboard

The desirable qualities of a keyboard are reliability, quietness and light operating pressure and in these terms keyboards vary considerably. If the keyboard is for a normal office use then a standard or Microsoft keyboard is appropriate.

Computerised tills in restaurants, pubs and hotels often use concept keypads tailored for all the items they sell. This ensures accurate pricing, as well as quicker service. Gas and electricity meter readers also use concept keypads to collect the readings. Security systems often include a concept keypad, for entry of pass codes. Dirty environments in factories or on building sites, for example, need equipment with extra protection, so membrane keyboards are used.

Pointing devices

Apart from the keyboard, which is an essential part of every computer system, pointing devices are the next most popular option for input. The devices in this group use different mechanisms and technologies, but they all allow the user to draw, erase, select and format text and graphics on screen. Figures 15.4 and 15.5 illustrate two such actions. Pointing devices are an essential component for the effective use of modern software. Two of the most popular types are described below.

Mouse

A mouse is a hand-held device which the user can move on a flat surface to direct a pointer on the computer screen. It has two or more buttons, which allow the user to draw, erase, select and format text and graphics on screen. Most computer systems are equipped with a mouse facility and many packages, including those for art, design, word processing and desktop publishing can only be operated effectively with a mouse or similar device. Graphical user interfaces such as that provided by the Windows 95/98 operating system, also depend heavily on its use.

Figure 15.4. *Selecting a menu option*

Figure 15.5. *Drawing a line*

Tracker ball

A tracker (or roller) ball is another variation of a mouse and is used for the same purposes. As shown here, a tracker ball is a bit like an upside-down mouse, with the ball visible on the top of the base. To use a tracker ball you simply move the ball in the required direction using your fingers. Buttons are supplied just like on a mouse. Like joysticks, tracker balls have the advantage over mice that a flat surface is not required for its operation, and for this reason they are often used with portable computers.

Tracker ball

Other pointing devices

Although the mouse and tracker ball are very popular, they are not the most suitable for every application. Three other pointing devices are described below.

❏ *Touch screen.* A touch sensitive display allows selection of screen options with a finger. It is commonly used in banks and tourist agencies to allow customers to obtain information on certain topics.

❏ *Digitising tablet.* A stylus (pen-like device) is used to 'draw' on the tablet; the movements of the stylus are reflected on screen. Used by architects and designers, it allows more precise drawing than a mouse.

❏ *Light pen.* This pointing device is moved over the screen and uses a light sensitive tip to allow the computer to track its movements. It can only be used with cathode ray tube (CRT) displays and cannot be used with laptop or notebook computers.

Choosing a pointing device

For most users, the mouse is standard equipment, but for architects, graphic artists and other designers, the mouse does not provide the precision control possible with a graphics tablet. The light pen is a possible alternative to the graphics tablet; it is cheaper but is not capable of the same accuracy. The roller or tracker ball is suitable for a portable computer because it does not need a flat surface. Touch-sensitive screens are suited to public display information systems, because no keyboard or other input device is needed. The user simply uses a finger to touch the required option on screen.

Sensors and ADCs

Sensors are used to detect continuously varying values, such as temperature, pressure, light intensity, humidity, wind speed and so on. These sensors detect analogue signals which are not compatible with digital computers. So, apart from several other components, an *analogue-to-digital converter* (ADC) is needed to convert analogue signals into the digital values a computer can understand. Suppose that the temperature of a washing machine is computer controlled, using a built-in microprocessor programmed for that purpose. The microprocessor can only handle discrete, that is separate, values, so the ADC in this machine takes a sample from the sensor every minute. Figure 15.6 illustrates the analogue wave form which represents the temperature variations detected by the sensor, over a 5 minute period. The figure also shows the temperature readings at each sample point (S1 to S5). For example, at the 3rd minute sample S3 = 40°C.

Continuous temperature readings detected by sensor during 5 minutes of the cycle

Temperature sample once a minute
S1 – 50°C – 5 volts; S2 – 20°C – 2 volts;
S3 – 40°C – 4 volts; S4 – 75°C – 7.5 volts;
S5 – 25°C – 2.5 volts

Figure 15.6. *Washing machine temperature variation, with a sample reading every minute*

Figure 15.7 shows a temperature sensor immersed in the water. The electrical signal (after being strengthened by an amplifier) produced by the sensor is converted by the ADC into an equivalent digital value for the microprocessor. Therefore, for each temperature sample, the microprocessor receives an equivalent digital value. It can then use these values to control the washing machine's heater.

Figure 15.7. *Sensor detects variations in temperature and ADC digitises sample values*

Microphone

Figure 15.8 illustrates the use of a microphone connected to a computer. Just as the temperature sensor produces a voltage which varies with the temperature, so a microphone acts as a sensor, converting sound waves to equivalent electrical voltage levels. The voltages are sampled and converted by the sound card inside the system casing into the binary codes

Figure 15.8. *Microphone as sensor for sound input*

which the computer can store and process. Most personal computers are equipped with a microphone to allow, with appropriate software, sound recording or the input of commands and text.

Digitiser

The term *digitiser* is used to describe more complex ADCs used for capturing video sequences (the digitiser is a *video capture card*) and scanning documents. Scanners are briefly described in the next section.

Other input devices

There are a number of devices designed to capture information, in the form of pictures or text, already printed on paper. These devices include the following.

❑   *Scanners.* These devices allow whole documents to be scanned optically and converted into digital images. Text can be captured in this way and then converted for use in a word processor. The conversion is carried out by *optical character recognition (OCR)* software.

❑   *Optical mark reader (OMR).* An OMR is designed to read simple pencil marks placed in pre-set positions on a document. A common application for OMR is a multi-choice examination paper, where the answer to each question has to be indicated by a pencil mark in one of several boxes located after the question number. The OMR can then scan the paper for the pencil marks and work out a grade. National Lottery tickets are completed and checked in a similar fashion.

❑   *Bar code readers.* Bar codes are commonly used to store a variety of data such as prices and stock codes relating to products in shops and supermarkets. A sticker with the relevant bar code is attached to each product, or alternatively, the packaging may be pre-coded. By using the data from the code, the cash register can identify the item, look up its latest price and print the information on the customer's receipt.

Output devices

Just as input devices allow human beings to communicate with computers, so output devices convert computer code into the information we can use. In this section we describe the devices that form part of typical personal computer systems, namely, *visual display units (VDUs)*, *printers* and *loudspeakers*.

Visual display unit

The most commonly used device for communicating with a computer is the *visual display unit* (VDU). The term VDU *terminal* is normally used to describe the screen and keyboard as a combined facility for input and output. On its own, the screen is called a *monitor* or *display*.

Technical features of VDUs

Screen size

A screen's size is quoted as a measurement across the diagonal, as shown. In practice, part of the screen is covered by the casing and the part of the screen you can see is usually at least an inch less, making the visible screen in the figure only 16". Some screen specifications quote this smaller measurement as the 'viewable area'.

For desktop personal computers, 14" or 15" is standard, but 17", 19" and 21" are also available. The larger screens are needed for applications such as computer-aided design (CAD). This is because the level of detail on some designs cannot be properly seen on a standard screen. Notebook computer screens, which use a different technology to desktop models, are obviously smaller and typically around 12" (12 inches) across the diagonal.

Screen resolution

A screen's *resolution* is one measurement indicating the clarity of sharpness of displayed text or graphics. Images are formed on the screen with pixels (picture elements). A pixel is one dot in a graphic image. A display screen is divided into thousands or millions of such pixels, organised in rows and columns. By varying the colours and luminosity (brightness) of individual pixels, text and graphic images are displayed. A high resolution screen packs pixels more densely to produce sharper images. A lower resolution will produce a more 'grainy' image, rather like a photograph which has been enlarged to many times its original size. To illustrate the idea of resolution, examine Figure 15.9, showing two pictures of a puma.

They are both the same size, but the top picture uses fewer pixels than the other. For this reason, the top picture is much less clear than the other. In fact, the resolution is so poor that the jagged edges of pixels can be seen.

The resolution of each image is indicated by the number of pixels in each row and column. So, the top picture has a resolution of 72 × 48 and the bottom picture has a resolution of 192 × 128. Expressed as an area, the low resolution picture is formed from 3,456 pixels (72 × 48) and the higher resolution picture from 24,576 pixels (192 × 128). As you would expect the higher resolution picture is sharper, more clearly defined.

Any given screen has a *maximum resolution*. This is the number of pixels it is capable of displaying. This maximum may be reduced, depending on several other things, such as the number of colours to be used and the amount of memory on the graphics card. The software which controls the graphics card

Figure 15.9. *Two pictures of the same size, but formed from different numbers of pixels*

can then be used to set the screen's resolution to the user's requirements (up to the screen's maximum).

A higher resolution allows the user to 'zoom in' and obtain a greater level of detail.

Screen size and resolution

A resolution of more than 1024 × 768 is only practical for screen sizes of 17" or larger. This is because higher resolutions on a small screen make the images too small to see.

Refresh rate

The contents of a display must be continually refreshed, that is re-displayed. Flicker occurs when the eye can detect a gap between each screen refresh cycle. If the refresh rate is quick enough, the eye will not detect any flicker. A screen may, for example, be refreshed 75 times every second (75 Hz), which is the minimum for modern displays.

Non-interlaced and interlaced display

When a screen's contents are refreshed, as described in the last paragraph, this involves a scanning process inside the monitor. Put simply, the image is built up line by line, although the process is too quick to be noticed.

There are two main types of scanning used by monitors. Most monitors are of the *non-interlaced* type, which means that all the lines that form the complete screen image are produced in a single refresh scan. An *interlaced* screen refreshes the screen in two separate passes.

The lines in Pass 1 leave alternate blank lines. Pass 2 fills in these blank lines. An interlaced screen can produce the same resolution as a non-interlaced one, but does it more cheaply by only replacing half the lines each time the screen is refreshed. A disadvantage of an interlaced screen is that it takes longer to completely refresh the display (two refresh cycles). Although this is not a problem for many applications, animation, video and redraws of complex diagrams are likely to produce noticeable flicker.

Monochrome and colour

A monochrome monitor uses one colour for the text or graphic images and one for the background, for example, white, green or amber on black. Colour monitors use red, green and blue, which can be mixed together in different quantities to produce different colours. For example, when red, green and blue are mixed in exactly the same quantities, we see white light; red and green in equal quantities produces yellow; two parts red and one part green gives orange. In fact, by varying the quantities and the mixtures, any colour can be produced.

Resolution and colour range

The more colours a screen can display, the more memory is required, so graphics cards (or adapters) have their own memory. In practice, the maximum number of colours, which can be up to 16·7 million, is set by the graphics adapter. Higher resolutions also use more memory, so although a graphics card may allow 16·7 million colours at a resolution of 1024 × 768, it may only permit 256 colours when the resolution is increased to 1600 × 1200. Typically, such a graphics card would have several megabytes of its own special RAM.

Text mode

For some applications, graphics display is not needed and when operated in text mode, the computer system needs to use less power and memory. This is an advantage when numerous VDUs are controlled by a central computer. In text mode, characters are formed using a matrix of *pixels* as shown in the adjacent example and the clarity of individual characters is determined by the number of pixels used. The same principle is used in character printers, such as the ink-jet

Dot matrix character

(see Printers). Selected dots within the matrix are illuminated to display particular characters. There are various main text modes, including one that displays 40 characters and another that displays 80 characters in each of 25 rows.

LCD Monitors

These monitors are very thin (about 1.5 inches thick) and occupy about a third of the space that CRT monitors require. They use much less energy than CRT monitors and because they are based on Thin Film Transistor (TFT) technology, they give off only one-third as much heat as many traditional monitors. Even more importantly, they produce virtually no electromagnetic emissions. In addition the flicker-free viewing of the TFT technology make them much easier on the eyes.

Figure 15.10. *LCD monitors*

Many LCD monitors swivel so that they can be used in either portrait or landscape orientation. Figure 15.10 shows two colour LCD monitors produced by IBM.

LCD monitors are capable of high resolutions such as 1280 x 1024 and can display millions of colours. Their extremely compact dimensions and energy-efficient features make them ideal for space- or energy-conscious environments. At the moment, however, they are considerably more expensive than equivalent conventional CRT monitors, though prices are coming down as they become more popular.

Choosing a monitor

Although specific recommendations cannot be given here, it is possible to provide advice for broad application areas.

Text-based applications

These are likely to be standard applications, such as ordering, sales and stock control systems. There is no graphics requirement. You are likely to see text-based displays at supermarket checkouts or a in a car parts department.

General office applications

These include use of word processors, spreadsheets and database. They all run under operating systems such as Windows 95, through a mouse-driven, graphical interface. For general office applications, a 15" monitor is probably the norm. Although larger screens are generally better, they take up more desk space and, of course, are more expensive.

A resolution of 800 × 600 is probably the best resolution to give the necessary clarity and image size. Although the graphics card may support higher resolutions, their use may well make icons, buttons and other images so small that viewing the screen may result in eye strain. The refresh rate is important, but provided it is 75Hz or more, the screen should be flicker-free.

To obtain the cheapest alternative, an interlaced screen could be chosen, because the applications do not require complex graphics and most users will not notice screen flicker. To avoid flicker on an interlaced screen, a higher refresh rate is usual. However, a non-interlaced screen should still provide a steadier image and this is important for users' eyesight.

Graphics-intensive applications

These include computer-aided design (CAD), photo-editing, graphic design, desktop publishing, video-editing and animation. Larger monitors, from 17" to 21" are essential for these applications. Higher resolutions of 1024 × 768, 1280 × 1024 and 1600 × 1200 need greater screen areas to ensure that images are large enough to allow detailed work on them. At the two highest resolutions, a refresh rate of 85Hz is desirable, to avoid screen flicker (the higher the resolution, the more pixels that have to be refreshed).

Printers

Computer printers vary according to: the technology they use for the printing process; the quality of their printed output; the speed of printing; whether they can print in black and shades of grey, or in colour, or both. We now examine, in some detail, ink-jet and laser printers. At the end of this section, a brief summary is provided of the other types of printer.

Ink jet printers

There are two main types of inkjet, liquid and solid.

Liquid inkjet

A typical *liquid inkjet* printer is shown alongside. Ink jet printers spray high-speed streams of ink droplets from individual nozzles in the print head onto the paper to form individual characters or smooth graphical images. Individual text characters are formed by the print head as a matrix of dots, as shown on the previous page. By a series of passes and adjustments to the head's position, graphics can also be produced. Although the output quality is high, print speeds for graphical work are very slow.

Typical ink jet printer

Liquid inkjets produce their best quality output on special paper, which is considerably more expensive than standard copier paper. The best glossy paper costs around £1 per sheet.

The fastest liquid inkjets can print 2 pages per minute (ppm) in economy mode (low resolution), but 0·5 ppm is more usual. Colour printing at the best resolutions of 600 to 700 dots per inch (dpi) is even slower. At these resolutions, near photographic quality can be achieved.

Solid inkjet

A *solid inkjet* uses sticks of ink (rather like crayons) and these are turned to liquid by being heated. In contrast to the more common liquid inkjet, the solid inkjet is quick at 3 to 4 ppm, using the base resolution of 300 dpi; this is good enough for general business graphics, but not for photographic quality. The solid inkjet achieves its high speed by using a print head the full width of an A4 sheet. Solid inkjet printers cost several thousand pounds.

Buffer memory

To enable the printer to print bi-directionally, that is from left to right and then right to left, alternately, it must have enough of its own *buffer memory* to store at least a complete line.

How colour printing works

Most inkjet printers print in monochrome, shades of grey and in colour. In colour printers, the ink is often supplied from two cartridges, one holding black ink and the other three colours (cyan, magenta and yellow) cartridge. As explained in the section on colour displays, a few colours can be mixed to produce all the others. As explained in the section on VDUs, colour displays use the RGB (red, green, blue) model. Colour printing uses a different colour mode to produce the full colour range; it is called CMYK (cyan, magenta, yellow and black -K). Figure 15.11 shows a dialogue box from CorelDRAW for the CMYK model. The displayed colour is navy blue, which is produced from different proportions of cyan, magenta and black.

Figure 15.11. CMYK model used in colour printing

Laser printers

Laser printers are called *page printers*, because they effectively print a complete page at one time. To do this, the printer must have received the contents of an entire page from the controlling computer, before it starts printing. This is illustrated in Figure 15.12.

Contents of complete page

Figure 15.12. Typical laser printer receiving complete page into its memory before printing

Laser printers may be monochrome only or both monochrome and colour. Printing speeds are far superior to ink jet printers, with similar quality output.

Monochrome laser printer

A *personal* model will print at between 12 and 17 ppm, typically at 600 dpi, but also up to 1200 dpi. The highest resolutions are used where very high quality output is needed, for example, in publishing. Some models of *network* laser, designed to serve the printing needs of many users, can print 32ppm at 600 dpi or even 50 ppm at 300 dpi. The lower of these two resolutions in perfectly good for standard printing, including invoices and general correspondence. However, such printers are expensive and aimed at high volume use, say a maximum of 900,000 pages per month. Figure 15.13 shows an example of a large network printer.

Figure 15.13. High volume, network laser printer

Colour laser printer

Alongside the solid inkjet, the colour laser produces the highest print speeds, ranging from 2 to 5 ppm. Resolutions are similar to the monochrome models, up to 1200 dpi. An advantage of colour lasers over liquid inkjets is that they can produce the best quality on standard paper. The quality of liquid inkjet printing depends on the quality of paper used. As you would expect, these advantages are gained at a price, colour laser printers costing significantly more than monochrome models. However, the speed of the laser printer allows it to be shared on a network, so the cost per user for colour printing may be little more than that of buying a personal inkjet for each user. Running costs are also much lower than for inkjet printers.

Printer memory

As a page printer, the laser printer must be able to hold the data for an entire page at one time. If the page has a large proportion of graphics, then the memory requirements for one page can be very large. Most laser printers are equipped with a basic memory of 2MB, but this is often insufficient for complex graphical documents; extra memory can be added if necessary. Some printers also make use of the computer's own RAM and thereby remove the need for buying extra, expensive, printer memory.

Printing speeds - quoted and real

Print speeds quoted as pages per minute (ppm) in manufacturer specifications cannot be used as a rule for all kinds of printing. The following points should be noted:

❑   Print speed will vary considerably, depending on the mix of graphics and text on a page. A small logo at the top of a page may not slow the printout much, but a full-page poster is likely to reduce the printing rate drastically.

❑   Printing a text page with a little colour highlighting will mean that the entire page is printed as a colour document and will take much longer than if it were plain text.

Other types of printers

❑   *Line impact.* As the name suggests, this type of printer uses hammers to print the characters onto the continuous stationery, a complete line at a time. They are used as system printers, for internal, high volume reports and can achieve speeds of between 500 and 1400 lines per minute (lpm).

❑   *Large format (plotters).* Used for design work, a large format printer can handle poster images up to 150 feet long and 54 inches wide. Monochrome and colour models are available. Figure 15.14 shows a typical example.

Figure 15.14. *Large format printer (plotter)*

Choosing a printer

Although specific recommendations cannot be given here, there follow some typical user examples and suggested choices.

❑   Personal computer printing. The user needs to print a few letters and perhaps produce the occasional colour poster. The choice is fairly straightforward here. Until recently, the choice would have included the impact dot matrix (not dealt with in this text), but the liquid inkjet provides excellent quality output, with the option of colour.

❏ Publishing and graphics for a single user system. The user needs to print large, monochrome publications, including some complex graphics. A laser printer is the necessary choice for this user, because an inkjet printer would be much too slow and the running costs too high; print cartridges have a much higher cost per page than the toner used in a laser printer.

❏ Network monochrome printing. Again, the only choice is a laser printer. Which model is chosen would depend on the number of users and the type of printing required. For text documents, a printer would support more users than would be the case for graphical work.

❏ Near-photographic quality printing. A liquid inkjet printer will produce the necessary quality at 600 or 720 dpi, but a colour laser will do the same, much more quickly.

If colour printing is needed by a number of users, then the higher cost of the colour laser could be shared by placing it on a network. The alternative is to provide as many liquid inkjet printers as there are users who need access at the same time.

❏ General-purpose colour printing. Either the solid inkjet or the colour laser printer would provide the necessary speed and the 300 dpi quality for general business graphics.

Exercises

1. Explain the need for input devices.
2. Name as many input devices as you can.
3. Why is an ADC necessary when using a sensor to capture temperature values?
4. Explain the need for output devices.
5. Name as many output devices as you can.
6. What is meant by the screen resolution of a monitor?
7. What is the difference between an interlaced and a non-interlaced monitor?
8. What advantages do LCD monitors have over traditional CRT monitors?
9. Name two types of printers commonly used. Give a typical print resolution and output speed (in pages per minute) for each one. What other factors need to be considered when choosing a printer?

Chapter 16

Storage systems

As explained in Chapter , backing storage is needed to hold programs and data files, from where they can be recalled as necessary by the computer. They are all *non-volatile* - their contents are not lost when power is removed. The purpose of main memory or RAM, which is volatile, is to hold programs and data currently in use - it is not a permanent storage area. A wide range of different backing storage systems is available, to suit every kind of computer system and user requirement. They vary according to:

❑ the technology they use and the way they operate;
❑ the speed with which they can record and retrieve data;
❑ capacity, that is, the amount of data they can hold;
❑ whether they are

   O read-only - the contents cannot be changed or

   O read-write - the contents can be changed.

The storage systems described in this chapter (there are numerous others) are those using:

❑ magnetic disk, including hard disk and removable disk media, such as floppy, Zip and Jaz.
❑ magnetic tape.
❑ optical media, including: CD-ROM (read only memory); CD-R (recordable - once only); CD-E (erasable - read and write); DVD (digital versatile disk).

A common feature of all disk storage systems is the way in which they are addressed by the computer system. Magnetic disk addressing principles are described in the following section.

Magnetic disk

All disk storage systems provide *direct access* to data. This is in contrast to tape systems where data has to be accessed *serially*, that is, in the order in which it is organised. When data is to be written to or read from disk, a specific *location* can be identified, by its *address*. Tape devices do not have locations which can be addressed, so data can only be accessed serially.

Magnetic disk addressing

In a similar fashion to the first line of a typical postal address of house number and street, magnetic disks use *sector* and *track*. This structure is illustrated in Figure 16.1. The figure illustrates a simplified magnetic disk structure, with 8 sectors numbered 0 to 7 and a number of tracks, numbered from 0, starting with the outermost track. In reality, on a hard disk, there would be hundreds of tracks. The Figure also shows an example address, Sector 5, Track 4. To read from or write to a disk location directly, the software must specify the address.

Hard disks and other high capacity systems use a number of disks within the one device and this makes the address structure slightly more complicated (not dealt with in this text).

Figure 16.1. *Addressing structure on disk surface*

Hard disk

A typical microcomputer has an internal hard disk with a capacity measured in gigabytes (GB). An illustration of its internal components is provided in Figure 16.2 . The illustration shows the top surface of a pack of hard disks on a central spindle. The disks are rotated at high speed, between 4,500 and 10,000 revolutions per minute (rpm). The read/write heads, through the use of a motor, can be moved in or out across the surface of the disk. This is how particular tracks are reached.

Figure 16.2. *Components of a microcomputer's hard disk drive*

Access speed

The speed with which data can be read from, or written to, a hard disk is measured as the *average seek time*, in thousandths of a second, or milliseconds (ms). This means that to access a location, the read/write heads have to move to the required track. The time taken to reach the track is known as the *seek time*. A typical average seek time is between 7 ms and 10 ms. The seek time is usually better in systems which use higher spin speeds. This means that the correct sector comes into position more quickly. Figure 16.3 illustrates seek time and spin speed delay. Another major influence on the speed of a disk drive is its *controller*. This is the interface between the disk drive and the computer system. The topic is not discussed further here, but well-known interface standards are SCSI (Small Computer Systems Interface), Ultra Wide SCSI, and UDMA (Ultra Direct Memory Access).

Figure 16.3. *Effects of seek time and spin speed*

Capacity

Modern software, with its provision of an ever-increasing range of features and the use of multimedia images, such as photographs and video clips, demands larger capacity disk drives. Typical capacities used to be measured in megabytes (MB), but are now measured in gigabytes (GB) - thousands of megabytes.

To understand how capacities can be increased in this way, you need to be familiar with some basic ideas about how the data is stored on magnetic disk. The binary codes used to represent data in a computer are stored as magnetic dots along the length of disk tracks. Figure 16.4 illustrates the tracks and magnetic dots which represent the data. Different methods are used to make the magnetic dot represent binary 1 or binary 0. One method uses polarity, positive for a 1 and negative for a 0. Increased capacity is achieved by packing the magnetic

Figure 16.4. *Disk surface showing magnetic dots representing binary data*

dots more closely together, that is, more densely. Until recently, it was thought that optical media, such as CD-ROM would far outstrip capacities of hard disk drives. This has not been the case, because technical advances mean that the magnetic dots can be packed more densely than was previously thought possible.

Usage

The hard disk, with its huge capacity and fast access times, remains the best product for the *primary drive* in a computer system, holding the operating system and main applications programs.

Removable magnetic disk

There is a wide range of products in this category, including: floppy; Iomega Zip; Jaz.

Floppy disk

The floppy disk has, until recently, been the main product for securing small files. Although several developments have increased its capacity, the 1·44 MB of the 3·5" floppy disk (see Figure 16.5), is insufficient for many users. A graphics image, for example, is often too large to fit on a floppy. It also provides very slow access times, with a spin speed of only 360 rpm.

Figure 16.5. *3·5" floppy disk*

Usage

Floppy disks are extremely cheap and a 3·5" drive is still standard equipment in a microcomputer system. For many home and small business users, it is adequate for making backup copies of data files held on the primary hard drive and passing copies of data files to other users. The increasing use of e-mail, which allows the *attachment* of such files, is likely to reduce the need for this practice. For many other users, who need to produce and store multimedia data and backup large parts of their primary hard drive, the 1·44 MB floppy disk is inadequate.

Data compression programs

It is possible to compress files so that they will fit onto a floppy disk, through the use of data compression programs, such as WinZip. Bitmap files, in particular will compress to about 2% or 3% of their original size. Compression may allow, for example, text and graphics files with a total capacity of 50MB (which would take at least 35 disks) to be stored on around 10 disks. Backing up to even 10 disks is still a laborious task and likely to discourage the vital task of frequent and regular backup.

Iomega Zip

A Zip disk cartridge holds 100MB of data on its single platter, the equivalent of approximately 70 × 1·44MB floppy disks. The Zip drive can be attached *externally*, to the parallel printer port. The printer and Zip drive connectors can be 'piggy backed' to allow both to connect to the port. It can also be attached *internally*, as another drive, to the hard disk controller.

Access speed

Attached externally, the Zip drive is still relatively slow, but when attached internally to the main hard drive controller, it has a seek time of around 30 ms. This compares with a typical hard drive seek time of between 7 and 12 ms.

Usage

Its 100MB capacity makes it ideal for users who need to store large files, such as those producing design and multimedia presentations. The quickness of the internal drive encourages regular backup and although not matching the hard disk drive, allows it to be used as an extension to the on-line storage system. Files could be efficiently retrieved from the Zip without first copying them to the hard drive.

Iomega Jaz

A single Jaz cartridge contains two platters and will store 1GB of data (2GB with data compression). It can be attached internally or externally, but only to a SCSI drive controller.

Access speed

The Jaz drive has an average seek time of between 10 and 12 ms, making it as quick as most fixed hard disks.

Usage

Its huge capacity and hard drive performance make the Jaz drive a true extension to on-line storage. Files can be retrieved from a Jaz cartridge as quickly as from the main hard drive. It is also suitable for backing up the contents of the primary hard drive.

Magnetic tape

In contrast to disk, tape does not have locations which can be separately *addressed*. For this reason tape storage systems provide only *serial access* to data, that is, the order in which it is stored. This is illustrated in Figure 16.6.

| data 1 | data 2 | data 3 | data 4 | data 5 | data 6 | data 7 | data 8 | data 9 |

Figure 16.6. *Serial access to data*

The figure shows that to reach a particular item of data on tape requires the device to read all the data that comes before it. Although magnetic tape systems can be used for some data processing applications, such as payroll, which do not need direct access, the systems described here are for backing up network servers, mini and mainframe computers. Although the arrangement of data on tape is different from that on disk, the magnetic storage principles are the same.

Tape backup systems

To prevent permanent loss of data, it is vital that a computer system's main hard drive is regularly backed up. The more frequently the contents of files change, the more frequent should be the backups. For a single microcomputer hard drive, a single tape is often sufficient. A single tape device is often referred to as a *tape streamer*. When several tapes are required for a complete backup, such as for a large network server a *tape library* is essential. This device includes an *autochanger*, which rather like a juke box, automatically loads the next tape. The alternative is to insert new tapes manually, which for a process that may take hours, is not desirable.

Capacity

The most popular tape backup systems use Digital Audio Tape (DAT) cartridges. For example, a 120 metre tape can store up to 4GB, and 8GB using data compression. A tape library system, capable of holding 8 such tapes, would be able to backup 64GB of data.

Data transfer rate

Typically, tape backup systems can transfer data to the tape at between 35 and 60MB per minute. If compression is being used the rate will vary during backup, because some kinds of data take longer to compress than others. At an average of 50MB per minute, a 4GB drive would take 80 minutes (4000MB ÷ 50MB).

Optical media

Instead of using magnetism to record data, optical media are read or recorded using laser light. To *record*, a high intensity laser beam burns tiny holes into the surface of the disk, each hole representing a binary 1 or a binary 0. To *read*, a lower intensity laser is used to detect the holes and the binary digits they represent.

The binary digits are recorded along tracks in a similar fashion to magnetic disk, but instead of using concentric tracks, optical disks use a spiralling track, similar to the old gramophone records. This is illustrated in Figure 16.7.

Figure 16.7. *Optical disk with spiralling track*

Compact disk (CD)

CDs are optical media and a single disk can hold approximately 650MB of data. Although data transfer rates are continually being improved, CD drives are slower than hard magnetic disks.

There are three types of CD.

❑ CD-ROM (compact disk-read only memory). As the name indicates, the data is recorded during manufacture and can only be read by a CD-ROM drive. The main uses of the CD-ROM are for:

O multimedia applications, such as games and encyclopaedia.

O software installation. The large memory requirement of many software packages means that delivery on floppy disk is impractical, whereas one CD-ROM disk is often sufficient to deliver an entire package

❑ CD-R (recordable - once only). This is a CD which can be written to once, with a suitable CD-Writer.

O Provided the contents do not need to be updated, this can be a useful medium for archiving documentary and other material.

O The falling cost of CD-Writers and the small cost of each disk, makes it possible for businesses and other organisations to produce their own multimedia training programmes.

❑ CD-R/W (read and write). Because data can be erased and updated, this type of CD is an alternative to magnetic disk, although its data transfer rates are still relatively slow.

DVD (Digital versatile disk)

Using the same basic principles as the CD, DVD packs the data more densely and can store 4.7GB, compared with the CD's 650MB. With this capacity and its quicker data transfer rate, a single DVD disk can hold 133 minutes of video, with Dolby surround sound.

It is probable that DVD drives will be an increasingly important removable storage device, particularly with the increasing use of video in multimedia products.

Exercises

1. What main factors determine the type of backing storage device to use for a particular IT application?
2. List as many types of backing-storage devices as you can.
3. How is data organised on a magnetic disk?
4. How is data organised on magnetic tape?
5. Give a major use of magnetic tape.
6. What is a tape streamer?
7. What is the main difference between CD ROM and magnetic disks for data storage?

Chapter 17

Setting up a computer system

This chapter deals with the following aspects of setting up a computer system:

- ❏ Connecting the hardware.
- ❏ Powering up the system.
- ❏ Installing device drivers, such as printer drivers.
- ❏ Tailoring a GUI 'desktop'.
- ❏ Installing and configuring applications software.

Connecting the hardware

Although some additional devices, such as a scanner and camera may be included in a system, the guidelines which follow deal with a typical minimum configuration. The connections to be made are:

- ❏ system unit;
- ❏ monitor;
- ❏ keyboard;
- ❏ mouse;
- ❏ printer;
- ❏ power supplies for the printer, monitor and system unit.

Figure 17.1 illustrates the connection of these devices. Obviously, safety requires that the entire task must be carried out without connection to the power supply.

Monitor connection

The system unit communicates with the monitor through a *data cable*. The data cable is permanently attached to the monitor as shown. The other end usually has a 15 pin, male, D-type plug to connect it to the 15 pin, female, D-type socket on the system unit. This is labelled 'Display port' in the figure. The 'D' shape of the plug and socket mean that the connection can only be made in one way. The screws on the side of the plug are used to secure the connection.

Keyboard connection

Keyboard to system unit; this is sometimes a coil stretch cable as shown in Figure 17.1. The cable is fixed to the keyboard. The other end has a 5 pin, male, round connector which connects to the 5 pin, female socket on the system unit. The plug simply pushes into the socket.

Mouse connection

A serial mouse connects to the serial port, commonly known by its MS-DOS name of COM1. The mouse has a fixed cable. The other end has a 9 pin, female, D-type plug which connects to the 9 pin male socket on the system unit. Screws are used to secure the connection. If the mouse is to be connected to the other serial port (labelled 'Spare serial port' in the figure), which has 25 pins, an adapter must be used. This port is known as COM2 and can be used to attach other serial devices, such as an external *modem*.

Parallel printer connection

Although some printers allow either serial or parallel connection, the parallel port is the usual connection point. Data can be transferred to a printer more quickly in parallel than it can seri-

Figure 17.1. *Connecting computer hardware*

ally. The parallel port is often known as a Centronics interface. The printer cable is not fixed to the printer and is usually bought separately. The printer end of the cable is a 25 way, (not pins) male plug which attaches to the 25 way, female socket on the printer. The system unit end of the cable has a 25 pin male plug which attaches to the 25 pin female socket on the system unit. Spring clips secure the cable to the printer. Screws are used to secure the cable to the system unit.

Power connections

The system unit, monitor and printer each have a separate power supply and these should be the final connections.

Powering up the system

Having checked that all components are properly connected, the power supply and switches on the printer, monitor and system unit should be switched on.

Power on self-test

The system goes through a self-checking procedure and if properly set up will load the operating system. If errors or faults are detected, a suitable error message may be displayed. Although you would need to check the computer manufacturer's user manual, the following table shows some example errors, possible causes and solutions.

Error	Possible cause	Possible solution
Keyboard error	Not properly connected	Push home connection

Non-system disk or disk error	Floppy disk left in drive on power up	Remove floppy disk
C: drive failure	Corruption of software on hard disk	Run ScanDisk
C: drive failure	Damaged hard disk	Call manufacturer
HDD controller failure	Hard disk ribbon cable or power supply not properly connected	Open system unit and check cables properly connected
FDD controller failure	Floppy drive ribbon cable or power supply not properly connected	Open system unit and check cables properly connected

Installing device drivers

Device drivers are programs which control the way a device works. All attached devices, including for example, the graphics card (to control the display), sound card, disk drive controller and printer need device drivers. For example, without the appropriate driver, the computer system will be unable to take advantage of all the printer's features. So, a particular make of printer, with facilities to print text and graphics at a resolution of 600 dpi, will only provide all those facilities with the correct driver. The incorrect driver may prevent printing of graphics or even print gobbledygook. A printer driver can be installed with the installation program provided by the printer manufacturer, or with the appropriate operating system utility.

Printer install program

A new printer will include its associated software on disk, and the driver is installed through the use of this software. The following notes illustrate a typical printer install process.

1. The operating system is instructed to 'Run Setup.exe'. In this case the setup program is on the first floppy disk supplied with the printer (Figure 17.2).

2. The setup program prompts for the parallel port to be used by the printer. In this case, the system only has one such port, LPT1, so this is the only option (Figure 17.3).

Figure 17.2

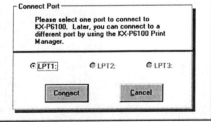

Figure 17.3

3. The user is asked to confirm the hard disk directory into which the programs will be installed. Generally, the default is chosen, unless there is a particular reason for changing it.(Figure 17.4)

Figure 17.4

4. The setup continues with the copying of files from the floppy to the named directory on hard disk (Figure 17.5).

5. If the setup programs occupy more than one floppy disk, the user is prompted when the next one is needed.

6. When the setup is complete, various configuration files may be altered and the process is completed.

7. For the changes to take effect, the operating system has to be restarted. This is because the changes to the configuration files are detected when the operating system is first loaded. Figure 17.6 shows the prompt to restart.

Figure 17.5

Figure 17.6

Printer install utility

In the case of Windows 95, a new printer can be installed with printer Install Wizard.

Figure 17.7 shows the Printers window with two installed printers and the 'Add Printer' utility. Running the 'Add Printer' utility, calls up the Wizard. This provides the options of selecting a driver already available on the hard drive, or one held on another disk (such as that provided by the manufacturer).

Figure 17.8 shows a list of drivers already available on the hard drive.

Downloading drivers from the Internet

Figure 17.9 shows the download page on the Brother.com Web Site. Manufacturers often modify their device drivers to improve the features or performance of the devices they control. It is often worth downloading the latest device driver from the manufacturer's Web site, to take advantage of such

Figure 17.7. *Printer install utility*

Figure 17.8. *List of available printer drivers*

improvements. Obtaining the latest graphics driver can improve the performance of a computer system, for example, by speeding up screen redraws. To download a particular driver, the user simply clicks on the appropriate driver name. The figure shows that the user has requested the download of the Brother 1260 printer driver. The dialogue box indicates that the downloaded file can be copied straight to memory or to the hard disk. The downloaded file will normally include a program to automate the installation process.

Figure 17.9. *Downloading drivers from the a Web site*

Setting GUI preferences

A major benefit of a GUI is that its appearance can be altered to suit an individual user or a group of users. If the settings are made for a group, then a generally accepted appearance has to be agreed. If one user in the group decides to change settings, without proper agreement, this can be annoying or even confusing for the other members of the group. There are too many different settings to deal with them all here, so we will concentrate on some of the most important. The examples used here refer to the Windows 9x GUI.

Display properties

The Windows 95 Display Properties window is shown in Figure 17.10. Each tab deals with a different aspect of the display. The displayed tab gives access to *Screen Saver* and energy saving controls. Setting a screen saver prevents a static image from remaining on screen and burning a permanent shadow into it. Energy saving features can only be used if the screen is compatible. This switches the

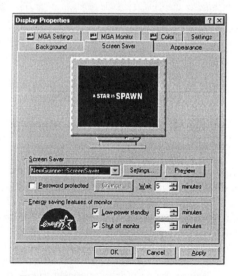

Figure 17.10. *Display properties window*

monitor power down or off after a certain period. The *Settings* tab allows the user to control the appearance of the screen display, including screen resolution, number of colours and the font size.

The figure also shows an MGA settings tab, which is specific to the installed graphics card, an MGA Matrox Millennium. It provides more varied controls than the standard Settings tab. Figure 17.11 shows the *Appearance* settings can be selected from a number of different standard models, or the user can alter individual parts of the screen, such as the colour of the desktop or spacing of icons.

Date and time

Figure 17.12 shows the date and time window in Control Panel. Figure 17.13 shows the MS-DOS prompt and the alteration of the date and time through typed commands.

Figure 17.11. *Appearance tab*

Figure 17.12. *Setting the date and time*

Figure 17.13. *Using DOS prompt to set date and time*

Software installation

Much of this process is automated through an *install program*. Figure 17.14 shows an example.

Install settings

Some installations are quite straightforward and the only major decision to be made concerns the drive and directory in which the programs are to be stored. The above example, shows that the directory is \qbooksw, on the E: drive. The default is usually C:, but E: was chosen because of limited space on the C: drive. Although the drive and directory can be changed from that suggested by the install program, it is usually sensible to accept the default. The C:\ drive is normally the preferred location for applications programs, but another hard drive, or partition of the hard drive can be used. If an alternative is chosen, the operating system will still require some files on its own drive, usually the C: drive.

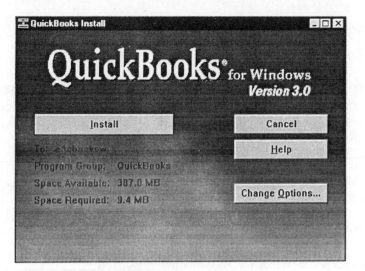

Figure 17.14. *A software install program*

Other entries include:

- [ ] acceptance of licence arrangements. This restricts the number of machines on which the software can be installed at the same time.

- [ ] user name and company; these details are required for technical support from the software supplier.

- [ ] key code. This is supplied to the licensee and is designed to discourage pirate copies. The key code must be entered before the installation can continue.

Type of installation

The *typical* installation is useful if you wish to be certain that the facilities required by most users are provided. However, if you are knowledgeable about the facilities, a custom installation is usually better. Custom installation ensures that all the facilities you require are installed (your needs may not be typical) and that facilities you do not need are not installed. This can save considerable disk space.

Testing the installation

Completion on installation involves:

- [ ] copying of program files to the named directory;

- [ ] alteration of configuration files which 'tell' the operating system that the program is installed and where it is located.

Sometimes, the system needs to be restarted for the settings to be detected by the operating system. Once the above tasks are completed, the program can be run and tested with sample tasks or data. Whether the installation meets all of the user's requirements cannot be thoroughly checked until the full range of tasks has been attempted. Obviously, if the range of tasks is wide, this may take a considerable time. If a required option has not been installed, the install program may:

❑   require the full installation to be repeated;

❑   allow the additional option to be installed without full installation.

Removing programs

Most commercial programs provide an *uninstall* program. The uninstall program should be used wherever possible. It is generally a bad idea to simply delete the program files. The configuration files will still contain details and the operating system will still 'think' that the program is installed. At best, only space will be wasted. At worst, the operating system may display error messages on startup, which although not damaging are a great nuisance.

Figure 17.15 shows the Windows 95 utility for starting the removal of programs from the system, with a list of the installed software.

System security

Loss of important data can be disastrous for an organisation. For example, if a business loses its sales accounting records, it may prevent collection of sales debts (amounts owed by customers for goods bought on credit). The loss of income may then prevent it from paying its suppliers, resulting in bankruptcy or liquidation. The causes of data loss are varied, but the computer *virus* is one important threat. An important part of the protection system is the virus protection program.

Data loss can also result when unauthorised persons gain access to a computer system. Protection systems include physical methods, such as the use of security staff and locked doors, and software methods, including passwords.

Figure 17.15. *Removing programs*

🔏Exercises

1. When setting up a typical PC what connections need to be made?
2. What are device drivers?
3. What is the main purpose of a screen saver program?
4. How are most modern commercial programs removed from computer systems?
5. What do you understand by the term computer virus?
6. What methods can be used to protect PCs from viruses?
7. Why are passwords often used in computer systems?

Chapter 18

PC assembly and upgrade

Modern PCs are designed to be assembled and upgraded quickly and easily. System cases, whether standard desktop or tower, have brackets, screw holes and connector slots that allow all essential, basic components to be fitted easily and without the need for special tools or extensive experience and training. In this chapter we describe the steps required to fit and connect basic PC components. Diagrams and photographs will help to identify standard PC components and show how they are fitted and connected. We describe fitting and connecting the

❑   motherboard ❑   memory modules ❑   processor chip

❑   expansion boards ❑   hard drive, floppy drive and CD ROM drive

It is assumed that the system case already has a suitable power supply and fan fitted since PC cases are usually sold this way.

Before you start

Precautions

There are three very important precautions that you must take before starting to work on assembling or modifying a computer:

1.   **Make sure that you have made backups of any essential files held on your system.** Things can go wrong when upgrading a computer so assume the worst and make backups of important files if you have not already done so.

2.   **Make sure that the power cable to the computer is physically disconnected.** Do not just switch off the power supply at the power socket - physically pull out the power supply lead from the power socket at the rear of the computer case. Always put the cover back on the case before re-connecting the power supply.

   These precautions are essential to remove the risk of getting an electric shock when working on components installed inside the case.

3.   **Draw a diagram of the back panel leads and connectors before you disconnect anything**. It is easy to forget which lead goes where. A good idea is to attach numbered labels to leads and use a marker pen to write corresponding numbers near to the appropriate back panel sockets.

4.   **Make sure that you have neutralised any electrostatic charge that might have built up in your body**. Without knowing it you can easily build up thousands of volts of static electricity on your body and if you have done so, and you touch an electronic component

such as a memory module, you could easily damage it. You can easily discharge yourself by touching a metal object that is plugged into a wall socket. For example, you could touch a metal part of a lamp or a power tool. The object does not need to be turned on for this purpose.

Tools

The only tools that you are likely to need are a Phillips screwdriver, a flat blade (ordinary) screwdriver and a pair of long-nosed pliers

The Motherboard components and connectors

Figure 18.1 shows the structure of a typical motherboard for a Pentium processor.

Figure 18.1. *Example layout of a motherboard for a Pentium processor*

Features of importance to the placement and connection of components are described below. This information is important when assembling a PC as described in a later section (see **Assembling a PC**)

Expansion board slots

The motherboard illustration shows three ISA and four PCI slots for expansion boards. The photograph in Figure 18.2 shows two empty PCI expansion board slots on a motherboard.

ZIF socket containing the CPU

The photograph shown in Figure 18.3 shows a Pentium processor package in a ZIF socket with its own cooling fan on top. Depending on the particular processor, there may not be a cooling fan mounted on the unit.

Figure 18.2. *PCI slots*

SIMM sockets

SIMMs (or DIMMs for more recent motherboards) are plugged into the four sockets. This motherboard requires SIMMs to be installed in identical pairs. These pairs can be FPM or EDO SIMMs and either parity checking or non-parity checking. (parity-checking SIMMs have eight chips on a single module, eight of them being memory chips and the ninth a parity checking chip; non-parity checking SIMMs have eight memory chips). For example the SIMM banks could contain two 16MB EDO SIMMs and two 8MB FPM SIMMs. Motherboard documentation will usually specify SIMM requirements. Figure 18.4 shows a bank of four SIMMs.

Figure 18.3. *CPU in ZIF socket with fan*

Figure 18.4. *SIMM banks*

Primary and secondary IDE connectors

These are connectors for connecting hard drives, CDROM drives and backup drives such as ZIP drives. These connectors are shown in Figure 18.5.

Ribbon cables are used to connect devices to the motherboard connectors. See the section on installing drives for more information about connecting and configuring hard drives and other types of drive.

The secondary connector can be used for a CDROM or ZIP drive or both if they are daisy chained together.

Figure 18.5. *Primary and secondary IDE connectors*

Floppy disk connector

In addition to the Primary and Secondary IDE connectors, Figure 18.5 also shows the smaller connector for the floppy disk drive.

Power supply connectors

There are two main forms of power supply plugs. The photograph in Figure 18.6 shows the old type of connector type that uses twin power supply plugs.

These plugs can be fitted incorrectly - when plugged in correctly, the four black wires are in the centre.

The other type of plug, which is for an ATX power supply, is a single unit that can only be fitted one way.

Figure 18.6. *Power supply connectors*

Port connectors

There are three port connectors shown in Figure 18.7. There are two serial port connectors, COM 1 and COM 2, and a single parallel port connector. These connectors are linked to sockets on the back of the PC chassis by means of ribbon cables as shown in Figure 18.7. Some motherboards have the port sockets mounted on them so that no ribbon cables are required.

Figure 18.7. *Port connectors*

Front panel connectors

These are connected to the various switches and indicators on the front of the PC case by means of small connectors. For instance there are connectors for the hard disk drive activity light, for the reset switch and for the internal speaker. There is also a connector for the internal fan. The uses of the pins are labelled on the motherboard or described in the documentation. Figure 18.8 shows a photograph of some of the front panel connectors on a typical motherboard.

Figure 18.8. *Front panel connectors*

Configuration switch block

This is a bank of tiny switches that change various motherboard and processor parameters. For instance some of the switches are used to specify processor speed for motherboards that can take processor upgrades. The function of each switch is dependent on the type of motherboard and will be described in documentation. You may need to use a small screw driver or a ballpoint pen cap to flip the switches if they need altering.

Installing and removing SIMMS

SIMM connectors pivot forward to allow memory modules to be installed and removed more easily. When installing SIMMs, angle the connector at about 45° and push the module in, as shown in Figure 18.9, until it snaps into position and is held by the two metal clamps at the two ends of the connector.

SIMM

Notch

Pull when
removing
SIMM

Pull

Figure 18.9. *A SIMM and connector*

To remove a memory module, first gently release the metal clamps at the ends of the socket. Then tilt the module forward and lift it out. The metal clamps **must** be released first to avoid damage to the module.

Installing and removing a processor

Inserting the processor

ZIF sockets have an integral handle to facilitate seating and removing the processor chip. Before installing the processor, unlatch and raise the handle.

Align the processor over the socket making sure that all the pins match the pin holes in the socket. Then push the processor into place being very careful not to bend any of the pins. Then lower and lock the handle. A heat sink and fan for the processor may also need to be locked in place over the processor once it is inserted in the socket.

Removing the processor

If there is a fan over the processor, release the sprung wire retaining brackets and lift the fan away. Then if necessary remove the heat sink from the top of the processor. The ZIF socket handle must then be unlatched and lifted to release the processor.

Installing and removing drives

PCs can accommodate a number of different types of drives, including hard disk drives, floppy disk drives, CDROM drives and ZIP drives. All of these drives are installed and removed in much the same way. The main difference is that since hard drives do not use removable media such as floppy disks or CD ROMs they do not have a face plate in the front panel of the computer; all of the other types of drives need to be accessed from the front of the computer so that disks or cartridges can be inserted or removed.

Installing a hard disk drive

Hard disk drives are usually located behind the front panel of the computer or in a bay above the power supply unit as illustrated in Figure 18.10. Before fixing the drive in place, make sure that the jumper settings are correct.

Figure 18.10. *Hard Disk Drive mounted above PSU*

Usually the main hard drive (the one that is used to boot the system on startup) is connected to the Primary IDE connector on the motherboard and a second hard drive can be daisy-chained to it using the same ribbon cable. Hard drive ribbon cables usually have two connectors at one end for this purpose. If two hard drives are being connected in this way, the main drive must be configured as the Master drive and the other as the Slave drive. These settings are made using *jumpers* which are tiny two-pin plugs that join pairs of connections on the hard drive jumper pins. The illustration of a hard drive in Figure 18.11shows the connections for the jumpers, the ribbon data cable and the power supply.

The jumper settings in the illustration will probably be different for other makes of hard drive. The settings are usually written on the casing of the hard drive or included in documentation for the device.

Jumper pin settings

Single drive

Master drive

Slave drive

Ribbon cable   Pin 1   Stripe on ribbon cable   Power supply connector

Figure 18.11. *Hard drive connections and jumper settings*

When plugging in the ribbon cables, make sure that they are the right way round; some connectors are constructed so that it is impossible to get them the wrong way round, but this is not always the case. In Figure 18.11 the right hand side of the ribbon cable connector, closest to the jumper pins, is Pin 1 and it corresponds to a stripe on the ribbon cable. The motherboard IDE connectors have the pins labelled from 1 to 40. (See Figure 18.5). Getting the connector orientation wrong won't damage the hard drive, but of course it won't work. (When you try to start the system, the hard drive light usually stays on permanently if the connector is the wrong way round).

Before installing the hard drive check the location of Pin 1 on the 40 pin socket so that the stripe on the ribbon cable can be aligned with it later.

Four small screws (two on each side) secure the drive unit to the drive bay as illustrated in Figure 18.10. The ribbon data cable and power supply connectors need to be plugged in once the drive is fixed in place.

Installing a CDROM drive

Before installing the CDROM drive, set any jumpers or switches. Details of jumper and switch settings should be included in the documentation for the device. Remember that if more than one CDROM drive or an IDE hard drive are to be installed on the same cable, they must be configured as master and slave.

The CDROM drive occupies one of the front panel bays. If necessary, remove a blank panel to allow the drive to be slid in from the front as shown in Figure 18.12.

ZIP drive

CDROM drive

Floppy disk drive

Figure 18.12. *CDROM drive being installed*

Once positioned flush with the front of the case, use the fixing screws to fix the unit in place and attach the 40 pin data ribbon cable and the power cable. As with hard drives, ensure that the ribbon cable stripe is positioned at pin 1 of the CDROM drive connector.

The secondary IDE connector on the motherboard is usually used for drives other than hard drives or floppy disk drives. In addition, so that the CDROM drive can output sound, an audio cable must be connected to the sound card, if there is one, or to the motherboard if it includes sound circuitry. Figure 18.13 shows an audio cable connected to a sound card from the CDROM drive..

Sound card

Audio cable and connector

Figure 18.13. *Audio cable from CDROM drive*

Installing a floppy disk drive

The procedure for installing a floppy disk drive is essentially the same as that for a CDROM drive, the main difference being that the ribbon cable has a split in it at the end that connects to the floppy drive A: and the other end goes into the floppy disk connector on the motherboard (see Figure 18.5) or to a floppy disk controller expansion board . The ribbon cable will usually have a connector in the middle for a possible second floppy disk drive B:. Check that any jumper settings are correct (usually the factory settings are appropriate) as detailed in the drive's documentation. Also note the position of pin 1 which is probably labelled on the case or circuit board of the floppy disk drive; the coloured wire of the ribbon cable goes to this pin.

For old-style cases it may be necessary to use an expansion frame for a 3.5 inch drive if the drive bay is too wide. Some older cases also require plastic or metal slide rails on each side of the bracket assembly. Four screws are used to secure the drive in position.

Attach the end of the ribbon cable with the twist to the floppy disk connector and plug in the power cable.

Installing Expansion boards

Expansion boards plug into the ISA or PCI slots on the motherboard. Figure 18.14 shows an expansion board prior to being installed.

Expansion boards are positioned such that the metal bracket at the end of the board (where there are usually connectors for peripheral devices) can be held in position by a single screw (see Figure 18.15).

If the position for the bracket on the rear of the chassis is covered by a plate, prise it off with a small flat-blade screwdriver (or unscrew it if this is possible). Then align the board over the appropriate expansion

Expansion board

Fixing bracket

Expansion board sockets

Figure 18.14. *Expansion board prior to installation*

socket and gently push the connector strip of the board into the socket. Make sure that the connector strip is fully inserted into the expansion socket before securing the board with a screw.

Figure 18.15. *Securing an expansion board*

Installing a new motherboard

Precautions

If you intend to upgrade a PC by installing a new motherboard in the old system case, before buying the motherboard it is a good idea to check the following details:

☐   CPU compatibility - if you are not changing the processor, make sure that it is compatible with the new motherboard. This includes the type of socket required as well as the type of processor.

☐   Power supply requirements - new motherboards (for Pentium IIs and above) generally require an ATX power supply which provides different voltages and motherboard connector from the older type power supply units. In addition ATX motherboards may not fit an older type system casing. If the new motherboard does require the ATX power supply, it is probably advisable to buy a new ATX system case with the power supply unit already installed.

☐   CMOS settings - modern hard disk drives auto-configure on startup. In other words they are able to provide the CPU with the drive type and the number of cylinders and tracks they have automatically; this information is essential to accessing data on the drive. For many older drives this information needs to be provided manually to the CMOS setup program (see Chapter 17). Just to be sure that there is no risk of losing essential setup information, make a copy of the current CMOS settings on paper before replacing the motherboard.

Read through **both** of the following two sections before removing and/or installing a motherboard; this is so that you know in advance what needs to be done in both cases. The section on the Motherboard Components and Connectors, referenced in the following sections, contains essential information for installing a motherboard. If you assume that anything that can go wrong, will go wrong, and take all possible precautions, you are more likely to be able to install a new motherboard without any major hitches.

Removing a motherboard

If there is already a motherboard installed in the system casing, first attach labels to all cables and draw a diagram of the connectors to which they were attached. This will be of great help when trying to connect the new mother-board. Then disconnect all cables attached to the motherboard.

Next, remove all expansion boards, first making a note of which expansion slots they occupied and labelling any connectors that need to be removed. The motherboard is usually secured to the PC chassis by a combination of several plastic standoffs (see Figure 18.16) that fix into slots and two or more screws that go through the motherboard and screw into hexagonal metal standoffs attached to the chassis. Figure 18.17 is a sectional view of a PC chassis showing a plastic and metal standoff.

Figure 18.16. *Installing and removing a motherboard*

Figure 18.17. *Motherboard standoffs*

Remove the screws and slide the motherboard sideways to free the plastic standoffs. The motherboard can then be lifted out.

Installing a motherboard

This is more or less the reverse of the process of removing a motherboard described in the previous section.

First set any switches or jumpers that are needed to configure the system; these settings should be explained in the documentation that came with the new motherboard.

Fit memory modules if not already installed. (See **Installing and removing SIMMs**).

If there are no standoffs already on the motherboard, push three or four of them into the motherboard fixing holes that align with appropriate chassis slots. Again if necessary, screw in and tighten two or three hexagonal metal standoffs into chassis screw holes. The metal and plastic standoffs should be evenly distributed over the motherboard, the intention being to keep the printed circuits on the underside of the motherboard from touching the metal casing, and also to prevent the motherboard from flexing too much when components such as expansion boards and memory modules are being fitted later.

Now align the motherboard with the plastic standoff holes and metal standoffs. Lower the motherboard so that the wide bases of the plastic standoffs go through the wide parts of the chassis slots and then slide the motherboard sideways so that the plastic standoffs are firmly engaged in the slots. Now fix the motherboard in position with metal screws that screw into the hexagonal metal standoffs attached to the chassis.

Connect the front panel LED wires and the internal speaker wires. The motherboard should have some markings to indicate where each of the small connectors is located.

Next connect the power supply cable or cables (see **Power supply connectors** earlier) making sure that where two connectors are required the black wires of both are together in the middle.

If IDE controllers are on the motherboard, connect ribbon cables from the appropriate drives to these. (See **Primary and secondary IDE connectors**). Also attach the cable from the floppy disk drive to the motherboard connector if appropriate.

If there are pins on the motherboard for serial and parallel ports, attach the ribbon cables to these. (See **Port connectors**).

Now re-install all expansion boards and connect any cables that were disconnected when the old motherboard was removed.

Before replacing the cover, check that all cables are connected and that all connectors are seated properly. Finally, replace the cover and reconnect cables to peripheral devices.

When you switch the machine on, you may get error messages regarding unrecognised disk drives. This has two most probable causes:

1.   IDE and floppy drive connectors have not been replaced properly. You will need to open the case and check that connectors are seated properly and that drives are configured correctly. Also check that the ribbon cables are connected to the drives the right way round, with the striped wire to pin 1 of the drive connectors.

2.   The CMOS memory requires drive information if drives do not autoconfigure. Before removing the old motherboard you should have made a note of the required CMOS settings for just this eventuality.

Exercises

1.   Explain safety precautions that should be taken before adding or removing components from the inside of a PC?
2.   What connectors are usually provided on a motherboard?
3.   What two main types of expansion board slots are usually provided on motherboards?
4.   What is a ZIF socket?
5.   What restriction often applies to installing SIMMs of different memory sizes on a motherboard?
6.   What is usually connected to the Primary IDE connector?
7.   When the motherboard's power supply socket requires two connectors, how should they be plugged in?
8.   What is the purpose of the *Configuration Switch Block* on a motherboard?
9.   What is the significance of Master and Slave disk drives? How is a hard disk drive set to be a single drive, a Master drive or a Slave drive.
10. What is the guideline for fitting a hard drive ribbon cable?
11. What precautions should be taken before installing a new motherboard?

Chapter 19

Assembly language programming

In this chapter we describe a simplified instruction set and assembly language for a hypothetical 16-bit microprocessor, the BEP/16. The BEP/16 instruction set has been shortened to allow us to present some typical microprocessor instructions, and to illustrate simple programming tasks. The ATL1 (Assembler Teaching Language 1) assembler produces machine code for the BEP/16. Full details of the BEP/16 instruction set, the ATL1 assembler and a program that will assemble and execute ATL1 programs can be found at www.bcpublications.co.uk.

The chapter concludes with a number of small assembly language programs to illustrate how some simple programming tasks may be implemented.

We start by describing the general characteristics of programs and, in particular, of low-level languages.

Programming Languages

At the level at which the computer operates, a program is simply a sequence of numeric codes. Each of these codes can be directly converted by the hardware into some simple operation. Built into the processor, the heart of the computer, is a set of these simple operations, combinations of which are capable of directing the computer to perform complex tasks. Computer programs, in this fundamental form, are termed *machine code*, that is code which is directly 'understandable' by the machine.

The numeric codes of the program are in binary form, or at least the electrical equivalent of binary, and are stored in the *memory* of the computer. Because this memory is volatile (in other words, it is temporary and can be changed), it is possible to exchange the program currently held in the memory for another when the computer is required to perform a different function. For this reason the term *stored program* is often used to describe this fundamental characteristic of the modern digital computer.

The numeric codes that direct the computer to perform such simple operations as those mentioned above are collectively called the *instruction set*. The instruction set of a typical computer would normally contain a number of the following types of instructions:

(a)   Data transfer. This allows data to be moved within the processor, between the processor and the memory of the computer system or between the processor and external devices such as printers, VDUs and keyboards.

(b)   Arithmetic operations. Such instructions direct the computer to perform arithmetic functions such as addition, subtraction, multiplication, division, increment, decrement, comparison and logical operations such as AND, OR, NOT and EXCLUSIVE OR.

(c)   Shift operations. These move data to the left or right within a *register* or memory location.

(d)   Transfer of control. This directs the machine to skip one or more instructions or repeat previously encountered instructions.

A program, consisting of a combination of the types of instructions outlined above, is *executed* by retrieving each instruction in turn from the memory of the computer, decoding the operation required and then performing this operation under the direction of the processor. This sequence of events is termed the *fetch-execute cycle*. On completion of each current instruction, the next instruction in the program's logical sequence of execution will be fetched from store automatically. This process ends, under normal circumstances, when a halt instruction in the program is recognised by the computer.

The example in Table 19.1 illustrates the form of a machine code program. Suppose that a computer has currently in its main store memory a simple machine code program to load two numbers into internal registers from memory, add them and store the result in memory.

Each instruction in turn, starting with that resident in memory location 1000, would be fetched from memory, decoded and executed. This process would continue until the halt instruction in location 1007 was decoded.

Memory location	Contents (Hex)	Comments
1000	220F	Load R0 from ..
1001	2000	..memory location 2000
1002	221F	Load R1 from ..
1003	2001	..memory location 2001
1004	0901	Add R1 to R0
1005	351F	Store R0 in ..
1006	2002	..memory location 2002
1007	FFFF	Halt execution

Table 19.1. *Example machine code program*

The particular binary code or combination of binary digits (0's or 1's) in the instruction (shown in hexadecimal notation in the example) causes the decoding circuitry of the CPU to transmit to other components of the hardware the sequence of control signals necessary to perform the required operation.

When it is considered that a typical program might contain tens of thousands of machine code instructions, it might seem that programming is a formidable task, well beyond the capabilities of all but the most determined and meticulous of computer professionals. Indeed, if machine code were the only computer language in use, it is extremely unlikely that society would today be experiencing such a widespread presence of computers in almost every aspect of industrial, commercial, domestic and social life. Fortunately for the computer industry, programming techniques have evolved along with advances in hardware. There is now a proliferation of programming languages designed to allow the programmer to concentrate most of his attention on solving the problem rather than on the tedious task of converting the solution to machine code form.

Low-level languages

In the history of programming languages, one of the first significant innovations was the development of *assembly languages*. A program written in an assembly language is much more readable and understandable than its equivalent in machine code. For example, a program, in some typical assembly language, equivalent to that given in Table 19.1 for the addition of two numbers, might take the form shown in Table 19.2.

Instruction	Comments
LDR R0, N1	;LoaD Register R0 with the contents of location N1
LDR R1, N2	;LoaD Register R1 with the contents of location N2
ADD R0, R1	;ADD Ro and R1 and store sum in R0
STR R0, N3	;STore Register R0 in location N3
HLT	;HaLT execution of program

Table 19.2. *Assembly language program for the addition of two numbers*

Notice that the operation codes LDR, ADD, STR and HLT (representing LOAD, ADD, STORE and HALT respectively) are now easily recognisable and easy to remember; such memory aids, or *mnemonics*, are chosen for these reasons. The references, N1, N2 and N3, relate to memory locations and are called *symbolic addresses*, and in many assembly languages it is possible to use more meaningful names such as HRS or RATE to indicate the type of data stored there. The internal registers, R0, R1, may be two of several available within the computer for use by the programmer.

The processor is unable to decode instructions in this coded form, so they must first be converted into the equivalent machine code. An *assembler* is a machine code program which performs this function. It accepts an assembly language program as data, converts mnemonic operation codes to their numeric equivalents, assigns symbolic addresses to memory locations and produces as output the required machine code program. The assembly language program is termed the *source program* and the final machine code program is the *object program*. Thus assemblers and assembly languages have removed the need to write machine code programs and a considerable burden has been removed from the programming task; the computer itself now does much of the work required to produce the object program.

Though assembly languages aid the programmer considerably, they are still closely related to machine code; there is a one-to-one correspondence between a machine code instruction and one in assembly language. In other words each machine code instruction must have a matching assembly language instruction. This fundamental correspondence has led to the term *low-level* being applied to this type of programming language.

Assemblers

Though a program written in an assembly language is much more readable and understandable than its equivalent in machine code, it is no longer directly executable by the computer. An *assembler* is a computer program which carries out the necessary translation.

The assembler accepts an assembly language program as data, converts *mnemonic* operation codes (op-codes) to their numeric equivalents, assigns *symbolic addresses* to memory locations and produces as output the required machine code program.

The assembly language program is termed the *source program* and the final machine code program is the *object program*.

Though it is true that by far the majority of computer programming today is in high-level languages such as Pascal, C or COBOL, programming in assembly languages is still essential for certain tasks. The reason for this, despite continual improvements in compiler design, is simply that the programmer, having total control over the structure of the machine code generated by the assembler, is able to write much faster and more efficient code than that produced by a compiler. The very nature of high-level languages, allowing us to deal with a greatly simplified, virtual machine, often precludes the programmer from being able to fine-tune code according to particular circumstances.

For example, a commonly used method of increasing the speed of a machine-code program is to utilize internal registers as much as possible in preference to memory locations, in order to minimize relatively slow memory accesses. While this type of code optimization is perfectly feasible in any assembly language, most high-level languages do not allow the programmer this degree of control (C is a notable exception, allowing identifiers to be specifically allocated to general purpose registers).

A consequence of the one-to-one correspondence between an assembly language instruction and its equivalent machine-code instruction is that assemblers are *machine dependent*, producing machine code for a specific type of processor. For instance, the machine code generated by an Intel 8086/88 assembler could not be used directly by a computer with a Motorola 68000 processor. For this reason, there is no single, archetypal assembler; rather, each assembler is related to the architecture of the processor for which it has been designed. Thus, if the processor supports two-address machine-code instructions, this will be reflected in the format of the assembly language instructions. In the following sections a number of fundamental characteristics, common to most assemblers, are introduced. It uses a hypothetical microprocessor and associated assembly language to illustrate simple programs and includes an example program to illustrate the assembly process.

Assembler tasks

Early assemblers did little more than convert instruction mnemonics to their equivalent numeric machine codes, but current assemblers do much more. Some of the most common assembler tasks are described below:

- ❑ *Op-code translation.* Numeric operation codes replace the mnemonic op-codes used in the source program.

- ❑ *Absolute address allocation.* Each instruction or data word in the source program must be allocated an absolute machine address (its physical location). The assembler maintains a *location counter* (sometimes referred to as a *load pointer*) which, having been set to an initial base address, is incremented by the length of each data or instruction word as it is assembled.

- ❑ *Symbolic operand conversion.* This refers to the assembly process of substituting any symbolic addresses, that is, user identifiers used in place of memory locations, with numeric machine addresses. A symbol table records each symbolic operand together with its corresponding absolute address; a similar table logs labels and their machine addresses. If relative addressing is used, labels and symbolic addresses are converted to offsets from the location counter; this enables a program to be relocatable.

- ❑ *Converting constants to their internal forms.* This will involve conversion from textual (ASCII, for example) representations of decimal, hexadecimal, octal or binary to pure binary.

- ❑ *Replacing identifiers by user-defined macros.* If the assembly language supports the use of *macro* instructions (a shorthand used by a programmer to express sequences of regularly used instructions by a macro name), any such macro must be expanded by the assembler and inserted into the source program prior to assembling it.

❑ *Obeying directives*. Many assemblers support the use of *pseudo-operations*, or *directives* which are instructions not directly translatable into machine instructions. These involve such things as reserving space for data, defining the values of identifiers used in the program and defining where the program is to be located in memory.

❑ *Generating error messages*. If the assembler detects any syntax errors in the source program, it must be able to issue a message indicating the source and nature of the problem.

❑ *Producing source-code listings*. These may take various forms including listings of the source-code, object-code and symbol table.

Assembly

The assembly process usually involves the assembler in executing several passes of the program's source code, each one carrying out certain of the tasks described above. The problem of forward referencing (an instruction uses a symbolic operand which is not defined until later in the program, so its address has not been allocated at that point and cannot be included in the instruction) means that assemblers usually carry out a minimum of two passes. Some assemblers, such as our hypothetical ATL1, perform an additional initial pass to simplify the main two passes described below.

Two-pass assembly

Pass 1. Any macro instructions are expanded as part of the pass or as a separate initial pass, making three in all. All instructions are examined and checked for syntactical correctness; any errors are recorded in a table. After each instruction has been dealt with, the location counter is incremented, and a symbol table is constructed to link any symbolic operands and labels with their corresponding absolute addresses.

Pass 2. By reference to the symbol tables, the assembler generates and outputs the object code.

A hypothetical microprocessor: the BEP/16

The BEP/16 is a simple, hypothetical 16-bit microprocessor loosely based on the Intel 8086/88. The BEP/16 processor contains the following 16-bit registers:

❑   11 general-purpose registers, R0-R10

❑   a 16-bit Program Counter, PC

❑   a 16-bit Stack Pointer, SP

❑   a 16-bit Flag Register, FR

❑   a 16-bit Overflow Register, VR

Addressable RAM is limited to 64K bytes, though an additional 16K bytes are used for the stack. Memory is accessed in 16-bit words. The *flag register* contains the following flags:

❑   the carry flag (C)-bit0

❑   the zero flag (Z)-bit1

❑   the sign flag (S)-bit2

❑   the overflow flag (V)-bit3

Carry flag: the C flag is set (C=1) if there is a carry out from the most significant bit (m.s.b.) as a result of an arithmetic operation. The C flag is *cleared* (C=0) if there is no carry out.

Zero flag: the Z flag is set if the result of an operation is zero. It is cleared if the result is non-zero.

Sign flag: the S flag reflects the state of the most significant bit of the result of an arithmetic operation. S = 0 represents a positive value and S = 1 represents a negative value.

Overflow flag: the V flag is set when an arithmetic overflow occurs, that is when, as a result of a signed arithmetic operation, the most significant bit of the result is lost.

Examples of instructions using two registers are

```
MOV R1,R2        ;Data transfer
ADD R2,R4        ;Arithmetic operations
```

A subset of the instruction set is first summarized and then described in more detail in the next sections. In the summary, the flags that are affected (if any) are indicated by a hyphen (flag not used) or * (depends on the result of the instruction).

Summary

A shortened instruction set for the BEP/16 is summarised in Table 19.3.

> *reg* refers to any one of the registers.

> *addr* is an address which may be a number or a symbolic address.

> *immed* is an immediate operand which may be a single character enclosed in single quotes, or a number, or an identifier preceded by the @ symbol. Immediate numeric constants may also be preceded by the & symbol for hexadecimal constants or the % symbol for binary constants.

mnemonic	operation	formats	words	flags
				V S Z C
ADD: Add	Adds reg2 to reg1	ADD reg1,reg2 ADD reg,immed	1	* * * *
CMP: Compare	Compares reg1 and reg2 and sets flags	CMP reg1,reg2 CMP reg,immed	1 2	- * * *
DEC: Decrement	Subtracts 1 from operand	DEC reg DEC addr	1	* * * *
DIV: Divide	Divides reg1 by reg2	DIV reg1,reg2 DIV reg,immed	1	- - - *
	Unsigned integer division		2	
HLT: Halt	Halts execution of the program	HLT	1	- - - -
INC: Increment	Adds 1 to operand	INC reg INC addr	1 2	* * * *
Jcondition	Conditional jump		2	- - - -
	Jump if equal	JEQ label		
	Jump if not equal	JNE label		
	Jump if plus	JPL label		
	Jump if minus	JMI label		
	Jump if greater or equal	JGE label		

	Jump if less than	JLT label		
	Jump if greater than	JGT label		
	Jump if less or equal	JLE label		
JMP: Unconditional jump		JMP label	2	- - - -
LDR: Load register	Copies memory address contents to register	LDR reg,addr	2	- * * -
MOV: Move	Copies reg2 to reg1	MOV reg1,reg2	1	- * * -
		MOV reg,immed	2	
MUL: Unsigned multiply	Multiplies reg1 by reg2 retaining sign of operand	MUL reg1,reg2	1	- - - *
		MUL reg,immed	2	
STR: Store register	Copies contents of register to memory	STR reg,addr	2	- * * -
SUB: Subtract	Subtracts reg2 from reg1	SUB reg1,reg2	1	* * * *
		SUB reg,immed	2	
SWI: Software interrupt	Invokes an operating system routine	SWI addr	2	- - - -

Table 19.3. *Instruction set*

Data transfer instructions: MOV, LDR, STR

This set of instructions deals with transferring data to and from memory, and between internal registers.

MOV: Copies a word from from a source operand to a destination operand. The source operand may be an immediate constant or a register, but the destination must be a register.

LDR: Copies the contents of a memory location to a specified register.

         LDR R1, &1234 or LDR R3, cost, where cost is a symbolic memory address;

STR: Copies the contents of a specified register to a memory location.

Arithmetic instructions: ADD, SUB, CMP, MUL, DIV, INC, DEC

This set of instructions allows simple arithmetic operations to be performed on the contents of registers. The multiply and divide instructions use the overflow register (VR) to hold part of the result of the operations.

ADD: Performs addition on two words, putting the sum in the first operand. For example, the instruction ADD R10, @3 would add 3 to the contents of R10.

SUB: Subtracts the second operand from the first operand, putting the difference in the first operand. For example, SUB R5, R3 subtracts the contents of R3 from R5 and stores the difference in R5.

CMP: Performs the same operation as SUB, but does not store the difference in the first operand. It is used to compare two values and set appropriate flags (V, C and Z) according to the result so that a conditional branch instruction may follow it.

MUL: Multiplies two 16-bit unsigned numbers to produce a 32-bit product. The carry flag is set if the product exceeds the size of a 16-bit register; in this instance, the overflow (the most significant word) is stored in VR, the overflow register, which is reserved for this purpose, though it may also be used as a general-purpose register.

DIV: Divides the first unsigned operand by the second and stores the integer quotient in the first. The remainder after division is stored in VR.

INC: Adds 1 to the specified register or memory location.

DEC: Subtracts 1 from the specified register or memory location.

Transfer of control instructions: JMP, Jcond

This set of instructions allows the normal sequential flow of instructions to be modified. Normally, the PC is incremented after every fetch cycle so that each instruction is performed in the order in which it is stored in memory; this set of instructions allows the contents of the PC to be changed to any value in the memory space so that program instructions may be executed in orders other than sequential. This allows, for instance, sections of code to be repeated in a loop.

JMP: Causes an unconditional jump by adding a signed offset to the PC. That is, it performs a relative jump forwards or backwards. The assembler automatically converts label addresses to the appropriate offsets.

JEQ: Performs the transfer of control only if Z=1, that is, if the result of an arithmetic operation was zero.

JNE: Performs the transfer of control only if Z=0, that is, if the result of an arithmetic operation was not zero.

JPL: Performs the transfer of control only if S=0, that is, the last operation produced a positive number with a sign bit of 0.

JMI: Performs the transfer of control only if S=1, that is, the last operation produced a negative number with a sign bit of 1.

JGE: This assumes that the previous operation used signed integers in two's complement representation. The branch is performed if the first operand was greater or equal to the second operand.

JLT: This assumes that the previous operation used signed integers in two's complement representation. The branch is performed if the first operand was less than the second operand.

JGT: This again assumes signed arithmetic with the first operand greater than the second.

JLE: Again assuming signed arithmetic with the first operand less than or equal to the second.

Input/output instructions: SWI

SWI: This instruction performs an indirect call to an operating system subroutine. It allows access to pre-written routines for standard tasks such as keyboard input and displaying text on the screen.

SWI getInt : get an integer from the keyboard and store in R0

SWI putInt: display the contents of R0 as an integer

SWI getChar: get a single character from the keyboard and store in R0

SWI putChar: display the contents of R0 as a character

Other instructions: HLT

HLT: Terminates program execution, returning control to the operating system.

The ATL1 assembler

The ATL1 assembler includes the following facilities:

- ❑   the use of mnemonics for operation codes;
- ❑   the use of labels for branching instructions;
- ❑   the use of comments for annotating programs;
- ❑   symbolic memory addresses.

ATL1 assembly language instruction format

Assembly language instructions, or statements, are divided into a number of fields:

(i)   *Operation code field.* This contains the instruction mnemonic and therefore must always be present in the instruction.

(ii)   *Operand(s) field.* The composition of this field depends on the operation and the addressing mode. It may contain zero or more operands which may be registers, addresses or immediate operands.

(iii) *Label field.* This optional field allows the programmer to establish a point of reference in the program. Certain other instructions, such as branch instructions, use these labels in their operand field.

(iv)   *Comment field.* This is another optional field, ignored by the assembler, to allow the programmer to annotate the program.

Assemblers provide varying degrees of flexibility in how these fields may be combined in program statements. Fields are separated from one another by means of *delimiters*, which are special characters (such as spaces, semi-colons or colons) recognised by the assembler as serving this function.

Listing 19.1 shows a short assembly language subroutine illustrating the concepts explained above. Internal registers are designated R0, R1, R2 etc. The subroutine adds the numbers 5 to 14 inclusive, that is, the 10 consecutive numbers starting with 5, by accumulating them in register R2.

Listing 19.1.   Addition of ten consecutive numbers

label	Opcode	Operand(s)	comments
start:	MOV	R0, @10	; init loop counter
	MOV	R1, @5	; start value, R1=5
	MOV	R2, @0	; clear running total, R2=0
loop:	ADD	R2, R1	; accumulate total, R2=R2+R1
	INC	R1	; add 1 to R1
	DEC	R0	; decrement R0
	JGT	loop	; branch to label if R0>0
	HLT		; halt program

These addresses form a table of addresses of the actual routines. The SWI instruction uses the operand provided in the instruction as a pointer to the appropriate routine. This allows for the operating system routines to be located in different areas in different machines while still retaining the same SWI call. Other SWI calls allow graphics operations to be performed and input/output devices to be used.

The ATL1 preprocessor

The ATL1 assembler uses a preprocessor to make an initial pass through the source program to perform the following functions:

- ❏ Remove unnecessary spaces
- ❏ Remove blank lines
- ❏ Convert text to upper case
- ❏ Process #DEF lines

These operations simplify the source program in preparation for the next two passes which produce the required machine code. The final bullet point in the list above requires some explanation.

#DEFines

The preprocessor looks for any lines starting with #DEF. It then expects to find an identifier followed by a value or another identifier. It then searches the source program and replaces any incidences of the identifier with the value following it. For example, the definition below causes all occurrences of width to be replaced by 10 in the source program.

```
#DEF width 10
```

The examples following illustrate some uses of #DEF.

Example 1

Use meaningful names for registers:

```
#DEF counter R1
```

This definition allows you to use the identifier counter instead of the register name R1. The assembler would replace every incidence of counter with R1. Thus, an instruction such as INC counter in the source program would become INC R1 after preprocessing.

Example 2

Define the values of constants used in the program:

```
#DEF asterisk '*'
```

The assembler would replace every incidence of asterisk with '*'. Thus, an instruction such as MOV R4, asterisk in the source program would become MOV R4, '*' after preprocessing.

The ATL1 assembly process

The ATL1 assembler performs three passes of the source code:

- ❏ *Pass 1*: Preprocessing. Comments are removed and #DEFs are processed.
- ❏ *Pass 2*: A symbol table is constructed, assembler directives are obeyed and instructions are converted into machine code where possible.
- ❏ *Pass 3*: Any forward referenced addresses are inserted with the aid of the symbol table.

Programming examples

The following examples illustrate a number of simple programming tasks.

Data transfer

Programming example 1

```
;Program to illustrate simple data transfer instructions using MOV
;LDR and STR. A register is set to zero and then stored in two
;memory locations
        #DEF n1 &1000      ; Allocate n1 to location hex 1000
        #DEF n2 &1002      ; Allocate n2 to location hex 1002
        ;
        MOV R0, @0         ; Move zero to R0
        STR R0, n1         ; Store in location n1
        STR R0, n2         ; Store in location n2
        HLT                ; Terminate program.
```

Simple arithmetic

Programming example 2

```
;Program to illustrate simple 16-bit integer arithmetic and simple
;data transfer instructions. The two numbers, a and b, are input
;from the keyboard and the program calculates a² - b², using
;(a+b)(a-b).
        ;
        SWI getInt         ; Operating system call to get a 16-bit
                           ; integer from the keyboard. Value is
                           ; returned in R0
        MOV R1, R0         ; Store the first value in register R1
        SWI getInt         ; Get the second value
        MOV R2, R0         ; Store in register R2
        MOV R3, R1         ; R3 = a
        ADD R3, R2         ; R3 = a+b
        MOV R4, R1         ; R4 = a
        SUB R4, R2         ; R4 = a-b
        MUL R3, R4         ; R3 = (a+b)(a-b)
        MOV R0, R3         ; Copy answer to R0
        SWI putInt         ; Operating system call to display the
                           ; 16-bit integer in R0.
        HLT                ; Terminate program.
```

Transfer of control

Programming example 3

```
;Program to illustrate conditional jump instructions. Two numbers
;are input and the smaller of the two is displayed.
        ;
        SWI getInt         ; Operating system call to get a 16-bit
                           ; integer from the keyboard. Value is
                           ; returned in R0
        MOV R1, R0         ; Store the first value in R1
        SWI getInt         ; Get the second value
        MOV R2, R0         ; Store in R2
        CMP R2, R1         ; compare numbers
        JLT L1             ; Jump to L1 if R2 < R1
```

```
          SWI putInt        ; Display second number (already in R0)
          JMP L2            ; Jump to end
L1:       MOV R0, R1        ; Move the first number into R0
                           ; ready for displaying
          SWI putInt        ; Display the first number
L2:       HLT               ; Terminate program.
```

Loop

Programming example 4

```
;Program to illustrate a loop. Positive numbers are input and
;added to R1 until a negative number is input. Then the sum of the
;numbers is displayed
          ;
          MOV R1,@0         ; Set R1 to 0
L1:       SWI getInt        ; Operating system call to get a 16-bit
                           ; integer from the keyboard into R0
          MOV R2,R0         ; Move number to R2
          JMI L2            ; Jump to L2 if number is negative
          ADD R1, R2        ; Add number to R1
          JMP L1            ; Get next number
L2:       MOV R0, R2        ; Move total into R0 ready for displaying
          SWI putInt        ; Display the total
          HLT               ; Terminate program.
```

Exercises

1. Write a program to input two integers and output their sum, difference and product.
2. Read two integer values, *a* and *b*, and perform the following calculations.

   $2a + 3b$

   $a^2 - b^2$

   $5a^2 + 3a - 1$

3. Write a program to arrange two characters into alphabetical order.
4. Write a program to read in a set of 10 positive and negative integers then add the positive and negative numbers separately and display the two totals.

Chapter 20

Software

The word *software* is used to describe all computer programs. *Systems software* is used to make the hardware operate as a general-purpose computer system. *Applications software* makes the computer operate in particular ways, for example, as a payroll, word processing, graphic design, route planning or games system. Figure 20.1 shows the systems and applications software groups and some of the sub-groups belonging to each.

Figure 20.1. *Main categories of software, with examples*

Relevant examples of commercial software products are shown in the figure, beneath each sub-group. Some of the examples should be familiar and should help you to understand the purpose of each software group and sub-group.

Summary of software types

Referring to Figure 20.1, the following types of software can be identified.

❑ *Operating system*. This set of programs has overall control of the computer system, both hardware and applications software and acts as the *interface* between the user and the machine. Frequently the interface is graphical and known as a *graphical user interface* (GUI). Sometimes, the user may communicate through a *command-driven* interface, typing commands at a simple screen prompt.

❑ *Utilities*. These are programs to help the user carry out general maintenance tasks on the system. For example, Windows 9x provides *Windows Explorer* to manage the disk filing system, *Disk Defragmenter* to recover wasted space on disks, *DriveSpace* to create additional disk space and *ScanDisk* to find and repair disk recording problems.

❑ *BIOS* (Basic Input/Output System). The BIOS specifies the details of the installed hardware and 'fine tunes' it for best performance and user preference. Note that the BIOS software is not a category that most users deal with. The BIOS deals with the direct control of the hardware components and is normally the concern of computer manufacturers. Experienced users of computer systems may access the BIOS when installing new hardware to upgrade their system.

❑ *Development tools*. These are used by programmers to create and maintain systems and applications software. They include *programming language* development tools.

❑ *Special-purpose* applications software. These are programs designed for a single purpose, such as stock control, invoicing, accounts or a game.

❑ *General-purpose* applications software. These are packages which can be used for many different applications. For example, a database package could be used to hold details about holidays, food, people or dogs. The packages are 'content free' and need tailoring to each particular purpose. They are often called *generic* software.

The rest of this chapter examines all these topics in more detail. The first major section deals with systems software and the second with applications software.

Systems software

Operating system

An operating system manages and communicates with the resources of a computer system, as illustrated in Figure 20.2. You should recognise these resources as the hardware components that form a computer system (see Chapter).

❑ *central processing unit (CPU)*. The operating system controls the CPU in its different tasks, which include, for example:

   ○ fetching program instructions and data from RAM;

   ○ starting a data transfer from an input device;

   ○ handling separate user requests for data, perhaps from the same file, in a *multi-user* system;

   ○ sharing the CPU's time between several tasks in RAM at the same time, a process known as *multi-tasking*.

Figure 20.2. *Purpose of the operating system*

❑ *Memory* or *RAM*. Programs (sometimes several) have to be accommodated in RAM, together with the data they are processing. The operating system:

O loads programs (or part programs) into memory as requested;

O unloads programs (or part programs) no longer required;

O moves programs around in memory to make best use of the space.

❑ *Input/output devices*. The operating system requests the use of devices as required and checks for conflict, for example, when two user programs try to print at the same time.

❑ *Backing storage*. Programs and data files are held on backing storage and loaded into RAM as needed. The operating system:

O manages the storage space;

O supervises transfers between RAM and backing storage.

Types of operating system

Computer systems vary in size, power and the number and variety of peripherals which can be attached. The biggest computer systems are called supercomputers. Coming down the scale, there are mainframe, mini and microcomputer systems. Because the resources for each are so different and the applications for which they are used also vary widely, there is a need for different kinds of operating system. So, for example, there are:

❑ simple operating systems like MS-DOS, designed for running one program at a time for a single user.

❑ multi-tasking operating systems, which allow a user to have several programs loaded at one time. Figure 20.3 illustrates a user operating several tasks through the Windows operating system.

Single user
Multiple tasks

Figure 20.3. *A user multi-tasking with the Windows operating system*

❑ network operating systems, such as Windows NT and Novell Netware, designed to control networked computer systems. Figure 20.4 shows several computers linked to a network using the Novell Netware operating system.

Figure 20.4. *Network controlled by a network operating system*

☐   A network operating system has the following features:

○ Facilities to control users' access to *shared resources*, including programs and data held on the network. They use login procedures to identify the user and request a password.

○ A user's access to the network is limited by their *network rights* and these are controlled and checked by the operating system. For example, a clerk in the personnel department may be able to view staff salary figures, but is not given access to the program which allows them to be changed.

Note from the figure that the individual workstations run their own 'local' operating system. The network operating system is designed to be able to communicate with workstations running under different *platforms*. So, for example, PCs and Macintosh workstations may be attached to the same network. There are many other operating systems, to suit every kind of use, including, for example, air traffic control, manufacturing processes and large-scale business systems such as those used by banks.

Operating system interfaces

An operating system is the interface for communication between the computer and its users and operators. The method or 'language' used for this communication can be:

☐   command driven. Commands are typed at a system prompt, such as that for the old MS-DOS operating system (often referred to as the C:\> prompt). This is a *command line interface* (CLI).

☐   graphical. A *graphical user interface* (GUI) provides a more user-friendly method of communication and avoids the need to learn complicated command sequences.

Command line interface (CLI)

Figure 20.5 shows the CLI for the MS-DOS operating system. With this type of interface, the user must enter commands. These commands may instruct the operating system to carry out some action, or provide the user with some information. At the bottom of the figure, there is a lengthy command sequence to copy a file from one directory to another. It is followed by the message "1 file(s) copied", which confirms that the command has been executed successfully.

Figure 20.5. *Command line interface in MS-DOS*

The main advantage of the CLI is that the short commands, though not particularly user-friendly, are ideal for rapid, expert use.

The main disadvantages of the CLI are:

❑   it is unsuitable for novice users;

❑   the commands must be learned and remembered;

❑   it can only be used with the keyboard.

Graphical user interface (GUI)

Figure 20.6 on the next page shows the graphical user interface (GUI) for the Windows operating system and illustrates the following features:

❑   a *pointer* on screen, moved by a pointing device, typically a *mouse*. The figure shows the pointer selecting a menu option.

❑   *icons* (small pictures) representing, amongst other things, programs, which can be run by pointing and clicking the mouse. The recycle bin icon is in the bottom right corner of the figure.

❑   *windows*. Applications run in their own self-contained areas called *windows*. There are three in the figure, one for Explorer, the Internet browser, another for CorelDRAW, a graphic design program and a third for Corel Ventura, a desktop publishing program. These are all examples of *applications software*.

❑   *pull-down menus* which provide access to standard functions. The figure shows such a menu in the Corel Ventura window.

Benefits of a GUI

Most users are not really interested in the technical details of a computer's operation and simply want to use it. However, to do so effectively, a user must learn routine maintenance tasks, such as creating folders, copying files and formatting disks as well as the use of the particular applications they need. A GUI is designed to make these tasks easier as follows.

Figure 20.6. *Graphical user interface (GUI) for Windows operating system*

❏   Methods of doing things are more *intuitive*. This means that a user can often anticipate what certain actions with the mouse will do. For example, selecting a file with a mouse pointer and dragging it to an *icon* (small picture) of a dustbin has the effect of deleting the selected file.

❏   Applications running under a GUI have common features, so, for example, it is easier to transfer skills learned using a word processor to those needed for a spreadsheet. The Figure 20.7 shows that two entirely different packages use several of the same menus and command buttons. As the figure also shows, common package requirements, such as creating new, opening existing and saving files, whether they relate to a spreadsheet from Microsoft or a publishing package from Corel, use the same buttons. Obviously, individual packages have extra buttons and menus which relate to their particular facilities.

Figure 20.7. *Common menus and buttons in two packages running under Windows*

Utilities

These are programs, usually included with the operating system, which do routine maintenance tasks on the computer system. The Windows Explorer, Disk Defragmenter, DriveSpace and ScanDisk utilities, provided by the Windows 9x operating system are described in this section.

Windows Explorer

Figure 20.8 shows the Windows Explorer view of a particular computer system.

Figure 20.8. *Using Windows Explorer to view files in a particular directory (or folder)*

This Windows 9x utility allows the user to see the disk file systems attached to the computer and carry out various maintenance tasks on the files stored there. To understand the purposes of this utility, you need to know some basic principles about a Windows 9x disk file system.

☐ Each physical disk drive in the system is identified by a letter. Usually, the main hard drive is C: and the floppy drive is A:. Other drives, such as the CD-ROM take other letters, D:, E: and so on. Note that a single physical drive may be partitioned into two or more drives, each with a different letter. Also, additional, compressed drives (see DriveSpace) can be created from a physical drive, each additional compressed drive being given a different letter. Note that the example system has six drive letters:

    O A: (floppy drive);

    O C: (first *partition* of the main hard drive);

    O D: (a 100MB Zip drive);

○ E: (second partition of the main hard drive);

○ F: (CD-ROM drive);

○ H: (a compressed drive - see DriveSpace, later).

❑ Each drive letter can be treated as a separate disk and storage area. For example, the C: drive contains the operating system and usually the main applications programs. In the example system, the E: partition drive contains other applications programs and the H: drive all the main data files. The A: and D: drives use removable disks and are used for taking security backups of important files.

❑ Each drive letter holds a hierarchical (different levels) directory or folder structure. Some folders are created for the operating system and applications programs. A user can create additional folders to organise the data files. Figure 20.8 shows Windows Explorer being used to view the various levels on the H: drive, to access files held in the COBOL directory. Clicking on a + next to a folder reveals any sub-folders, whilst clicking on a − hides its sub-folders and clicking on a folder or sub-folder reveals its contents. In the figure, the COBOL folder is opened to show the files it holds.

❑ Files or folders can be selected and deleted, or copied or moved to other folders or drive letters. Usually, these operations use the mouse to drag the selection to the required destination.

Disk Defragmenter

This utility is extremely important for the efficient operation of the main hard drive(s) in a computer system. To understand its purpose, you need to be familiar with a number of facts relating to disk storage. Disk space is allocated in *clusters*, which are units of disk storage. For example, the cluster size may be 16 kilobytes (KB). When a file is stored on disk it takes up as many clusters as it needs. For example, if a document is of size 525 KB, it will need $525 \div 16 = 33$ clusters (to the nearest whole cluster).

When a file is first stored on disk it is given, if possible, a *contiguous* (no gaps between) chain of clusters. Each time it is altered and made larger, it may not fit in its original place, so the extra has to be placed somewhere else. This *fragmentation* of files leads to slower disk performance, because the read/write heads may have to go to several different parts of the disk to retrieve a single file. Such a fragmented file is illustrated in Figure 20.9. Note the following points in the figure:

The figure represents a small area of disk space, with each square as a single cluster. The white squares are empty clusters. The 24 light grey squares are the clusters occupied by a particular File A. The clusters numbered 1 to 9 shows where the original version of File A

Figure 20.9. *Area of disk clusters, showing File A fragmented*

is stored. Numbers 10 to 24 are clusters filled as File A has been altered and made larger. The dark grey clusters are filled by other files. Ideally, File A would be in a contiguous (without gaps) set of clusters, but each time it has been updated and made larger, the extra clusters have been taken from separate areas of the disk. The white clusters, although empty now, may not have been at the times File A was updated.

The defragmentation utility rearranges the disk space so that each file is held in a contiguous set of clusters. The empty space is also organised into a contiguous block of clusters. Figure 20.10 shows how the disk space may appear after defragmentation is complete.

Figure 20.10. *Disk space after defragmentation*

Figure 20.11 shows the Windows 9x utility, Disk Defragmenter in progress, together with a legend explaining the different states of clusters on the disk. As the legend shows, the utility also identifies any damaged areas of the disk.

Figure 20.11. *Disk Defragmenter in progress*

DriveSpace

This utility is used to increase the amount of disk space, by compressing some of the existing physical space. So, for example, using a compression ratio of 2:1, a disk can be made to hold twice as much data. An example will help to explain what happens. Figure 20.12 shows the properties of Drive E:, a physical hard drive. The figure shows that it is a 'physical', uncompressed drive with a capacity of 1.16GB and around 379MB of unused space. Figure 20.13, shows the properties for a compressed drive H: with a capacity of 506 MB, of which around 170MB is unused. The compression ratio indicates that data stored on drive H: is compressed between 2 and 3 times.

Figure 20.13 also shows that physical drive E: is the *host*. This means that H: is not a new drive, simply a compressed storage area on drive E:. As a result the physical space on the host drive E:

is reduced because it is storing the compressed drive H:. The next figure illustrates how extra space has been created (Figure 20.14).

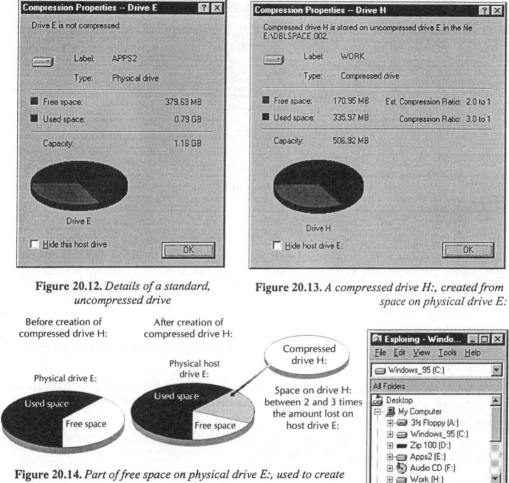

Figure 20.12. *Details of a standard, uncompressed drive*

Figure 20.13. *A compressed drive H:, created from space on physical drive E:*

Figure 20.14. *Part of free space on physical drive E:, used to create compressed drive H:*

Figure 20.15. *Explorer with drives, including compressed drive H:*

The amount of space gained with drive H: is, in this example, 2 to 3 times the amount of space lost to the compressed drive on drive E:. Figure 20.15 of Windows Explorer shows that a compressed drive appears to the user as just another drive.

ScanDisk

This utility detects and repairs disk recording errors. Some locations on disk may not record data properly and if they are not found and repaired, data may be stored in those locations and be corrupted or lost. ScanDisk also finds 'lost' files. When a program 'crashes', or more seriously, when the operating system crashes, corrupted files, or bits of files, may be left on disk. These lost files take up valuable disk space and often contain meaningless information or 'garbage'. The ScanDisk dialogue box is shown in Figure 20.16. The figure shows the following options:

❑ The standard check finds files and folders for errors, including 'lost' files. It is a good idea to run this check whenever the operating system crashes.

❑ The thorough check carries out the standard check, plus a surface scan for possible disk recording errors. This check should be carried out regularly to find and fix disk recording problems before vital data is lost.

Figure 20.16. *ScanDisk with options for file and folder check and surface scan*

BIOS

A computer system's BIOS (Basic Input/Output System) holds details of what hardware is installed and settings for individual components. The settings are held in CMOS RAM. This is a special type of RAM, which can retains its contents with only a tiny amount of battery power - the battery is attached to the motherboard and recharged whenever the machine is switched on. The BIOS settings are used to control the *system start-up* and carry out diagnostic checks on the hardware.

System start-up

When a computer system is 'powered on' the BIOS starts the Power-On Self-Test (POST) routine. The POST routine is in two stages:

1. The *motherboard* (also known as the *system board*) and its components (processor, RAM etc.) are checked for their normal operation. The RAM test is visible on screen while it is being carried out.

2. The hardware actually installed is checked to see that it matches with the system's BIOS (Basic Input/Output System) settings.

If an error is identified, the system reports it, either with a 'beep' or an error message on screen. The Power-On Self-Test (POST) sequence checks the hardware to see that the major components, including RAM, are present and working properly.

BIOS Setup utility

The BIOS Setup utility is held in ROM so that it is not lost when the machine is switched off. The program is used to enter details of the computer system's hardware, that is, the BIOS settings. When a computer is powered on and before the operating system starts to load, the operator has the opportunity to access the BIOS Setup utility, normally by pressing the <delete> key. Because settings entered through this program are then stored in CMOS RAM, the program menu includes options for the Standard CMOS setup and the BIOS Features (or Advanced CMOS) setup.

Standard CMOS setup

Standard CMOS Setup is used to record details of the basic hardware in the computer system.

The settings are recorded when the motherboard is installed, normally by the manufacturer. This is usually the first BIOS Setup menu option. An example of a Standard CMOS Setup screen is shown in Figure 20.17.

Figure 20.17. *Example Standard CMOS Setup*

The exact settings will vary according to the computer hardware, but note the following details labelled in the figure.

❑ The Primary Master is the main hard disk drive inside the system unit and in this example, it has a capacity of 2·5 GB. The Primary Slave, in this example, is a 100MB Zip drive, which uses removable disk cartridges. There is only one floppy disk drive, designed for 1·44 MB floppy disks.

❑ The 'Halt on' setting specifies that any hardware error will cause the powering up sequence to stop, until the error is corrected. The only other options are to ignore keyboard and/or floppy disk errors. Failure of RAM or the hard disk drive, for example, would always halt the system.

❑ The RAM total is 128 MB.

❑ The screen type is EGA or VGA. These are screen resolution standards. VGA is a minimum 800 × 600 resolution.

The Standard CMOS Settings option would only need to be used if:

(a) the CMOS contents are corrupted or lost, perhaps through battery failure (as can happen if a machine is switched off for a long period). It is important that the settings are written down, so that if the contents are lost or corrupted, they can be re-entered. Without the correct settings, the machine may not work properly or at all;

or

(b) the system configuration is altered, perhaps through replacement of the hard disk or installation of a new motherboard.

BIOS Features setup

This option is used to 'fine tune' the hardware configuration, to improve performance and to set certain user preferences. Figure 20.18 shows an example BIOS Features screen.

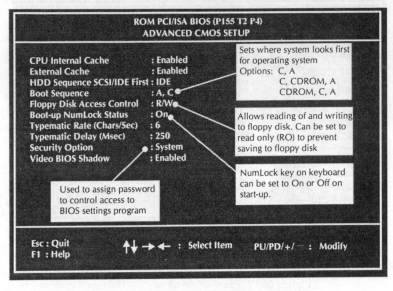

Figure 20.18. *Example BIOS Features setup*

The Figure is labelled with the following four features:

1.   Boot sequence. Following a successful Power-On Self-Test (POST) routine, the BIOS loads the operating system, normally from the hard drive. The boot sequence dictates the order in which the BIOS checks the various disk drives to find the operating system. Setting the A: (floppy) drive as the first to be checked, allows for an emergency 'boot' if the operating system will not load from the hard drive. Windows 9x provides an option to create such a Startup Disk (see Figure 20.19). To carry out the emergency boot, the Startup disk is placed in the floppy drive before the machine is powered up. As soon as the BIOS finds the Startup disk boots the system from there, rather than trying to load the operating system from the hard drive. For this reason, an error message is displayed if a 'non-system' disk (one not containing special start-up files) is left in the floppy drive during start-up.

2.   Floppy disk access control. The default setting is R/W (read/write), but to prevent users copying files from the hard drive onto floppy disk, it may be set to RO (read only). This may be done for security reasons.

Figure 20.19. *Option to create Windows 95 Startup disk*

3. Boot-up NumLock status. Setting the NumLock key to 'On' ensures that it is automatically on when the system is powered up. The keys on the numeric keypad then operate as such. If set to 'Off' the numeric keys have an alternate use as navigational keys (cursor left, right, page up and so on). Whatever the boot setting, the user can switch the NumLock key on or off as necessary.

4. Security option. As the earlier warning point out, altering BIOS settings has to be carried out with great care and only by someone who knows what they are doing and has the authority to do it. This option allows a password to be set. If a user tries to access the BIOS Setup program during startup, he or she will be asked for the password.

Plug and Play BIOS

Plug and Play operating systems use a BIOS which is automatically updated when a new device is added. On a Windows 9x machine, the BIOS details then appear in the System Properties window, as shown in Figure 20.20.

The Device Manager tab lists all the categories of device attached to the computer system. In the figure, three of the items are expanded, to show details of the actual attached device:

Figure 20.20. *Example BIOS details in a Windows 9x System Properties window*

☐ The CD-ROM is identified as a TEAC CD-58E;

☐ The display adapter, or graphics card, is a Matrox Millennium;

☐ The monitor is identified as Plug and Play (VESA DDC). 'VESA' indicates that it meets the Video Electronics Standards Association requirements for monitors.

Once a new device, such as a disk drive, or extra RAM, has been connected, the BIOS detects it during the next startup. If the device is not Plug and Play compatible, the installation settings have to be made through the BIOS setup utility.

Development tools

This is a group term for software which is used to develop applications and systems software. Examples of development tools are *programming languages* and *database packages*. To understand the purpose of development tools generally, you need to be familiar with the idea of a *computer program*.

Computer programs

The words *software* and *program* are often used to describe the same thing, but what exactly is meant by these two terms? To be usable by a computer, a program has to be in *machine code*. Machine code is *binary code*, a series of 1's and 0's, represented electrically inside the computer. A computer program consists of a series of machine code instructions which make the computer perform the required tasks.

The program is stored in memory. It is fetched, decoded and executed, one instruction at a time, by the CPU (processor) until a Halt instruction is reached. The CPU has its own *instruction set*, which it uses to understand the instructions in a computer program. The set includes instructions for:

❑ *Arithmetic operations*, such as add, subtract, divide and multiply and logical operations, such as AND, OR, NOT.

❑ *Data transfer*, to enable data to be moved between the various devices in the computer system, including input, storage and output devices.

❑ *Transfer of control*, which allows the computer to skip one or more instructions or repeat previous instructions.

The storage of a computer program in memory and its execution by the CPU are illustrated in Figure 20.21.

Figure 20.21. *A computer program in memory being executed by the CPU*

Writing computer programs

Although the computer needs programs to be in the binary codes it understands (according to its instruction set), it is not practical for programmers to write the same codes. Instead, programmers use *programming languages* and other development tools to write programs in a form that they understand; this is known as *source code*. The computer is then given the job of translating the source code into the machine's own code, known as the *object code*.

The next section deals with the various software development tools used by programmers.

Programming languages

C++, Visual C, Visual BASIC, Pascal, Java, Delphi and COBOL are all examples of programming languages. All programming languages can be used to produce software, although some languages are suited to particular applications. For example, COBOL is mainly for business data processing applications, while Java is particularly suited to Internet applications. Pascal is used for commercial applications, but is particularly popular in education for teaching programming skills. Like English and other languages, a programming language has a *vocabulary*. These are keywords which form the language. Each keyword has a particular meaning. In Pascal, for example, the keywords begin and end are used to mark the beginning and end of a program, or separate groups of instructions within it. The words if and then are used in the writing of *conditional* statements. For example, the statement

```
if age < 16 then writeln('Junior Member');
```

will display the message in quotes if a the memory location labelled *age* contains a number less than 16.

There are also rules of grammar. These are rules on the formation of program instructions. The example statement above would fail the rules for Pascal grammar if it were written as

```
if age < 16 writeln('Junior Member');
```

The word then must be used as part of an if statement. A programming language's rules for spelling and grammar are known as its *syntax*.

Program development

Programming language software includes a number of components to assist the programmer, including:

- ❑ an *editor* to allow entry of the source code. Figure 20.22 illustrates this process;

- ❑ *debugging* utilities to help find and correct errors in syntax;

- ❑ a *translator* to convert the source code into the object machine code. There are two main types of translator:

Use editor to enter source code

Source code stored on disk

Figure 20.22. *Editor used for entry and storage of program source code*

○ *compiler*. This is the most common and produces a separate machine code program which the computer can use without further use of the translator.

○ *interpreter*. This type does not produce an independent machine code program. The program must be translated each time it is run. Many versions of BASIC use an interpreter.

A translator only checks the syntax of a program, not its *logic*. Before it can be used a program must be thoroughly tested to check that it performs exactly as required.

Figure 20.23 illustrates the translation process with a compiler.

Compiler

Display syntax errors

Source code

compiler

Object code (if no syntax errors)

Run compiler to translate to machine's object code

Figure 20.23. *Translating the source code to the machine's object code*

Applications software

This category of software includes all the purposes for which organisations and individuals use computers.

Specific applications packages

The needs of accounts and other special applications may be met by *specific* applications package, such as Sage Accounts and Quickbooks. Specific means that each one can only be used for a certain purpose and has no other use. Other applications in this category include, for example, payroll and stock control.

Some applications software is *tailor-made*, that is, developed specifically for a particular organisation. Off-the-shelf packages, such as QuickBooks are cheaper but they cannot always meet the exact needs of an organisation.

General-purpose software packages

Word 97 and Excel 97 are examples of *general-purpose* applications packages. General-purpose means that they can be used for a range of different purposes. Word 97 is a word processor and could be used to produce any text and graphics documents, for example, letters and reports or magazines and books with colour graphics. Excel 97 is a spreadsheet package and can be used for any number-based work, such as a sales forecast or a statistical analysis of the health of a population. It can also produce graphs or charts, to present the information in different ways. Other examples include drawing and paint packages, such as CorelDRAW and PhotoPaint and desktop publishing (DTP) packages, such as Corel Ventura.

There are many different such packages, among the most important being: word processors; spreadsheets; databases; graphics, including desktop publishing (DTP), business graphics, graphic design and computer-aided drawing (CAD).

Exercises

1. What is the function of the following types of software?
   (i) Operating system
   (ii) Utilities
   (iii) BIOS
   (iv) Development tools
   (v) Applications
2. Name three operating systems commonly used on PCs.
3. What is an operating system interface?
4. What are the main features of a GUI?
5. Name and briefly describe the purpose of four types of utility software used by Windows 95/98.
6. What is the purpose of the CMOS settings? Typically, what information is stored by the CMOS? What BIOS settings are accessible via the CMOS?
7. Name 4 programming languages.
8. Give examples of special-purpose and general-purpose applications programs.

Assignments

3.1. Software installation
Task 1

Install an applications package, from floppy disk or CD-ROM, onto the hard disk of a stand-alone computer. Record the details of your experience as you go. Although your experience will vary with different packages, you should record the following.

(a) Package details, including the name and type.

(b) Operating system required.

(c) Hardware requirements for the package. The documentation should detail minimum and recommended requirements for the: amount of disk space; type of processor; type of display;

(d) How the target computer system met the requirements in (a) and (c).

(e) Initial instructions for running the 'install' or 'set-up' program.

(f) The name of the directory into which the program was installed. This is most likely to be the one suggested by the install program, but you could choose to install the package in a different directory.

(g) If options are given, which package configuration you chose. Typical alternatives are 'minimum', 'full' or 'custom' install. Record the amount of disk space taken by the chosen configuration.

(h) The action taken once installation was completed.

It is likely that the screen display driver is already installed. If so, check the resolution and colour settings. Record the settings and how you found them.

Task 2

Install the driver program for the system printer. Record the steps you followed and add them to the installation log. Re-save the log and print it.

3.2 Software applications and hardware requirements
Task 1

For this task you are to describe purposes of various kinds of application software and give examples of their uses. First, use appropriate software to create Table 1, which lists various types of application software. Then complete the 'Purpose and Typical Applications' column to demonstrate that you are familiar with their purposes. Each entry in the column should include:

(a) a brief statement of the software's general purpose;

(b) one or more examples of typical applications.

To complete this task use a software catalogue or computer magazine to find the names of two or three commercial package examples, for each software type in the Table 1. Enter the names into the table, save and print it.

Application software type	Purpose and typical applications	Commercial examples
Database		
Word processor		
Spreadsheet		
Graphic design		
2D Computer-aided drawing		
Desktop publishing		
3-D Modelling		
Presentation		

Table 1

Task 2

This task requires you to select hardware for different types of application software. You need to refer to two tables, Table 1, which you completed in Task 1 and Table 2.

Table 2 lists a range of hardware devices For each item in the table provide specification figures for commercial devices you find in hardware catalogues, computer magazines or on the Internet. For example, a hard drive has a *storage capacity*, an *average access time* and *data transfer rate*.

CPU	RAM
Hard disk drive	CD-ROM drive
Mouse	DVD-drive
Laser printer	Graphics card
Monitor	Backup device
Plotter	Scanner

Table 2

For **each** application in Table 1, select one or more of the hardware entries from Table 2. You should only select entries which are **of particular importance** to the application.

Using the information from these two tables, prepare a **User Guide** on the selection of suitable hardware for particular types of application software. The Guide should be ordered in the same sequence as the application software types in Table 1.

For each type of application software, the User Guide should:

(a) describe the purpose of each type of application software;

(b) describe the hardware devices required for each type of application software, emphasising those which are of particular importance.

(c) briefly explain why the selected hardware is needed, for each application;

(d) quote some actual quality/performance figures for recent examples of the hardware devices.

3.3. Matching application requirements

In this assignment you identify system requirements from a case study. Then, you select appropriate hardware and software which meets those requirements. Before starting this assignment, read the three case studies which follow.

Case study: ComDesign

ComDesign is a graphic design company. Their work requires the use of computers to produce graphics for book covers, book illustrations, CD sleeves, brochures, posters and other similar applications. They also design and create multimedia productions and web sites. Customers provide materials for ComDesign to use in many different formats, including picture and text files on disk, CD-ROMs and paper. Consequently their computer systems must be flexible and capable of storing handling very large multimedia files. The web design work is expanding so rapidly that they are using Internet facilities continuously for most of each working day.

Case study: Condew Properties

Condew Properties is a local estate agency. The agency sells houses on behalf of *vendors* to *buyers* who come to the agency looking for houses to buy. Records need to be kept of every house for sale, including its address, number of rooms, size of gardens, sale price and so on. When a buyer makes an offer for a house, this also needs to be recorded. Usually, there are several buyers after the same house, so all their details and the prices they have offered also need to be recorded. At any one time there may be hundreds of houses for sale and even more buyers who have put in offers for them. Condew Properties need a system which will store all this information securely and allow details of individual houses and offers to be retrieved quickly. They also need to produce posters with descriptions of the houses for sale. Pictures of the houses are not held on computer, and prints are simply stuck on the posters manually. The posters are put in the agency window to help advertise the properties. Some buyers may spend months looking for the right house and are kept informed of properties as they become available. This is done by keeping their details on a mailing list. The firm has also been considering the possibility of advertising their properties on-line to allow potential customers with Internet access to be able to view property details from their homes.

Case study: Top Flight Accountancy Services

Top flight is run by David Micawber who is a qualified accountant. The firm offers a full range of accountancy services, including the auditing of business accounts and handling of personal and business tax returns to be sent to the Inland Revenue. The law requires that businesses of a certain size must have their annual accounts checked or audited. This must be done by a professional accountant before the accounts are sent to the Inland Revenue to calculate the tax due from the business. The final accounts (a *trading and profit and loss account* and a *balance sheet*) of any particular business are similar from year to year. Although the amounts vary, the layout and the headings tend not to change. This means that David could hold the appropriate layout and headings for each client's final accounts on computer and then fill in the figures to automatically check them. Top Flight is a small firm and only has about 150 regular clients. The volume of printing is fairly low, but the quality should be good enough to give a professional image to David's clients.

Tasks

Write a report that identifies the *system requirements* for each of the three case studies - ComDesign, Condew Properties or Top Flight Accountancy Services.

The report should answer the following questions.

(a) What are the main uses of the computer system?

(b) What application software would be required? There may be more than one type of software that could be used for a particular purpose, but state which one you think would be the most suitable and why.

(c) What computer hardware would be needed? Give details of keyboard; mouse; monitor type and size; processor type and speed; RAM capacity; hard drive capacity and average access time; printer type, resolution and speed; number and types of port. Justify your choice of hardware.

3.4. PC connection

Task 1

Using the checklist, demonstrate the connection of stand alone computer system components.

Task 2

Produce a short report on the procedures carried out in Task 1, identifying any difficulties experienced.

1. Power cable to system unit.
2. Keyboard to system unit.
3. Mouse to system unit.
4. Display to system unit.
5. Power cable to display
6. Printer to port in system unit
7. Power cable to printer.
8. Connect power supply and power up.

3.4. PC hardware assembly and removal

In this assignment you are required to demonstrate your ability to install and remove PC hardware components located in the system case. For each of the components listed below you will need to demonstrate that you can remove it and replace it while observing appropriate safety precautions.

Each component must be safely removed and then replaced separately, and the system tested for correct operation each time. For example, when you remove and replace a particular component, you must make sure that the computer is switched off and that the power cable is disconnected and unplugged from the case before removing the case cover. You must then perform the particular task and replace the cover. Then you can reconnect external cables and switch the computer on in order to make sure that the computer functions correctly. You will need to keep a log of any problems encountered, the causes of the problems and how you dealt with them, and how you tested the computer for correct operation in each case.

Tasks

Remove and replace the following system components:

> The CPU
> A memory module (eg SIMM or DIMM)
> An expansion card
> A hard drive
> The floppy drive
> The CD-ROM drive

Unit 4

Introduction to software development

Chapters

- 21. Program design
- 22. Program testing, debugging and documenting
- 23. Pascal programming

Unit 4 Outcomes and assessment criteria

Outcomes	Assessment criteria To achieve each outcome a student must demonstrate the ability to:
1. Apply **simple analysis and design** techniques to the software development process.	• produce an analysis report for a given specification stating the requirements and data needs for 'what' the system is to do • design a solution for a given set of requirements using appropriate documentation tools for both the text data and graphical representations.
2. Develop basic high-level code using an appropriate **procedural programming language**.	• select appropriate variable types and use simple input/output operators for linear program structures • identify and use appropriate selection methods for single and nested program applications • identify and use appropriate interaction methods for various loop examples ensuring that suitable exit criteria is maintained at all times • produce programs to desired programming standards including layout, commenting and a 'user friendly' approach.
3. Produce appropriate **documentation** for a given program application.	• produce user documentation for a completed programming application • develop technical documentation for a prescribed program application.
4. Use suitable **testing methods** to ascertain the correctness of a working piece of code.	• use an appropriate tool to analyse a piece of code to ascertain its semantic correctness • produce suitable test data for a working program application.

Chapter 21
Program design

The single most important requirement of a computer program is that it runs without error at all times, since a program that either produces erroneous results or hangs up under certain circumstances is almost useless. Because of this stringent requirement, computer program design and production is a very skilled activity demanding meticulous attention to detail. It is not sufficient to address only the relatively easy problem of designing and implementing a program which produces the correct output when provided with ideal data. Rather, the program must be able to cope with non-ideal data such as that provided by a user who may be unfamiliar with its operation or data input requirements. Such a user might supply inappropriate input by, for example, entering alphabetic instead of numeric characters, and even experienced operators of the program might accidentally enter invalid data on occasions.

In fact there are many ways that a program could be presented with exceptional - that is, invalid or unreasonable - data and it is the responsibility of the program designer to allow for such. Consequently, the program design stage of program production, in which possible problems - and their solutions - are identified, is of vital importance. As a result, there are now a number of established program design methodologies to aid the program designer to produce well-crafted, error-free programs. The design method described here is a form of *structured programming* using *top-down, stepwise refinement*.

Two forms of notation that we will use to express solutions to design problems are *pseudocode* and *structure charts*; these are called *program design languages* (PDLs). Structure charts provide a graphical representation of a program, allowing its logical structure to be easily appreciated, whereas pseudocode, having a form similar to program instructions, aids program writing and testing.

Problem solving

Whether a problem is computer-related or otherwise, the strategy for solving it has essentially the same three main stages:(1) *understand the problem*, (2) *devise a solution*, and (3) *test the solution*. In addition, for program design tasks there is a further stage which is to (4) *document the solution*.

1. Understand the problem

This first stage requires a *thorough* understanding of the problem being addressed so that you can identify what assumptions can be made and what can't in order to test your solution in the correct context. Some problems are apparently straightforward but, when analysed with a view to producing a program design, become much more complex. As an example, consider the following outline program specification:

Write a program to read in a date and convert it to the number of days from the start of the calendar year.

It sounds simple enough until you start to consider what the problem implies. For example, what format is to be used for the date? - 15th January, 1995 or 15 Jan 95, or 15/1/95, or 15-01-95 or 150195, or 950115, and so on. Is a particular format to be adopted and incorrectly formatted dates to be rejected, or is the program to attempt to interpret different formats? Are leap years to be considered when calculating the day number? Do you assume that the date is for the current year or can the date be for a different year? You may be able to think of more problems that could arise.

2. Design a solution

The method adopted here to design the solution involves tackling the problem in a number of steps. An outline program is designed first, showing the main modules of the program, and the order in which they are to be executed. Each main module is then reduced to a number of smaller, simpler, and more manageable components, and this process of refinement continues until the program designer judges that there is sufficient detail in the design for a programmer to be able to convert the design directly into a programming language. The process of reducing components into sequences of smaller components in stages is often termed *stepwise refinement*. Top-down, stepwise refinement encourages program design to be tackled methodically in a number of stages of increasing detail. Although structure charts and pseudocode are both suitable program design languages, we recommend that you adopt our approach of first using structure charts to produce your program designs in outline form and then translating them into detailed pseudocode prior to testing and subsequent conversion to program code.

An example of a simple structure chart and the equivalent pseudocode for the addition of two real numbers are shown in Figure 21.1. (Note that a *real* number is a number with a fractional part such as 23·456, whereas an *integer* is a whole number such as 32). Answer, a and b are called variables which serve a similar function to the symbols used in algebra - they are gen-

Structure chart   Pseudocode
                               1. read a, b
                               2. Answer = a+b
                               3. write Answer

Figure 21.1. *Simple program design for addition of two real numbers*

eral, symbolic representations of data that is to be processed. Thus, the pseudocode statement 1 in Figure 21.1 means 'read two values from the input device (such as a keyboard) and call them a and b respectively'. Statement 2 adds the two values and calls the result Answer. Statement 3 displays Answer on the output device (such as a display screen). By using variables rather than actual numbers, this sequence of statements defines how a computer is to deal with the addition of *any* two numbers. In addition to the problem solution itself, another part of the design is a

data table which defines the purpose and type of the variables used in the solution. The data table (Table 21.1) would identify whether these variables were integers or real numbers and their purpose.

name	description	type
Answer	Holds the sum of the two numbers	real variable
a	First number entered	real variable
b	Second number entered	real variable

Table 21.1

3. Test the solution

This involves using test data to manually step through the solution statements so that the computed output can be compared with the expected output. For instance, the date example mentioned earlier should give an answer of 70 for 10th March 2000, assuming that the days are calculated from 1st January, 2000. This value would be compared with that provided by the design - if the answer was different then the apparent design fault would need to be investigated and corrected before continuing with further testing. The design of test data is considered in Chapter 29.

4. Document the solution

The documentation contains the following: (i) the problem statement; (ii) the top-level program design; (iii) the final detailed program design; (iv) the data table. These are produced during the course of the first three stages of program design. The examples in later sections show the form of this documentation.

Structured programming

Most current program design methodologies are based on *structured programming* concepts. Structured programming is generally associated with certain basic principles:

1. **Restricted use of control structures**. These are limited to three types: *sequence* consisting of instructions which are performed one after the other in the order that they appear in the program; *selection* of one set of instructions from several possible sets of instructions so that the program is able to deal with a number of different circumstances; *repetition*, or *iteration*, of a set of instructions using some kind of program loop. Restricting design to using only these three constructs does not necessarily produce error-free code, but it does help to produce a program which is clear and relatively easy to test.

2. **Modularity**. This is the subdivision of a program into easily identifiable and manageable segments, or *modules*. Each module should require no more than about one page of code. A module may be realised in the final program as one or more small subprograms. Using modules helps to clarify the logical structure of a program for human readers and, by incorporating subprograms, aids its construction.

3. **Top-down, stepwise refinement**. This program design method was described in the earlier section *Problem Solving*.

4. **Clear program format**. This is concerned with the layout of the program instructions. Each page of coding should contain clearly identifiable control structures and blocks of code. One main method of achieving this clarity of structure is by the consistent use of indentation showing the limits of loops, selections and blocks of instructions. Formatting standards apply both to pseudocode and actual program code.

5. **Comments**. The thorough use of comments within the pseudocode design and the actual program in order to explain the purpose of each variable and each few lines of logically related code.

6. **Simplicity.** Where there is a choice between a simple solution to a problem and a slightly more efficient solution which perhaps uses less code, then the simple solution is to be preferred. Straightforward, simple code is easier to test, modify and understand than obscure, 'clever' code.

Basic control structures

As explained earlier, structured programs are constructed using the three control structures sequence, selection and iteration. In order to illustrate how each of these is expressed and used in program design, consider the following programming problem:

> *Read a set of ten positive and negative numbers entered from a keyboard and find the separate totals of the positive numbers and the negative numbers. Print the two totals.*

It is assumed that only valid real numbers such as $1 \cdot 2$, $-7 \cdot 3$, 25, -6 will be entered. The program can be considered to be a *sequence* of three simple modules:

1. **Initialise variables.** Two variables will be required: one for the total of the positive numbers and the other for the total of the negative numbers.

2. **Process the numbers.** This involves a loop to read numbers typed in from the keyboard until ten values have been entered. A count will be incremented every time a number is read in.

3. **Display the results.** This will involve writing out the two totals.

This top-level design is illustrated by the structure chart shown in Figure 21.2. The equivalent pseudocode for the top-level design is shown in Listing 21.1.

Figure 21.2 *Top level design as sequence of three modules*

Listing 21.1.

```
{Totals}
1    Initialise
2    Process numbers
3    Display results
```

The first refinement of the design results in the structure chart shown in Figure 21.3.

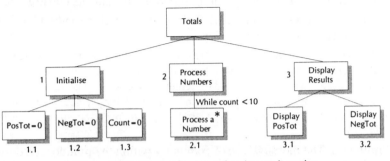

Figure 21.3. *First refinement showing an iteration*

The loop that reads the ten numbers, in other words the *iteration*, is indicated in the structure chart by an asterisk in the top right-hand corner of the component that is to be repeated. The condition governing the loop is written above this component; in this case the loop continues while the count variable has a value less than ten.

The equivalent pseudocode is shown in Listing 21.2.

Listing 21.2.

```
{Totals}
1.1   PosTot=0
1.2   NegTot=0
1.3   Count=0
2     while Count < 10
2.1       Process Number
2     endwhile
3.1   write PosTot
3.2   write NegTot
```

Each of the Listing 21.1 statements, numbered *1*, *2* and *3*, have all been refined in Listing 21.2; statement *1* (initialise) has been replaced by three detailed instruction, *1.1*, *1.2* and *1.3*. Similarly, statements *2* and *3* in Listing 21.1 have also been refined in Listing 21.2. (These statement level numbers reflect the depth of the structure diagram; a single statement level such as *1* indicates a top-level module, a statement number such as *1.2* indicate the second step of a refinement of level *1*. Number *2.3.1* indicates the first step of a refinement of statement *2.3*, and so on. A refinement of a statement is denoted by adding another level to the statement number.) Notice that the end of the loop is indicated by endwhile and the instruction inside the loop, Process Number, is indented. A loop thus translates into three pseudocode statements: one statement for the type of loop and the condition that governs it, another for the item that is to be repeated, and the third for the end of the loop. The final refinement is to expand Process Number, since this is the only statement that has not yet been fully defined: we need to show *how* a number is to be processed. The full design is shown in Figure 21.4.

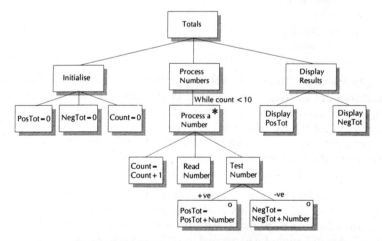

Figure 21.4. *Final refinement showing a selection*

The structure chart shows that the repeated component Process Number involves three steps: increment the count, read a number, and test the number to determine its sign. Positive numbers are to be accumulated in PosTot and negative numbers are to be accumulated in NegTot. The test involves a *selection*, each independent choice being indicated by a small circle in the top right-hand corner of the box. The condition governing each choice is written above the appropriate box as shown. This version of the design needs no further refinement since it is now in a suitable form for conversion to pseudocode and subsequently to a programming language such as COBOL or C.

The pseudocode in Listing 21.3 uses a `select` statement for the selection. If the condition following the first `select` is true, the statement or statements following are obeyed, otherwise the next `select` is considered. The `endselect` statement must be used to terminate the `select` statement.

Note that the number of alternative sets of statements is not limited to two - as many as necessary can be chained together in this way. If some action is necessary when none of the `select` statements is true then the `select when otherwise` statement can be included before `endselect`.

Listing 21.3.   Totalling positive and negative numbers

```
      {Totals}
1.1       PosTot = 0
1.2       NegTot = 0
1.3       Count = 0
2         while Count < 10
2.1          Count = Count + 1
2.2          Read Number
2.3          select
2.3.1a          when Number > 0
2.3.1b             PosTot = PosTot + Number
2.3.2a          when Number < 0
2.3.2b             NegTot = NegTot + Number
2.3          endselect
2         endwhile
3.1       write PosTot
3.2       write NegTot
```

The numbering follows the refinement levels of the structure charts. Thus if the first module is refined as a sequence of two statements, these statements are labelled *1.1* and *1.2*. In the case of an iteration, the start and end statements are given the same number. Thus in Listing 21.3, the `while` and `endwhile` both are labelled *2* showing that the iteration is the second top-level module in the program. The start and end statements of a selection are similarly labelled, but each option, which might involve a number of steps, has a small letter added to indicate that it is a step within the option. (For example, *2.3.1a* and *2.3.1b*).

In addition, in the examples that follow, where a structure chart step has been expanded in the pseudocode, each part of the expansion is also designated with a lower case letter. This frequently occurs when the structure chart shows that a value is to be entered by a user through a keyboard; the pseudocode might be expanded thus: *5.1* read Number becomes

```
5.1a   write 'Enter a number'
5.1b   read Number
```

This helps to prevent the structure chart from becoming too detailed and thus unclear. To complete the design, the three variables must be defined in a data table (see Table 21.2).

name	description	type
Count	Counts how many numbers have been entered	integer variable
PosTot	The sum of the positive value numbers	real variable
NegTot	The sum of the negative value numbers	real variable

Table. 21.2. *Definition of variables*

Summary

Figure 21.5 summarises the structure chart and pseudocode notation used for the three basic control structures, sequence, selection and iteration. Iteration is shown in a commonly used alternative form in which the condition is expressed as `repeat..until <condition>`. In this form the condition is tested at the end of the loop rather than at the beginning; this means that the statements within the loop will be repeated at least once. The `repeat..until` loop is illustrated in the worked examples.

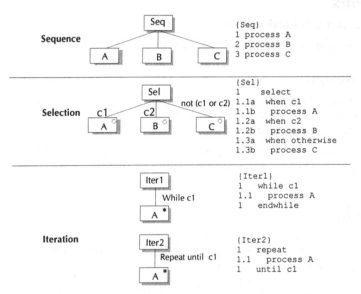

Figure 21.5. *The three basic control structures used in structured programming*

Worked examples

The worked examples presented in the next sections use a combination of structure charts and pseudocode to arrive at the final program design. Structure charts are used for the design refinements in order to express the overall logic in a clear, easily understandable form. The design is then presented in pseudocode, a form more suitable for testing and subsequent conversion to a programming language. At this stage some fine detail may also be added to the design.

The program design technique presented here, rather than being targeted at a particular programming language such as COBOL, is in a form suitable for conversion to any one of a number of quite different high-level languages.

Each of the following worked examples is in the format:

(i)   the problem statement;

(ii)   any assumptions that have been made;

(iii)   structure charts showing the top-level design and any further refinement stages;

(iv)   pseudocode for the final design;

(v)   the data table for the complete design;

(vi)   comments.

Reading and displaying information

Problem statement

Design a program which will accept from the keyboard a value representing a number of inches and display the equivalent number of centimetres.

Assumptions

1.   The input is a valid real number.

2.   There is no preferred format for the output.

Top-level design

The top-level design, shown on the right, now re-quires only minor refinements concerned with the precise form that the output is to take.

This can be accomplished conveniently in pseudocode without the need to draw another structure chart.

Pseudocode

```
{Convert inches to centimetres}
1a    write 'Enter the length in inches: ', <newline>
1b    read Inches
2     Centimetres = Inches*2.54
3a    write <newline>
3b    write 'A length of ', Inches, ' inches is equivalent to ',
                      centimetres, ' centimetres', <newline>
```

Data table

name	description	type
Inches	Value entered at the keyboard and converted to centimetres	real variable
Centimetres	The value to be output	real variable

Comments

<newline> indicates that the cursor is to move to the beginning of the next line.

Loops - Running totals

One very frequent programming task is to keep a running total when a number of values are read within an iteration (that is, *loop*). This next example illustrates the technique usually adopted to accumulate a total in a variable.

Problem statement

Design a program to read ten numbers from a keyboard and display their sum.

Assumptions

1. Exactly ten valid real numbers will be entered using a keyboard.

2. The sum of the numbers is to be accumulated as the numbers are entered, and thus there is no requirement to store them.

Top-level design

The top-level design is a simple sequence of three modules. The second module, `Process Numbers`, involves a loop which is to repeat a known number of times (namely 10). It can therefore be implemented using a count variable as shown in refinement #1.

Refinement #1

The variable `Total` is to be used to accumulate the sum of the ten numbers and therefore must start with an initial value of zero. `Count` is to start at 1 because it must be increased by one each time a new number is read. Each time through the loop a new number is read into the variable `Number` and then added to `Total` which accumulates the numbers. When `Count` reaches 10, the loop terminates.

Refinement #2

The statements required for processing a number and incrementing the loop control variable have been added; this represents the final structure chart form of the design.

Pseudocode

```
{Sum of 10 numbers}
1.1    Total = 0
1.2    Count = 1
2      while Count <= 10
2.1a     write <newline>, 'Enter
           number #', Count
```

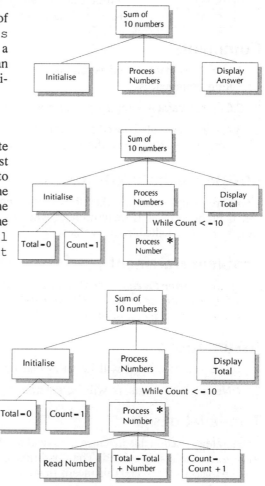

```
2.1b      read Number
2.2         Total = Total + Number
2.3         Count = Count + 1
2        endwhile
3        write <newline> , 'The sum of the 10 numbers is: ', Total
```

This pseudocode form of the final refinement is to make the program a little more user friendly by adding some text to prompt the user to enter a number - this is much better than presenting the user with a blank screen and expecting him/her to know exactly what to do. The final instruction adds some text to announce the answer.

Data table

name	description	type
Total	Accumulates the ten numbers	real variable
Number	Stores the latest number input	real variable
Count	The control variable for the loop	integer variable

Comments

1. Variables that are used as running totals and counts must always be initialised before a loop commences.

2. Control variables for loops are always of type `integer`.

3. A count variable is used to control the duration of a loop when the number of repetitions is known before the loop commences.

Loops - Rogue values

There are many occasions when the exact number of repetitions of a loop is not known in advance. Frequently loops are terminated when a special value is entered by the user. Such special values are often called 'rogue values'.

Problem statement

Design a program to read a set of numbers representing the cost of some purchased items. The end of the list is to be indicated by entering 0 for the cost. Display how many items were purchased and the total cost of the items.

Assumptions

1. The values entered will be valid real numbers

2. No negative numbers will be entered

Top-level design

The strategy used in this instance is to read a value before the loop represented by the module, `Process Items`, is started. The condition governing the continuation of the loop will be `While Amount > 0` and this means that `Amount` must have been assigned a value before the loop starts.

Refinement #1

This refinement now shows that if the user initially enters zero for the amount, the loop is not executed at all because the condition, Amount > 0, is false. This is a very important characteristic of the while loop and a reason for not using the repeat..until loop construct in this instance.

Refinement #2

Processing an item requires a sequence comprising incrementing a count for the number of items, adding the current item's cost to the running total and finally obtaining another item cost. Again, if this latter amount is zero, the condition for continuing the loop becomes false and the loop is terminated. The results are then displayed.

Notice that the last statement executed in the loop is a read statement which obtains the data to be processed next. Since no further detail is required for the structure chart, this is the final refinement before writing the pseudocode.

Pseudocode

```
{Enter and total costs}
1.1    Total = 0
```

```
1.2     Count = 0
2.1a    write 'Enter the cost of the first item, or 0 to end'
2.1b    read Amount
3       while Amount > 0
3.1       Count = Count + 1
3.2       Total = Total + Amount
3.3a      write <newline>, 'Enter cost of next item, or zero to end'
3.3b      read Amount
3       endwhile
4.1a    write <newline>,
4.1b    write <newline>, Count, 'items were purchased'
4.2a    write <newline>
4.2b    write 'The total cost was: £', Total
```

The detail added to the pseudocode is again to improve communication with the user by displaying prompts such as that in statement *2.1a* and by using blank lines (that is, `write <newline>`) to improve the clarity of the output.

Data table

name	description	type
Total	Accumulates the cost of the items	real variable
Amount	Stores the current item's cost	real variable
Count	Counts the number of items	integer variable

Comments

Try to avoid using a `while` condition such as `Amount <> 0` (not equal to zero) instead of `Amount > 0` because real numbers may not be represented exactly within a computer; the representation of zero might not be **exactly** zero and the condition `Amount <> 0` may still be true even when zero is entered for `Amount`.

Making decisions - the select statement

This example introduces the idea of taking one of several courses of action depending on the value of a variable read in from the keyboard. A loop is again terminated by testing for a rogue value, this time a negative value.

Problem statement

Design a program to accept a number of values representing student examination marks. Each mark is to be displayed as a grade as follows:

Mark	Grade
80 or over	Distinction
60 or over	Merit
40 or over	Pass
less than 40	Fail

A negative value is to be used to indicate the end of the set of marks.

Assumptions

The marks are entered as valid integers.

Top-level design

The third module in this sequence is an iteration which repeatedly reads and grades a mark until a negative mark is entered.

Refinement #1

The threshold values for the grades are assigned to integer constants. Any negative value entered will be regarded as the signal to terminate the program.

Refinement #2

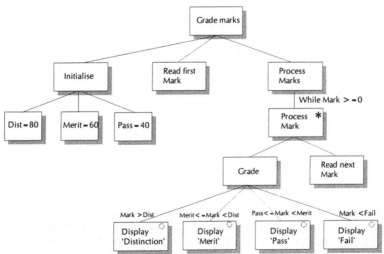

The four actions comprising the selection statement, Grade, which determine the message to be displayed should not be considered as a sequence of tests; the selection notation simply shows which action is to be taken depending on the one condition which is true, and as such the four actions could have been drawn in any order.

Pseudocode

```
{Grade marks}
1.1        Dist = 80
1.2        Merit = 60
1.3        Pass = 40
2.1a       write 'Enter the first mark(-1 to end):'
2.1b       read Mark
3          while Mark >= 0
3.1           select
3.1.1a           when Mark >= Dist
```

```
3.1.1b              write 'Distinction', <newline>
3.1.2a          when Mark >= Merit and Mark < Dist
3.1.2b              write 'Merit', <newline>
3.1.3a          when Mark >= Pass and Mark < Merit
3.1.3b              write 'Pass', <newline>
3.1.4a          when Mark < Pass
3.1.4b              write 'Fail', <newline>
3.1          endselect
3.2a         write 'Enter the next mark(-1 to end):'
3.2b         read Mark
3         endwhile
```

The three thresholds for the grades are stored in the integer constants Dist, Merit and Pass. The advantage of doing this rather than using the actual values 80, 60 and 40 respectively is that if any of these values need to be modified, they need only be changed in the initialisation module and nowhere else.

Data table

name	description	type
Dist	The distinction mark	integer constant = 80
Merit	The merit mark	integer constant = 60
Pass	The pass mark	integer constant = 40
Mark	The student's exam mark	integer variable

Comments

The precise form of a selection statement in a programming language can vary considerably; it is the responsibility of the programmer to choose the most appropriate form available in the target language that exactly represents the required logic.

Decisions - A menu program

Where a program offers a user a number of different options, a menu-based program structure is often employed. The options are displayed and the user is invited to choose one of them by, for example entering its first letter. The program then performs the requested operation and re-displays the menu after it is completed. One of the options always allows the user to exit the program. This example illustrates the structure of a program which presents the user with four options concerned with currency conversion.

Problem statement

Design a menu-based program to allow a user to choose between converting pounds sterling to German marks, American dollars or French francs. The program will ask the user to enter the number of pounds and it will display the equivalent amount in the chosen currency before returning to the menu. The menu is to appear at the top of a blank screen and appear as follows:

```
Currency conversion program

(M)arks
(D)ollars
(F)rancs
e(X)it
```

```
Which currency do you want to convert to Pounds?
```

Assumptions

1. Invalid choices (that is entering a letter other than M, D, F or X) will produce an error message and an invitation to try again.

2. Upper and lower case letters will be allowed.

3. The amount in pounds entered by the user will be a valid real number.

4. A single statement, `ClearScreen`, is available to blank the display screen.

Top-level design

The top-level design in this instance is very simple: the initialisation module sets the values for the three currency conversion factors and the remaining module, `Main`, repeatedly displays the user options and executes the one chosen.

Refinement #1

Three constants used for the currency conversion calculations are defined at this point (don't rely on these figures for holiday plans!).

Further, the iteration is defined as a `repeat..until` loop with condition c_1. Logical conditions governing loops and selections can be coded in this way so that defining their precise form can be deferred until the design has been completed. We will see later in refinement #3 that c_1 is the condition that indicates the user has chosen the exit option. Remember that the `repeat` loop causes the statements within the loop to be repeated at least once, and that the test for continuing to repeat the statements is made at the end of the loop.

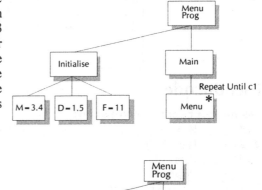

Refinement #2

This refinement now shows that the loop controls a sequence of two modules. The first, `Display menu`, repeatedly clears the display screen, shows the menu of options and then reads the user's choice. The second module is a selection statement which processes the option chosen. The final refinement defines the operation of each of the options and under what circumstances each is chosen.

Refinement #3

The first three options are concerned with the actual currency conversions. The fourth option displays a message to confirm that the user has chosen to exit the program. The final `select` statement is only invoked if the user has entered an invalid choice, that is, the letter entered is not 'M', 'D', 'F' or 'X'.

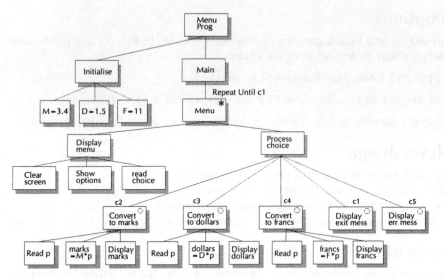

The condition codes c1–c5 are defined in the next table.

c1	choice = ('X' or 'x')
c2	choice = ('M' or 'm')
c3	choice = ('D' or 'd')
c4	choice = ('F' or 'f')
c5	choice <> ('X' or 'x')or
	('M' or 'm')or
	('D' or 'd')or
	('F' or 'f')

Pseudocode

```
{Menu currency conversion}
1.1       M = 3.4
1.2       D = 1.5
1.3       F = 11
2         repeat
2.1.1       ClearScreen
2.1.2a      write 'Currency conversion program', <newline>
2.1.2b      write <newline>
2.1.2c      write '(M)arks'
2.1.2d      write '(D)ollars'
2.1.2e      write '(F)rancs'
2.1.2f      write <newline>
2.1.2g      write 'Which currency do you want to convert to pounds?'
2.1.3       read Choice
2.2         select
2.2.1a        when Choice = ('M' or 'm')
2.2.1b            write <newline>, 'Enter amount'
2.2.1c            read p
```

```
2.2.1d          Currency = M*p
2.2.1e          write ' = ', Currency, ' Marks'
2.2.1f          write <newline> 'Press <Enter> to return to menu'
2.2.1g          read key
2.2.2a       when Choice = ('D' or 'd')
2.2.2b          write <newline>, 'Enter amount'
2.2.2c          read p
2.2.2d          Currency = D*p
2.2.2e          write ' = ', Currency, ' Dollars'
2.2.2f          write <newline> 'Press <Enter> to return to menu'
2.2.2g          read key
2.2.2a       when Choice = ('F' or 'f')
2.2.3b          write <newline>, 'Enter amount'
2.2.3c          read p
2.2.3d          Currency = F*p
2.2.3e          write ' = ', Currency, ' Francs'
2.2.3f          write <newline> 'Press <Enter> to return to menu'
2.2.3g          read key
2.2.4a       when Choice = ('X' or 'x')
2.2.4b          write 'Exiting program..'
2.2.5a       when otherwise
2.2.5b          write 'Invalid option. Please try again'
2.2.5c          write <newline> 'Press <Enter> to return to menu'
2.2.5d          read key
2.2        endselect
2.3     until Choice = ('X' or 'x')
```

Data table

name	description	type
M	Conversion factor for pounds to marks	real constant = 3.4
D	Conversion factor for pounds to dollars	real constant = 1.5
F	Conversion factor for pounds to francs	real constant = 11
p	The number of pounds to convert	real variable
Choice	The user's menu choice	character variable
Currency	The equivalent value in the currency chosen	real variable
key	Dummy variable to accept the <Return> key	character variable

Comments

1. This is a good model for constructing menu-driven programs.

2. The manner of implementing the select statement can vary considerably with the target programming language. Pascal provides if and case statements which each have their particular advantages and disadvantages. The programmer is responsible for choosing the most appropriate selection construct from those available.

Chapter 22

Program testing, debugging and documenting

Once a program has been written, it must go through two stages in order to remove errors which almost inevitably will be present. No matter how much care has been taken in the design and coding of a program, it is still very likely to contain *syntax* errors, that is incorrectly formed statements, and probably errors in *logic* as well. *Debugging* is the term given to the process of detecting and correcting these errors or *bugs*.

The first stage in the removal of errors is the correction of syntax errors. Fortunately for the programmer, modern interpreters and compilers will provide a large amount of assistance in the detection of syntax errors in the source code. Badly formed statements will be reported by a compiler after it has attempted to compile the source code; an interpreter will report illegal statements as it attempts to execute them.

Logic errors, however, are largely undetectable by the translating program. These are errors which cause the program to behave in a manner contrary to expectations. The individual statements in the program are correctly formed, but when executed it does not operate correctly; it may give incorrect answers, or terminate prematurely, or not terminate at all. Hopefully, even the most puzzling logic errors, having been detected, eventually can be removed. But how can the programmer be confident that the program will continue to behave properly when it is in use? The answer is that the programmer never can be absolutely certain that the program will not fail. However, by the careful choice of test data in the second stage of the debugging process, the programmer can test the program under the conditions that are most likely to occur in practice.

Test data is designed to determine the robustness of the program: how well it can cope with unexpected or spurious inputs, as well as those for which it has been designed specifically to process. The purpose of *documentation* is to provide the user with all the information necessary to fully understand the purpose of the program and how that purpose has been achieved. The precise form that the documentation takes will be determined by a number of factors:

❏ The type of program.

❏ Who is likely to use the program.

❏ Whether it will be necessary to modify the program coding after it has been finally tested and accepted.

General guidelines for the contents of program documentation are given at the end of this chapter.

Detecting logic errors

If after examining program code for a reasonable amount of time the cause of an error remains a mystery, there are a number of courses of action which probably will be much more productive than continuing to pore over the listing:

1. Ask a fellow programmer to listen while you explain the operation of the program and the way it is behaving. Quite often you will see the cause of the error as you are making the explanation. Alternatively, your helper might recognise the type of error and its probable cause from his/her own experience, or might ask a question which makes you reconsider some aspect of the program which you have assumed to be correct or had no direct bearing on the problem. It is surprising how often this simple approach works.

2. Examine the values of key variables while the program is running by inserting temporary lines of code throughout the program to display the values of key variables. Comparison of the values actually displayed with expected values will normally identify the likely source of the error.

3. Use debugging utilities provided in the language itself or separately in the system software. Most high-level language development systems provide debugging aids. These allow the programmer to do such things as step through the program line by line and display the value of variables, or to insert break-points to interrupt the execution of the program so that the state of variables can be examined. It is the responsibility of the programmer to investigate the debugging aids available and make good use of them.

Test data

When the programmer feels that the more obvious program errors have been detected and removed, the next stage is to test the program using carefully selected data. The nature of the test data should be such that:

- ❑ every statement in the program is executed at least once;
- ❑ the effectiveness of every section of coding devoted to detecting invalid input is verified;
- ❑ every route through the program is tried at least once;
- ❑ the accuracy of the processing is verified;
- ❑ the program operates according to its original design specification.

In order to achieve these aims, the programmer must be inventive in the design of the test data. Each test case must check something not tested by previous runs; there is no point in proving that a program which can add successfully a certain set of numbers can also add another similar set of numbers. The goal is to strain the program to its limit, and this is particularly important when the program is to be used frequently by a number of different people. There are three general categories of test data:

1. *Normal data*. This includes the most general data for which the program was designed to handle.

2. *Extreme values*. These test the behaviour of the program when valid data at the upper and lower limits of acceptability are used. The process of using extreme values is called 'boundary testing' and is often a fruitful place to look for errors. For numeric

data this could be the use of very large or very small values. Text could be the shortest or longest sequence of characters permitted. A program for file processing could be tested with a file containing no records, or just a single record. The cases where zero or null values are used are very important test cases, frequently highlighting programming oversights.

3.   *Exceptional data.* Programs are usually designed to accept a certain range or class of inputs. If invalid data is used, that is data which the program is not designed to handle, the program should be capable of rejecting it rather than attempting to process it. This is particularly important when the program is to be used by people other than the programmer, since they may be unaware of what constitutes invalid data. A programmer should from the outset assume that incorrect data will be used with the program; this may save a great deal of time looking for program errors which may actually be data errors.

Test logs

Once test cases have been devised, the program must be executed using the test data. The effect of using the test data is recorded in a *test log*. Since the point of program testing is to find errors, the log will indicate a <u>successful</u> test <u>if an error is found</u>, and an unsuccessful test otherwise.

The test log will form part of the documentation of the program so that if the program is subsequently modified, the same test data can be re-applied to ensure that no program errors have been accidentally introduced by the modifications. For each set of test data, the expected output must be determined before running the program so that it can be compared with the actual output produced by the program.

The test log could be set out in tabular form as follows.

TEST LOG

Date:

Program name:

Version:

Author:

Tested by:

Test case	Expected output	Observed output	Result	Comments
1				
2				
3				
4				
etc				

Validation

At some point the programmer must decide that the program has had sufficient testing. He or she will be confident that the program will operate according to specification and without 'crashing' or 'hanging up' under extreme or unexpected circumstances; the reputation of a professional programmer relies on this. Prior to release, the final testing is then performed by the user for whom the program was developed. The programmer may have overlooked areas of difficulty because it is often hard to consider a problem objectively or entirely from the view-point of the user. If this is the case, that the operation of the program is not entirely satisfactory, the program will be modified and re-tested until all user requirements are met.

Program documentation requirements

The documentation produced for a program will depend on a number of factors. For instance, a program which validates a temporary file prior to creating it permanently will probably require a minimum of user interaction and only a small number of user instructions. However, at some later date, it might be necessary for the author of the program, or a different programmer, to modify it. This possibility means that the structure of the program will have to be explained in great detail, and test procedures to ensure its correct operation will need to be provided.

A general purpose program such as a spreadsheet, designed for people who just want to use the computer as a tool, will require extremely detailed instructions regarding its function and use. Such programs are generally accompanied by detailed user manuals and tutorials. On the other hand, users would not be expected (and definitely not encouraged) to modify the program cod-ing; thus no details would be provided regarding the way the program has been written. This latter type of documentation would only be required for the people responsible for producing the program. In addition to the documentation requirements of users and programmers, there is a third category of person to be considered. These are people such as managers who are neither likely to use programs extensively nor want to attempt to modify them. They merely need to have an overview of the program - its function, capabilities, hardware requirements etc.

Thus there are many factors governing the coverage of documentation, and for this reason in the next section it is only possible to provide a checklist of items which might reasonably be included.

Documentation checklist

The documentation for a simple program generally falls into four sections:

- ☐ Identification.
- ☐ General specification.
- ☐ User information.
- ☐ Program specification.

Most users will need access to the first three sections; in general the fourth section will only be needed if the program is to be modified. The amount of detail in each section will depend en-tirely on the particular application and, to some extent, the implementation language. COBOL, for example, is largely self-documenting: it contains an Identification Division containing all the information listed in the first section below; the Data Division of a COBOL program con-tains precise details regarding all of the files used by the program and which devices are required; the Procedure Division is written in 'English-like' sentences which are generally easy to understand, even by a non-programmer. Consequently, a program written in COBOL will generally require less documentation than one written in Pascal or C, languages which are not self-documenting. The following checklist is a guide to what might reasonably be included in the documentation for a program.

1. Identification.
   - ❏ Title of program.
   - ❏ Short statement of its function.
   - ❏ Author.
   - ❏ Date written.
   - ❏ Language used and version if relevant.
   - ❏ Hardware requirements.

2. General specification.
   - ❏ Description of the main action(s) of the program under normal circumstances.
   - ❏ File specifications.
   - ❏ Restrictions and/or limitations of the program.
   - ❏ Equations used or references to texts explaining any complex procedures /techniques involved.

3. Program specification.
   - ❏ Structure charts/flowcharts/decision tables.
   - ❏ Annotated listing.
   - ❏ Testing procedure including test classes and test data with expected output and a test log.

4. User Guide.
   - ❏ Installation instructions
   - ❏ Detailed explanation of the operation of the program
   - ❏ Tutorial
   - ❏ Screen shots
   - ❏ Troubleshooting guide

Chapter 23

Pascal programming

This chapter addresses the task of developing a piece of software using the programming language Pascal. Here we look at Pascal in enough depth for you to be able to develop your own simple programs, provided of course that you have access to a Pascal compiler. The programs presented in this unit were written and tested using Borland's Turbo Pascal. However, apart from a small number of possible exceptions, the programs should work with any standard version of Pascal. Any special features of Turbo Pascal used in example programs are noted and explained; if you are not using Turbo Pascal, your version will most likely have very similar features that you can substitute, but you will need to refer to the appropriate language reference manual for the precise instruction format required. Turbo Pascal was chosen because it provides an ideal, easy to use environment for developing programs since it combines in one package all the tools required for the task. For example, it has: (i) an *editor* for creating and editing source programs; (ii) a *compiler* to check the syntax of a program, to report and identify errors and to produce object code; (iii) a *linker* to produce executable code; (iv) a *debugger* to help with locating runtime errors; (v) a *file manager* to allow you to quickly save, retrieve and print source programs.

The structure of a Pascal program

A Pascal program consists of four main parts: (i) the *name* of the program; (ii) a *declarations* section in which the programmer defines global *identifiers*. These are the variables and constants used in the program; (iii) *function* and *procedure definitions*; (iv) The main *procedural* part of the program which defines the sequence of instructions to be performed by the program. This section uses the identifiers, functions and procedures defined in the previous two sections of the program. It starts with the word begin and ends with end. Listing 29.1. shows the general structure of a Pascal program.

Listing 29.1. General structure of a Pascal program

```
program Name(input, output);

   {Declarations of global variables and  and constants}

   {Procedures and functions definitions}

begin
  {The main body of the program containing a sequence of
  instructions to be performed}
end.
```

As a simple example to illustrate these ideas, Listing 29.2 shows a program which calculates the total cost of a purchased item by calculating VAT and adding it to the price of the item. The algorithm on which the program is based is as follows:

1.   *Ask the user to enter the price of the item*

2.   *Store the price*

3.   *Calculate the VAT at 17.5% (i.e. multiply the price by 0.175)*

4.   *Calculate the total price by adding the VAT to the price*

5.   *Display the total cost on the screen.*

Note that the line numbers preceding each line in the program are included in the example programs presented in this chapter simply for ease of reference to specific lines when describing them. *Line numbers are not part of the Pascal language and should not be included if you intend to compile and run the example programs.*

The operation of program `Example1`

Line *1* declares that this program is called `Example1` and `(input, output)` indicates that the program uses the keyboard for the input of data and the screen for the display of data.

Lines *2 and 3* declare that VAT is a *constant* value.

Listing 29.2.	A simple program to calculate the total cost of a purchase

```
1       program Example1(input, output);
2       const
3         VAT = 0.175;
4       var
5         Price :real;
6         Tax :real;
7         TotalCost :real;
8       begin
9         write('Enter price of the item');
10        readln(Price);
11        Tax:= Price*VAT;
12        TotalCost:= Price + Tax;
13        writeln('The total cost is:' , TotalCost:8:2);
14        end.
```

Lines *4 - 7* declare three *variables* `Price`, `Tax` and `TotalCost` (hence the word `var` on line *4*) each as being of type `real`. Variables are used to store data, which in this case are in the form of real numbers, that is, numbers which are not whole numbers. Every variable used in a Pascal program must be declared in this way.

Up to this point the programmer has defined a number of *identifiers* that will be used in the procedural part of the program which follows.

Line *8* indicates the beginning of the procedural part of the program, that is, the section of the program which states what operations are to be performed. This is the part of the program in which the tasks identified by the algorithm are coded.

Line *9* causes the message Enter price of the item to be displayed on the screen.

Line *10* stores causes the computer to pause and accept numeric data typed in to be stored in the variable `Price` before continuing.

Line *11* stores the result of `Price` multiplied by `VAT` in the variable `Tax`.

Line *12* stores the result of adding `Price` and `Tax` in `TotalCost`.

Line *13* then displays the text, 'The total cost is: ' followed by the value stored in `TotalCost`. The total cost is shown as a total of eight characters with two figures after the decimal point.

Finally in **Line *14***, the word `end` followed by a full stop indicates the end of the program.

Some general remarks

Before going on to explore Pascal in more depth, it is worth mentioning a few general points at this stage:

1. Pascal does not distinguish between the use of capitals and lower-case letters. Thus it regards BEGIN, begin and Begin as being exactly the same.

2. Pascal uses the semicolon to indicate the end of an instruction, which is why you will see a semicolon at the end of most of the lines in a program. (You will quickly learn where a semicolon is not necessary). If you forget to terminate a complete instruction with a semicolon, the compiler will 'think' that the instruction is continued on the next line and, more often than not, it will say that there is an error in the next line.

3. It is a good idea to include comment lines (that is, text enclosed between '{' and '}') to describe the purpose of lines or sections of your program. Particularly for large, complex programs, this is very helpful if it is necessary to change the program at some later date.

4. Using spaces, blank lines and indentation can greatly improve the appearance and the clarity of a program, thus making the program easier to read and understand if it has to be modified later for any reason.

5. Programming involves meticulous attention to detail; omitting punctuation marks, including them in the wrong place or making spelling mistakes will usually lead to the compiler reporting syntax errors, but sometimes such slips might cause serious errors which are more difficult to detect, so be very careful to form instructions precisely.

Identifiers and data types

The term *identifier* is a general term used for *variables*, *constants* and other programmer-defined names such as *procedures* and *functions*. Variables and constants are always associated with a data *type*. Pascal requires that variables are given a type such as integer or real so that the necessary amount of memory can be reserved for their use.

Variables

A variable, which represents an item of data such as a single number, has a name and a current value. Variables are given names such as `Amount`, `Total` or `Numb3` and are assigned values by program instructions. These values are stored in the memory of the computer and they are accessed whenever a variable is referenced in a program instruction. So, for example, in the instruction

```
        Total := Price + Tax;
```

the value associated with the variable `Price` is added to the value of the variable `Tax` and the sum is then assigned to the variable `Total`. If in a previous instruction total had already been assigned a value, that value would be replaced by the new one.

Constants

Constants too are assigned values but only once after the word `const` preceding the main program. The constant VAT in Listing 29.2 is an example. Constants retain their values throughout the execution of a program; Pascal does not allow you to use a constant in an instruction which tries to change the value of the constant. Thus, if in Listing 29.2, you included an instruction such as

```
        VAT := 0.2;
```

in the main program, the Pascal compiler would report an error. Notice that a constant is assigned a value using only the '=' sign without the ':'.

Special identifiers and reserved words

Certain words in Pascal are classed as *special,* or *standard, identifiers* because they perform the same function as programmer-defined identifiers but they are recognised by the compiler as being pre-defined and they are therefore to be used only in a certain context. Examples of special identifiers are the words `write`, `writeln`, `read`, `readln`, `input` and `output`. If you use any of these words for identifiers, for example by declaring

```
        var
          Read :integer;
```

then Pascal will not necessarily regard this as a mistake, but you will have overridden the standard definition of `read` as an input instruction, and you will have to use it as an integer variable; you will not be able then to use read as an input instruction since, in effect, you will have redefined its function. The moral is to avoid using these special identifier names for your own, programmer-defined identifiers. Reserved words such as `begin`, `end`, `real` and `program` are words which are actually part of the Pascal language and are unavailable for use as identifiers. Pascal's reserved words and special identifiers are shown below.

Reserved words

and	array	begin	case	const
div	do	downto	else	end
file	for	function	goto	if
in	label	mod	nil	not
of	or	packed	procedure	program
record	repeat	set	then	to
type	until	var	while	with

Special identifiers

abs	arctan	boolean	char	chr
cos	dispose	eof	eoln	exp
false	get	input	integer	ln
maxint	new	odd	ord	output
pack	page	pred	put	read
readln	real	reset	rewrite	round
sin	sqr	sqrt	succ	text
true	trunc	unpack	write	writeln

Rules for naming identifiers

Pascal imposes a number of restrictions concerning the formation of names for identifiers:

1. The name must consist only of alphabetic and numeric characters.

2. The name must start with an alphabetic character.

3. The name must not be a special identifier or a reserved word.

Examples of valid identifiers

```
firstNum         NUMBER1        abc31          Counter    x
```

Examples of invalid identifiers

```
12abc            (starts with a numeric character)
first-number     (contains a non-alphabetic/numeric character)
var 1            (contains a space)
End              (a reserved word)
READ             (a special identifier)
```

Data types

As well as having a names and values, variables are also given a *type*. Three commonly used types are integer, real and char (character). Data types are declared before the main program. For variables, the type must be shown after the name of the variable, as illustrated on lines *5-7* of Listing 29.2. More examples of type declarations are shown below.

```
var
    Amount           :real;
    CodeLetter       :char;
    NumberOfItems    :integer;
```

The type real means that these variables can be used for numbers such as 123.456, 0.22 or –9.93, that is, *signed* numbers that are not whole numbers. The computer holds real numbers in floating-point form so that very large, and very small numbers can be stored.

Signed whole numbers, that is, integer values are stored as two's complement binary values in the computer. Some examples of integers are 23, 0, –1, 32767 and –559.

Type char means that the named variable (CodeLetter in the example above) stores a single character such as 'a', 'D', '6' or '?'.

Turbo Pascal provides a further data type to handle *strings*. A string is simply a number of characters which are collected together and used as a unit. For example, a person's name is a string of alphabetic characters, and a stock number such as 100-234/ABC in a mail order catalogue is a string containing a mixture of alphabetic, numeric and special characters. String variable declarations are illustrated in the examples below.

```
    Surname          :string[20];
    StockNumber      :string[12];
    Address1         :string[30];
```

The number inside the brackets specifies the maximum number of single characters to be handled by the named variable.

A further standard data type is the type boolean. This type of variable has only one of two possible values, namely `true` or `false`. A boolean variable declaration is made as follows:

```
Morevalues         :boolean;
```

Pascal provides the two reserved words `true` and `false` which can be used to assign a value to a boolean variable, as in:

```
Morevalues:= true;
```

The use of boolean variables will be explored in a later section.

Performing calculations

Probably every program that you will ever write will contain at least one calculation, and this is true of the majority of programs. It is not surprising therefore that Pascal and other high-level languages make calculations easy to perform. Arithmetic instructions simply involve defining what arithmetic operations are to be performed on numeric identifiers and constants. The four common arithmetic operations: add; subtract; multiply; divide, use the symbols +, –, * and /, respectively. The examples of arithmetic operations provided in Table 29.1 assume that the following data declarations have been made.

```
const
   PI        =3.14;
var
   Length, Width, Perimeter          :integer;
   Area, Radius, Gallons, Miles, Mpg :real;
   a, b, c, x, y                     :real;
```

Expression	Pascal statement
$Area = length \times width$	`Area:= Length*Width;`
$Area = \pi r^2$	`Area:= PI*Radius*Radius;`
$Perimeter = 2 \times (length + width)$	`Perimeter:= 2*(Length + Width);`
$Mpg = gallons \div miles$	`Mpg:= Gallons/Miles;`
$x = 0$	`x:= 0;`

Table 29.1. Examples of arithmetic operations with real variables

All of the statements in Table 29.1 involve calculating a value using `real` or `integer` variables or a combination of `reals` and `integers`. Pascals rules concerning how such calculations may be expressed are called *assignment compatibility* rules. They state that a calculation which involves: (i) a mixture of integers and reals must be assigned to a real variable; (ii) only integers may be assigned to either an integer variable or a real variable. Another point to note is that Pascal provides two divide operators. The '/' divide operator may be used with any values, `real` or `integer`, but if both values are `integers`, the result is a `real` value and must be assigned to a `real` variable. The second divide operator, `div`, is only allowed to be used with integers. If the result of a division does not produce a whole number, the fractional part is ignored. In other words, the result is rounded down to the nearest integer. The remainder when one integer is divided by another is produced by the `mod` operator.

Some examples should help to clarify these points and these are shown in Table 29.2.

Operands	Example	Answer	Answer type
real/real	7.3/0.2	36.5	real
	0.5/0.25	2.0	real
real/integer	13.9/5	2.78	real
integer/real	1116/7.2	155.0	real
integer/integer	33/11	3.0	real
	33/10	3.0	real
	3/5	0.6	real
integer div integer	33 div 11	3	integer
	33 div 10	3	integer
	3 div 5	0	integer
integer div real	Not allowed		
real div integer	Not allowed		
real div real	Not allowed		
integer mod integer	33 mod 10	3	integer
	10 mod 33	10	
integer mod real	Not allowed		
real mod integer	Not allowed		
real mod real	Not allowed		

Table 29.2. *Examples of divide operations*

Listing 29.3 is an example of the use of integer division. The program converts a number of seconds into hours, minutes and seconds.

Listing 29.3.	The div and mod integer division operators

```
1    program ModAndDiv(input, output);
2        {Program to convert a time given in seconds
3        to hours, minutes and seconds}
4
5    const
6        SECONDSPERMINUTE    =60;
7        MINUTESPERHOUR      =60;
8
9    var
10       Hours           :integer;
11       Minutes         :integer;
12       Seconds         :integer;
13       Duration        :integer;
14       Temp            :integer;
15
16   begin
17       writeln;
18       write('Enter the time in seconds: ');
19       readln(Duration);
20       Seconds := Duration mod SECONDSPERMINUTE;
21       Temp := Duration div SECONDSPERMINUTE;
22       Minutes := Temp mod MINUTESPERHOUR;
23       Hours := Temp div MINUTESPERHOUR;
24
25       writeln;
26       writeln(Duration, ' seconds is: ');
27       writeln;
```

```
28
29          write(Hours, ' hours ');
30          write(Minutes, ' minutes ');
31          writeln(Seconds, ' seconds.');
32        end.
```

On line *17* the user is requested to enter the time to be converted from seconds to hours, minutes and seconds. The number of seconds is stored in the variable Duration. The first stage in the calculation is to calculate the remainder when Duration is divided by the number of seconds per minute stored in the constant SECONDSPERMINUTE which has the value 60. Suppose, for example, the user entered the number 6573 when asked for the time in seconds. Line *20* would produce the value 6573 mod 60, that is, 33. This is assigned to the variable, Seconds. Next, the temporary variable Temp is given the value 6573 div 60, that is, 109. The remainder when this last number is divided by the number of minutes per hour, that is 60, gives the value for Minutes: 109 mod 60 = 49. The number of hours is calculated using 109 div 60 = 1. Thus, when the program is run, it produces the following output:

Enter the time in seconds: *6573* ⏎

6573 seconds is: 1 hours 49 minutes 33 seconds.

Operator precedence

The term *operator precedence* applies to the order in which the operators in an arithmetic expression are used. For example, to evaluate the expression

$$x = y + 3z$$

z is multiplied by 3 before the result is added to *y*; the multiply operator thus has precedence over the addition operator. If *y* had a value of 2 and *z* had a value of 4, *x* would be calculated as

$$x = 2 + 3 \times 4 = 2 + 12 = 14$$

The higher the precedence of an operator, the sooner it is used in the evaluation of an expression. The use of parentheses within an expression can alter the way a calculation is performed. So, in the above expression, to force the addition to be performed before the multiplication, we would write x = (y + 3) × z. This would result in y being added to 3 before multiplying by z. Thus,

$$x = (2 + 3) \times 4 = 5 \times 4 = 20$$

In Pascal, the operators * and / have equal precedence; this means that in an expression involving two or more of them, they are simply used in the order that they appear in the expression. These two operators have higher precedence than + and –. Again, + and – have the same precedence. As a further example, consider the program in Listing 29.4.

Listing 29.4.	Illustration of operator precedence

```
1        program Example2(input, output);
2        var
3          x1 :real;
4          y1 :real;
5          n :integer;
6        begin
```

```
7          n:= 11;
8          y1:= 5;
9          x1:= 1.0/2.0*(y1 + n div y1);
10         writeln(x1:8:2);
11     end.
```

The order of evaluation of line *9* is as follows:

1.	1.0/2.0	i.e.	0.5
2.	n div y1	i.e.	11 div 5 = 2
3.	y1 + n div y1	i.e.	5 + 2 = 7
4.	1.0/2.0*(y1 + n div y1)	i.e.	0.5*7 = 3.5

Reading and displaying information

Practically every program requires that data are provided by some input device such as a keyboard and that results are produced on an output device such as a monitor. Pascal provides a number of instructions to simplify these operations. The example program in Listing 29.4 used three input-output instructions, namely `readln`, `writeln` and `write`. In this section we examine these instructions in a little more detail.

The `readln` instruction uses data provided by a standard input device such as a keyboard to assign values to variables. The word `input` inside the brackets after the program name at the beginning of a Turbo Pascal program tells the Pascal compiler that a keyboard is to be used to enter character-based data (see Listing 29.4 for an example). You use the readln instruction to read real numbers, integers, single characters or strings into appropriately declared variables. For example, the statement

```
readln(Price);
```

would cause the program to wait for the user to enter a number to be stored in the real variable price. The user presses the ENTER key (⏎) to signify the end of data entry. It is good practice to include a write instruction to precede readln to inform the user what information is required. So, for example, the statements

```
write('Please enter the price of the item: ');
readln(Price);
```

would cause the computer to display

```
Please enter the price of the item:
```

on the display screen and then, with the text cursor remaining on the same line, wait for the user to type in a value and press the ⏎ key. The `writeln` instruction is almost identical to `write`, except that the text cursor is automatically moved to the beginning of the line immediately following the line on which the message is displayed. Which one of the instructions `write` and `writeln` you use depends on how you want your output to appear. Listing 29.5 illustrates the use of `write`, `writeln` and `readln`.

Listing 29.5.	Using `write`, `writeln` and `readln` instructions

```
1      program convert1(input, output);
2          {Program to convert inches to centimetres }
3      const
4          CENTIMETRESPERINCH =2.54;
```

```
  5        var
  6           Centimetres   :real;
  7           Inches        :real;
  8        begin
  9           write('Enter the length in inches: ');
 10           readln(Inches);
 11           Centimetres := Inches*CENTIMETRESPERINCH;
 12           writeln;
 13           write('A length of ', Inches:5:2,' inches');
 14           write(' is equivalent to ');
 15           writeln(Centimetres:5:2, ' centimetres');
 16        end.
```

The program would produce the following output when run:

```
Enter the length in inches: 12 ⏎
```

```
A length of 12.00 inches is equivalent to 30.48 centimetres
```

Notice the different form of the `writeln` instruction on line *12*: it simply produces a single blank line when the round brackets are not used. This is useful for making your output clear and easy to read. The output shows that the user entered the number *12* followed by ⏎ when prompted to type in the length in inches.

In line *13*, `write('A length of ', Inches:5:2,' inches');`, the purpose of the numbers after the variable `Inches` is to control the number of characters printed, that is, the *field width* and the number of decimal places of the displayed variable. In this instance the field width, including the decimal point, is to be restricted to five, with two figures after the decimal point. When the variable is of type `integer`, only one figure representing the total number of digits to be displayed is provided. If the field width is larger than the item to be displayed, the output is padded with blanks. Using a field width of zero, as in `Inches:0`, or less than the number of digits in the number, causes the minimum number of digits to be displayed. Table 29.3 contains a number of examples using various output formats.

value	type	format	output	remarks
15.234	real	:10:1	******15.2	Six leading spaces are added
6.6666	real	:10:1	*******6.7	The figure after the decimal point is rounded up
6.6666	real	:0:2	6.67	The minimum number of digits is displayed
−8.3124	real	:0:3	−8.312	As above
234.56	real	:1	2.3E+02	Number is displayed in floating-point form
234.56	real	none	2.3456000000E+02	The maximum number of decimal places is displayed
123	integer	:5	**123	Two leading spaces included in the field
123	integer	:2	123	Minimum number of figures displayed and no leading spaces
'hello'	string	:10	*****hello	Strings are treated like integers
'hello'	string	:0	hello	As above

Table 29.3. *Examples of various output formats and their effects*

Note that the instructions that we have covered in this section, namely `readln`, `write` and `writeln`, are actually implemented as *standard procedures* which are explored later in this chapter.

Loops

A very frequent programming requirement is to perform a set of instructions several times. Rather than writing the set of instructions several times (which is impractical for all but a small number of repetitions), they are controlled by a special instruction which causes them to be repeated as many times as desired. Such program constructs are called *loops*, and each repetition of a set of statements is often called an *iteration*. For example, suppose a program is required to read 10 numbers, add each one to a running total and then display the final total. The program in Listing 29.6 accomplishes this task using a loop.

Listing 29.6.   Using a loop to add numbers

```
 1    program RunningTotal2(input, output);
 2      {Program to add ten numbers }
 3    var
 4      Number        :real;
 5      Total         :real;
 6      Count         :integer;
 7    begin
 8      Total:= 0;
 9      writeln('Enter ten numbers: ');
10      for Count:= 1 to 10 do
11      begin
12         readln(Number);
13         Total:= Total + Number;
14      end;
15      writeln('The total is: ', Total:10:2);
16    end.
```

Listing 29.6 uses a `for` loop to repeat the two instructions which repeatedly read a number and add it to a running total. The `for` loop requires that a control variable, called `Count` in this example, is defined as type `integer`. The control variable is automatically given the first value specified (1 in this example) and, each time the statements within the loop are repeated, it is increased by 1 until it finally reaches the second value specified (10 in this example). Thus the same program, but with the value 10 replaced by the required number, could be used to add any number of numbers. Statements to be repeated are enclosed between `begin` and `end`. Listing 29.7 is a further example of the use of the `for` loop.

Listing 29.7.   Using a `for` loop to display a conversion table

```
 1    program ConvTab(input, output);
 2      {Program to display a conversion table for inches to
 3         centimetres using a for loop}
 4    const
 5      CONVERSIONFACTOR =2.54;
 6      MAXINCHES =12;
 7    var
```

```
8          Inches :integer;
9          Centimetres :real;
10
11      begin
12        writeln;
13        writeln('Inches':20, 'Centimetres':20);
14        writeln('——':20, '———-':20);
15
16        for Inches:= 1 to MAXINCHES do
17          begin
18            Centimetres:= Inches*CONVERSIONFACTOR;
19            writeln(Inches:17, Centimetres:20:2);
20          end;
21      end.
```

The output produced looks like this:

```
Inches        Centimetres
------        -----------
   1             2.54
   2             5.08
  etc             etc
  12            30.48
```

Notice that the end value in the `for` statement on line *16* is a constant called MAXINCHES; this could also have been defined as a variable used in a `readln` instruction.

A slight variation in the format of a `for` statement allows the count variable to go down from a high value to a low value. For example, you could write

```
for i:= 12 downto 1 do ....
```

which would cause the variable `i` to start at 12 and go down to 1 in steps of 1.

The `for` statement is a very useful means of implementing a loop, but certain programming problems require a different approach to repeating a set of instructions. For example, consider the following outline program description:

> *Read a set of real numbers representing the cost of a number of items. Accumulate the total cost of the items until a value of zero is entered, then display the number of items purchased and their total cost.*

Here it is not known how many times the loop is to be repeated: the user decides when to terminate the loop by entering a *rogue value*, (zero in this case). The rogue value is used in another type of loop instruction, the `while` instruction. Listing 29.8 shows how a `while` loop can be used in conjunction with a rogue value. The rogue value is defined as a constant on line *5*. Because the user may want to terminate the program immediately, without entering any values, the program asks for a purchase amount before entering the loop starting on line *18*. The `while` instruction requires that a true/false expression is included after the word 'while'. Thus the expression, Amount > ROGUEVALUE, will be true if Amount entered is greater than zero, and it will be false if Amount is not greater than zero, that is if it is equal to, or less than zero. When the expression is true, the statements between the immediately following `begin` and `end`, that is lines *20* to *23*, will be executed; as soon as the expression becomes false, the loop terminates and the program goes on to line *26*.

Notice that the last instruction in the lines to be repeated is the `readln` instruction to read another value: this means that because the next instruction to be executed is the `while` instruction, the value typed in by the user is immediately compared with the rogue value. This ensures that the rogue value is not processed as an actual data item.

Listing 29.8.	Using a `while` loop and a rogue value

```
1       program RogueVal(input, output);
2         {program to illustrate the use of a rogue value
3            to terminate a loop}
4       const
5         ROGUEVALUE =0;
6       var
7         Count :integer;
8         Amount :real;
9         Total :real;
10
11      begin
12        Total:= 0;
13        Count:= 0;
14
15        write('Enter the cost of the first item, or 0 to end :');
16        readln(Amount);
17
18        while Amount > ROGUEVALUE do
19           begin
20              Count:= Count + 1;
21              Total:= Total + Amount;
22              write('Enter the cost of the next item, or 0 to end :');
23              readln(Amount);
24           end;
25
26        writeln;
27        writeln(Count, ' items were purchased.');
28        writeln;
29        writeln('The total cost was: £', Total:0:2);
30      end.
```

Here is a typical output from the program:

```
        Enter the cost of the first item, or 0 to end :23.45 ⏎
        Enter the cost of the next item, or 0 to end :6.12 ⏎
        Enter the cost of the next item, or 0 to end :5.99 ⏎
        Enter the cost of the next item, or 0 to end :0 ⏎

        3 items were purchased.
        The total cost was: £35.56
```

Notice that the assignment instruction on line *20*, `Count := Count + 1`, is used as a means of counting the number of times the loop is executed. The instruction simply adds 1 to the variable, `Count`, each time the instructions within the loop are repeated. The true/false expression on line *18* in the `while` statement uses the *relational operator*, >, meaning 'greater than', to compare `Amount` with ROGUEVALUE. There are in fact six different relational operators that can be used in such logical expressions, and these are shown in Table 29.4.

relational operator	meaning
>	Greater than
>=	Greater than or equal to
<	Less than
<=	Less than or equal to
=	Equal to
<>	Not equal to

Table 29.4. *Relational operators used in logical expressions*

The operators in Table 29.4 are used according to the relationship to be established between two values. Whatever logical expression is used, the result of the comparison will either be true or false - if true, the `while` loop will repeat; if false the loop will terminate. More examples of the use of these operators are provided in the next section, which deals with the use of logical expressions in making program decisions.

Decisions

Suppose a program is required to display multiple-choice questions with one correct answer out of three possible choices. For example, one of the questions could be:

```
A BYTE is the name given to

    (a)  Four bits
    (b)  Eight bits
    (c)  Sixteen bits

Your answer is:
```

The program is also required to display the message

```
Correct - well done!
```

if the answer is correct, and display a message such as

```
Sorry, the correct answer is (b)
```

if the answer provided is incorrect.

The program must therefore be able to take two alternative courses of action depending on the answer supplied. An `if` statement is one possible way of achieving this requirement. The appropriate form of the `if` statement is illustrated in Listing 29.9 which shows the Pascal code required to display the question above and provide the response appropriate to the letter `'a'`, `'b'` or `'c'`, typed in.

Listing 29.9.   Using an `if` statement

```
1      program Decisions1(input,output);
2        {Program to illustrate the use of the if statement}
3      var
4        Answer      :char;
5      begin
6        writeln('Enter the letter corresponding to the ');
7        writeln('correct answer for the following question:');
8        writeln;
9
```

```
10        writeln('A BYTE is the name given to');
11        writeln('(a) Four bits');
12        writeln('(b) Eight bits');
13        writeln('(c) Sixteen bits');
14        writeln;
15        write('Your answer is: ');
16        readln(Answer);
17
18        if Answer = 'b' then
19           writeln('Correct - well done!')
20        else
21           writeln('Sorry, the correct answer is (b)');
22     end.
```

The if statement extending over lines *18* to *21* shows how the program can take one of two possible courses of action depending on the value of a variable. We saw in the last section concerning the use of the while statement that logical expressions are either true or false. This is also the case with the logical expression Answer = 'b' in the if statement on line *18*. If the letter stored in the character variable Answer is the letter 'b', then the logical expression Answer = 'b' will be true, otherwise it will be false. If it is true, the statement following the word then is executed (that is, line *19*), otherwise the statement after else is executed (that is, line *21*). The general form of the if statement is

```
if {logical expression} then
   {statement 1}
else
   {statement 2}
```

Note that {statement 1} is the instruction that is performed if {logical expression} is true; {statement 2} is performed if {logical expression} is false. Note also that either {statement 1} or {statement 2}, or both of them, can be a block of instructions enclosed between begin and end as follows.

```
if Answer = 'b' then
  writeln('Correct - well done!')
else
  begin
    writeln('Sorry, the correct answer is (b)');
    writeln('There are eight bits in a byte');
  end;
```

Sometimes it is necessary to choose between more than just two courses of action in a program. For example, Listing 29.10 shows a program which converts a percentage mark to a pass, merit, distinction or fail grade. The program repeatedly accepts marks and converts them to grades until the mark entered is the rogue value –1 (or any negative integer value) signifying the end of the mark inputs. The rules that are used to determine the grade are as follows:

For a distinction the mark must be over 80.

For a merit the mark must be greater than or equal to 60 and less than 80.

For a pass the mark must be greater than or equal to 40 and less than 60.

Below 40 is a fail.

Listing 29.10.   The if..else if construction

```
1        program Decision2(input, output);
2          const
3            DIST     =80;
4            MERIT    =60;
5            PASS     =40;
6
7          var
8            Mark       :integer;
9
10       begin
11         writeln;
12           write('Please enter the first mark(-1 to end): ');
13         readln(Mark);
14
15         while Mark >=0 do
16           begin
17             if Mark >= DIST then
18                 writeln('Distinction')
19             else if (Mark >= MERIT) and (Mark < DIST) then
20                         writeln('Merit')
21                     else if (Mark >= PASS) and (Mark < MERIT) then
22                             writeln('Pass')
23                         else writeln('Fail');
24             write('Please enter the next mark(-1 to end): ');
25             readln(Mark);
26           end;
27       end.
```

The if statement between lines *17* and *23* reflects this logic exactly. It is possible to chain if statements in this way to cope with quite complex lines of reasoning. Added flexibility is provided by the use of the logical and operator used for the the logical expressions on lines *19* and *21*. The and operator requires that both of the minor logical expressions it connects are true for the complete logical expression to be true. If either or both are false, then the whole expression is false. Logical operators are discussed in more detail in the next section.

Here is a typical output from the program:

```
Please enter the first mark(-1 to end):46 ⏎
Pass
Please enter the next mark(-1 to end):68 ⏎
Merit
Please enter the next mark(-1 to end):32 ⏎
Fail
Please enter the next mark(-1 to end):83 ⏎
Distinction
Please enter the next mark(-1 to end):-1 ⏎
```

Logical operators

Logical operators allow you to combine logical expressions. There are three logical operators in Pascal : and, or and not. An example of the use of the and operator was provided in Listing 29.10. The and and the or operators are always placed between two logical expressions, and they each combine these logical expressions to produce a value of true or false. Table 29.5 shows the rules that are applied by Pascal to determine whether a compound logical expression is true or false. This type of table is usually called a *truth table*.

(Expr 1)	(Expr 2)	(Expr 1) or (Expr 2)	(Expr 1) and (Expr 2)
true	true	true	true
true	false	true	false
false	true	true	false
false	false	false	false

Table 29. 5. *Truth table for the* **and** *and* **or** *logical operators*

Referring back to Listing 29.10 in the previous section, on line *19*, where the compound logical expression (Mark >= MERIT) and (Mark < DIST) is used to determine whether the mark is equivalent to a merit grade. In the expression, (Mark >= MERIT) is an example of (Expr 1) and (Mark < DIST) is an example of (Expr 2) shown in Table 29.5. The next table (Table 29.6) shows how the and operator combines these two logical expressions for a number of cases.

Mark	(Mark > = MERIT)	(Mark < DIST)	(Mark > = MERIT and (Mark < DIST)
45	false	true	false
86	true	false	false
67	true	true	true

Table 29. 6. *Truth table for the* **and** *logical operator.*

Thus, both logical expressions must be true for the complete expression to be true; with the or operator, however, only one of the expressions needs to be true for the complete expression to be true. For example, consider the program in Listing 29.11 which reads some text and counts how many vowels it contains. The program uses a for loop to test each letter in turn in the text against each possible vowel. If the current letter is a vowel, that is 'a', 'e', 'i', 'o' or 'u', a count is incremented.

Listing 29.11.   Illustrating the use of the or logical operator

```
1        program Vowels(input, output);
2        var
3        VowelCount      :integer;
4        Letters         :string[80];
5        LengthOfText    :integer;
6        c               :integer;
7        begin
8          VowelCount:= 0;
9          writeln('Type text followed by ENTER: ');
10         readln(Letters);
11         LengthOfText:= length(Letters);
12
```

```
13        for c:= 1 to LengthOfText do
14           if (Letters[c] = 'a') or
15              (Letters[c] = 'e') or
16              (Letters[c] = 'i') or
17              (Letters[c] = 'o') or
18              (Letters[c] = 'u')
19           then
20              VowelCount:= VowelCount + 1;
21
22           writeln;
23           writeln('The text contained ', VowelCount, '
      vowels');
24        end.
```

The text is held in a string variable called Letters. Each letter in Letters is accessed by specifying its position within the text. For example, if the text entered was the string 'hello there', then Letters[1] is the letter 'h', Letters[2] is the letter 'e', Letters[3] is the letter 'l', and so on. The for loop control variable, c, starts at 1 and goes up in steps of 1 to the length of the string (11 for the string 'hello there'). The length of the string is determined by the pre-defined Pascal function length(), on line *11*, which requires a string as its single argument. (See the later section on Pascal functions for more detail about functions). Here is the output from the program when the string, 'the cat sat on the mat' is typed in:

Type text followed by ENTER: *the cat sat on the mat* ⏎

The text contained 6 vowels

Note that the program will only work with lower-case text. The reason is that lower-case letters 'a', 'b', 'c', etc are represented in a computer using a different set of codes from the equivalent upper-case letters 'A', 'B', 'C', etc.

The third logical operator is the not operator which simply reverses the logical value of a logical expression. Thus, the logical expression not (x > 3) is true only when x is less than or equal to 3. Similarly, the logical expression not (Balance <= 0) is true only when Balance has a value that is greater than zero. The truth table shown in Table 29.7 defines the operation of the not logical operator.

Expr	not Expr
true	false
false	true

Table 29.7. *Truth table for* not *logical operator*

More control statements

Listing 29.12 draws together two further Pascal control statements, namely the repeat..until and the case statements using a progam which allows you to convert Pounds Sterling into one of three foreign currencies: American Dollars, German Marks or French Francs. The repeat..until statement provides a third method of constructing a loop. It is similar to the while statement in that it uses a logical condition to determine when to exit the loop, but the difference is that the condition appears at the end rather than at the beginning of the loop. This means that the loop will be executed at least once, which is appropriate for this example in which the loop repeatedly executes instructions which display a menu and ask the user to choose one of the menu options. In this example, the repeat statement repeats the statements between lines *13* to *63* until the condition following the word until is true, that is, when the user enters the letter 'X' or 'x' to indicate the desire to exit the program.

Listing 29.12.   Using the case and repeat statements in a menu program.

```
1     program menu1(input, output);
2     uses CRT;
3     const
4       DOLLARS      =1.5;
5       MARKS        =3.4;
6       FRANCS       =11;
7     var
8       Choice       :char;
9       Currency     :real;
10      Pounds       :real;
11    begin
12      repeat
13        clrscr'
14         writeln('Currency conversion program');
15        writeln;
16        writeln('(M)arks');
17        writeln('(D)ollars');
18        writeln('(F)rancs');
19        writeln('e(X)it');
20        writeln;
21        write('Which currency do you want to convert to Pounds? ');
22        readln(Choice);
23        writeln;
24
25        case Choice of
26            'D', 'd':
27                begin
28                    writeln('Enter the amount to convert to Dollars');
29                    readln (Pounds);
30                    Currency:=Pounds*DOLLARS;
31                    writeln('You would get ',Currency:0:0,
32                            ' Dollars for',Pounds:0:0, ' Pounds');
33                    writeln('Press ENTER to return to the menu');
34                    readln;
35                end;
36            'M', 'm':
37                begin
38                    writeln('Enter the amount to convert to Marks');
39                    readln(Pounds);
40                    Currency:=Pounds*Marks;
41                    writeln('You would get ',Currency:0:0,
42                            ' Marks for ',Pounds:0:0, ' Pounds');
43                    writeln('Press ENTER to return to the menu');
44                    readln;
45                end;
46            'F', 'f':
47                begin
48                    writeln('Enter the amount to convert to Francs');
49                    readln(Pounds);
50                    Currency:= Pounds*FRANCS;
51                    writeln('You would get ',Currency:0:0,
52                            ' Francs for ',Pounds:0:0, ' Pounds');
53                    writeln('Press ENTER to return to the menu');
54                    readln;
55                end;
56            'X', 'x':
57                writeln('Exiting program..');
58            else
59                begin
60                    writeln('Invalid option. Please try again');
```

```
61                         writeln('Press ENTER to return to the menu');
62                         readln;
63                      end;
64            end;
65       until (Choice = 'X') or (Choice = 'x');
66    end.
```

The case statement is an alternative method to the if statement for choosing between alternative courses of action wihin a program. It has the following general format:

```
case {variable name} of
    value list 1: statement 1;
    value list 2: statement 2;
    etc...
    ......
else statement N
end;
```

The variable name after the word case can be of type integer, character or boolean, but string and real variables *are not allowed*. Pascal matches the value of the variable against the values specified on the subsequent lines; when a match is found, the corresponding statement is executed after which the case statement is immediately exited without considering any remaining values. If there are no values that match the variable, the case statement does nothing unless the else option is used, in which circumstances, the supplied statement (shown as statement N above) is executed. Note that some versions of Pascal may not support the use of the else option: you may need to consult the language manual for your version of Pascal. In Listing 29.12, the case statement is used to select the block of statements corresponding to the menu option chosen by the user. The user can choose one of four options using the letters 'D', 'M', 'F' or 'X'; to allow for the possibility of either upper or lower case letters being entered, both are included in the case statement value lines. Here are some program fragments which should help to clarify the use of the case statement:

Example 1

```
var
  Month, Days    :integer;
.......
.......
case Month of
   1, 3, 5, 7, 8, 10, 12   :Days:= 31;
   4, 6, 9, 11             :Days:= 30;
   2                       :Days:= 28;
end;
```

Month contains a number corresponding to the month of the year, where January = 1, February = 2 ..... December = 12. The case statement is used to store, in the variable, Days, the number of days in the month whose number is stored in Month. Thus if Month contained the number 8 corresponding to August, Days would be assigned the value 31.

Example 2

```
var
  Smoker :boolean;
  ......
  ......
```

```
case Smoker of
  true :writeln('Smoking seriously damages your health!');
  false :writeln('Good for you!');
end;
```

If the boolean variable, Smoker, has been assigned a value of true prior to the case statement, the health warning will be displayed, otherwise the complimentary message 'Good for you!' will be displayed. This is equivalent to using the if statement

```
if Smoker then
  writeln('Smoking seriously damages your health!')
else
  writeln('Good for you!');
```

Note that it is because Smoker is a boolean variable having a value of true or false, that it can be used as a logical expression in an if statement as illustrated above.

Example 3

```
var
  Letter :char
  VowelCount :integer;
  ConsonantCount :integer;
  .....
  .....
case Letter of
  'a', 'e', 'i', 'o', 'u' : VowelCount:= VowelCount + 1;
  'A', 'E', 'I', 'O', 'U' : VowelCount:= VowelCount + 1;
  ',', '.', ';', ':', '(', ')', ' ':{No action required}
else ConsonantCount:= ConsonantCount + 1;
end;
```

Here the program adds one to a vowel count if Letter contains either an upper or lower case letter; otherwise it adds one to a consonant count. Punctuation marks, brackets and spaces are ignored. Note that using if statements to perform this task would be much more difficult.

Arrays

An *array* is a data structure which allows you to store a number of items of data without having to allocate separate variable names to them. Arrays, like all other identifiers, must be declared before they are used. For example, the following declaration is for an array of five integers:

```
var
  Array1    :array[1..5] of integer;
```

This single declaration is in effect defining five variables called Array[1], Array[2], Array[3], Array[4] and Array[5], each of which can store a single integer value. The integer value inside the square brackets is called the array's index, and it is allowed only to take the range of values specified in the declaration (1 to 5 inclusive in this example). Each of these identifiers can be used just like any ordinary integer variable. For instance, to set each of them to zero could be accomplished as follows:

```
Array[1]:= 0;
Array[2]:= 0;
```

```
Array[3]:= 0;
Array[4]:= 0;
Array[5]:= 0;
```

However, we could accomplish the same operation by using an integer variable as an *index* and by putting a single assignment statement in a `for` loop:

```
for i:= 1 to 5 do Array[i]:= 0;
```

Now the count variable `i` takes on the integer values 1 to 5 and again each element in the array is set to zero. The obvious advantage of using a variable for an index is that arrays can then be used very effectively within loops, and they allow the manipulation of as many or as few numbers as appropriate to the task in hand; notice that the same `for` loop could initialise 5000 array elements as easily as 5 elements:

```
for i:= 1 to 5000 do Array[i]:= 0;
```

This would be an exceedingly difficult task to accomplish without the use of an array. Listing 29.13 illustrates the use of an array of real numbers. The program reads five numbers into an array and then finds the position within the array of the smallest number. It then swaps this number with the first number in the list before displaying the re-ordered array.

Listing 29.13. Using an array.

```
1    program TopList(input, output);
2    uses CRT;
3    const
4      MAXNUMS      =5;
5    var
6      Array1       :array[1..MAXNUMS] of real;
7      Temp         :real;
8      i            :integer;
9    begin
10     clrscr;
11     writeln('Enter ', MAXNUMS, ');
12     writeln;
13     for i:= 1 to MAXNUMS do
14        begin
15           write('Enter number ', i, ' and press ENTER :');
16           readln(Array1[i]);
17        end;
18     for i:= 2 to MAXNUMS do
19        if Array1[i] < Array1[1] then
20           begin
21              Temp:= Array1[1];
22              Array1[1]:= Array1[i];
23              Array1[i]:= Temp;
24        end;
25     writeln;
26     writeln('The new list is as follows:');
27     for i:= 1 to MAXNUMS do write(Array1[i]:10:2);
28   end.
```

Line *2* contains a non-standard statement which allows you to clear the screen by using the pre-defined *procedure* `clrscr` shown on line *10*. You may have to omit these two lines if you are not using Turbo Pascal. Note that *procedures* and the `uses` statement are discussed later.

The program first defines a constant MAXNUMS to be the maximum size of the `real` array, Array1. Lines *11* to *17* are to read in the ten numbers with appropriate user prompts. Thus the first number is read into Array1 [1], the second into Array1 [2], and so on up to the last number which is read into Array1 [10]. The second `for` loop starting on line *18* compares each number in the array in turn with the first number; if one is found that is greater than the first, they are swapped over. By the time the last number in the array has been compared with the first one, the largest number is in the first position in the array.

A typical output from the program might be as follows:

```
Enter 5 numbers

Enter number 1 :5.7 ⏎
Enter number 2 :3.9 ⏎
Enter number 3 :9.1 ⏎
Enter number 4 :1.7 ⏎
Enter number 5 :98.4 ⏎

The new list is as follows: 1.7   3.9   9.1   5.7   98.4
```

As a final example in this section on arrays, Listing 29.14 shows a program which uses a random number generator to select five lottery numbers in the range 1 to 49.

Listing 29.14.   Using random numbers and an array to generate lottery numbers

```
1       program Lottery(input, output);
2       uses CRT;
3
4       const
5         NUMOFNUMS    =5;
6         MAXNUM       =49;
7       var
8         LuckyNums    :array[1..MAXNUM] of integer;
9         Num          :integer;
10        i            :integer;
11        Count        :integer;
12
13      begin
14        clrscr;
15        writeln('Lottery random number generator');
16         writeln;
17
18        randomize;
19
20        for i:= 1 to MAXNUM do LuckyNums[i]:= 0;
21
22        for Count:= 1 to NUMOFNUMS do
23          begin
```

```
24          Num:= random(MAXNUM + 1);
25          while LuckyNums[Num] <>  0 do
26              Num := random(MAXNUM + 1);
27
28          LuckyNums[Num]:= Num;
29          write(Num:5);
30        end;
31
32      writeln;
33      writeln;
34      write('Press ENTER to exit program');
35      readln;
36    end.
```

The random numbers are generated using the pre-defined function `random(N)` which produces a random number in the range specified by its single integer argument, N, within the brackets. For example, `random(11)` would produce a random number between 1 and 10 inclusively. Thus the statement

```
Num:= random(MAXNUM + 1);
```

assigns a random number between 1 and 49 to the variable Num. The `randomize` instruction on line *18* simply initialises the random number generator so that it does not produce the same sequence of random numbers every time the program is run. Line *20* initialises each element to zero in the array `LuckyNums[]` which is to be used to store the five random numbers. The reason for the `while` loop on lines *25* and *26* is to ensure that the same random number is not used more than once. The loop keeps generating random numbers until it finds one that has not been generated previously. For instance, if the first random number generated on line *24* was the number 36, then this would be stored in Num. The `while` loop will only generate another random number if `Luckynums[36]` contains zero, showing that 36 has not previously been generated. As soon as the `while` loop finds an empty slot, the number is stored in the array and immediately displayed on the screen. The process repeats until five different numbers have been generated.

Pre-defined procedures and functions

High-level languages almost invariably provide libraries of useful pre-written programs that are available to the programmer. These programs, which are often termed *pre-defined procedures* and *functions*, have previously been written, compiled and thoroughly tested so that they can be used by programmers with confidence that they are error-free.

In Turbo Pascal such libraries of programs are declared with the nonstandard instruction, `uses`, followed by the name the library file, or *unit*, as it is called. We have already used a unit called `Crt` containing the procedure `clrscr` which was used to clear the display screen Some library programs require you to provide information in the form of *parameters* at the time they are called. An example of such a program is the `delay(T)` procedure which requires you to supply a delay, T, in milliseconds inside the brackets. Functions always return an item of information when they are used. For example, in Listing 29.14 we saw that the function `random(N)` returned to the calling program a random number in the range 1 to N-1, where N is an integer value. Whatever the version, however, Pascal always provides a number of *standard procedures* and *functions* which are available without the need to declare them in programs. They comprise procedures and functions which are considered to be the most frequently used. It was noted earlier that `readln`, `write` and `writeln` are in fact such standard procedures, rather than instructions such as `for` and `if` which are integral parts of the Pascal language. Turbo Pascal keeps the standard procedures and functions, plus quite a few more, in a library unit called `System` which is automatically available when a program is compiled. Pascal's standard functions are described at the end of this chapter, and in addition we have provided further descriptions of a selection of procedures and functions that are available in some of Turbo Pascal's other units.

Simple user-defined procedures

Procedures are often called *subprograms* or *subroutines* because they form only part of a complete program. We saw in the previous section that Pascal provides a number of pre-written functions and procedures that you can use in your own programs, but it is also possible for you to write your own. These are called *user-defined* procedures and functions.

A Pascal procedure is very similar to a Pascal program, the main difference being that a procedure cannot stand by itself - it must form part of another program. Like identifiers such as constants and variables, procedures must also be declared at the beginning of the program before they are used. The structure of a program containing two procedures, called `Procname1` and `Procname2`, would have the outline structure shown in Listing 29.15.

Listing 29.15. The structure of a program containing two procedures.

```
1     program Progname(input, output);
2     const
3       {Progname constants are declared here}
4     var
5       {Progname variables are declared here}
6
7     procedure Procname1;
8     const
9       {Procname1 constants are declared here}
10    var
11      {Procname1 variables are declared here}
12    begin
13      {Procname1 code goes here}
14    end;
15
16    procedure Procname2;
17    const
18      {Procname2 constants are declared here}
19    var
20      {Procname2 variables are declared here}
21    begin
22      {Procname2 code goes here}
23    end;
24    begin
25      ........
26      ........
27      Procname1;
```

```
28        ........
29        ........
30        Procname2;
31        ........
32      end.
```

The two procedure definitions, shown in the shaded sections of the program, appear after the constants and variables declarations of the main program. The definitions of the procedures look exactly like a main program, each having their own constants and variables declarations (if required) and their own main code between begin and end.

The program in Listing 29.16 illustrates the use of simple procedures to cycle through three rudimentary pictures of faces in order to give the appearance of a face winking alternate eyes. The program uses three procedures, Face1, Face2 and Face3, each of which uses keyboard characters to display a face. The procedures are executed in the main program by simply naming them. Thus line *36* Face1 causes the instructions in procedure Face1 to be executed. The program then continues with line *37* delay(500), a pre-defined procedure which causes a delay of 500 milliseconds.

Listing 29.16.   Using procedures to make a face wink.

```
1       program Winker(input, output);
2       uses CRT;
3       var
4         i      :integer;
5
6       procedure Face1;
7       begin
8         clrscr;
9         writeln('    _ _    ');
10        writeln('  < 0 0 > ');
11        writeln('   | ^ |  ');
12        writeln('    \_/    ');
13      end;
14
15      procedure Face2;
16      begin
17        clrscr;
18        writeln('    _ _    ');
19        writeln('  < 0 o > ');
20        writeln('   | ^ |  ');
21        writeln('    \_/    ');
22      end;
23
24      procedure Face3;
25        begin
26        clrscr;
27        writeln('    _ _    ');
28        writeln('  < o 0 > ');
29        writeln('   | ^ |  ');
30        writeln('    \_/    ');
```

```
31      end;
32
33    begin
34    for i:= 1 to 10 do
35      begin
36        Face1;
37        delay(500);
38        Face2;
39        delay(500);
40        Face1;
41        delay(500);
42        Face3;
43        delay(500);
44      end;
45    end.
```

Each of the procedures uses the pre-defined `clrscr` procedure to clear the screen so that the face stays in the same place and appears to wink. Notice that the logic of the main program is easy to follow by the use of procedures - this is one of their major advantages. Another feature of this program is that although the procedure `Face1` is used twice, the code required for it appears only once in its definition. This economical use of program code is another major advantage of using procedures in programs.

Global vs local variables

Earlier we said that a procedure is allowed to have its own `var` declarations. When this is the case, the variables declared in the procedure are termed *local* variables. This means that these variables only have values while the procedure is being executed; once the procedure has been completed and control has returned to the main program, local variables cannot be accessed. On the other hand, *global* variables which are defined in the main program are always available, even to procedures, while the program is running. Note, however, that if a variable declared in a procedure has the same name as a variable declared in the main program, the local variable only, can be used in the procedure. These ideas are best illustrated with the aid of an example such as that shown in Listing 29.17.

Listing 29.17.   A program to illustrate the difference between global and local variables

```
1       program Scope(input, output);
2       uses CRT;
3       var
4          Greeting1      :string[20];
5
6       procedure Proc1;
7       var
8          Greeting1      :string[20];
9       begin
10         Greeting1:= 'How do';
11         writeln('Proc1':15, 'Greeting1':15, 'local ':15,
           Greeting1:15);
12      end;
13
```

```
14    procedure Proc2;
15    var
16      Greeting2      :string[20];
17        begin
18      Greeting2:= 'Hi ';
19      writeln('Proc2':15, 'Greeting2':15, 'local ':15,
        Greeting2:15);
20      writeln('Proc2':15, 'Greeting1':15, 'global':15,
        Greeting1:15);
21    end;
22
23    begin
24      clrscr;
25      writeln('Source':15, 'Variable':15, 'Scope':15, 'Value':15);
26       writeln;
27       Greeting1:= 'Hello ';
28      writeln('Main ':15, 'Greeting1':15, 'global':15,
        Greeting1:15);
29      Proc1;
30      Proc2;
31      end.
```

The program declares three string variables: Greeting1 which is a global variable defined on line *4*, Greeting1 a variable local to procedure Proc1 and declared on line *8*, and finally Greeting2, a local variable declared in Proc2 on line *16*. The main program assigns a value ('Hello') to Greeting1 on line *27* and displays it. Then, when Proc1 is executed, the local variable Greeting1 is assigned a different value ('How do') on line *10* and then displays that string. Finally, when Proc2 is executed, it displays the contents of the local variable Greeting2 followed by the global variable Greeting1. Note that an attempt to include a line such as

```
    writeln(Greeting2);
```

after line *30* in the main program would result in an error since, once Proc2 has terminated, the local variable Greeting2 does not exist. Here is what the program produces as its output:

Source	Variable	Scope	Value
Main	Greeting1	global	Hello
Proc1	Greeting1	local	How do
Proc2	Greeting2	local	Hi
Proc2	Greeting1	global	Hello

Each line of the output indicates the source of the line, that is whether it is generated from the main program or from a procedure, the name of the variable whose value is being displayed, whether the variable is local or global, and the contents of the variable.

Using parameters in procedures

The 'wink' program shown in Listing 29.16 uses the simplest form of procedure which performs a task without any need to communicate with the main program. However, there will be many instances when you will want to use information available in the main program. As we saw in the previous section, global variables provide one means of accomplishing this, but for sound reasons current programming practice discourages the use of global variables for this purpose. Usually a much better method is to use procedures which have either *value parameters* or *variable parameters*.

Value parameters

Listing 29.18 is a modification of the program shown in Listing 29.16. Notice that another procedure, Wink(), has been included. This new procedure uses a *value parameter*, called Eye, which is defined within brackets after the procedure name on line *34*. A value parameter allows you to pass a value to a procedure from the main program or from another procedure. Thus, on line *47*, the value of the for loop variable k is passed to the procedure Wink. k takes the values 1, 2 and 3 which are used to decide which of the three procedures, Face1, Face2 or Face3 to execute. In effect, this causes each of the latter three procedures to be executed in turn. The outer for loop makes this cycle of three procedures to repeat ten times. When one loop is controlled by an outer loop in this fashion, they are called *nested loops*.

Listing 29.18.   A program to illustrate the use of value parameters

```
1      program Winker2(input, output);
2      uses CRT;
3      var
4        i        :integer;
5        k        :integer;
6
7      procedure Face1;
8      begin
9        clrscr;
10       writeln('    _ _     ');
11       writeln(' < 0 0 > ');
12       writeln('   | ^ |   ');
13       writeln('    \_/    ');
14     end;
15
16     procedure Face2;
17     begin
18       clrscr;
19       writeln('    _ _     ');
20       writeln(' < 0 o > ');
21       writeln('   | ^ |   ');
22       writeln('    \_/    ');
23     end;
24
25     procedure Face3;
26       begin
27       clrscr;
28       writeln('    _ _     ');
29       writeln(' < o 0 > ');
30       writeln('   | ^ |   ');
31       writeln('    \_/    ');
32       end;
33
34     procedure Wink(Eye:integer);
```

```
35    begin
36      case Eye of
37        1 :Face1;
38        2 :Face2;
39        3 :Face3;
40      end;
41    end;
42
43    begin
44    for i:= 1 to 10 do
45      for k:= 1 to 3 do
46        begin
47          Wink(k);
48          delay(500);
49        end;
50    end.
```

The number of parameters that you can use in a procedure is not limited to one - you can use as many as you like as long as you declare them in the procedure definition and include them within the brackets when you call the procedure from the main program. For example, suppose that we wanted to include the pre-defined delay procedure on line *48* within the procedure Wink() as shown in the program fragment below.

```
procedure Wink(Eye:integer, Time:integer);
begin
  case Eye of
      begin
        1 :begin
             Face1;
             delay(Time);
           end;
        2 :begin
             Face2;
             delay(Time);
           end;
        3 :begin
             Face3;
             delay(Time);
           end;
  end;
```

Now Wink() has two value parameters and these would both be included in any call to the procedure, as shown in the example below.

```
for i:= 1 to 10 do
    for k:= 1 to 3 do Wink(k, 500);
```

An important point about value parameters is that they provide a *one-way transfer of information* from the main program to a procedure. Variables used as value parameters when a procedure is called are unaffected by any processing that has occurred within the procedure; this is not the case, however, with *variable parameters*.

Variable parameters

Listing 29.19 is an example of a program which incorporates a procedure that uses a variable parameter.

Listing 29.19.   A program to illustrate the use of variable parameters.

```
1    program VarParam(input, output);
2    var
3      Smaller      :real;
4      Larger       :real;
5
6    procedure Sort(var a, b:real);
7    var
8      Temp         :real;
9    begin
10     if a > b then
11       begin
12         Temp:= a;
13         a:= b;
14         b:= Temp;
15       end;
16   end;
17
18   begin
19     write('Enter two numbers: ');
20     readln(Smaller, Larger);
21     Sort(Smaller, Larger);
22     write('The sorted numbers are: ');
23     writeln(Smaller:10:2, Larger:10:2);
24   end.
```

The program simply sorts two numbers into ascending order of magnitude using a procedure. The procedure has two variable parameters, a and b, which it compares: if a is greater than b, the values in a and b are swapped over. The main program asks the user to enter two numbers, it calls the procedure using the two numbers stored in Smallest and Largest, and then displays them when the procedure has finished. Here is a typical run of the program:

```
Enter two numbers: 34.6 17.32 ⏎

The sorted numbers are: 17.32 34.6
```

Notice that the values contained in Smallest and Largest, which were exchanged in the procedure using the variables a and b, have been swapped over. Thus, *variable parameters allow a two-way exchange of data* between a program and a procedure.

User-defined functions

As well as being able to write your own procedures you can also devise your own functions. Functions also accept value or variable parameters, but in addition they require that you declare what type of value they return. So, for a function, you would need to write its first line using the following format:

```
function FunctionName(parameters):return type;
```

In addition, you must assign the return value to FunctionName somewhere within the function. For example, for a function called `TriangleType` which accepts three positive real numbers, in ascending order of magnitude, representing the three sides of a triangle and which returns an integer value of 0, 2 or 3 indicating how many of its sides are equal, the function definition in Listing 29.20 might be appropriate.

Listing 29.20.   A function to determine the type of triangle represented by three numbers

```
20    function TriangleType(a, b, c:real):integer;
21      var
22        Count      :integer;
23    begin
24      Count:= 0;
25      if a = b then Count:= Count + 1;
26       if b = c then Count:= Count + 1;
27       if c = a then Count:= Count + 1;
28      case Count of
29         0 :TriangleType:= 0;
30         1 :TriangleType:= 2;
31         2 :{not possible}
32         3 :TriangleType:= 3;
33       end;
34      end;
```

The three sides are passed as value parameters to the variables a, b and c. The `if` statements on lines *25* to *27* increment `Count` if any two sides are the same. The values that `Count` can assume are 0 for no sides equal, 1 if two sides are equal and 3 if all three sides are equal; a value of 2 is not possible when the three sides are arranged in ascending order of magnitude. The number of equal sides is stored in `TriangleType` by the `case` statement and it is this value which is returned by the function to the calling program. Note that because a function always returns a value it can be used like a variable in an arithmetic expression or in a logical expression or in a `write` statement. For example, it would be perfectly valid to write

```
if TriangleType(x, y, z) = 3 then writeln('Equilateral triangle');
```

Writing programs using procedures and functions

Listing 29.21 illustrates the use of user-defined procedures and functions in a program which allows two people to use the computer to play noughts and crosses. The program illustrates the use of procedures and functions appropriate to a variety of situations. The main program alternately gets X and O moves, checking each time for a winning or drawn position. The program terminates when someone has won or after nine moves have been made.

Listing 29.21.   Noughts and crosses game

```
1    program Oxo(input, output);
2
3    {-----------------------------------------------------------------}
4    {A program which makes use of functions and procedures to allow }
5    {two players to play noughts and crosses. The computer checks    }
6    {for a win  or draw automatically, and ensures that illegal      }
7    {moves are not made. The board is a grid numbered 1 to 9. Each   }
```

```
8    {Player in turn selects a number and the grid is redrawn with   }
9    {the X or O in that position. X always starts first.            }
10   {----------------------------------------------------------------}
11
12   uses CRT;{The screen handling unit to allow screen to be cleared}
13
14   var
15     Grid       :array[1..9] of char;
16     Move       :integer;
17     Count      :integer;
18      Winner    :boolean;
19      XMove     :boolean;
20
21   procedure InitGrid;
22   {----------------------------------------------------------------}
23   {Sets up the board with the positions numbered from 1 to 9       }
24   {----------------------------------------------------------------}
25
26   begin
27     Grid[1]:='1';
28     Grid[2]:='2';
29     Grid[3]:='3';
30     Grid[4]:='4';
31     Grid[5]:='5';
32     Grid[6]:='6';
33     Grid[7]:='7';
34     Grid[8]:='8';
35     Grid[9]:='9';
36   end;
37
38   procedure DrawGrid;
39   {----------------------------------------------------------------}
40   {This draws the current board after every move                   }
41   {----------------------------------------------------------------}
42
43   begin
44     clrscr;
45     writeln(' ',Grid[1], ' | ', Grid[2], ' | ', Grid[3]);
46     writeln('--|--|--');
47     writeln(' ',Grid[4], ' | ', Grid[5], ' | ', Grid[6]);
48     writeln('--|--|--');
49     writeln(' ',Grid[7], ' | ', Grid[8], ' | ', Grid[9]);
50     writeln;
51   end;
52
53   function CheckMove(Move:integer):boolean;
54   {----------------------------------------------------------------}
55   {This validates every move to make sure that a number           }
56   {from 1 to 9 is chosen and that the selected position is        }
57   {not already occupied by an X or O.                             }
58   {Parameters: Move - integer value parameter                     }
59   {Return value:boolean - true if valid, false if invalid move    }
60   {----------------------------------------------------------------}
61
62   begin
63     CheckMove:= true;
64     if (Move < 1) or (Move > 9) then
65       begin
66         writeln('Invalid position - number between 1 and 9');
67         CheckMove:= false;
68       end
69     else if (Grid[Move] = 'X') or (Grid[Move] = 'O') then
```

```
70       begin
71          writeln('This position has already been used');
72          CheckMove:= false;
73       end;
74    end;
75
76    function GetXmove:integer;
77    {------------------------------------------------------------------}
78    {Accepts the X move from the player. If the move is invalid, the}
79    {player is required to enter the move again.                     }
80    {Parameters: None                                               }
81    {Return value: Integer in the range 1 to 9                      }
82    {------------------------------------------------------------------}
83    var
84       Xpos          :integer;
85       ValidXMove    :boolean;
86    begin
87      repeat
88         writeln;
89         writeln('Enter position( 1 to 9 ) for X move');
90         readln(Xpos);
91         ValidXMove:= CheckMove(Xpos);
92      until ValidXMove;
93      GetXmove := Xpos;
94    end;
95
96    function GetOmove:integer;
97    {------------------------------------------------------------------}
98    {This accepts the O move from the player. If the move is         }
99    {invalid the player is required to enter the move again.         }
100   {Parameters: None                                               }
101   {Return value: Integer in the range 1 to 9                      }
102   {------------------------------------------------------------------}
103   var
104      Opos          :integer;
105      ValidOMove    :boolean;
106   begin
107     repeat
108        writeln;
109        writeln('Enter position( 1 to 9 ) for O move');
110        readln(Opos);
111        ValidOMove:= CheckMove(Opos);
112     until ValidOMove;
113     GetOmove:= Opos;
114   end;
115
116   function CheckForWinner :boolean;
117   {------------------------------------------------------------------}
118   {Checks for a line of Xs or Os in one of the 7 possible ways    }
119   {Determines whether row, column or diagonal contains the same   }
120   {character (ie an X or an O)                                     }
121   {Parameters: None                                               }
122   {Return value: Boolean - true if there is a winner, else false  }
123   {------------------------------------------------------------------}
124
125   begin
126      if  (Grid[1]=Grid[2])  and  (Grid[2]=Grid[3])  or
127          (Grid[4]=Grid[5])  and  (Grid[5]=Grid[6])  or
128          (Grid[7]=Grid[8])  and  (Grid[8]=Grid[9])  or
129          (Grid[1]=Grid[4])  and  (Grid[4]=Grid[7])  or
130          (Grid[2]=Grid[5])  and  (Grid[5]=Grid[8])  or
131          (Grid[3]=Grid[6])  and  (Grid[6]=Grid[9])  or
```

```
132          (Grid[1]=Grid[5]) and (Grid[5]=Grid[9]) or
133          (Grid[3]=Grid[5]) and (Grid[5]=Grid[7])
134    then
135          CheckForWinner:= true
136    else CheckForWinner:= false;
137 end;
138
139 begin   {Main program }
140   InitGrid;          {Call procedure to initialise the board }
141   Count:= 0;         {Counts the number of valid moves made  }
142   Winner:= false;    {Boolean variable which becomes true     }
143                      {when there is a winner                  }
144   XMove:= true;      {Keeps track of whose move it is:        }
145                              {true for X move                 }
146                              {false for Y move                }
147   DrawGrid;          {Display the initial board position      }
148
149   {Loop to repeat the playing sequence                       }
150   while (Count < 9) and not Winner do
151     begin
152        case XMove of
153        true:                   {Do this if it is X's move    }
154           begin
155              Move:= GetXmove;{Get the X move position        }
156              Grid[Move]:='X';{Store it in the data structure}
157              XMove:= false;  {Make it O's move next          }
158           end;
159        false:                  {Do this if it is O's move    }
160           begin
161              Move:= GetOmove; {Get the O move position        }
162              Grid[Move]:= 'O';{Store it in the data structure}
163              XMove:= true;    {Make it X's move next          }
164           end;
165     end;
166
167     Count:= Count + 1;        {Increment count after every move}
168
169     DrawGrid;                 {Show the current board position }
170
171     {Check to see if the game is a win or draw                 }
172      Winner:= CheckForWinner;
173      if Winner
174        then writeln('End of Game:', Grid[Move], ' has won')
175      else if Count=9
176        then writeln('A draw');
177     end;
178
179     readln;
180 end.
```

The two procedures, InitGrid and DrawGrid, and the four functions, CheckMove, GetXMove, GetYMove and CheckForWinner, are described in the following sections.

InitGrid

This procedure initialises the character array, Grid[], which is a global array used throughout the program by every procedure and function. The procedure is used once only and does not require any parameters.

DrawGrid

This procedure draws the current board position. Initially the board is displayed like this:

```
1 | 2 | 3
--|---|--
4 | 5 | 6
--|---|--
7 | 8 | 9
```

The numbers are replaced by Xs and Os as the game progresses.

CheckMove

This function has a single integer value parameter called Move which represents the current player's choice of board position. The function first checks that the integer is in the range 1 to 9 before checking the contents of Grid[Move] to ensure that the position is not already occupied with an X or an O. If the move is valid, the function returns a boolean value of true, otherwise it returns false. CheckMove is used by the following two functions.

GetXMove

This function asks the X player to type in a number from 1 to 9 representing a board position. If the move is valid, the function terminates and the position entered by the player is returned as an integer value; if the move is invalid (see function CheckMove) the player is requested to try again.

GetOMove

This function asks the O player to type in a number from 1 to 9. Otherwise it is structurally identical to GetXMove.

CheckForWinner

This function checks individually the three rows, three columns and two diagonals, to see that they contain the same character. If one of these lines does contain the same character, then one of the players has won. For example, if the diagonal represented by Grid[1], Grid[5] and Grid[9] all contain an X, then the X player has won.

Advantages of using procedures and functions

All good programmers make full use of procedures and functions, and in fact their use is essential to the development of all but the most trivial programs. There are a number of good reasons for making this statement, including the following: (i) they allow a large, complex program to be built up from a number of smaller of more manageable units. This facilitates a team approach to program development by allowing each unit to be written and tested independently of the rest of the program; (ii) they can reduce the amount of code required for a program. Once a subprogram has been developed, it can be used as many times as required within a program using the same code; (iii) they can reduce the amount of time required to write a program if libraries of re-usable functions and procedures are available. This is much the same as building electronic circuits using standard electronic components.

Screen handling

Turbo Pascal's CRT unit contains a number of useful screen handling functions and procedures. We have already used two of the procedures in the unit: clrscr to clear the screen and d delay() to make the computer pause while executing a program. More functions and procedures in the CRT unit are described below.

Window procedure

Defines a text window on the screen. The syntax of the procedure is

Window(X1,Y1,X2,Y2) where the four parameters are explained by the following diagram.

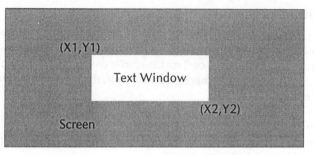

To set a text window containing ten lines at the top of the screen use

        window(1,1,80,10)

To return the current window to the full screen size use

        window(1,1,80,25)

ClrEol procedure

Clears all characters from the cursor position to the end of the line without moving the cursor. It uses the current text window.

DelLine procedure

Deletes the line containing the cursor in the current text window.

GotoXY procedure

Moves the cursor to X, Y, where X is the column and Y is the row relative to the top left corner of the current window which has the coordinates (1, 1). Thus to move the cursor to row 5, column 10, you would use GotoXY(10,5).

InsLine procedure

Inserts a line in the current text window, above the line that the cursor is on.

TextColor procedure

This sets the colour for subsequently displayed text. There are sixteen colours and you can specify each one by name or by using the equivalent number as shown in the Table 29.8. Thus, to set the text colour to red, you could use either TextColor(Red) or TextColor(4).

By using the pre-defined constant, blink, you can make the text flash, for example, TextColor(Blue + Blink).

colour	value	colour	value	colour	value	colour	value
Black	0	Red	4	DarkGray	8	LightRed	12
Blue	1	Magenta	5	LightBlue	9	LightMagenta	13
Green	2	Brown	6	LightGreen	10	Yellow	14
Cyan	3	LightGray	7	LightCyan	11	White	15

Table 29.8.

TextBackGround procedure

This allows you to set one of sixteen different colours for the text background. The colours are shown in the table. Thus to set the background colour to light grey you could use either TextBackGround(LightGray) or TextBackGround(7). Note that if you clear the screen using clrscr after setting the background colour, the whole of the current text window will change to that colour.

Example program 1

The example shown in Listing 29.22 illustrates the use of text windows and text colours by drawing random windows of different colours.

Listing 29.22. Using text windows

```
1    program Screen1(input,output);
2
3    {-------------------------------------------------------------}
4    {Illustrates some screen handling facilities by               }
5    {drawing randomly sized and coloured windows                  }
6    {-------------------------------------------------------------}
7
8     uses CRT;
9    var
10     x       :integer;
11     y       :integer;
12     i       :integer;
13
14   begin
15     textbackground(Black);    {Clear screen             }
16     clrscr;
17
18     for i:= 1 to 100 do
19        begin
20        {Draw random windows                              }
21           x := Random(60);      {Random x position      }
22           y := Random(15);      {Random y position      }
23           window(x, y, x + Random(10), y + Random(8));
24           textbackground( Random(16) + 1);
25           clrscr;    {Set window to random colour       }
26                                {in the range 1 to 16 }
27           delay(200); {Pause for 200 millisecs          }
28        end;
29
30     end.
```

KeyPressed and Readkey

Two other useful functions to be found in Turbo Pascal's CRT unit are KeyPressed and ReadKey. KeyPressed returns a boolean value of true if there is a character in the keyboard buffer and false if the buffer is empty. The keyboard buffer is simply an area of memory which is used to store, temporarily, characters entered through the keyboard. KeyPressed can therefore be used to detect any use of the keyboard. A common application of KeyPressed is as a means of terminating a loop, as illustrated by the following program fragment.

```
repeat
     {instructions to be repeated}
until keypressed;
```

Each time through the repeat loop KeyPressed tests the keyboard buffer: if a key has been pressed, the keyboard buffer will have at least one entry, KeyPressed returns true and the loop terminates, otherwise KeyPressed returns false and the loop repeats once more.

Readkey allows you to capture a keystroke by reading the first character in the keyboard buffer. If the keyboard buffer is empty, it waits until a character is available and then returns its value. The advantage of using ReadKey rather than read or readln is that it is not necessary to press ⏎.

Example program 2

The program shown in Listing 29.23 echoes only numeric characters to the screen, ignoring characters that are not in the range 0 to 9. The repeat loop terminates as soon as the space bar is pressed.

Listing 29.23.   Using readkey.

```
 1     program EchoNumbers(input,output);
 2     {-----------------------------------------------------------}
 3     {Program to display numeric digits entered at keyboard      }
 4     {and to ignore any other characters typed. The program      }
 5     {terminates when the space bar is pressed.                  }
 6     {-----------------------------------------------------------}
 7
 8     uses CRT;
 9
10        var
11        key     :char;
12
13     begin
14        repeat
15          key:= readkey;
16          if (key = '0') and (key '9') then write(key);
17        until key = ' ';
18        end.
```

Sound and NoSound

Finally, these two procedures allow you to use your computer's built-in speaker. Sound(Pitch) causes the speaker to emit a tone whose pitch is determined by the integer parameter, Pitch. Thus, Sound(500) produces a tone with pitch 500Hz. NoSound terminates the tone produced by Sound. Thus to produce a tone of 300Hz for half a second within a program you could use:

```
sound(300);
delay(500);
nosound;
```

Example program 3

As a final example Listing 29.24 uses all of the screen handling functions and procedures discussed in a program which measures how quickly you are able to press a key after being given a signal.

Listing 29.24.   Screen handling example.

```
1    program reflexes(input, output);
2
3    {----------------------------------------------------------------}
4    {A program to illustrate some screen handling facilities.        }
5    {The user is invited to test his/her reflexes by pressing a key }
6    {as quickly as possible. The average of three attempts is        }
7    {calculated and displayed in millisecond units.                  }
8    {----------------------------------------------------------------}
9
10   uses crt;
11     const
12     ROW          =2; {The row base position for screen text        }
13     COLUMN       =5; {The column base position for screen text      }
14
15     var
16     i              :integer; {A for loop control variable           }
17     Total          :integer; {The total time for the three attempts }
18   {.........................oOo....................................}
19
20     procedure FlushKeyboardBuffer;
21
22   {----------------------------------------------------------------}
23   {This makes sure that there are no characters in the standard     }
24   {input buffer. The function readkey removes a single character   }
25   {from the keyboard buffer. Keypressed is true while there is at  }
26   {least one character in the buffer                               }
27   {----------------------------------------------------------------}
28
29     var
30     key :char;
31
32     begin
33       while keypressed do
34         key:= readkey;
35     end;
36   {.........................oOo....................................}
37
38     procedure PressAnyKey;
39
40   {----------------------------------------------------------------}
41   {A procedure that waits until a key is pressed before            }
42   {continuing with the next instruction                            }
43   {----------------------------------------------------------------}
44
45     begin
46     FlushKeyboardBuffer;        {Ensure that the keyboard buffer is  }
```

```
47                                   {empty                                    }
48      repeat until keypressed; {Do nothing until a key is pressed }
49   end;
50   {............................oOo................................}
51
52   procedure instructions;
53
54   {-------------------------------------------------------------------}
55   {Displays the instructions for using the program                    }
56   {-------------------------------------------------------------------}
57
58   begin
59     window(10,10,70,20);        {Define the text window              }
60     textcolor(yellow);          {Text colour set to yellow          }
61     textbackground(blue);       {Background text clour is blue      }
62     clrscr;
63     gotoxy(COLUMN, ROW);
64     writeln('Put your finger on any key and as soon as');
65     gotoxy(COLUMN, ROW+1);
66     writeln('this window changes colour, press it');
67     gotoxy(COLUMN, ROW+3);
68     writeln('You will get three tries and the program');
69     gotoxy(COLUMN, ROW+4);
70     writeln('will calculate your average response time');
71     gotoxy(COLUMN +5, ROW+6);
72     write('Press any key to begin');
73     PressAnyKey;
74   end;
75   {............................oOo................................}
76
77   function Time(attempt:integer):integer;
78
79   {-------------------------------------------------------------------}
80   {Uses the delay() procedure to determine the response time in      }
81   {milliseconds required for hitting the space bar.                  }
82   {-------------------------------------------------------------------}
83
84   var
85      Millisecs :integer;
86
87   begin
88     clrscr;
89     textcolor(yellow);
90     gotoxy(COLUMN, ROW);
91     case attempt of
92       1:write('First attempt starting..');
93        2:write('Second attempt starting..');
94         3:write('Third attempt starting..');
95     end;
96     randomize;                {Initialise the random number generator }
97
98     Millisecs:= 0;
99     delay(1000);                   {Pause for one second before timing }
100      textcolor(red + blink);
101      write(' NOW!');
102      delay(random(5000));    {Random delay of up to 5 seconds        }
103      FlushKeyboardBuffer;    {Make sure that there are no            }
104                              {characters in the keyboard buffer      }
105      textbackground(Red);
106      clrscr;                 {The signal to press the space bar      }
107
108      repeat
```

```
109          delay(1);
110          Millisecs:= Millisecs + 1;{Count how many msecs expire    }
111       until keypressed;              {Look for user hitting any key }
112     Time:= Millisecs;               {Return time taken to respond  }
113   end;
114 {..........................oOo...............................}
115
116 procedure Results(Average:real);
117
118 {————————————————————————————}
119 {Displays the average time taken over the three attempts      }
120 {————————————————————————————}
121
122 begin
123   textbackground(LightGray);
124   textcolor(Black);
125   clrscr;
126   gotoxy(COLUMN, ROW);
127   write('Your average response time was ', Average:5:0,
128             ' milliseconds');
129   gotoxy(COLUMN, ROW + 5);
130   write('Press any key to continue');
131   PressAnyKey;
132 end;
133
134 begin
135   Total:= 0; {Set the total time to 0 }
136   for i:= 1 to 3 do          {Repeat the trial three times        }
137   begin
138     Instructions; {Display the user instructions }
139     Total:= Total + Time(i);{Accumulate time for each trial     }
140   end;
141   Results(Total/3);          {Display result of the three trials}
142 end.
```

The main program starts on line *134*. The procedure `Instructions` explains that the user is to press a key as quickly as he/she can when a rectangular window changes colour. The function `Time()` times how long it took to do so in milliseconds. This time is added to a running total which accumulates the times for three attempts. `Results()` displays the average time the user took to respond. The program makes good use of user-defined functions and procedures, and the comments in the program Listing 29.24 explain their operation, but it is worth adding some further explanation regarding the procedure `PressAnyKey` and associated functions and procedures. As mentioned earlier, the buffer memory associated with the keyboard temporarily stores the values of key depressions made while the program is running, and these values can be accessed using the `ReadKey` function which extracts the first available character in the buffer. By repeatedly using this function to read single characters until there are no more left in the buffer, `FlushKeyboardBuffer` empties the buffer in preparation for using the `KeyPressed` function. This is to ensure that `KeyPressed` will detect only the next key depression and not any that have been made previously.

Reference section

This section describes a number of Pascal's standard functions and some of the additional functions provided by Turbo Pascal.

Standard Pascal functions

abs

Returns the absolute, that is unsigned, value of a real or integer value.

Examples

If x is a real variable then

   1.   `x:= abs(-3.7)`   gives   x = 3.7

   2.   `x:= abs(24.3)`   gives   x = 24.3

If i is an integer variable then

   3.   `i:= abs(-6)`   gives   i = 6

   4.   `i:= abs(3.232)`

      is not allowed since the type of the returned value (real) is not the same as the type of the argument (integer).

exp

Returns the exponential of the argument, that is e^a, where a is the value of the parameter supplied in brackets and e is a mathemetical constant approximately equal to 2.72.

Example

If x is a real variable then

      `x:= exp(2)`   gives   x = 7.39 (that is, x=e^2)

ln

Returns the natural logarithm of the argument, that is, the inverse of the `exp` function.

Example

If x is a real variable then

      `x:= ln(7.39)`   gives   x = 2

sqr

Returns the square of the argument, that is x^2 , where x is the argument.

Examples

If x is a real variable then

   1.   `x:= sqr(-3.1)`   gives   x = 9.61

   2.   `x:= sqr(3.1)`   gives   x = 9.61

If i is an integer variable then

   3.   `i:= sqr(-6)`   gives   i = 36

   4.   `i:= sqr(3.232`

      is not allowed since the type of the returned value (real) is not the same as the type of the argument (integer).

Sqrt

Returns the square root of the operand, that is √x, where x is a positive valued argument.

Examples

If x is a real variable then

1.   `x:= sqrt(16.3)`   gives   x = 4.04

2.   `x:= sqrt(-16.3)`   is not allowed since x is negative

If i is an integer variable then

3.   `i:= sqrt(16)`   gives   i = 4

4.   `i:= sqrt(-16)`   is not allowed since i is negative

sin

Returns the sine of the argument which must be in radians.

Example

Since 1 radian $= \dfrac{180}{\pi}$ degrees, to convert an angle from degrees to radians we must divide the

angle by $\dfrac{180}{\pi}$ where $\pi \approx 3.1416$

Thus, if x is a real variable and we want the sine of 30^0, then

$\quad$ `x:= sin(30/(180/3.1416))`   gives $x = sine(30^0) = 0.5$

cos

Returns the cosine of the argument which must be in radians. See sin above for converting degrees to radians.

Example

If x is a real variable and we want the cosine of 30^0, then

$\quad$ `x:= cos(30/(180/3.1416))`   gives $x = cosine(30^0) \approx 0.87$

Note that the `sin` and the `cos` functions can be used together for finding the tangent of an angle, since $\tan \theta = \sin \theta / \cos \theta$

arctan

Returns the arc tangent of the argument in radians. This is the inverse of finding the tangent of an angle.

Example

If x is a real variable and we want to find the arc tangent of 1 then

$\quad$ `x:= arctan(1)*(180/3.1416)`   gives $x = arctangent(1) = 45^0$

round

Returns the nearest integer type value to the real type value provided.

Examples

If i is an integer variable then

1.   i:= round(34.3)   gives   i = 34

2.   i:= round(34.8)   gives   i = 35

trunc

Converts a real type value to an integer type value by removing the fractional part of the real value.

Examples

If i is an integer variable then

1.   i:= trunc(34.3)   gives   i = 34

2.   i:= trunc(34.8)   gives   i = 34

3.   i:= trunc(.975)   gives   i = 0

ord

This gives the ASCII numeric value for characters.

Examples

If c is an integer variable then

1.   c:= ord('a')   gives   c = 97

2.   c:= ord('A')   gives   c = 65

3.   c:= ord('?')   gives   c = 63

chr

Returns the character equivalent of a numeric code in the range 0 to 255

Examples

If c is an character variable then

1.   c:= chr(97)   gives   c = 'a'

2.   c:= chr(65)   gives   c = 'A'

3.   c:= chr(230)   gives   c = '?'

The following program prints the full character set:

```
program CharSet(input, output);
var
c :char;
i :integer;
begin
     for i:= 0 to 255 do
     writeln(i:10, chr(i):10);
end.
```

odd

Returns TRUE if the argument is an odd number and FALSE if it is an even number. The argument must be an integer. The sign of the argument is ignored.

Examples

If t is a boolean variable then

1.   `t:= odd(23)`   gives   t = TRUE

2.   `t:= odd(22)`   gives   t = FALSE

3.   `t:= odd(-23)`   gives   t = TRUE

4.   `t:= odd(0)`   gives   t = FALSE

3.   `t:= odd(7.5)`   is not allowed since the argument must be an integer.

Some Turbo Pascal functions

These functions are always available in Turbo Pascal and do not require a unit declaration.

Length

Returns the length of a string.

Example

If `s1:= '1234567'` and len is an integer variable then

　　　`len:= length(s1)`   gives   len = 7;

Concat

Joins together a number of strings. The strings are provided as arguments to the function.

Examples

If string variables s1, s2 and s3 have the values

```
s1= 'One, two, three o clock '
s2= 'four o clock '
s3= 'rock'
```

and s4 is another string variable then

　　　`s4:= concat(s1, s2, s3)` gives s4= 'One, two, three o clock four o clock rock'

Copy

This allows a set of characters, or a *substring*, to be copied from a string. It has the form:

　　　`copy(Str, StartChar, NumOfChars)`

where Str is the string from which the substring is to be copied,

StartChar is the position within Str from which to start copying and NumOfChars is how many characters are to be copied.

Examples

If s1 = `'Copy me please'`

1. `s2:= copy(s1, 6, 2)`   gives   s2 = 'me'
2. `s3:= copy(s1, 1, length(s1))` gives   s3= 'Copy me please'

Pos

Returns the starting position of a substring within a string. Returns zero if the substring is not found.

Examples

1. `p:= pos('Koteikan, Windsor Tce', ',')` gives   p=9
2. `p:= pos('abcde', 'z')`   gives   p=0

Upcase

Converts a letter to capitals, that is, upper case. Non letters are not affected.

Examples

1. `Capital:= upcase('x');`   gives   Capital='X'
2. `Capital:= upcase('X');`   gives   Capital='X'
3. `Capital:= upcase('3');`   gives   Capital='3'
4. `readln(Answer);`
5. `if upcase(Answer) = 'Y' then writeln('The Y key was pressed');`

(This is a good way to ensure that pressing both 'y' and 'Y' can be detected).

Random

Generates a random number in the range 0 to *n*-1 where *n* is the integer value supplied to the function.

Example

```
writeln(random(10) + 1)
```

generates a random number between 1 and 10 inclusively.

Randomize

This is a procedure used in conjunction with random function described above. It initialises the random number generator using the system clock so that each time a program is run it does not generate exactly the same set of random numbers.

Exercises

For each of the following problems, design, implement and thoroughly test the program.

Decisions

1. Read a number and display a message which states whether the number is positive, negative or zero.
2. Read a number and print it only if it is between 10 and 20.
3. Read a number followed by a single letter code. The number represents the price of an item and the code indicates whether tax is to be added to the price. If the code is "V" then the tax is 20% of the item's cost. If the code is "X" then the item is not taxed. Print out the total cost of the item.
4. Read three positive, non-zero integers which may represent the sides of a triangle. The numbers are in ascending order of size. Determine whether or not the numbers do represent the sides of a triangle.
5. Read in a single character and print a message indicating whether or not it is a vowel.

Loops

6. Write separate programs to produce conversion tables for:
    (i)   Inches to centimetres (1 to 20 inches, 1 inch = 2.54 centimetres);
    (ii) Pounds to kilograms (1 to 10 pounds, 2.2 pounds per kilogram);
    (iii) Square yards to square metres (10, 20 ,30,..., 100 sq yds 1yd = .91 m)
7. The cost and discount code of a number of items are to be entered by a user. The program must print out each item's cost, discount and cost less discount. The discount codes are as follows:

    The program will terminate when the user enters 0 for the cost of the item. The program must then print the total cost of all the items entered.

Code	Discount
A	5%
B	10%
C	15%

8. Write a program to repeatedly display a menu containing a number of options for converting between different units, plus one option to exit the program. The user must enter a number or letter corresponding to a menu item. Valid entries are to accept a numeric value from the user and apply and display the appropriate conversion, invalid entries are reported and the user is reminded about what choices are valid, and the exit option terminates the program. An example follows.

    Menu

    1 Inches to centimetres

    2 Centimetres to inches

    3 Pounds to Kilograms

    etc

    4 Exit

    Please enter option number :

9. A program reads an integer representing the number of gas bills to be processed, followed by that number of customer details. Each set of customer details consists of a customer number, a single character code representing the type of customer and the

number of units used. Customers are of type 'D' (domestic) or 'B' (business). Domestic customers are charged 8p per unit and business customers are charged 10p per unit. For each customer print the customer number, the number of units used and the cost of the gas used. Print the total number of units used for this batch of customers and the total amount charged.

10. Repeat the previous question assuming that all the domestic users are first and that separate totals are required for domestic and business users.

Strings

11. Read two strings and compare them. Print a message to indicate whether or not they are identical.

12. Repeat the previous problem but ignore case. For example, your program should regard the strings

    "Hello There", "HELLO THERE", and "hello there" as being identical.

13. Read a string representing a sentence and print the number of words in the sentence. Assume that words are separated by no more than one space and that there are no punctuation marks in the text.

14. Write separate programs to enter and store a string of up to 80 characters and then:

    (i)   Count the number of leading spaces;

    (ii)   Count the number of trailing spaces;

    (iii) Count the number of embedded spaces;

    (iv)   Count the number of leading, trailing and embedded spaces;

    (v)   Remove leading and trailing spaces from a string, and reduce multiple embedded spaces to single spaces.

15. Read a string containing a sentence and print the words in reverse order. For example, the sentence "the cat sat on the mat" would become, "mat the on sat cat the".

16. Read a string and determine whether it is purely alphabetic, purely numeric or a mixture of alphabetic and numeric characters.

Arrays

17. Read 15 values into a numeric array and then:

    (i)   print the contents the array;

    (ii)   find the average of the numbers stored in the array;

    (iii) copy the array into a duplicate array, but in reverse order. Print the contents of both arrays.

18. Read a set of numbers and swap the first number with the largest in the set. Then, starting from the second value, find the largest number in the remaining list and swap it with the second value.

    Repeat this process until the list has been sorted into ascending order of magnitude.

Validation

19. Post codes have the following possible formats:

    (i)   aa99 9aa

    (ii)   aa9 9aa

    (iii) a9a 9aa

    where *a* represents an alphabetic character and *9* represents a numeric character. Write a program to validate a post code, assuming that only uppercase letters are used and there is a single space separating the two parts of the post code.

20. As for the previous problem but allow upper and lower case letters, leading spaces, trailing spaces and more than one space between the two parts of the code.

Encoding

21. Many names that sound the same are often spelled differently and this can cause problems in information systems. For example, Waites, Waits and Whaites all sound the same though they are all spelled differently and contain different numbers of letters. A coding system called Soundex can be used to solve this problem by converting a name into a code based on the following algorithm.

    (i)   The first letter of the name is used as the first letter of the code.

    (ii)   All subsequent vowels, and the letters H, W and Y are ignored.

    (iii)   Double letters are replaced by single instances of the letter.

    (iv)   Then this code, apart from the first character, is converted into a number by substituting the letters in the following table by numeric digits.

Letter	Substitute
BFPV	1
CGJKQSXZ	2
DT	3
MN	4
L	5
R	6

    (v)   The code is restricted to four characters including the leading letter.

    (vi)   If the code is less than four characters it is padded with zeros.

22. Write a program to convert a name into its equivalent Soundex code. Some examples are given below.

    Morton becomes M635

    Morten becomes M635

    Waites becomes W320

    Whaites becomes W320

    Waits becomes W320

23. The table illustrates the Morse code.

A	. −	N	− .
B	− . . .	O	− −
C	− . − .	P	. − − .
D	− . .	Q	− − . −
E	.	R	. − .
F	. . − .	S	. . .
G	− − .	T	−
H	. . . .	U	. . −
I	. .	V	. . . −
J	. − − −	W	. − −
K	− . −	X	− . . −
L	. − . .	Y	− . − −
M	− −	Z	− − . .

(i)   Write a program to read in a word (or a sentence if you wish) and output it in Morse code.

(ii) Add sound so that when a letter is pressed on the keyboard the appropriate Morse code is heard.

24. A form of encoding used on the Internet is called "rot13" encoding. It involves taking each letter of the alphabet and replacing it by the letter 13 positions further on in the alphabet as shown in the following table.

Letter	Replace with	Letter	Replace with	Letter	Replace with
A	N	J	W	S	F
B	O	K	X	T	G
C	P	L	Y	U	H
D	Q	M	Z	V	I
E	R	N	A	W	J
F	S	O	B	X	K
G	T	P	C	Y	L
H	U	Q	D	Z	M
I	V	R	E		

(i)   Write a program to read a block of text and encode it using rot13. Spaces and punctuation marks do not need to be encoded.

(ii)   Write a program to decode text which has been encoded using rot13.

(iii) Invent and implement your own encoding and decoding scheme using a different form of substitution.

Assignment

4.1.

A program is required to read in three numeric values representing the three sides of a triangle. The numbers are to be entered from a keyboard one after the other, separated by one or more spaces and followed by pressing the Enter key. The program outputs a number of messages regarding the type of triangle that the three numbers represent:

- ❑ Invalid data: these values cannot be used to form a triangle;
- ❑ Invalid data: non-numeric input;
- ❑ Scalene;
- ❑ Isosceles;
- ❑ Equilateral;
- ❑ Obtuse;
- ❑ Right-angled.

The program may print out more than one message. For instance, if the three values were 3, 3, 5, the program should say that the triangle is 'Obtuse' and 'Isosceles'.

Task 1

Using a standard design methodology design the program. Your design should adhere to top-down, structured design principles and should include a data dictionary specifying the name, type, size and use of all identifiers used in the design.

Task 2

1. Use appropriate testing methods to devise test cases which would test the program thoroughly.
2. For each test case specify the expected output from the program.
3. You should assume that the program has code to validate the input so that it can detect invalid inputs. Your test data should cover every possible output from the program for invalid and valid data.

Task 3

Write the program using the design in Task 1.

After identifying and removing syntax and runtime errors, test the program using the test cases devised in Task 2. Keep a log of test results and of how errors were corrected and the program re-tested.

You will need to research the characteristics of each type of triangle in order to devise test data that represents each possible type of triangle.

Unit 5

Business information systems

Chapters

Unit 5 Outcomes and assessment criteria

Outcomes	Assessment criteria To achieve each outcome a student must demonstrate the ability to:
1. Examine the need for **information in organisations.**	• explain why organisations are formed • describe how information varies in different sizes of organisations.
2. Investigate the **functional areas** within organisations.	• describe the activities of each of the functional areas • identify and graphically illustrate the flow of information between functional areas (eg DFD).
3. Examine the methods for **data handling and processing** of information within organisations.	• document the ways in which information gets processed.
4. Understand the physical and operational requirements of a **business system.**	• analyse the factors that need to be taken into account with regards to the layout of a business • explain the factors that need to be taken into account with regards to the protection and use of data.

Chapter 24

Organisations

Need for organisations

The society in which we live is complex and sophisticated. As consumers we demand a variety of goods and services to enable us to maintain the quality of life we enjoy. In order to satisfy these demands, suppliers must produce the goods and services which the consumer wants by combining factors of production such as land, labour and capital in the most efficient manner. By this we mean producers must hire workers, rent or buy premises, perhaps invest in plant and machinery and purchase raw materials, and then organise the manufacture of the final product in such a way that they will make a profit. Society may also gain, as its scarce resources are being used in the way consumers wish rather than being wasted in producing things people do not need. Suppliers under such a system are known as commercial organisations. Many public sector organisations also provide goods and services to society and, in the same way as commercial organisations, these public sector bodies must employ staff, occupy premises and raise capital. The fundamental difference between these two types of organisation lies in the objectives they seek to fulfil. The private sector tends to be motivated by profit, while public sector organisations will often have a much less mercenary motive, such as providing for the public good and improving the state of society. If we wish to see society ordered and governed in such a way that individuals are free to express their demands and producers are able to meet such wants, it becomes necessary to form organisations to control and regulate society through a variety of administrative structures. These are the bodies which make up the organisations of the state. In the UK, these are Parliament, the Government and its Executive, the Civil Service, the Local Authorities and the Courts and justice system. These bodies are required to carry out legislative, administrative and judicial functions.

If you examine the nature and range of individual demands in an industrialised society you soon realise that most of them cannot be met other than by organisations. Individually we lack the knowledge, skills and physical resources to manufacture products that fulfil our needs, whether these are simple or sophisticated. It would be as difficult for us to make a biro or a floppy disk as it would a television or a computer. Admittedly, some goods and services can be supplied by an individual working alone. A farmer may be able to grow sufficient food to satisfy himself and his family without any help from others. But what if he requires other goods and services? It is unlikely that the farmer will also have the ability or resources to produce his own combine-harvester or tractor. If he did not have such products which are manufactured by others, his life would be much simpler, but no doubt much harder.

A similar situation exists in the supply of services. A strong and resourceful individual may try to protect himself and his property from the dangers imposed by thieves or vandals. If he cannot, however, then he may turn to the state to demand protection. Recognising that a failure to respond to such demands from its citizens would lead to an anarchic system, the government must accept the responsibility and establish a legal system incorporating law enforcement agencies to provide the protection being sought.

How, then, are these goods and services produced? It is clear that individuals working independently would be unable to meet our complex physical and social needs. Therefore society has developed a system where people join together to form organisations. These bodies are extraordinarily diverse. They manufacture products, which they distribute and sell. They also provide all the services that we need. Thus, both the BBC and the Ford Motor Company are organisations, although their products are very different.

Clearly, then, if individuals within society are to have all their various needs satisfied, there must be co-operation between workers. Each must specialise in a certain aspect of the supply process. These workers must be organised and allocated a specific role in which to perform co-ordinated tasks. These tasks are normally organised with the aim of producing a given product or service, although there are some organisations which do not specialise and which make an extremely diverse range of products. In the private sector of the economy, such businesses will usually have the objective of making a profit for their owners. Of course, this is just one example of an organisation. As we have already noted, the state is another form of organisation which is clearly more complex than a business, and it has a variety of objectives, such as increasing the wealth of citizens, improving their quality of life and protecting them if they are threatened. We are all members of organisations, some of which are formal while others are informal. Your family is an example of an informal organisation, as is the group of friends you mix with. Other more formal organisations to which you may belong or may have belonged are the school you attended as a child, your employing body, or your trade union.

The tendency to form groups is a characteristic of human nature. Human beings are highly socialised, they need to 'belong' and will generally find it uncomfortable and disturbing if they cannot find 'acceptance' within a social group. An employee who is capable and confident in his or her job, and who is in turn regarded by the employer and the rest of the work force as a professional, gains a 'role' satisfaction through identifying as a vital part of the group. So organisations have an important role to fulfil in meeting the social needs of man. However, perhaps more important in the context of this course of study is the function of organisations as the satisfiers of needs. They allow individual workers to develop their specialist skills, and this in turn allows productive capacity to increase.

Since differing organisations concentrate on the supply of different goods and services, there must be a system established whereby products can be distributed to the consumers. Thus shops, wholesalers, transport companies and so on must all be involved. The fabric of the social and economic environment is based on a process whereby individuals form organisations which are dependent upon other organisations to survive. In just the same way as the needs of the individual cannot be met by that individual alone, so the same also holds true for organisations. They are interdependent. Organisational activity involves a perpetual interaction, one organisation with another, as society steadily evolves in a direction that individually and collectively we try to guide. However, as we shall see, even though the overall aim of society is the advancement of our physical well-being, the methods for achieving this are the subject of much disagreement.

Characteristics common to all organisations

The specific reasons for the formation of organisations are many and varied, and may not, of course, always be clearly defined. Some are the result of the need for individuals to find company for a social or leisure reason, for example by forming a sporting or working-men's club.

Others are formed with a more precise economic objective in mind, such as the desire to make a profit for the person who has established a business organisation. Some, such as the organisations which make up the state and government, evolve as a result of the emergence of particular needs in society which require government intervention. For example, the Government established the National Health Service in 1946 to meet the needs of society for a high standard of free health care, available to all. Nevertheless, most formal organisations have some common characteristics. These may be simply stated as follows:

(i)   The establishment of an organisation is usually for a specific purpose.

For example, the Automobile Association was founded with the precise objective of promoting the interests of motorists within this country. Other organisations may be launched with one prime aim, but may later diversify in order to follow alternative causes or objectives. For instance, Guinness, the brewery company, was established to produce alcoholic drinks, but now has subsidiaries making a variety of products such as fishing tackle boxes and cassette cases. This illustrates how a business may try to evolve as the commercial environment changes and new commercial opportunities emerge.

(ii)   Organisations usually have a distinct identity.

People belonging to a specific organisation can identify themselves as being part of a group either as a result of where they work or of what they do. A Manchester United footballer wears a red shirt to show he is part of the particular organisation. A member of a trade union is given a membership card to signify he belongs to that union. Manufacturing companies promote their brand names through advertising. This sense of identity, which we have already seen is an important need for most people, can produce extreme loyalty to the organisation.

(iii) Most organisations require some form of leadership.

We have seen that organisations are normally formed for a specific purpose. In order to achieve this purpose, it is necessary to co-ordinate the efforts of the members of the organisation. This requires management, or leadership. Formal organisations such as companies or a club have a specified management hierarchy which may be appointed by the owners of the organisation. For instance, the shareholders of a company appoint the directors. Alternatively, the leadership may be elected, as in the case of a club or society where the members vote to have a chairman, secretary and committee. However, once appointed this management team has the responsibility for ensuring the organisation achieves its objectives.

(iv)   Organisations are accountable.

Such accountability applies both to those the management team deals with and those it employs.

Objectives of organisations

The objectives of an organisation are the targets it hopes to achieve. Clearly the objectives which are set will vary considerably between different types of organisation. As we shall see later in this section, the objectives of commercial organisations will largely be based around the goal of profit. For organisations within the public sector, profit may not be the sole aim. Factors such as benefit to the community or the creation of jobs may also feature as targets for the public sector. It should be noted, however, that the profit motive has grown substantially in importance in recent times.

A classification of organisations

Initially, it is convenient to categorise organisations as follows:

❏   public service;

❏   commercial and industrial.

Public service organisations

Many public services are provided by central and local government (the public sector) Central government takes responsibility for a wide range of services and has specific organisations, referred to as Departments, to manage each. Thus, there are separate departments, each responsible for the provision of, amongst others, health, education, defence and social welfare services. The role of local government is continually changing as successive governments pursue policies which tend to centralise power, or devolve it to locally elected council bodies. The provision of water, electricity and gas services used to be provided by 'public utilities', but they have been 'privatised' and now operate as commercial and industrial businesses. Some services, traditionally provided by the public sector, are now partly in the private sector; for example, some prisons are privately owned and private companies may carry out the work of refuse collection. Even so, overall control of such services is still the responsibility of central and local government departments. Table 24.1 lists some major central government organisations and briefly describes the responsibilities of each. Table 24.2 does the same, in respect of local government.

Government departments	Responsibilities
Education	Schools
Transport	Road and building
Home Office	Law and order, police and prison services policy
Health	Hospitals,
Trade and Industry	Business and industrial policy
Social Security	Benefits such as income support.
Treasury	Economic policy
Defence	Armed Forces

Table 24.1. *Central Government Departments and areas of responsibility*

It should be noted that although the government departments retain overall responsibility for the areas listed in the Table, private companies carry out some of the work. For example, some hospitals, prisons and schools are privately owned. As part of the government's 'privatisation' programme, local councils have to allow private businesses to tender for (compete for) work traditionally carried out by their own departments; this is called Compulsory Competitive Tendering (CCT).

For example, private businesses can tender for contracts to carry out street sweeping or refuse collection. In addition, some schools have 'opted out' and receive their funding directly from central governments.

Local Government departments	Responsibilities
Social Services	Home helps, children's homes, meals on wheels, day nurseries, residential homes and day centres for the mentally ill.
Education	Nursery, and secondary schools.
Housing	Council housing provides affordable accommodation for those who cannot buy their own homes.
Environmental Services	Refuse collection and disposal, street sweeping and pollution control.
Police and Fire Services	Although there is co-operation between forces, these services are still locally controlled.
Planning and Building Control	Consider applications for local building and enforce regulations on building standards.

Table 24.2. *Local Government Departments and areas of responsibility*

Industry and commerce

The term 'industry' covers a wide range of organisations which form part of a country's economy. We tend to link factories with the idea of industry, but the term also covers: *extraction* industries, such as coal-mining and fishing; *manufacturing* businesses which take raw materials and process them into finished products, such as cars and clothing, as well as those assembling ready-made components into, for example, computers and televisions; *retail* and *wholesale* businesses, concerned with buying, selling and distributing goods for personal and business consumption; *service* industries, such as hotel, catering, travel and banking. The word 'commerce' overlaps with 'industry' and includes all forms of trading organisation and those which support trade, such as banking and insurance.

Organisational structures

A structure can be defined as having component parts, which are connected in a particular way. Structures are designed to fulfil purposes. For example, a house is a structure, consisting of rooms, windows, floors, ceilings, doors and connection passages; the mix of these component parts and the way they are put together determines the design of the house. Two main types of organisational structure are considered here: *hierarchical*; *flat*.

Hierarchical structure

An organisation with a hierarchical structure includes different levels of authority and responsibility. Heads of Department may be directly responsible to one of the Directors. For example, the Accounts Department Head may be subject to the authority of the Financial Director. Such authority relates to the operation of the organisation and enables tasks to be completed. There may be Section Supervisors who are responsible to their respective Heads of Department for particular functions within departments. Each section supervisor may have authority over a number of clerks.

Generally, there are more 'workers' than 'bosses', so a hierarchical structure can be viewed as a pyramid, as shown in Figure 24.1; the lower down the pyramid you descend, the larger the number of staff you are likely to find employed. The jobs at the top of the pyramid carry the most authority and the greatest responsibility for the success or failure of the organisation.

Operatives and clerical staff are unlikely to have any authority in the organisation, but they have responsibility for the completion of their own jobs.

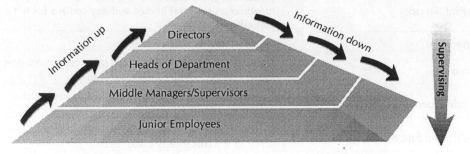

Figure 24.1. *Hierarchy of authority, responsibility and information flow*

Downward communication

Figure 24.1 shows that, within the pyramid, communications go up and down. Policy decisions taken at board level by the directors are implemented by instructing the relevant departmental heads to see that the policy is carried out. The heads of department brief their middle managers and the final stage in the process is the communication between middle managers and their subordinates.

Upward communication

The communication also passes from the bottom upwards. Staff provide feedback to their seniors. This may take many forms; it may involve monitoring shortages of materials, absences of staff, production problems, grievances and suggestions for improving work methods. Anything which requires the authority or approval of someone further up the organisational hierarchy and which has been generated or identified below, will pass back up the system. Only in extreme circumstances is it likely that an issue arising at the bottom of the pyramid will pass right back to the top for consideration and decision. For the most part, an immediate senior is likely to have sufficient authority to make a decision; ultimately however, it is a question of the extent of *delegated* responsibility held by senior employees that determines whether they can deal with it personally, or must pass it back to their own superiors. As organisations grow bigger it is inevitable that communications have much further to travel. This is not ideal since it is likely to take longer to transmit information and there is greater distancing between the giver and the receiver, which can lead to a 'them and us' view of the organisation by junior staff. However, it is clear that as the organisation grows, so its communication system must be become increasingly refined. Information technology support is crucial to the efficiency of communications.

Flat structure

In contrast to a hierarchy, a flat structure generally has a single level of management, as shown in Figure 24.2. Except for the smallest organisations, very few will have an entirely flat structure. It is possible, that an organisation wishes to avoid a cumbersome hierarchy and attempts to keep the number of management levels to a minimum; they are thus aiming for a 'flatter' structure. As mentioned earlier, hierarchies with many levels of authority can make communication difficult. A flatter structure can encourage 'team spirit' through the avoidance of the 'them and us' feelings, which can be characteristic of hierarchies

Figure 24.2 represents a firm of solicitors, where each partner has the same level of authority and responsibility, specialises in a particular aspect of the law and has joint authority over the Office Manager and articled clerks ('apprentice' solicitors). The Office Manager is responsible for supervision of the clerical staff. Although there are hierarchical elements in the organisation, its structure is fairly 'flat'.

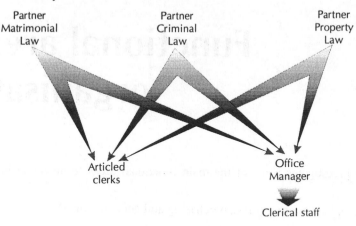

Figure 24.2. *Flatter structure*

Exercises

1. Choose three formal organisations with which you are familiar and for each:
   (a) identify its main *purpose*;
   (b) select an aspect which gives it its distinct *identity*;
   (c) briefly describe how it is *lead* - its top management structure;
   (d) identify to whom the management are ultimately *accountable*.
2. Use the examples you provided in 1. to illustrate characterstics which are common to all organisations.
3. The water industry used to be in the public sector, but is now run by private companies, overseen by a regulator (OFFWAT). Briefly list features which allow the privatised water company to be classified as both commercial and public service.
4. (a) Choose a hierarchically structured organisation with which you are familiar and using Figure 24.1 as a guide, draw a pyramid structure to show the main levels of authority.
   (b) Identify two benefits and two drawbacks of the structure for the chosen organisation.

Chapter 25

Functional areas of organisations

This Chapter investigates some of the main functional areas to be found in organisations, namely:

- ❑ financial accounting (sales, purchasing and general ledger);
- ❑ invoicing and stock control;
- ❑ marketing;
- ❑ payroll and personnel;
- ❑ design and production;
- ❑ ICT services.

Financial accounting

Financial accounting or 'book-keeping' is the process of recording financial transactions arising from the day-to-day operation of a business. The sale of goods to a customer and the subsequent settlement of the debt are two examples of financial transactions. More detailed information on financial accounting systems is provided in Chapter .

Sales accounting

When credit sales are made to customers, a record needs to be kept of amounts owing and paid. Payment is normally requested with an invoice, which gives details of goods supplied, quantities, prices and VAT. Credit sales are usually made on for example, a 14, 21 or 28 day basis, which means that the customer has to pay within the specified period to obtain any discounts offered. Overdue payments need to be chased, so sales accounting systems normally produce reports analysing the indebtedness of different customers. Debt control is vital to business profitability and computerised systems can produce prompt and up-to-date reports as a by-product of the main application.

Purchase accounting

This function is concerned with controlling amounts owed and payments made to suppliers of services, goods or materials which are used in the main business of the company. For example, a car manufacturer will need to keep records of amounts owing to suppliers of car components and sheet steel manufacturers. Delayed payments to suppliers may help cash flow, but can harm an organisation's image, or even cut off a source of supply when a supplier refuses to deliver any more goods until payment is made.

Nominal or general ledger

The general ledger keeps control of financial summaries, including those originating from payroll, sales and purchase accounting and acts as a balance in a double entry system. Computerised systems can automatically produce reports at the end of financial periods, including a trial balance, trading and profit and loss account and balance sheet.

Other finance-related functions

Stock control

Any organisation which keeps stocks of raw materials or finished goods needs to operate a stock control system. Although stock constitutes an asset, it ties up cash resources that could be invested in other aspects of the business. Equally, a company must keep sufficient quantities of items to satisfy customer demand or manufacturing requirements. To maintain this balance a stock control system should provide up-to-date information on quantities, prices, minimum stock levels, and re-order quantities. It should also give warning of excessively high, or dangerously low levels of stock. In the latter case, orders may be produced automatically. A stock control system may also generate valuable management reports on, for example, sales patterns, slow-moving items, and overdue orders.

Sales order processing

This function will normally be concerned with:

☐ the validation of orders, checking, for example, that the goods ordered are supplied by the business or that the customer's credit status warrants the order's completion;

☐ the identification of individual items ordered. A customer may request several different items on the same order form and any particular item will probably appear on many different order forms, so the quantities for each are totalled to produce picking lists to enable warehouse staff to retrieve the goods for despatch;

☐ the monitoring of back orders. If an order cannot be fulfilled, it may be held in abeyance until new stocks arrive, so all outstanding back orders need to be available on request.

Invoicing

This function deals with the production of customer invoices, requesting payment for goods or services delivered. Information stored in the customer files and stock files is used to produce invoices, usually on pre-printed continuous stationery.

Payroll

Payroll systems are concerned with the production of payslips for employees and the maintenance of records required for taxation and other deductions. In a manual system, the preparation of payroll figures and the maintenance of payroll records is a labour intensive task. Although tedious and repetitive, it is a vitally important task. Most employees naturally regard pay as being the main reason for work and resent delays in payment or incorrect payments, unless of course it is in their favour! The repetitive nature of the task makes it a popular candidate for computerisation, especially with organisations which employ large numbers of people. The automatic production of reports for taxation purposes also provides a valuable benefit. Smaller organisations with only several employees probably do not regard payroll as a high priority application for computerisation. The benefits are not as great if the payroll can be carried out by one or two employees who also carry out a number of other tasks.

Human resources

The human resources (personnel) function is responsible for the selection (usually by interview), recruitment, training and development of staff. Personnel records will store all the information needed by Salaries and Wages to make the correct payments to employees; this will include details of, for example, gross salary, tax code, statutory sick pay and holiday entitlement. Depending on the size of the organisation, information may also be held concerning: qualifications, courses attended; personal and career development plans.

Design

The design function is present where an organisation develops its own products and services; a trader who simply buys and sells goods has no need of a design team. Design is part of the research and development R& D) function, which is vital to organisations wishing to radically develop their product range. The nature of design teams depends on the product or service being designed. The skills and talents of a car design team are clearly very different from those of a team designing a cover for a magazine.

Production

The production function should, ideally, be driven by the market for the business's products. In other words, it should be geared to produce the necessary mix and quantities of products required by customers. If goods are perishable within a short time, and large reserve stocks cannot be held, then production should be flexible and responsive to the day-to-day sales requirements. Of course, this is an ideal and production plans cannot always be changed at short notice; ships and other large items take months or years to build.

The production department must know exactly what is required and when; it must also have the staff with the necessary skills and any machinery must have the appropriate facilities and production capacity. For example, a production department which is geared to produce 1000 units of a product per day, will probably find it difficult to produce 2000 units, without modification of the system of production.

Marketing

A marketing function is a vital part of many large national and international businesses; it aims to generate information, from a wide range of data sources, to support marketing decisions. Three such decision areas are:

(i)   *strategic* and relating to, for example, expansion of the company's existing market share and the identification of new marketable products;

(ii) *tactical*, for example, planning the marketing mix;

(iii) *operational*, for example, day-to-day planning of sales calls and ad hoc promotions.

At the operational level, for example, data gathered from sales invoices, sales force staff and accounting information can be used to establish customer types. Thus, customers can be classified as 'low', 'medium' or 'high' volume users according to the frequency and volume of their orders. This information can help sales staff to target particular categories of customer and to plan the timing of sales calls. At the tactical level, invoices provide information on sales variance between different market segments over time or sales projections based on current patterns.

Distribution

Distribution concerns the delivery of a company's products to its customers and is obviously of great importance. An organisation can have the best products in the world and the most effective marketing campaigns, but if it cannot distribute its goods efficiently it will fail. Distribution systems include the management and control of a company's own delivery vehicles and drivers, the scheduling of deliveries to ensure rapid response to orders and efficient use of the transport fleet. If a company does not have its own vehicles, then it must arrange for suitable contracts with other companies, such as Parcel Force, UPS and Securicor. Systems must also be in place for the handling delayed deliveries and customer complaints, order tracking (buyers can check on the progress of their order) and the return of unwanted or damaged goods.

Controlling the costs of distribution, which can be considerable, is of major importance. For example, the breakdown of distribution costs across manufacturing industry is typically as follows: administration 17%; transport 29%; handling 8%; packaging 12%; warehousing 17%; stock control 17%.

Administration

Administration systems provide support and services across the organisation. They include, for example, the handling of telephone switchboard and fax and photocopying services, document production, room booking (for meetings etc), requisitioning of equipment and consumables, and general secretarial support. ICT services are part of that administration support service.

ICT Services

Apart from small firms, most organisations need specialist staff to develop, introduce, maintain and update the various systems which make use of information technology. The term 'information communication technology' covers all computer-based information processing systems, plus those which make use of data communications, such as computer networks, fax machines, photocopiers and telephone systems. The responsibilities of ICT Services are, therefore, much broader than those traditionally held by wholly centralised computer services or data processing departments. The development of cheaper and more powerful microcomputer systems, which can be networked with one another, as well as with larger mini and mainframe systems, has resulted in computer facilities being distributed more widely. For this reason, ICT Services needs to provide a much more flexible service and support user systems at the point of use. For example, users of network workstations need support when equipment, such as a shared printer, breaks down or they may require help in the use of software on the network. This contrasts with a centralised department, which holds all the computer equipment, carries out all computer processing and restricts user access to specialised applications, run through dedicated terminals. ICT Services may be known variously as Computer Services, Management Information Services or less commonly now, the Data Processing Department.

Role of ICT Services

ICT Services fulfils a servicing function for the whole organisation. In larger organisations, there is a centralised computer facility, possibly in the shape of a mainframe or mini-computer system, with the responsibility for major applications, such as payroll and stock control. User departments may have access to the centralised facility through attached terminals or net-worked microcomputers. Individual members of staff may also use stand-alone microcomputer systems or portable devices, such as notebooks and personal digital assistants (PDAs). ICT Services staff need to support users in the use of these distributed facilities, as well as control the operation of any centralised system. IT Services provides facilities to satisfy both *operational* and *managerial* information needs.

Operational requirements

Each functional area has its own operational information needs. For example, Wages and Salaries need payroll details and payslips, and Sales Order Processing require the production of customer invoices. Common examples of routine operations include:

- ❑ keeping stock records
- ❑ sales accounting and purchase accounting;
- ❑ payroll;
- ❑ invoicing and production of delivery notes;
- ❑ routine costing;
- ❑ filing of customer orders.

Managerial requirements

Routine processing work forms the bulk of the activity within ICT Services, but there is an increasing demand for management information. This includes assistance with functions which require management involvement and thinking, but which can be partially automated or assisted by computers. Examples of such functions include:

- ❑ production planning;
- ❑ short term and long term forecasting;
- ❑ setting of budgets;
- ❑ decision-making on financial policies;
- ❑ marketing decisions and sales management;
- ❑ factory maintenance and management;
- ❑ price determination;
- ❑ selection of suppliers.

Function of ICT Services

Figure 25.1 shows the typical functions within an ICT Services department.

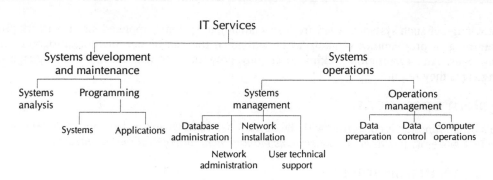

Figure 25.1. *Typical structure of ICT Services department*

Systems development

This function relates to the development of new computerised systems and the maintenance of existing ones. This function is staffed primarily by *systems analysts* and *programmers*. In small organisations, hybrid skills are often needed, so job titles such as *analyst programmer* may be used.

Systems analysis

Systems analysis is a process used in the design of new systems, as requested by corporate management. Systems analysis follows stages of *investigation*, *design* and *implementation*. Each stage should involve close consultation with potential users, in the various functional areas of the organisation, to ensure that their information and operational requirements are met.

The design stage should produce a *system specification* which, rather like an architect's plans for a building, details all necessary materials and procedures needed to fulfil the specification. The specification should detail the necessary clerical procedures, hardware requirements and the inputs, processing and outputs required of the computer software.

After implementation of a system, it will require continual monitoring and probably, occasional modification, when the operational or information requirements of users change. This maintenance task is the responsibility of the systems analysts,

Programming

Programming lacks some of the creative aspects of systems analysis and involves the use of a programming language (for example, C++, COBOL, Visual BASIC) to code the necessary computer programs. The program requirements are detailed in the *program* or *software specification*, which forms part of the system specification prepared by systems analysts.

Most programmers who work in an ICT Services department are likely to be *applications programmers*, responsible for the development or modification of applications, such as stock control or payroll. Systems programmers are concerned with the development of operating systems and utilities, which are normally developed by large computer manufacturers or software companies, such as Microsoft. An ICT Services department may also employ *systems programmers*, but they are likely to have a more limited role than applications programmers. Much software is now in commercial package form, but not all applications can be satisfied by such means and applications programmers continue to be needed for tailoring of programs specifically for their employer.

The growth of network use has created the need for *network programmers*, who have specialist knowledge of such systems. Apart from specialising in systems, applications or network programming, a programmer is likely to be skilled in the use of one or more programming languages. An organisation seeking to employ programmers will specify the language or languages they require.

System operations

This broad function is concerned with the operational, rather than the developmental aspects of the ICT systems. It is divided into *systems management* and *operations management*.

Systems management

This function deals with the general operation of all the ICT systems and is not directly concerned with particular applications.

There are a number of separate areas within this function: *network installation*; *network administration*; *intranet and extranet management*; *user technical support*; *database administration*.

Network installation and administration

Computer networks are a feature of most organisations and tasks of selecting, purchasing and installing the hardware and software, both systems and applications, may be carried out by specialist staff in this area. Staff employed in this area need to be familiar with the network operating system and its utilities. They are responsible for setting up and managing network user accounts, controlling passwords, managing printer queues, allocating and maintaining and backing up network storage and monitoring the performance of the network.

User technical support

The distribution to users, of computer resources through networks, desktop and portable computer systems has hugely expanded the need for ICT user support. Users often have access to a range of different devices, such as printers, scanners, plotters and fax modems and apart from needing initial training in their use, they also require occasional support when things go wrong. Support staff may also give guidance in the use of software and help trouble-shoot problems which users will inevitably encounter at some stage. User technical support is extremely important if users are to use ICT resources efficiently and for the benefit of the organisation.

Database administration

If applications are implemented through a database system, then specialist staff, known as database administrators, are employed to control access to the database by applications and ensure consistency in the use of data within it. Systems analysts and programmers involved in the development of database applications need to work closely with the responsible *database administrator* (DBA).

Operations management

This function, led by an operations manager, has three main areas of responsibility: *data control*; *data preparation*; *computer operations*; *media library*. These responsibilities relate particularly to centrally controlled applications.

Data control

Data control staff are responsible for the co-ordination and control of data flowing through the operations section. For example, data received from Salaries, to update the payroll master file and produce payslips, have to be controlled to ensure their accuracy and completeness at all stages of processing.

Data preparation

Batch processing systems require the transcription and encoding of data gathered from source documents, such as order forms or invoices, on to magnetic storage. The input is then effected directly from the magnetic tape or disk on which the data has been accumulated. On-line, transaction processing systems, do not usually require this data preparation stage.

Computer operations

Computer operators are responsible for the day-to-day running of the computer hardware. In the case of mainframe computer systems, their responsibilities include the loading and unloading of magnetic tape reels or magnetic disk packs, according to the on-line requirements of applications currently in use. For example, before a payroll run, the media containing the master and transaction files have to be loaded onto the relevant devices, so that they can be accessed by the computer which is running the payroll program. The computer hardware is under the control of operating system software and an operator needs to communicate with the operating system regarding jobs to be processed and to deal with error conditions which may arise. A separate terminal is normally dedicated as an *operator console* and access to it is restricted both physically and through software-controlled passwords.

Exercises

1. Machem Ltd is a large manufacturing business. It buys in raw materials from a number of suppliers and uses the raw materials to produce its range of specialist outdoor clothing and equipment, which it sells to retailers. It has a warehouse next to the factory, to store the stocks of raw materials and finished goods.

   (a) Explain the circumstances when Machem Ltd is a *debtor* and when it is a *creditor*.

   (b) Explain circumstances when Machem will receive *invoices* and when it will issue them.

   (c) List the processes involved in invoicing a retailer and settlement of the debt.

   (d) Identify features of a typical *stock control* system which Machem Ltd could use to maintain sufficient, but not excessive levels of stock.

   (e) Machem Ltd is planning to extend its range of products and needs to ensure that there will be sufficient demand for the new products to make a profit. As well as its production function, the company has its own research and development (R&D) and marketing departments. Suggest ways in which these three functions may co-operate to maximise Machem Ltd's chances of success.

2. Machem Ltd has its own *ICT Services* function, employing systems analysts, programmers, network engineers, network administrators and user technical support assistants.

   Briefly outline the likely role of each of these categories of staff at Machem Ltd.

Chapter 26

Information in organisations

Role of information

In business, making decisions or taking actions without all the relevant information can be risky. For example, if a company decides to increase the price of a product because the product is selling well and ignores information that competitors have launched similar products, it is acting without all the relevant information. Similarly, fulfilling a customer order without checking their credit record risks an increase in bad (unrecoverable) debt. Information can vary in quality and to provide the best possible basis for decision-making, organisations should attempt to control the quality of the information they use. If it is to act with any purpose, an organisation needs information about itself, its customers (or clients) and suppliers (if any) and the *environment* in which it operates. Environment includes influences which are external to an organisation, such as government legislation and bank lending rates. Without such information, an organisation cannot properly plan for the future (*strategic planning*), or control and monitor its present performance (*operational control*).

Strategic planning

Planning for the future is never risk-free, but with a range of appropriate information the risks of decision-making can be minimised. Suppose, for example, that a manufacturing company is planning its production output for the next month; it needs to specify the particular product mix and the number of units of each product to be manufactured. In making these decisions, it is likely to draw on two main sources of information:

- ❏ past sales figures;
- ❏ market research results.

Decisions of this nature are likely to be made at corporate (Board of Directors) level and fall into a category known as *strategic* decision-making.

Operational control

When a company monitors its production figures, its stocks of raw materials and finished products, its is controlling its day-to-day, manufacturing operations. Other functions in the company, such as sales, payroll and accounts require similar operational control. Operational information permits day-to-day control to be exerted and allows measurement of present performance, as opposed to future prospects. Examples of operational information include:

- ❏ balances of customer accounts;
- ❏ invoices for customer sales;
- ❏ delivery notes for goods received from suppliers.

Periodic monitoring through Annual Accounts

The production of statements, such as a Trading and Profit and Loss Account and Balance Sheet, provides information on the financial health of a company, at the time the statements are produced. These statements are a legal requirement for all but the smallest businesses, but are useful for periodic monitoring of performance. Accounting records are essential to effective decision-making and also produce information demanded by, for example, shareholders, the Inland Revenue or the VAT authorities. Not all information generated within or used by an organisation can be categorised as wholly operational or corporate. Information which is classed initially as operational can become part of corporate information. For example, the operational information that a customer has failed to pay their account in two successive months may result in a suspension of further credit. Subsequently, this information may be combined with details of similar customer accounts to produce a bad debts report, which results in a corporate decision to alter customer credit and debt collection strategy.

Information systems

The production of information needs to be a controlled process, exercised through the use of information systems. An organisation can be divided into a number of *internal* functions, such as Sales, Marketing, Production and Accounts and each function requires its own information systems or sub-systems. The information system for any one functional area should not be considered in isolation, because it forms only part of an organisation-wide information system. This is made particularly clear when database systems are used. The various information systems within an organisation interact and affect one another. An organisation also interacts with and is influenced by organisations, such as banks and the Inland Revenue, in the surrounding environment; these are *external* functions. Co-ordination of an organisation's separate information systems or sub-systems is essential if its common aims are to be achieved.

Information needs

To operate, different functions within an organisation need access to particular types of information, some examples of which are briefly described below.

Design specifications; before a product is manufactured a specification is produced detailing, for example, the types, qualities and quantities of required materials, physical features, performance requirements (such as for a car) and so on. Some products, such as computer software, need to include design features concerning, for example, the user interface.

Construction drawings. As the term indicates, these are used to guide the person or persons building or constructing the product. An architect produces construction drawings for the house builder to follow; design specification details are also included, so that the builder knows the types and quantities of materials.

Market research. This information is often gathered through surveys, either using questionnaires or monitoring consumer buying patterns. A company should carry out market research before beginning the production or sale of a new product in its range.

Advertising is essential to any organisation wishing to promote its image or product range. Advertising uses market research information to target the most appropriate areas of the population. For example, market research may indicate that a product is most likely to be bought by professional people living in the south of England; advertising can be directed, perhaps through mails shots, to that section of the population.

Sales orders detail customer order requirements, including item details, quantities and delivery dates; *purchase orders* detail the organisation's purchase requirements from suppliers.

Payments and receipts. These may relate to sales orders or purchase orders. Receipts are amounts received from debtors. Payments are made by a business to settle debts with creditors (suppliers to the business).

Transport requirements. This information will detail, for example, a goods list, the delivery address, special requirements, such as refrigeration and possibly the route to be taken.

Information flow diagrams

Figure 26.1 illustrates some information flows within a typical manufacturing and wholesaling organisation. An examination of the Figure shows that each functional area is dependent on one or more other areas for the information it needs to operate. For example, to charge the retail outlets (their customers) for the goods supplied, the Accounting function requires the necessary sales information, which is supplied by the Sales function. The information allows the Accounting function to prepare the necessary invoices to send to customers. Similarly, Purchasing must be kept informed by the Warehouse (stock control) of raw materials which need re-ordering from suppliers, to replenish stocks.

Figure 26.1. *Information flows between functions*

These examples of *operational* information allow day-to-day decisions to be made on the operation of the business. To keep the diagram fairly simple, certain vital functions, such as Production Control and Marketing, are not shown. Obviously, their inclusion would increase the number of information flows and the complexity of the diagram. The information flows shown in Figure 26.1 are all 'triggered' by *events*. For example:

(i)   a customer order is generated when a customer orders goods;

(ii) credit limit details flow from Accounting to Sales, when a customer order is checked;

(iii) an invoice is raised when goods are despatched to a customer;

(iv) a payment to a supplier is triggered when the invoice payment falls due.

An information flow diagram may also illustrate the transmission medium or method used for each flow. For example, an interaction between two functions may be face-to-face, by e-mail, a video conferencing link, fax, electronic point-of-sale (EPOS), web site, or one of several other methods outlined at the end of this chapter.

ICT support of information flows

Teleconferencing

This service allows users to support a discussion over the telephone with a shared computer application, such as a word processor, spreadsheet or drawing package and a common whiteboard (an area of the display screen) visible to the conference users. The whiteboard is a comment or drawing area which users can use to illustrate points they wish to make. Each user has the ability to control the application, allowing co-operative development of, for example, a drawing or a spreadsheet model. Of course, such application sharing needs to be carefully managed and controlled to avoid inefficiency and time-wasting, which may result if users have different views on how the drawing or model should develop. The voice communications may be carried out over a conventional telephone network or over the Internet as part of the teleconferencing package. Microsoft's NetMeeting is built into the Explorer browser and supports all these facilities.

Video conferencing

Using computers with attached video cameras, microphones and speakers, conference participants are able to see and hear one another. The audio and video signals are carried over the Internet for real-time display as the conference takes place. The availability of cheap mini video cameras has radically increased the popularity of this service. Both tele and video conferencing have the potential to make significant savings for organisations in staffing, travel and accommodation costs. The main cost derives from local rate telephone charges.

Bibliographic databases

These databases provide information on specialised or widely ranging subjects. For example, BLAISE, which is provided by the British Library, gives information on British book publications. Euronet Diane (Direct Information Access Network in Europe) provides information extracted from publications, research documents and so on, which may be of interest to specialists, such as scientists, engineers, economists and lawyers. Each extract provides the relevant bibliographic references to allow users to access the original sources more fully.

Bulletin boards

A bulletin board (BB) is simply a means by which users can, for example, exchange ideas, pass on information and buy or sell items to one another. Frequently, no charge is made. Chat lines are often included; this means that two users can carry on a conversation, through the use of screen and keyboard.

Telex

Telex is a well established communications system which, rather like the public telephone network, allows subscribers to communicate with one another. There are over a million subscribers in this country at present. Each subscriber is given a telex code (you will often see it at the top of business letter headings next to the telephone number) and must have a teleprinter which is a combination of keyboard and printer. There is no screen, so all messages sent or received are printed onto hard copy. The transmission rate of approximately 6 characters per second is slow compared with more modern telecommunications systems, but the limitations of keyboard entry and printer speed on the teleprinter, make any faster speed unnecessary. The main benefit of telex is that a permanent record of communications is kept and the receiver does not have to be on the spot when the message arrives. Its main disadvantage is that there is no storage facility for messages. Any transmission has to be printed as soon as it is transmitted so that if the receiver is faulty, the system comes to a halt. Although it is inferior to e-mail (see next paragraph), it is still the only method (apart from telephone) of instant communication with less developed countries, where Telex machines are still widely used.

Electronic mail (e-mail) services

E-mail systems based on computer networks are paper-less (except when a user requires hard copy). A major advantage is the facility for message storage if a destination terminal is busy, or has a temporary fault. When it is free, the message can be transmitted. Certain basic features can be identified as being common to all e-mail systems:

- ❏ a terminal for preparing, entering and storing messages. The terminal will be intelligent, possibly a microcomputer, mainframe terminal or dedicated word processor. In any event, it should have some word processing or text editing facilities to allow messages to be changed on screen before transmission. A printer may also be available for printing out messages received over the system;
- ❏ an electronic communication link with other workstations in the network and with the central computer controlling the system;
- ❏ a directory containing the electronic addresses of all network users;
- ❏ a central mailbox facility (usually the controlling computer) for the storage of messages in transit or waiting to be retrieved.

Ideally, the following facilities are available to e-mail users:

- ❏ messages are automatically dated upon transmission;
- ❏ messages are automatically acknowledged as being received when the recipient first accesses it from the terminal;
- ❏ multiple addressing, that is the facility to address a message to an identified group, without addressing each member of the group individually;
- ❏ priority rating to allow messages to be allocated different priorities according to their importance.

Networks require two particular features in order to support e-mail:

- ❏ a message storage facility to allow messages to be forwarded when the recipient is available;
- ❏ compatibility with a wide range of manufacturers' equipment. Devices attached to a network have to be able to talk to the communications network using protocols or standards of communication.

Benefits of e-mail

The following major benefits are generally claimed for e-mail systems:

- ❏ savings in stationery and telephone costs;
- ❏ more rapid transmission than is possible with conventional mail;
- ❏ e-mail can be integrated with other computer-based systems used in an organisation;
- ❏ all transmissions are recorded, so costs can be carefully controlled;
- ❏ e-mail allows staff to telework, that is, to work from home via a terminal;

❑ the recipient does not have to be present when a message is sent. Messages can be retrieved from the central mailbox when convenient.

Electronic data interchange (EDI)

Similar to E-mail, EDI allows users to exchange business documents, such as invoices, delivery notes, orders and receipts over the telephone network. EDI can drastically reduce the volume of paperwork and business can be transacted much more quickly than is possible through the normal postal system.

Web site

The World Wide Web has made possible new ways for a business to communicate with its customers. Some sites are 'brochure' sites and are simply another way of promoting a business's corporate image, whilst some e-commerce (Chapter) sites are the basis of the entire business. Amazon.com is probably the most famous of such sites, selling books, CDs and other publications entirely through the Web.

Intranet and extranet

Some organisations may use their internal networks to form an intranet, effectively a private Internet. Its appearance is that of the Web and the familiar browser is its user interface. 'Out of the box' Web servers provide a convenient and relatively cheap method of developing internal network requirements and many organisations have built intranets as part of their overall Internet strategy. Employees are usually familiar with the Web and require little training to access the resources they need on the company intranet. Web tools, such as HTML (code for developing Web pages) editors, are relatively cheap and application development only becomes expensive when large and complex databases are needed, as in the case of an on-line store's product database.

To provide access external access to their intranet a company may use its Web site, with suitable access controls, including the use of *firewalls* (software protection), encryption (scambling of incoming and outgoing messages) and passwords. As an intra/extranet, outside access only requires the use of a Web browser, which is generally available. Extranets can be a valuable way of providing customer support and services. For example, the progress of a project can be monitored by the client, products can be developed by sharing information with partner organisations, customers can check on product availability, or the status of a delivery.

New generation mobile phones

Apart from voice transmission, mobile phones can be used to transmit text messages and those that support Internet Protocol (IP) or the newer WAP (Wireless Application Protocol) can be used to access Internet services, albeit very slowly. The delivery of Internet services through mobile networks is hampered by the mobile phone itself, with its slow processor, poor battery life, mono display and awkward keypad, as well as by limited bandwidth. The development of *broadband* mobile networks and more sophisticated phones will full potential of the Internet's multimedia content is to be made as accessible through a mobile phone as it is through a PC. In the meantime, services are largely text-based and perfectly adequate for the viewing of such information as travel, weather, sport results, share prices and the delivery of bank, ticket and message services. New generation mobile phones are making use of larger flip-up screens with touch-sensitive input and handwriting recognition as additions to the usual keypad.

EFTPOS (electronic funds transfer at point-of-sale)

This service provides for the automatic debiting of customers' bank accounts at the checkout or point of sale. Many garages now have a device for reading the magnetic strip details on bank and credit cards. The system saves considerable time when contrasted with payments by cheque and as an alternative to cash, reduces the likelihood of theft. The retailer also has the assurance that the payment is authorised before the sale is made. Usually, a retailer will have a floor limit, or amount above which a telephone call needs to be made to the credit card company for authorisation of payment.

EFT (electronic funds transfer)

This system is used to transfer money between the branches of the same bank and between different banks. In the UK, the system is known as the Bankers Automated Clearing Service (BACS). The service is not restricted to bank use; organisations can pay their employees salaries directly into their bank or building society accounts. Business accounts can also be settled through this EFT system. Apart from the banks, other users usually link into the pstn through a dial-up connection (unless the volume of data justifies a leased line).

Facsimile transmission (FAX)

This service allows the transmission of facsimiles or exact copies of documents or pictures through a data communications network. Using a fax machine connected to a telephone line, the user simply dials the fax number of the recipient, waits for the correct signal and the document is fed though the fax machine and transmitted. The fax machine sends picture elements or pixels obtained by scanning the document in a series of parallel lines; a synchronised fax machine at the other end prints a facsimile from those pixels. Fax/modems allow computer communication by fax with other fax modems or with conventional fax machines.

Example of ICT support of information flow

To illustrate the role of ICT in managing information flow, we use a simple example of a small electrical company, Wingrove Electrical Ltd, based on the outskirts of London. It employs 38 people and produces electrical components for use in central heating equipment. The following examples of activities and information flows are used to show the potential benefits of using IT.

An enquiry from a potential buyer

A telephone enquiry from a potential customer is received by the company's telephonist, who attempts to connect the caller with the company sales manager, who is out of the office. She makes a note of the caller's name and the nature of the enquiry and promises to pass these details on to the sales manager when she returns to the office. Unfortunately, the paper with the message is lost and so is the potential order. Clearly, the system could have been improved by a number of methods.

If Wingrove had a local area network, the telephonist could have obtained sufficient product information to meet the initial enquiry of the potential buyer. The message could have been transmitted through the electronic mail system, for the sales manager to access when she returned. If the sales manager used a notebook computer, she could download such messages remotely, through the telecommunications or mobile phone network.

It is also possible that the customer's enquiry could have been satisfied through the company web site. Information on products, prices, anticipated delivery times, technical support details and the answers to frequently asked questions (FAQs) can be stored and kept up to date through customer support pages.

Receipt of an order

Wingrove receives a substantial order by post. The manual procedures involve copying the order, sending a copy to Accounting and a copy attached to a 'job sheet' to Production. When the order is completed and despatched, Accounting will invoice the customer and await payment. Unfortunately, when the customer eventually pays, he submits a cheque for an incorrect amount, but the clerk fails to notice that the amount on the invoice and the amount on the cheque do not agree; as a result, he processes the invoice as paid. Wingrove has thus lost some of its profit.

The company could improve its financial control by installing a computerised order processing and invoice verification system. As each order is received into the company, the appropriate details, such as customer, item, quantity, price and so on, are entered into its computer, which automatically generates an invoice, statements and increasingly harshly worded reminders, until the customer settles the debt. When the cheque arrives, its value is also entered and the program automatically checks to ensure that the amount matches both the original price quoted and the invoice value. As protection against the miskeying of the cheque amount, a further check involves the automatic reconciliation, each month, of totals for paid and unpaid invoices.

Production of a quotation

Wingrove's managing director is informed that Birmingham City Council is intending to replace the central heating systems in all its public buildings, over the next three years and is seeking tenders for the component parts of the system. Wingrove would very much like to gain the contract and decide to submit a detailed quotation document. The quotation is 28 pages long and contains an extensive amount of technical detail, as well as product specifications, prices and delivery details. Typed manually, reference would have to be made to numerous files for component specifications and prices and the inevitable modifications to the tender would involve extensive re-typing. The following improvements are possible.

Using a word processor and quotation template, the task can be completed much more quickly. Layout alterations and editing can easily be done before a final copy is printed. A high quality printer, possibly with colour facility, will contribute to a highly professional appearance and improve the image of the company. Component specification and price data can be imported from the company's database of such information, directly into the document. If speed is important, the document could be faxed or e-mailed to Birmingham City Council.

ICT applications for strategic decision-making

Management information systems (MIS)

Although computers can perform routine processing tasks very efficiently, it is generally recognised that limiting a computer's use to the processing of operational information constitutes a waste of computer power. An MIS is designed to make use of the computer's power of selection and analysis to produce useful management information. An MIS has a number of key features:

    ❑   it produces information beyond that required for routine data processing;

❑   timing of information production is critical;

❑   the information it produces is an aid to decision-making;

❑   it is usually based on the database concept.

The claims for MIS are sometimes excessive. It is rarely the complete answer to all a company's information needs, but when successfully implemented, it provides a valuable information advantage over competitors.

Decision support systems (DSS)

A DSS aims to provide a more flexible decision tool than that supplied by a MIS which tends to produce information in an anticipated, pre-defined form and as such, does not allow managers to make ad hoc requests for information. DSS tend to be narrower in scope than MIS, often making use of general-purpose software packages. Examples of DSS include electronic spreadsheets, such as Microsoft Excel and relational database management systems such as Access and Paradox. Additionally, *financial modelling* and statistical packages are considered to be DSS tools. A major benefit is the independence they allow for information control by individual managers and executives. When, for example, a sales manager requires a report on sales figures for the last three months, a microcomputer with database package may provide the report more quickly than a centralised data processing department.

✎Exercises

1.   Study the information flow diagram in Figure 26.1 and answer the following questions.

(i)   When a customer places an order with Sales, to which function must they refer for a credit limit?

(ii)   When a customer order is accepted why are the details passed to Accounting?

(iii)   What information does accounting need from the Warehouse function before paying an invoice sent from a supplier?

(iv)   What use does the Warehouse function make of the requisitions it receives from the Factory?

2.   With the use of suitable examples, explain the role of e-mail, video conferencing in supporting communications within and between organisations.

3.   Distinguish between an *Intranet* and an *Extranet* and indicate how each can be used to improve the way an organisation communicates internally and with its customers and suppliers.

4.   Distinguish between EFT and EFTPOS.

5.   Suggest one benefit and one drawback of using a mobile phone to access the World Wide Web.

6.   List the key features of a Management Information System (MIS).

7.   A Sales Manager uses a spreadsheet to identify sales patterns across each of the five areas for which she is responsible. The data will be used to identify one area which is to be targeted for a special sales drive. What is the general term for this type of information system>

Chapter 27

Data handling systems

The data processing cycle

Computer-based data handling systems employed at the *operational* level of an organisation, for example, in the areas of payroll calculation or sales order processing, frequently involve a repeated cycle of events, which can be identified as follows:

- ❑ data collection and input;
- ❑ processing of the data, including reference to and the updating of relevant files;
- ❑ reporting of output.

Data collection

Depending on the application, this stage may include one or more of the following procedures.

Source document preparation

To ensure standardisation of practice and to facilitate checking, data collected for input, for example, customer orders, are transcribed onto source documents specially designed for the purpose.

Data transmission

If the computer centre is geographically remote from the data collection point, the source documents may be physically transported there, or be keyed and transmitted through a terminal and telecommunications network to the computer.

Data encoding and verification

This involves the transcription, usually through a keyboard device, of the data onto a storage medium such as magnetic tape or disk; a process of machine verification, accompanied by a repeated keying operation assists the checking of keying accuracy. Key-to-disk and key-to-tape systems are used for encoding, commonly making use of diskette and cassette tape storage, from which media the data is then merged onto a large reel of magnetic tape or onto magnetic disk for rapid subsequent input.

Data input and validation

Data validation is a computer-controlled process that checks the data for its validity according to certain pre-defined standards. For example, an account number may have to comprise 6 digits and be within the range 500000 to 900000.

Sorting

To improve the efficiency of processing sequentially organised files, input data is sorted into a sequence determined by the primary key of each record in the relevant master file.

Processing, storage and retrieval

This stage is entirely computer controlled and involves the processing of input data according to the requirements of the program currently in use. Thus, for example, in payroll processing, data on hours worked for each employee may be input and processed against information regarding rates of pay and tax codes held on the payroll master file, to produce the necessary payslips. In addition, the payroll information regarding, for example, pay to date and tax paid to date is updated on the master file.

Reporting of output

The destination of the results of processing also depends on the application and the requirements of the users. Output may be in the form of thousands of printed payslips or invoices or it may be simply a screen display of information in response to a user enquiry.

Processing methods

Data handling systems make use of one or more processing methods, depending on the requirements of the application. The methods can be categorised according to the ways in which data is controlled, stored and passed through the system; the major categories are:

- ❏ batch processing;
- ❏ on-line processing, which includes real-time and time-share processing;
- ❏ distributed processing and centralised processing.

To allow particular methods of processing a computer must have the necessary *operating system* software; thus any particular computer system is equipped with, for example, a batch processing or real-time operating system, or even a combination of types, depending on the needs of the user organisation.

Batch processing systems

Such systems process batches of data at regular intervals. The data is usually in large volumes and of identical type. Examples of such data are customer orders, current weekly payroll details and stock issues or receipts. Although associated with large organisations using mainframe or minicomputer systems, the technique can be used by a small business using a microcomputer.

The procedure can be illustrated with the example of payroll, which is a typical application for batch processing. Each pay date, whether it is every week or every month, the payroll details, such as hours worked, overtime earned or sickness days claimed, are gathered for each employee (these details are referred to as transactions) and processed in batches against the payroll master file. The computer then produces payslips for all employees in the company. A major feature of this and similar applications is that a large percentage of the payroll records in the master file are processed during the payroll 'run'. This percentage is known as the hit rate. Generally, high hit rate processing is suitable for batch processing and if, as is usual, the master file is organised sequentially, then the transaction file will be sorted into the same sequence as the master file. In the case of magnetic tape, transactions must be sorted because the medium only allows serial (one record after another in their physical order) access.

Batch processing method closely resembles manual methods of data handling, in that transactions are collected together into batches, sent to the computer centre, sorted into the order of the master file and processed. Such systems are known as 'traditional' data processing systems. There is normally an intermediate stage in the process when the data must be encoded using a key-to-tape or key-to-disk system. A disadvantage of batch processing is the delay, often of hours or days, between collecting the transactions and receiving the results of processing and this has to be remembered when an organisation is considering whether batch processing is suitable for a particular application. Conversely, batch processing has the advantage of providing many opportunities for controlling the accuracy of data (Chapter 14) and thus is commonly used when the immediate updating of files is not crucial.

On-line processing systems

If a peripheral, such as a Visual Display Unit or keyboard, is on-line, it is under the control of the computer's processor or Central Processing Unit (CPU). On-line processing systems therefore, are those where all peripherals in use are connected to the CPU of the main computer. Transactions can be keyed in directly. The main advantage of an on-line system is the reduction in time between the collection and processing of data. There are two main methods of on-line processing: *real-time* and *time-share*.

Real-time processing

Process control in real-time

Real-time processing originally referred only to process control systems where, for example, the temperature of a gas furnace is monitored and controlled by a computer. The computer, through an appropriate sensing device, responds immediately to the boiler's variations outside pre-set temperature limits, by switching the boiler on and off to keep the temperature within those limits. Real-time processing is now used in everyday consumer goods, such as video cameras, because of the development of the 'computer on a chip', more properly called the microprocessor. The important feature common to all real-time applications is that the speed of the computer allows almost immediate response to external changes.

Information processing in real-time

To be acceptable as a real-time information processing system, the response-time (that is the time between the entry of a transaction or enquiry at a VDU terminal, the processing of the data and the computer's response) must meet the needs of the user. The delay or response time may vary from a fraction of a second to 2-3 seconds depending on the nature of the transaction and the size of the computer. Any delay beyond these times would generally be unacceptable and would indicate the need for the system to be updated. There are two types of information processing systems which can be operated in real-time. These are *transaction processing* and *information storage and retrieval*.

Transaction processing

This type of system handles clearly defined transactions one at a time, each transaction being processed completely, including the updating of files, before the next transaction is dealt with. The amount of data input for each transaction is small and is usually entered on an interactive basis through a VDU. In this way, the user can enter queries through the keyboard and receive a response, or the computer can display a prompt on the screen to which the user responds. Such 'conversations' are usually heavily structured and in a fixed format and so do not allow users to ask any question they wish.

A typical example of transaction processing is provided by an airline booking system (see Booking Systems, later).

Information storage and retrieval

This type of system differs from transaction processing in that, although the information is updated in real-time, the number of updates and the number of sources of updating is relatively small.

Consider, for example, the medical records system in a hospital. A record is maintained for each patient currently undergoing treatment in the hospital. Medical staff require the patient's medical history to be available at any time and the system must also have a facility for entering new information as the patient undergoes treatment in hospital. Sources of information are likely to include a doctor, nurses and perhaps a surgeon, and new entries probably do not number more than one or two per day.

This is an entirely different situation from an airline booking system where the number of entries for one flight record may be 200-300 and they could be made from many different booking offices throughout the world. A further example of a library system is provided later (see Library Systems)

Time-share processing

The term time sharing refers to the activity of the computer's processor in allocating time-slices to a number of users who are given access through terminals to centralised computer resources. The aim of the system is to give each user a good response time. These systems are commonly used where a number of users require computer time for different information processing tasks. The processor time-slices are allocated and controlled by a time-share operating system. The CPU is able to operate at such speed that provided the system is not overloaded by too many users, each user has the impression that he or she is the sole user of the system.

A particular computer system will be designed to support a maximum number of user terminals. If the number is exceeded or the applications being run on the system are 'heavy' on CPU time the response time will become lengthy and unacceptable. Time-share systems are possible because of the extreme speed of the CPU in comparison with peripheral devices such as keyboards, VDU screens and printers. Most information processing tasks consist largely of input and output operations which do not occupy the CPU, leaving it free to do any processing required on other users' tasks.

Distributed processing

As the term suggests, a distributed processing system is one which spreads the processing tasks of an organisation across several computer systems; frequently, these systems are connected and share resources (this may relate to common access to files or programs, or even the processing of a single complex task) through a data communications system (Chapter 7). Each computer system in the network must be able to process independently, so a central computer with a number of remote intelligent terminals cannot be classified as distributed, even though some limited validation of data may be carried out separately from the main computer. Examples of distributed systems include mini or mainframe computers interconnected by way of wide area networks, or a number of local area networks similarly linked.

Distributed systems provide a number of benefits:

❑ *Economy*. The transmission of data over telecommunications systems can be costly and local database storage and processing facilities can reduce costs. The radical reduction in computer hardware costs has favoured the expansion of distributed systems against centralised systems;

❑ *Minicomputers and microcomputers*. The availability of minicomputer and microcomputer systems with data transmission facilities has made distributed processing economically viable. An increasingly popular option, in large multi-sited organisations, is to set up local area networks of microcomputers at each site and connect them through communications networks to each other and/or to a central mainframe computer at the Head Office. This provides each site with the advantages of local processing power, local and inter-site communications through *electronic mail* (Chapter 7) and access to a central mainframe for the main filing and database systems;

❑ *Local management control*. It is not always convenient, particularly where an organisation controls diverse activities, to have all information processing centralised. Local management control means that the information systems will be developed by people with direct knowledge of their own information needs. Responsibility for the success or otherwise of their division of the organisation may be placed with local management, so it is desirable that they have control over the accuracy and reliability of the data they use.

Centralised systems

With this type of system, all processing is carried out centrally, generally by a mainframe computer. The continuing reduction in hardware costs and the increase in computer power has led the move towards distributed processing systems. This is achieved through computer networks.

Financial accounting systems

The following section describes the various financial accounting systems of a typical business and the main features of accounting software. To begin with some associated terminology is defined and some basic concepts are explained.

The ledgers

Business accounts are needed to record:

❑ *debtor* transactions; debtors are people or organisations who owe money to the business for goods or services provided (credit sales);

❑ *creditor* transactions; creditors are people or organisations to whom the business owes money, for the supply of goods (credit purchases).

These transactions are recorded in the *sales ledger* and the *purchases ledger* respectively. A third ledger, the *nominal* (or *general*) *ledger* is used to record the overall income and expenditure of the business, with each transaction classified according to its purpose.

Sales ledger

General description

The purpose of the sales ledger is to keep a record of amounts owed to a business by its trading customers or clients. It contains a record for each customer with a credit arrangement. Most businesses permit their customers to buy goods on credit. The goods are usually supplied on the understanding that, once payment has been requested, the debt will be paid for within a specified period of, for example, 14 or 30 days. Payment is requested with the use of a customer addressed *invoice*, which contains details of goods supplied, the amount owing and credit days given. Once a customer order has been accepted and processed, the total amount due for the order is recorded in the relevant customers account in the sales ledger and the balance owing is increased accordingly. When a payment is received from the customer, the amount is entered to the customer's account and the balance owing is decreased by the appropriate amount.

Software requirements and facilities

Customer master file

When setting up the Sales Ledger system, one of the first tasks is to open an account for each customer. These accounts are maintained in a sales ledger *master file*, which is updated by sales and account settlement transactions. A typical package should provide as a minimum, the following data item types for each customer record:

- ☐ *account number* - used to identify uniquely a customer record;

- ☐ *name and address* - this will normally be the customers address to which statements of account and invoices are sent;

- ☐ *credit limit* - the maximum amount of credit to be allowed to the customer at any one time. This is checked by sales staff before an order is authorised for processing;

- ☐ *balance* - this is the balance of the customer's account at any one time.

Normally, when the file is first created, a zero balance is recorded and outstanding transactions are entered to produce a current balance. An *open item* system stores details of any unpaid invoices. Each invoice can be associated with a particular customer account through the account number.

Transaction entries

Transactions may be applied directly to customer accounts in the sales ledger (*transaction processing*) or they may be initially stored as a transaction file for a *batch* updating run. Whichever method the package uses, it should allow for the entry of the following transaction types:

- ☐ *invoice* - this is sent to the customer requesting payment concerning a particular order. The amount of the invoice is debited to the customer's account in the sales ledger, thus increasing the amount owing;

- ☐ *credit note*. If, for example, goods are returned by a customer or there is a dispute concerning the goods, a credit note is issued by the business to the customer. The amount of the credit note will be credited to the customer's account in the sales ledger, thus reducing the balance owing. Credit notes are often printed in red to distinguish them from invoices;

- ☐ *receipt* - this is any payment or remittance received from a customer in whole or partial settlement of an invoice. Such an entry will be credited to the customer's account and reduce the balance owing accordingly.

The following data may be entered with each type of transaction:

- ☐ *account number* - essential to identify the computer record. Although some packages allow for the entry of a shortened customer name (if the account number has been forgotten) the account number is still necessary to identify uniquely a record;

❑   *date of transaction* and *amount of transaction*;

❑   *transaction reference* - this is the invoice number to which the transaction relates.

Outputs

The following facilities may be expected:

❑   *single account enquiry* - details of an individual customer's account can be displayed on screen. Retrieval may be by account number or a search facility, using a shortened version of the customer name. If more than one record is retrieved by this method they may be scanned through on screen until the required record is found;

❑   *customer statement printing* - it is essential that the system can produce monthly statements for sending to customers;

❑   *debtors age analysis* - this provides a schedule of the total amounts owing by customers, categorised according to the time various portions of the total debt have been outstanding (unpaid). It is important for a business to make financial provision for the possibility of *bad debts*. These are debts which are unlikely to be settled and may have to be taken out of business profits. From their own experience of the trade, the proprietor of a business should be able to estimate the percentage of each debt that is likely to become bad. Generally, the longer the debt has been outstanding, the greater the likelihood that it will remain unpaid;

❑   *customers over credit limit* - this may form the basis of a black list of customers. Any new order from one of these customers has to be authorised by management. On the other hand, the appearance of certain customers on the list may suggest that some increased credit limits are needed. When a business is successful, it often needs more credit to expand further;

❑   *dormant account list* - if there has been no activity on an account for some time, it may warrant removal from the file. Alternatively, it may be useful to contact the customer to see if further business may be forthcoming.

Validation and control

The package should provide for careful validation of transactions and the protection of records from unauthorised access or amendment. Generally, for example, a customer record cannot be removed from the sales ledger while the account is still live (there is a balance outstanding). More details of validation and control are given in Chapter 29.

Purchase ledger

General description

The purchase ledger function mirrors that of the sales ledger, except that it contains an account for each *supplier*, from whom the business buys goods. When trading with a supplier, it is usually through credit arrangements, similar to those provided by the business for its own customers. Thus, the business receives an invoice requesting payment, within a certain period, for goods purchased. The amount of the invoice is credited to the supplier's account and the balance owing to the supplier is increased accordingly. When payment is made to a supplier, in full or part settlement of an invoice, the supplier's account is debited by the appropriate amount and the balance is decreased.

Most purchase ledger systems operate on an open item basis. Each supplier invoice is given a reference number and when payment is made to a supplier, the reference number can be used to allocate the payment to a particular invoice.

Software requirements and facilities

Supplier master file

The supplier master file contains the suppliers' (*creditors'*) accounts. It is updated by supplier invoices and payments to suppliers. A typical package should provide, as a minimum, the following data item types for each supplier record:

☐ *account number*- used to identify uniquely a supplier record;

☐ *name and address* - the name and address of the supplier business;

☐ *credit limit* - the maximum amount of credit allowed to the business by the supplier at any one time. A check should be kept on this to avoid rejection of orders;

☐ *settlement discount* - this is the amount of discount given by a supplier if an invoice is settled within a specified discount period;

☐ *due date* - the system may issue a reminder when payment is due. A report may be printed, on request, listing all invoice amounts due for payment within, say, 7 days;

☐ *balance* - the current balance on the account.

Transactions

Transactions may update the supplier accounts directly (transaction processing) or they may be initially stored as a transaction file for a later updating run. A purchase ledger package should allow for the following transactions:

☐ *supplier invoices* - before entry, each invoice must be checked against the appropriate order and then against the relevant delivery note, for actual receipt of goods. The balance on a supplier's account (the amount owed to the supplier) is increased by an invoice entry. Some packages allow unsatisfactory (there may be doubt about the delivery of the goods) invoices to be held in abeyance until cleared;

☐ *approved payments* - once an invoice has been cleared for payment, a voucher may be raised to ensure payment, on or before a due date, and discount for prompt payment. The entry of the payment value decreases the balance of a supplier's account and thus the amount owed by the business to the supplier. Cheques may be produced automatically on the due date, but there should be some checking procedure to ensure that payments are properly authorised;

☐ *adjustments* - to reverse entries made in error.

Outputs

The following output facilities may be expected:

☐ *single account enquiries* - details of an individual supplier's account can be displayed on screen; retrieval may be through a supplier code;

☐ *payment advice slip* - this may be produced to accompany a payment to a supplier. Each payment slip details the invoice reference, the amount due and the value of the payment remitted. Payment advice slips help the supplier, who may be using an open item sales ledger system;

❑ *automatic cheques* - the package may, with the use of pre-printed stationery, produce cheques for payment to suppliers, as and when invoices fall due. There must be a careful checking and authorisation procedure to prevent incorrect payments being made;

❑ *unpaid invoices* - a list of all outstanding invoices, together with details of supplier, amount owing and due date;

❑ *creditors' age analysis* - this is the supplier equivalent of debtors' age analysis. The report provides a schedule of total balances owing to suppliers, analysed according to the time the debt has been outstanding. The report may be used to determine which payments should be given priority over others.

Nominal ledger

General description

The nominal ledger is used to record the income and expenditure of a business, classified according to purpose. Thus, for example, it contains an account for *sales*; sales totals are entered on a daily basis. The sales ledger analyses sales by customer, whereas the *sales account* provides a cumulative total for sales, as the accounting year progresses. The *purchases account* in the nominal ledger fulfils a similar purpose for purchases by the business. Other income and expenditure accounts recorded in the nominal ledger may include, for example, *rent*, *heating* and *wages*. If some items of income and expenditure are too small to warrant separate analysis, there may also be *sundry income* and *sundry expenditure* accounts. The information held in the nominal ledger accounts is used to draw up a *profit and loss account*. This account provides information on the trading performance of the business over the year. A *balance sheet* can then be produced to give a snapshot view of the assets and liabilities of a business, on a particular date.

Software requirements and facilities

Nominal accounts master file

When an account is opened in the nominal ledger, the following should be available:

❑ *account code* - each account is given a code, to allow the allocation of transactions. For example, an entry for a gas bill payment may be directed to the Heating account by the code 012;

❑ *account name* - for example, Sales, Heating, Rent;

❑ *balance*.

Associated with each account are a number of transactions processed during the current accounting period.

Transactions

❑ *sales and purchases* - these may be entered periodically as accumulated totals or, in an integrated accounts system, values may be posted automatically, at the same time as they update customer and supplier accounts in the sales ledger and purchase ledger;

❑ *other income and expenditure* - entries concerning, for example, wages, rent, rates or heating.

Outputs

Typical output facilities include:

☐ *trial balance* - this is a list of debit and credit balances categorised by account. The balances are taken from the nominal ledger and the total of debit balances should agree with the total of credit balances;

☐ *transaction report* - a full list of transactions which may be used for error checking purposes, or as an audit trail, to allow the validity of transactions to be checked by an external auditor.

☐ *trading and profit and loss account* - a statement of the trading performance of the business over a given period;

☐ *balance sheet* - a statement of the assets and liabilities of a business, at a particular date.

The major benefit of the computerised nominal ledger is that these reports can be produced easily and upon request. The manual production of a trial balance, trading and profit and loss statement and balance sheet can be a laborious and time consuming task. Many small businesses, operating manual systems, have difficulty in completing their annual accounts promptly for annual tax assessment.

Apart from the basic ledgers described in the previous section, there are other applications which can benefit from computerisation. They include:

☐ stock control;

☐ sales order processing and invoicing.

Stock control

General description

Different businesses hold different kinds of stock. For example, a grocer holds some perishable and some non-perishable stocks of food and a clothing manufacturer holds stocks of materials and finished articles of clothing. Any trader's stock needs to be controlled, but the reasons for control may vary from one business to another. For example, a grocer wants to keep the full range of food items that customers expect, but does not want to be left with stocks of unsold items, especially if they are perishable. A clothing manufacturer's stocks will not perish if they are unsold, but space occupied by unwanted goods could be occupied by more popular items. On the other hand, if the manufacturer runs out of raw materials the production process can be slowed or even halted. Apart from such differences, there are some common reasons for wanting efficient stock control:

☐ excessive stock levels tie up valuable cash resources and increase business costs. The cash could be used to finance further business;

☐ inability to satisfy customer orders promptly because of insufficient stocks, can often lead to loss of custom.

It is possible to identify some typical objectives of a stock control system and these can be used to measure the usefulness of facilities commonly offered by computer packages:

☐ to maintain levels of stock which will be sufficient to meet customer demand promptly;

☐ to provide a mechanism which removes the need for excessively high safety margins of stock to cover customer demand. This is usually effected by setting minimum stock levels which the computer can use to report variations outside these levels;

☐ to provide automatic re-ordering of stock items which fall below minimum levels;

☐ to provide management with up-to-date information on stock levels and values of stock held. Stock valuation is also needed for accounting purposes.

Stock control requires that an individual record is maintained for each type of stock item held. Apart from details concerning the description and price of the stock item, each record should have a balance indicating the number of units held. A unit may be, for example, a box, 500 grammes or a tonne. The balance is adjusted whenever units of that particular stock item are sold or purchased. Manual or computerised records can only give recorded levels of stock. Physical stock checks need to be carried out to determine the actual levels. If there is a difference between the recorded stock level of an item and the actual stock of that item, it could be because of pilferage or damage. Alternatively, some transactions for the item may not have been applied to the stock file.

Software requirements and facilities

Stock master file

The stock master file contains records for each item of stock and each record may usefully contain the following data item types:

☐ *Stock code or reference* - each stock item type should have a unique reference, for example, A0035. The code should be designed so that it is useful to the user. For example, an initial alphabetic character may be used to differentiate between raw materials (R) and finished goods (F) and the remaining digits may have ranges which indicate particular product groupings. The stock file may also be used to record any consumable items used by a business, for example, stationery and printer ribbons. The initial character of the stock code could be used to identify such a grouping. The number and type of characters in a code, as well as its format, are usually limited by the package because the code will also be used by the software to determine a record's location within the file;

☐ *Description* - although users may become used to referring to individual products by their codes or references, a description is needed for the production of, for example, purchase orders or customer invoices;

☐ *Analysis code* - this may be used in conjunction with sales orders so that they can be analysed by product group. If, for example, a clothing manufacturer produces different types of ski jacket, it is important for production planning purposes to know the relative popularity of each type;

☐ *Unit size* - for example, box, metre, tonne, kilo;

☐ *Re-order level* - this is the stock level at which an item is to be re-ordered, for example, 30 boxes. Reaching this level may trigger an automatic re-order when the appropriate program option is run. Alternatively it may be necessary to request a summary report which highlights all items at or below their re-order level. The decision on what the re-order level should be for any particular item will depend on the *sales turnover* (the number of units sold per day or week) and the *lead time* (the time taken for delivery after a purchase order is placed with a supplier). Seasonal changes in sales figures will require that re-order levels for individual items are changed for time to time;

❑ *Re-order quantity* - this is the number of item units to be re-ordered from a supplier when new stock is required;

❑ *Bin reference* - this may be used to indicate the physical location of stock items within, for example, a warehouse;

❑ *Minimum stock level* - when an item falls to this level, a warning is given that the stock level of the item is dangerously low. As with the re-order level, the warning may be produced by a request for a special summary report which highlights such items. Even though the re-order level warning may have already been given, it is possible that no new stocks were ordered or that the supplier was unusually slow with deliveries;

❑ *Cost price* - the price paid by the business for the stock item;

❑ *Sale price* - the price charged to the customer. The package may allow the storage of more than one sale price to differentiate between, for example, retail and wholesale customers;

❑ *VAT code* - different items may attract different rates of Value Added Tax (VAT);

❑ *Supplier code* - if orders can be produced automatically, then the supplier code may be used to access a supplier file, for the address and other details needed to produce an order;

❑ *Quantity issued* - generally, several values may be entered, so that the turnover of an item can be viewed for different periods, for example, from 3 months ago to date, the preceding 3 month period and so on;

❑ *Stock allocated* - a quantity may not have been issued but may have been allocated to a customer order or factory requisition;

❑ *Quantity in stock* - the current recorded level of stock. This will change whenever an issue, receipt or adjustment transaction is entered.

Transactions

❑ *Goods received* - stock received from a supplier;

❑ *Goods returned* - for example, stock returned by a customer or unused raw materials returned from the factory;

❑ *Goods issued* - this may result from a customer order or from a factory requisition, if the business has a manufacturing process;

❑ *Stock allocated* - this will not reduce the quantity in stock figure but the amount allocated should be used to offset the quantity in stock when judging what is available;

❑ *Amendments* - for, example, there may be amendments to price, re-order level or supplier code.

The method used to update the stock master file will depend on how up-to-date the figures need to be (this will depend on how tight stock levels are) and how often the data entry operator can get at the computer. To keep the file up-to-date throughout the day, physical stock changes have to be notified immediately to stock control and the transactions have to be entered as they occur. Unfortunately, this means that a single-user system would be unavailable to any other users, such as sales staff, who needed to know quantities in stock. A networked system with central file storage, would allow continual updating and enquiry access. If the stock levels are sufficiently high to allow differences to arise between physical and book totals without risking shortages, then daily batch updating may be acceptable. In such a situation, an enquiry on a stock item may reveal, for example, a book stock of 200 units, when the physical stock is only 120 units (80 having been issued since the last update at the end of the preceding day).

Outputs

Typical outputs from a stock control package include:

☐ *Stock enquiry* - details concerning a stock item may be displayed on screen, or printed;

☐ *Stock out report* - a list of stock items which have reached a level of zero;

☐ *Re-order report* - a list of stock items which have fallen to their re-order level, together with supplier details and recommended re-order quantities;

☐ *Stock list* - a full or limited (for example, within a certain stock code range) list of stock items, giving details of quantities held and their value. The value may be calculated using the cost or sale price, depending on the costing method used by the business;

☐ *Outstanding order report* - a list of all purchase orders not yet fulfilled and the dates ordered. This may be used to chase up orders when stocks are falling dangerously low.

This is not an exhaustive list and some packages offer many other analytical reports which can help a business to maintain an efficient customer service and plan future production and purchasing more effectively.

A stock control case study

The Astex Homecare chain of DIY stores has branches all over the country and each branch maintains stocks of thousands of items used in the home. These items range from building materials such as sand and cement to bedroom furniture, fitted kitchens, bathroom suites, ceramic wall and floor tiles, lights and light fittings, garden materials such as plants, plant pots and garden furniture, nails, screws, paint, wallpaper and numerous other common household goods.

Each branch has its own small computer system dedicated to dealing with the *point of sale* (POS) terminals located at the customer tills. The POS terminals are used to record purchases and provide customer bills by scanning the bar code on each purchase using a hand-held scanner. The stock number contained in the bar code is fed by the POS terminal to the local computer which returns the description and price to be printed on the customers' receipts as well as the bill totals.

Each branch maintains its own stock file on the local computer but ordering stock is controlled by a mainframe computer at the Astex head office. Each Astex branch is laid out according to a *merchandise layout plan* (MLP) in which the store is organised into a large number of four foot sections, each having its own MLP code. Each item of stock is allocated to one MLP section and its computer record contains the MLP code together with the minimum and maximum stock level for that particular section of the store. When an item has been sold, the relevant information is transmitted automatically by the local computer to the mainframe at head office. The head office computer determines from the MLP data whether the item needs to be re-ordered from a supplier. It uses the MLP information regarding minimum and maximum stock levels in order to determine how many of a particular item to order.

Overnight, while the stores are closed, the head office computer transmits suggested ordering information back to the individual branches where order sheets are printed out on local laser printers, so that they can be checked manually by the appropriate personnel before stock is ordered. This manual monitoring of computer-generated information allows the information system to cope with unexpected situations and prevents the occurrence of gross errors. About ninety percent of all orders can be made electronically using communication links to the computers used by suppliers. Other suppliers not linked to the central Astex computer are contacted manually by telephone.

The security of the Astex information systems are ensured in two major ways. Firstly, because of the importance of the local computer system for producing customer bills, a backup processor is always available for use in the event of the primary processor failing. Secondly, access to the various users of the computer systems is provided on several different levels. Each person who uses the computer system has his or her own access code which provides access to only those areas he or she is authorised to use. These measures are essential to maintain the security and reliable operation of such large-scale systems.

Some sophisticated stock control systems enable the supply of materials just before they are needed for manufacture. Nissan car plants operate using this *just in time* principle, using satellite supply companies located around or near the main plant.

Sales order processing and invoicing

Sales order processing

Sales order processing is concerned with the handling of customers' sales orders. It has three main functions:

❑ validation of orders. This means checking, for example, that the goods ordered are supplied by the business or that the customer's credit status warrants the order's completion;

❑ to identify quantities of individual items ordered. A customer may request several different items on the same order form. An item will probably appear on many different order forms and the quantities for each need to be totalled to provide lists (picking lists) for warehouse staff to retrieve the goods;

❑ to monitor back orders. If an order cannot be fulfilled it may be held in abeyance until new stocks arrive. The system should be able to report all outstanding back orders on request.

The efficient processing of customer orders is of obvious importance to the success of a business and in whatever form an order is received, the details should be immediately recorded. Preferably, the details should be recorded on a pre-designed order form which ensures that all relevant details are taken. The order details should include:

❑ the date the order is received;

❑ the customer's order number;

- ❏ a description of each item required including any necessary stock references or codes;
- ❏ the quantity of each item ordered;
- ❏ the price per item excluding VAT;
- ❏ the total order value excluding VAT;
- ❏ any discount which is offered to the customer;
- ❏ the VAT amount which is to be added to the total price;
- ❏ the total order value including VAT;
- ❏ the delivery date required.

Invoicing

The invoice is the bill to the customer, requesting payment for goods or services supplied by the business. The following section describes typical package facilities which allow the integration of the sales order processing and invoicing systems.

Package requirements and facilities

To be effective, the sales order processing system needs to have access to the customer file (sales ledger) for customer details and to the stock file, so that prices can be extracted according to stock item codes entered with the order. This latter facility means that the system may also be integrated with invoicing.

Files

- ❏ *Customer file.* When a customer account number or name is keyed in with an order, the package usually accesses the customer file and displays the address details, so that the operator can confirm the delivery address or type in an alternative address if this is required. The process also ensures that all orders are processed for registered customers;
- ❏ *Stock file.* As stock item codes are entered from an order form, the system accesses the price and displays it on the screen for confirmation by the operator. Access to the stock file also ensures that only valid stock codes are used;
- ❏ *Completed order file.* This is used for the generation of invoices after an order's completion;
- ❏ *Back order file.* This is needed to ensure that orders which cannot be fulfilled immediately are kept on file and processed as soon as goods become available.

Transactions

- ❏ *Sales order* - details concerning an individual order, including customer number, items required (by item code), quantity of each item, delivery date, discount allowed and the date of the order.

Outputs

- ❏ *Invoice* - an invoice can be generated by using the details of customer number, stock codes and quantities from the order, together with information retrieved from the customer and stock files;
- ❏ *Back order report* - a report can be requested detailing all unsatisfied orders. This is

useful for planning production schedules or generating special purchase orders;

❑ *Picking list* - a summary of the quantities required of each item ordered. These are used by warehouse staff to extract the goods needed to make up orders for delivery;

❑ *Sales data* - details of each customer's order need to be extended to include the financial ledgers (sales, purchase and nominal ledger). Such integration should not usually be attempted all at once but full integration does reduce the number of inputs necessary and automates many of the updating procedures.

Payroll

The task of calculating wages for a large company having hundreds or even thousands of employees is an enormous task. It involves taking into account some or all of the following factors:

❑ number of hours worked;

❑ amount of overtime;

❑ bonus payment;

❑ sickness leave;

❑ type of employee (for example, waged or salaried, shop floor or management);

❑ deductions (for example, national insurance contributions and union fees);

❑ holidays;

❑ tax code;

❑ tax rate;

❑ cash analysis.

The gross pay is calculated from the hours worked and hourly pay rate, for weekly paid employees, and is a standard sum for salaried employees. Added to this gross payment are any allowances from overtime or bonuses, for example. Tax is calculated and subtracted from the total earnings and other deductions such as national insurance, union fees and pension contributions are also taken from it. Thus the total calculation is quite complicated, and it will probably be different for each employee. Producing payslips manually is therefore very time consuming and prone to error, so computers are particularly well suited to the task. Most computerised payroll systems use batch processing in which long-term employee information held on a master file is used in conjunction with a transaction file containing recent information such as hours worked and overtime details. The transaction file changes from week to week or month to month but most of the information on the master file either does not change at all or changes only occasionally. If employees are paid weekly, at the end of each week details of hours worked, bonus payments, overtime payments and deductions are recorded on a payroll transaction file which contains a record for every employee. This sequential transaction file is then sorted into employee number order so that it is in the same order as the payroll master file. The two files are then used by the computer to calculate and print the payslips, and to update the master file which must keep track of such things as tax paid to date, total national insurance contributions and holiday and sickness leave for each employee for the current tax year. A *systems flowchart*, as illustrated in Figure 27.1, is often used to describe business data processing systems such as this.

The systems flowchart shows the computer operations involved in a payroll run. Payroll systems normally use batch processing when the majority of the employees need to be paid. This lends itself to the use of magnetic tape devices (the flowchart does not specify the medium) which are restricted to sequential access. The payroll data is first stored on the payroll transaction file using keyboards as the input devices.

Each employee's pay information is stored in a separate record identified by employee number. Because the master file records are stored on tape in order of employee number, the transaction file must also be sorted into the same order. This is to avoid having to search for matching master file and transaction file records for each employee - because both files are in the same order, the next record in each file should be for the same employee. The sorted transaction file must be validated by the computer before processing the payroll data to produce payslips. This process performs various checks on the transaction file to ensure that only correct data will be processed. Any errors detected at this stage must be corrected before the payslips are generated.

Finally, the validated and sorted transaction file is processed against the payroll master file in order to produce the payslips. In addition to updating the master file, the payroll system might also produce summary reports for the management personnel of the company, and, if employees are paid by cash rather than by cheque or transfer to a bank account, a *cash analysis* might be produced. The cash analysis calculates exactly how many of each currency denomination will be re-

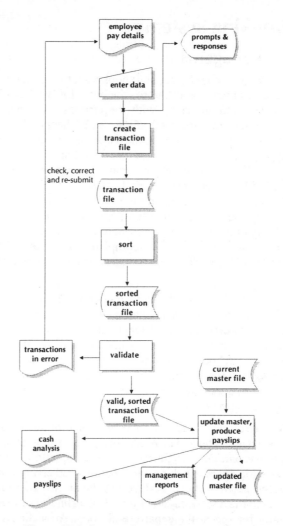

Figure 27.1. *Systems flowchart for payroll system*

quired for all the pay packets, so that the correct money can be obtained from a bank. Each payslip would also have a corresponding breakdown for a single pay packet to make it easier for the cashiers to make up the pay packets.

A large company will probably use a mainframe computer for the task of processing the payroll information. Data entry will often be carried out using key-to-tape systems by a number of data entry clerks, and the output of the payslips will probably be by means of pre-printed stationery used on a line printer for speed. Backing storage will normally be in the form of magnetic tape or magnetic disk, but sequential *batch processing* will almost invariably be used. Of course, small companies having only a few employees might use a microcomputer system for the payroll, or even produce the payslips manually without the use of a computer at all.

Booking systems

Travel agents

If you go to a travel agent to book a seat on a major international airline, the travel agent will need to check the airline for the availability of the flight that you require. This normally involves communicating with the airlines computer to obtain up-to-date flight information. Remember that the same thing can be happening from all over the world: numerous travel agents could be accessing the same airlines computer at the same time, several of them even trying to book seats on the same flight that you want. To cope with this type of demand, the airline will use a mainframe computer allowing on-line communication with each travel agent via the public telephone network. Each travel agency will have one or more terminals connected by modem to the airlines computer. Flight reservations will be performed in *real-time*, that is, the mainframe's flight and passenger information will be updated immediately to prevent the possibility of double-booking a seat on a particular flight. This ensures that the information that the travel agent obtains will be completely accurate and reliable. This form of processing, where a master file is updated immediately, is called *transaction processing*.

The process of reserving a seat on a flight is further complicated by the fact that several airlines might have scheduled flights to your destination, each offering different flight times, facilities and costs. Rather than contacting each one separately, a process that could take a considerable amount of time, the travel agent links into a wide area network(WAN) which connects the main computers of the different airlines. This allows the agent to choose the most appropriate flight for you and book it immediately. Though each airline in the system might have a different passenger reservation information system, the network software presents the same information format to the travel agents and takes care of transferring data in the correct format to the individual computer systems of the airlines.

When you have decided on your choice of airline and flight, your details are entered at the travel agent's terminal. While this is happening, other travel agents are prevented from accessing that particular flight record. On completion of the reservation, the flight record becomes available again. Booking cancellations and changes are handled in the same way. Your ticket, which will have been produced by the airline's computer, is usually sent out to you a few days prior to the departure date. Individual airline's computers also produce passenger lists automatically for use at the departure airports. An airline's master passenger reservation and flight information file will be held on a high-capacity magnetic disk drive. For backup purposes, in case the master file is in some way lost or partly erased, or the disk drive fails, a separate disk drive will be used to hold an exact duplicate of the master file, and this duplicate file will be updated at the same time as the other master file. This duplication is necessary because the master file will be in constant use, night and day, and there will be no opportunity to stop updating it in order to make a backup on magnetic tape. For the same reasons of security, there will also be a duplicate main computer immediately ready to be used if the other one fails for some reason. Because of the importance of the fast response time required of the system, it will almost certainly be used exclusively for passenger booking purposes, and it will have been designed to operate without break, 24 hours a day, every day of the year.

Similar real-time systems are used by holiday firms, some of which are able to offer thousands of holidays all over the world. Travel agents must have access to accurate information regarding the availability of all the holidays on offer. Again it is important to ensure that exactly the same holiday is not sold to more than one customer, so the booking file held on the holiday company's main computer must be completely up-to-date.

Hotel booking

Hotels frequently use booking systems for keeping track of room reservations made by guests. These systems generally provide additional facilities relating to hotel management, typically keeping track of guests accounts and producing hotel room usage information. When someone reserves a room in the hotel, a record is created in the guest file. The file contains three types of data:

- ❏ details of the guest, such as name, address, telephone number;

- ❏ room details, such as type (single, double etc.), number, period of occupancy;

- ❏ charges incurred by the guest during the stay at the hotel. For each charge, the item code, cost and date will be recorded.

The first two types of data are entered at the time the reservation is made; items and services bought by the guest during his or her stay, such as telephone calls, drinks, newspapers and extra meals, are recorded as and when they occur. When the guest leaves, the hotel system calculates the total bill and prints out an itemised list that the guest can check.

A hotel management system such as this can easily be implemented with a microcomputer system, though large hotel chains might also have a large central computer at their headquarters for general accounting purposes (such as producing financial reports covering the whole chain of hotels, and for payroll calculations).

Library systems

Dotherstaff College is a split site college of further and higher education. Each site has a large library which has recently been supplied with a microcomputer network for a library automation system called Alice, produced by a software company called Softlink. The software has a number of interlinked modules covering all aspects of typical library operation.

- ❏ Catalogue and Classification - managing the book database;

- ❏ Circulation - managing borrowers;

- ❏ Enquiries - information retrieval;

- ❏ Acquisition - ordering books;

- ❏ Reports and utilities- producing reports of publishers' details, author details and library usage figures;

- ❏ Periodicals- managing the ordering of magazines.

Catalogue and classification

This module is mainly used for the addition of new titles to the book database. Book details can be created, edited and deleted, as well as allowing the file to be browsed through, or searched.

Circulation

The circulation module is used for managing borrowers' details. To borrow a book from the library a borrower must produce his or her ticket on which there is a unique bar code. This bar code is scanned by a librarian and the borrower's record then appears on the screen. When the bar code of the book is scanned, the code is stored in the borrower's record. To return a book, the bar code of the book is scanned or typed in and the book is automatically removed from the borrower's record. The system also allows the display of all books currently borrowed by any person. Periodically, about every two weeks, the borrower file is searched for overdue items so that reminders can be generated automatically.

Enquiry

The enquiry module is used by staff and students to search the book database for books satisfying certain criteria. For example, a user can type in the name of an author and obtain a list of all books in the library written by that person. The title of a book, or part of the title can be entered and a list of books closely matching the title will be displayed. Alternatively, one or more keywords can be used to produce a list of books which contain the keywords in the title. The book information retrieved by an enquiry is summarised on the screen in several sections containing such things as the book titles, subjects covered and author(s). Any book selected from the list can have its full details displayed on screen or printed. This type of enquiry facility can save a great deal of time searching shelves or catalogues for specific information.

The network used for the library information system currently supports about 20 terminals, but it is also linked to the main college networks which provide access to other software such as word processors and spreadsheets.

E-commerce

Many businesses including, for example, supermarkets, travel agents, wine merchants, booksellers and car sales companies now sell their products through e-commerce web sites. With a computer, Internet connection and Web browser, consumers can visit these virtual stores and view, select and pay for goods which can often be delivered within 24 to 48 hours. Until the 1960s it was common practice for shops to make home deliveries or orders taken over the telephone and Internet shopping has the potential to reduce the volume of traffic visiting, for example, out of town shopping centres. It is extremely unlikely that demand for conventional 'bricks and mortar' will disappear because Internet shopping provides no social interaction and many consumers will wish to view and handle many types of goods before buying.

More formally, e-commerce can be defined as *"conducting business transactions over electronic networks"*. E-commerce is fundamentally changing the way business operates. Because of e-commerce, businesses of all sizes are changing their internal operations and their relationships with suppliers and customers. When properly implemented, e-commerce can improve the efficiency of all stages of the business process, from design and manufacture to retailing and distribution.

E-commerce is playing a major role in the establishment of a global economy. The major catalyst for the expansion of international electronic retailing is the Internet. Its users, the number of which is rapidly increasing, can communicate with the Web sites of countless organisations all over the world, and it is through these *World Wide Web* sites that companies can provide 'on-line stores'. The Web-based on-line stores are accessible by Web browsers, such as Microsoft Explorer and Netscape Communicator and a standard feature of all modern home computers. An Internet store provides all the facilities that the customer needs, including a product catalogue, a 'virtual shopping basket' and a secure credit card payment system (see later).

Business to business e-commerce

Business to business e-commerce is well established and one of the fastest growing areas. Many office equipment and consumables suppliers, for example, are able to take orders on-line and provide direct delivery to business customers. Because transactions such as the submission and settlement of invoices are all conducted electronically, the participating businesses enjoy significant cost savings.

Benefits of e-commerce for business

Businesses can benefit tremendously from e-commerce in many important ways, reducing costs and improving efficiency. For instance, expensive printed catalogues and service guides can be replaced by a single, up-to-date electronic product database that is accessible at all times. Many businesses use mail shots to inform customers of new products or special offers, a time consuming and expensive exercise. Instead the latest information can be held on the company web site and existing customers can obtain up-to-date information on new products or services at any time. A business can maintain closer contact with its customers and suppliers, and direct communication allows improved pre- and post-sales support.

Direct selling shortens the supply chain so delivery times and costs are reduced. Staffing costs can be a fraction of those for conventional sales outlets. For example, Web site software can handle routine sales transactions automatically, leaving sales staff to deal with more complex orders. E-commerce also provides opportunities for entirely new products and services. These include network supply and support services, web site design and hosting, and various types of on-line information services.

Business to consumer e-commerce

Business to consumer e-commerce, or electronic retailing, is expanding rapidly as businesses become informed of the new opportunities it presents for market expansion. Physical products, information and various services are all available for purchase over the Internet. For example, consumers can buy cars, books, CDs, wine, stock market information and computer software from numerous Internet shops.

Benefits of e-commerce for consumers

Consumers can gain considerable benefits from electronic commerce. The range of products that can be bought on-line is continually being extended. There are virtual stores all over the Internet offering a wide range of goods, including books, wine, newspapers, cakes, computer hardware, software and even cars. Similarly, numerous services are available on-line. These include education, entertainment and information services.

There is the convenience of 24-hour home shopping and access to a wider range of goods and services than is conventionally available within their locality. A conventional shopping chain rarely offers its full product range at every shop, whereas a virtual shop can make its full product range available globally. The consumer is given global choice. If a product or service is available from a number of suppliers, the consumer can choose without regard to geographical location.

Consumers may benefit from lower prices because electronic commerce drastically reduces transaction costs. A transaction involving human interaction may be measured in £s, but the same transaction carried out electronically can cost a few pence.

Orders may be fulfilled more quickly. Direct supply from manufacturer to customer can also be effected with mail order or telephone order catalogues, but the human and paper-based transactions are more costly and involve longer delays than is possible with e-commerce. For products that can be delivered electronically, such as software, video and newspapers, the time delay between order and delivery can be reduced to an absolute minimum, and intermediaries in the traditional supply chain are entirely redundant.

By bringing products and services to the home, electronic commerce also has the potential to benefit the disabled, the elderly and those living in remote areas.

Social and employment costs of e-commerce

Clearly, some of the above benefits will not apply to all consumers and there will be social costs as well.

❑ If residents of rural communities choose to shop on the Internet local stores may be unable to compete and have to close. Not everyone will have, or wish to have, access to the Internet and such closures will bring serious social deprivation to some.

❑ Many aspects of electronic shopping are automated and fewer staff are needed to process orders. Much customer support can be provided through the Web site, which further reduces staff requirements. Of course, e-commerce will also create jobs, but the skills and working practices are very different from those in many traditional businesses.

❑ E-commerce businesses may have access to global markets, but they may also be subject to global competition. This means that the business must be able to respond much more quickly to changes in consumer demand and to the activities of its competitors. Working practices, therefore, tend to demand a much more flexible and multi-skilled approach than is usual in traditional business.

E-commerce relies entirely on the operation and effectiveness of electronic systems and there are greater demands for people with suitable technical skills. Rapid delivery is considered to be a vital requirement if an e-commerce business is to keep its customers jobs in distribution are likely to increase.

An organisation's network needs to be secure against unauthorised access to maintain the integrity and confidentiality of its resources and protect the privacy of any clients whose details they hold. There are general security issues which apply to all networks, closed and open, but here we are concerned with the particular problems thrown up by the Internet and the new security measures developed to cope with those problems.

Objectives of data handling systems

A number of general objectives can be identified as being of relevance to most applications, in most organisations:

❑ Improved *operational efficiency*. *Speed* and *accuracy* of operations should be radically improved. This is not automatic as the computer-based system may be badly designed and the staff may be ill-trained, but given proper design and implementation, administrative systems will normally be more efficient.

❑ Better *control of resources*. Administrative systems such as those for financial control and the control of resources such as staff and raw materials, benefit particularly from the rapid production of up-to-date information by computer.

❑ Improved *productivity*. Redundancy does not always follow computerisation, particularly if the organisation is an expanding business. Computer-based systems should permit large increases in the volumes of business which can be handled without the need for extra staff.

❏ Improved *security of information*. With proper physical security, clear operational procedures to restrict access to computer facilities to those properly authorised, and with sophisticated use of software control mechanisms such as passwords, information can be made more secure than equivalent manual systems.

❏ Opportunities to *share data*. This is most likely where database systems and networked computer systems are employed.

❏ Improved *quality of information* for *decision taking* at the operational, strategic and corporate levels in an organisation. *Operational decisions* concern day-to-day operations, such as handling of customer orders or delivery of new stocks. At the *strategic level*, decisions may relate to issues such as production planning and the selection of suppliers. *Corporate decision* examples include the setting of prices, targeting of markets and the manufacture of new products. Most systems generate a range of management information reports, drawn from the routine processing of transactions and these are primarily of use at the strategic level, but may also help with corporate decisions. Accounts software, for example, produces reports on outstanding debts, potential bad debtors, dates when payments to suppliers are due and analysis of sales patterns.

❏ Improved *external image*. An organisation can improve its external image by the improved presentation of correspondence and by an improved service to its customers or clients, but badly designed procedures can also make life more difficult for them.

❏ Improved *working conditions*. This is highly debatable in respect of an office environment, but computer-based manufacturing systems usually provide a less dirty and dangerous environment for employees, as much of the work is done by robots and other computer-controlled machinery.

Choosing a system type

Whether batch processing, one of the on-line types, or distributed processing is appropriate depends on a number of factors:

❏ the type and size of organisation. Large organisations generally have larger volumes of data to handle, than do small ones. Batch processing is efficient in the sense that it is a concentrated activity and if transactions can be accumulated and handled together, then it may be more efficient than dealing with each transaction as it arises. On the other hand, delay may prevent achievement of an important objective, such as the provision of up-to-date management information. Distributed processing through computer networks is an increasingly popular option for a medium or large organisation, because it gives local control to branches and allows data to be shared and communicated across the whole organisation.

❏ the activity (for example, financial accounts, hotel booking);

❏ the objectives of the activity (see previous section).

A batch processing system provides numerous opportunities to ensure the accuracy of data, as it passes through the system. In this way, the type satisfies one of the main objectives of many systems and if this were the only criterion for selection, all systems would use batch processing. Of course, there are other criteria which must be applied to the selection process, including: system purpose(s); size and type of organisation; other objectives, such as security, speed, or the provision of extra management information. For example, an airline's passenger reservation system cannot be effective unless files are updated at the time each reservation is made and transaction processing is found to be appropriate. An organisation's stock control system may need to reflect stock changes on the same basis as the airline reservation system, particularly if delivery has to be immediate. Discount stores, such as Argos, sell a huge range of consumer items and some are expensive; it is not desirable to hold high stock levels, because this ties up large amounts of cash, so the stock records need to be updated as goods are delivered and sold. In some organisations, stock movements (stock received and stock issued) do not have to be instantly reflected in stock records, because delivery times to customers can be longer, perhaps up to several weeks. If the goods are not of high value, then it may be convenient to hold larger stocks, which ensure the satisfaction of customer demand. For example, if the stock record for an item shows 1000 units and 50 units is the maximum customer requirement, then a physical stock level which is only 800 units, is not an immediate problem.

The size of the organisation is also a significant factor in determining the most appropriate type of data handling system. A small plumbing firm, perhaps consisting of two partners and a couple of employees is unlikely to include anyone to keep the accounts; this will probably be the job of one of the partners, who will only have time to do the work at weekends. Thus, customer invoices and payments are dealt with in a batch, perhaps every week. As a small firm, a major objective will be to collect customer debts as quickly as possible and the computerised system can help to do this, in the limited time that the partner has to deal with such matters.

Exercises

1. Which *ledger* would a business use to record:
   (a) balances owing by customers for goods bought on credit?
   (b) expenditure on heating, light and wages?
   (c) balances owing to suppliers for goods bought on credit.?
2. Name the type of document which is sent to a customer:
   (a) requesting payment for goods bought on credit;
   (b) to show a refund on their account to the value of goods returned.
3. Which accounting package report would be useful for identifying potential *bad debts*?
4. Which report details the assets and liabilities of a business on a particular date?
5. Which report shows the profit made by a business over a specified period?
6. Which fields in a stock record are concerned with maintaining optimum levels of stock?
7. List three transaction types which may be entered into a stock control system.
8. (a) Assuming a fully integrated financial accounting system, identify the files which would need to be accessed to produce an invoice.
   (b) What data would be extracted from each file identified in (a), to produce the invoice?
9. List the components an organisation needs to support an e-commerce operation.

Chapter 28

System life cycle

In business, *systems analysis and design* is the process of investigating a business, existing or new, with a view to determining how best to manage the various procedures and information processing tasks that it involves. Though it frequently means considering the use of a computer system to replace some manual operations, this need not always be the case. The *systems analyst,* whose job it is to perform the investigation, might recommend the use of a computer to improve the efficiency of the information system under consideration, but he/she might equally well decide that a manual system is adequate, or even preferable. Thus, the intention in systems analysis is to determine how well a business copes with its current information processing needs, and whether it is possible to improve the procedures involved in order to make it more efficient, or more profitable, or both. Systems design involves planning the structure of the information system to be implemented. In other words, analysis determines what the system should do, and design determines how it should be done.

The job of the systems analyst starts with studying the current, or proposed, system; this involves collecting facts which will help the analyst to determine whether a computer would improve the information system, and if so, in what areas it would be most beneficial. Once the decision has been made to go ahead with a new or improved system, the analyst must develop a plan for putting the proposed system into practice. This includes specifying all the procedures involved, computerised or otherwise, how data is to be captured, what software will be required to process the data, what equipment will be necessary, what staff will be needed and how they will be trained, and so on. In other words, the analyst must provide a complete plan of every detail of the proposed system. A key feature of this complex task is communicating with staff, whether they are ordinary employees or managers. The people who work in the business are most likely to know what works and what does not, what causes problems and how they can be avoided, and where improvements to the current system are most necessary.

This Chapter describes the *system development life cycle* (Figure 28.1) the sequence of activities involved in analysing, designing and implementing an information system. As well as systems analysts, who play key roles in the process, other personnel such as computer programmers and computer managers are also involved to a large

Figure 28.1. *System life cycle*

degree. Though the steps are described separately, in practice they may be performed in a different order, or even be difficult to distinguish one from another; sometimes one part of the system will be in the process of being implemented while another is still being analysed. The cyclic nature of system development is illustrated in Figure 28.1. The system development stages illustrated in the diagram may be repeated a number of times during the life of a system. Each time a significant change or improvement is required, the cycle is repeated.

Preliminary study

Before an organisation embarks on a costly project involving the development of a new information system, it is necessary to determine whether the system is possible to achieve and, if so, whether there will be sufficient benefits in doing so. The main part of this investigation is called a *feasibility study*. However, even before the feasibility study commences, it will be necessary to fully clarify what is being proposed. The systems analyst dealing with the proposal will talk with the people who have suggested the project in order to determine exactly what they have in mind and their reasons. Once the proposal has been fully clarified, the feasibility study can be undertaken. The feasibility study is usually carried out by a team of people with experience in information systems techniques, with a knowledge of the type of system being proposed and who are skilled in systems analysis and design. The team will be responsible for determining whether the potential benefits of the proposed system can justify the costs involved in developing it. It may be that the consequences of not adopting the new system make the change essential. For example, if a company is unable, through volume of work, to deal with customers effectively, the latter may take their business to more efficient competitors. It then becomes essential to the company's survival to improve its information system.

The feasibility study must also establish whether the new system can operate with available technology, software and personnel. In most instances, for example where a currently manual system is to be replaced or improved by using a computer system, the existing technology will most probably exist, but a new, innovative idea might require hardware or software that don't exist. If this is the case, the feasibility study team will attempt to determine whether the new items can be developed within a reasonable time. Finally, the team will consider how well the system will be received by the people who will have to use it. This must have been a prime concern, for instance, of the first analysts who considered the use of cash points such as those now commonly provided by banks and building societies: would customers trust them and would they be sufficiently easy to use?

Investigation and analysis

If the feasibility study produces a favourable report, the next stage, that of making a detailed analysis of the current system, will commence. The systems analyst will investigate all aspects of the current system:

- ☐ what services are being offered;
- ☐ what tasks are being performed;
- ☐ how they are being performed;
- ☐ how frequently they are done;
- ☐ how well they are done;
- ☐ what staff are involved and the nature of their involvement;
- ☐ what is lacking in the system;
- ☐ any faults with the system;
- ☐ how the system can be improved.

Finding the answers to these questions requires the analyst to talk to all the people involved in operating the current system, from ordinary employees to managers and directors. This will frequently involve the use of questionnaires as well as personal interviews with employees, the study of manuals and reports, the observation of current working practices, and the collection and study of forms and other documents currently used. As this process is going on, the analyst will be starting to form views on how the new system should work in order to overcome the problems with the current system. At the end of this stage, the systems analyst will thoroughly understand how the current system works and be in a position to begin to design and produce a *Requirements Specification* for the new system.

The Requirements Specification should clearly present what the system is meant to do and achieve, but design considerations should be left until the Design stage. Of course, some design aspects, such as the need for bar code scanning for an EPOS (electronic point of sale) system, may be obvious and can be taken for granted. Some parts of the design may be constrained by the need for compatibility with existing hardware and software. Otherwise, creating a precise design at this stage is unwise because as the development proceeds new design possibilities or unforeseen 'glitches' are almost certain to arise. Although the systems analyst is responsible for drawing up the Requirements Specification, he or she needs to ensure that users are closely involved in its development. The systems analyst should listen carefully to users and ensure that their comments and suggestions have been properly interpreted before incorporating the information into the specification.

System design

This stage produces the details of how the system will meet the requirements identified in the previous analysis stage. A major part of this stage involves identifying the inputs to the system (what they are and how they are to be captured), and the outputs from the system, such as reports, invoices, bills and statements. The designers will also specify in detail what files will be needed, their structures and what devices and media will be used to store them. All this information will be written down in the form of reports, tables and diagrams. Such diagrams as system flow charts and data flow diagrams (Chapter) will be used to show how the overall system is integrated. The system designers will also provide detailed specifications on what the software is required to do so that programmers in the next stage will have a clear idea of what they are expected to produce.

Software development

Depending on the system requirements, existing software may be purchased or it may be necessary to have software written specially. Software that is already available will usually be much cheaper than software that has to be custom-designed, but in many instances suitable software will not be available. Large organisations frequently employ their own systems analysts and programmers, but smaller firms may have to resort to using a software house for the necessary programs.

System testing

Before the system is put fully into operation, all aspects of it must be tested, not just the software that has been developed, but also the manual procedures involved. Personnel who have not been directly involved in developing the system will often be used to test the system after they have been given some appropriate training; such people may do things that were not anticipated by the system designers. In fact, the people testing the system will often deliberately attempt to make it fail in some way. It is vitally important to discover any serious shortcomings in the new information system before it is fully operational.

System documentation

System documentation serves much the same purposes as program documentation described briefly in the earlier section on software development. All aspects of the system's operation will need to be described in detail. The documentation will include:

- ❑ user manuals describing the operation of the system;
- ❑ technical manuals for the computer hardware;
- ❑ program documentation.

This documentation serves a number of purposes:

- ❑ To provide reference material for training purposes. This will be of value to all employees using the new system. Each task and procedure will be clearly detailed and explained in terms appropriate to the staff involved.
- ❑ To explain in detail how the system is intended to work so that the people using the system can cope with problems and unfamiliar situations. This will be of particular value to managers and supervisors responsible for organising the work.
- ❑ To specify how to test the system to ensure that it is working correctly.
- ❑ To make it easier to modify or improve the system in future.

Implementing the system

In this stage the system designers will actually install the new system, putting new equipment into operation, installing and setting up software, creating data files and training people to use the system. A common practice is to run the new system in parallel with the old one to ensure that if anything does go wrong, the business will not come to a grinding halt.

When the system has become fully operational, there will still be the possibility of unforeseen events causing problems. The system developers will therefore need to be available to deal with any problems that do arise, as well as making modifications as circumstances change. If an outside firm has developed the system, this system maintenance, normally will be subject to a separate financial arrangement such as an annual charge.

Monitoring and review

The final phase of the system development process is the assessment of the completed system. In this review, or evaluation, a number of factors are examined, including:

- ❑ How well the system is performing with reference to the needs that were initially identified.
- ❑ The final cost of the system compared to how much was originally budgeted.
- ❑ The time taken to complete the work.

Even after the system is fully operational its performance is continually *monitored* throughout its life. At some stage, monitoring will identify needs that are no longer satisfied by the current system, and the system development process will begin once more with a preliminary study.

Chapter 29

System controls

Computerised information systems present particular problems for the control of data entering the system, because for much of the time this data is not in human-readable form and even when it is stored, the information remains invisible unless it is printed out or displayed on a VDU screen. If proper system controls are not used, inaccurate data may reach the master files or un-authorised changes to data may be made, resulting in decision-making which may be based on incorrect information. System controls can be divided into three main types, according to the purposes they serve: data control; data security.

Data control

A number of data control mechanisms, including for example, the validation of input data, can be employed. Controls should be exerted at all stages in the data processing cycle, which commonly recognises the following stages: (i) data *collection*; (ii) *input*; (iii) *processing*, including file processing; (iv) *output*. Controls can be implemented by clerical and software procedures. It is only through the combined application of both clerical and software controls that errors can be minimised, although their entire exclusion can never be guaranteed.

Data collection and input procedures

Before describing the controls it is necessary to outline the activities which may be involved in the collection and input of data. Depending on the application these may include one or more of the following:

❑ Source document preparation. To ensure standardisation of practice and to facilitate checking, data collected for input, for example, customer orders, are clerically transcribed onto source documents specially designed for the purpose.

❑ Data transmission. If the computer centre is geographically remote from the data collection point, the source documents may be physically transported there, or be keyed and transmitted through a terminal and telecommunications link to the computer.

❑ Data encoding and verification. This involves the transcription, usually through a keyboard device, of the data onto a storage medium such as magnetic tape or disk; a process of machine verification accompanied by a repeated keying operation assists the checking of keying accuracy. *Key-to-disk* and *key-to-tape* systems are used for encoding, commonly making use of diskette and cassette tape storage, from which media the data is then merged onto a large reel of magnetic tape or a disk pack for subsequent rapid input.

❑ Data input and validation. Data validation is a computer controlled process which checks the data for its validity according to certain pre-defined parameters, so it must be input to the computer first. The topic of validation is examined in more detail later.

☐ Sorting. In order to improve the efficiency of processing, input data is sorted into a sequence determined by the *primary key* of each record in the relevant master file; this is always necessary for efficient sequential file processing, but direct access files allow records to be processed by transactions in the same order that they are received.

Collection and input controls

Transcription of data from one medium to another, for example, from telephone notepad to customer order form, or from source document to magnetic disk, provides the greatest opportunity for error. A number of strategies can be adopted to help limit data collection and input errors:

☐ minimising transcription. This may involve the use of automated input methods such as bar code reading. Another solution is to use *turnaround documents*, which are originally produced by the computer and later become input documents, for example, remittance advices which, having been sent to customers, are then returned with their payments. Because these remittance advices already show customers' details, including account numbers, only the amounts remitted need to be entered for them to become complete input documents;

☐ designing data collection and input documents in ways which encourage accurate completion;

☐ using clerical checking procedures such as the re-calculation of totals or the visual comparison of document entries with the original sources of information;

☐ using codes with a restricted format, for example, customer account numbers consisting of two alphabetic characters, followed by six digits, permits easy validation;

☐ employing *batch* methods of input which allow the accumulation and checking of batch control totals, both by clerical and computerised methods;

☐ using screen verification before input data is processed and applied to computer files. Screen dialogue (the form of conversation between the computer and the user) techniques, which allow data verification and correction at the time of entry, can be used to provide this facility;

☐ checking input data with the use of *batch* or *interactive* screen validation techniques;

☐ ensuring that staff are well trained and that clerical procedure manuals are available for newly trained staff;

☐ controlling access to input documents. This is important where documents are used for sensitive applications such as payroll. For example, input documents for changing pay rates should only be available to, say, the Personnel Manager.

File processing controls

Once validated data has entered the computer system, checks have to be made to ensure that it is; (i) applied to the correct files; (ii) consistent with the filed data.

Header records

Files can have header records which detail the function, for example, Sales Ledger, *version number* and *purge date*. The purge date indicates the date after which the file is no longer required and can be overwritten. Thus, a file with a purge date after the current date should not be overwritten. Such details can be checked by the application program to ensure that the correct file is used and that a current file is not accidentally destroyed.

File validation checks

Some validation checks can only be made after data input when reference can be made to the relevant master file data. These are described in the later section on data control in batch processing systems.

Data integrity

The printing of all master file changes allows the user department and auditors to check that all such changes are *authorised* and *consistent* with transaction documents. All data used by applications for reference purposes should be printed periodically; price lists, for example, may be held as permanent data on master files or in table form within computer programs.

Output controls

It might reasonably be supposed that input and file processing controls are sufficient to ensure accurate output. Nevertheless, a number of simple controls at the output stage can help to ensure that it is complete and is distributed to the relevant users on time. They include:

- ❑ the comparison of *filed* control totals with *run* control totals. For example, when an entire sequential file is processed, the computer counts all processed records and compares the total with a stored record total held in a *trailer record* at the end of the file;

- ❑ the *conciliation* of control totals specific to the application, with totals obtained from a related application. For example, the sales transactions total posted to the Sales Ledger for one day should agree with the total sales transactions recorded in the Sales Day Book or Journal;

- ❑ the following of set procedures for the treatment of error reports;

- ❑ the proper checking and re-submission of rejected transactions.

Data control in batch processing

It is extremely important that all relevant data is processed and that accuracy is maintained throughout the data processing cycle. The controls which are used will depend on the type of processing method in operation, but batch processing provides the greatest opportunity for exerting control over the data, from the input stage through to the output stage.

Amongst the control methods outlined above, there are two which are particularly important - *verification* and *validation*. These control methods can be used to maximum advantage in a batch processing system and typical procedures are described below.

The stages involved in a batch processing *system cycle* are illustrated in Figure 17.1 with a systems flowchart for a payroll run.

The following controls can be used at certain stages within the cycle.

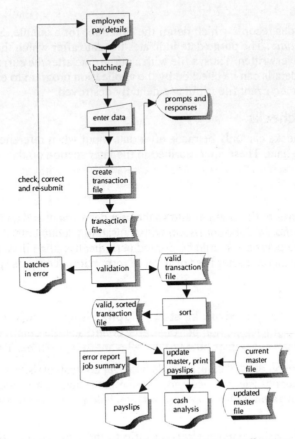

Figure 17.1. *System flowchart of batch payroll system*

Clerical controls

These can be used at any stage in the cycle when the data is in a human-readable form. The types of check include:

- ❑ visual checking of source documents to detect missing, illegible or unlikely data values, an example of the latter being a total of 100 in the weekly overtime hours entry for an individual worker;

- ❑ the verification of entries by checking them against another source, for example, the price catalogue for the price of a stock item on an invoice;

- ❑ the re-working of calculations on a source document, for example, the checking of additions which make up the total quantity for an item on an order form.

Verification

Before processing, data has to be transcribed from the source documents onto a computer input medium, usually involving a keying operation to encode the data onto magnetic tape or magnetic disk. This stage can be prone to error, particularly if large volumes of data are involved and verification, which is usually a machine-assisted process, can ensure that data is encoded accurately. Magnetic tape encoders (*key-to-tape* systems), for example, can operate in two modes, *record* and *verify*. The operation involves one person keying the data in the record mode, after which a second person re-keys the data with the machine in verify mode. In effect the machine reads the data from the first keying operation and then checks it against the second keying as it occurs. The machine signals if characters do not agree, thus indicating a possible transcription error. *Key-to-disk* systems operate on a similar principle, either with stand-alone workstations or through terminals linked to a minicomputer and usually incorporate some facility for *validation* of data.

Validation

This process is carried out after the data has been encoded onto the input medium and involves a program called the *data vet* or *validation program*. Its purpose is to check that the data falls within certain parameters defined by the systems analyst. A judgement as to whether or not data is valid is made possible by the validation program, but it cannot ensure absolute accuracy. That can only be achieved by the use of all the clerical and computer controls built into the system at the design stage. The difference between *validity* and *accuracy* can be illustrated by the following example.

Example of validation

A company has established a Personnel file. Each record in the file may contain a field for the Job Grade. The permitted values of job grade are A, B, C or D. An entry in an individual's record may be *valid* and accepted by the system if it is recorded as A, B,C or D, but of course this may not be the *correct* grade for the individual worker concerned. Whether or not the grade is correct can only be established by the clerical checks discussed earlier.

Types of validation check

Character, field and record checks

❑ *Size*. The number of characters in a field is checked. For example, an account number may require 6 characters and if there are more or less than this, then the item is rejected.

❑ *Mode*. It may be that particular fields must contain particular types of character, for example alphabetic or numeric. If the system is programmed to accept only numbers then letters would be rejected.

❑ *Format*. This refers to the way characters within a field are organised. For example, an Item Code may consist of 2 alphabetic characters followed by 6 numeric characters, so the system would reject any entry which did not correspond to this format.

❑ *Reasonableness*. Quantities can be checked for unusually high or low values. For example, a gas consumer with one small appliance may have a meter reading appropriate to a consumer with a large central heating system and a reasonableness test could be used to reject or highlight it.

❑ *Presence*. If a field must always have a value then it can be checked for existence. For example, the field 'Sex' in a Personnel record would always have to have an M(ale) or F(emale) entry.

❑ *Range*. Values are checked for certain upper and lower limits, for example, account numbers may have to be between 00001 and 10000.

❑ *Check digit*. An extra digit calculated on an account number can be used as a self checking device. When the number is input to the computer, the validation program carries out a calculation similar to that used to generate the check digit originally and thus checks its validity. This kind of check will highlight transposition errors caused by, for instance, keying digits in the wrong order.

All the above checks can be carried out prior to the master file updating stage. Further checks on data can be made through the use of a validation program at the *update* stage, by comparison with the master file. They are as follow:

❑   *new records*. When a new record is to be added to the master file, a check can be made to ensure that a record does not already use the entered record key .

❑   *deleted records*. It may be that a transaction is entered for which there is no longer a matching master record.

❑   *consistency*. A check is made that the transaction values are consistent with the values held on the master record which is to be updated. For instance a deduction for pension contributions by an employee who is not old enough to be in a pension scheme would obviously be inconsistent.

Validation using batch controls

Batch totals

The purpose of batch totals is to allow a conciliation of manually produced totals for a batch with comparable computer-produced totals. Differences are signalled and the batch is rejected for checking and re-submission. Following the arrangement of source documents into batches of say 30 in each batch, totals are calculated on add-listing machines for each value it is required to control. On an order form, for example, quantities and prices may be separately totalled to provide two control totals. Totals may also be produced for each account number or item code simply for purposes of control although they are otherwise meaningless. For this reason such totals are called hash or nonsense totals.

The totals are recorded on a *batch control slip* (Figure 17.2), attached to the batch, together with a value for the number of documents in the batch and a batch number. The batch number is kept in a register held by the originating department so that missing or delayed batches can be traced. It should be noted that *hash totals* may produce a figure which has a large number of digits, so extra digits over and above the original length of the data item are truncated.

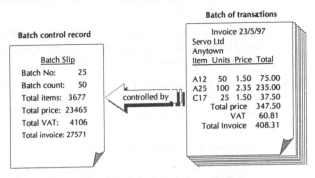

Figure 17.2. *Batch control slip*

Reconciliation of batch totals

The details from each batch control slip are entered with each batch of transactions at the encoding stage. The serial transaction file which results may be arranged as in Figure 17.3.

The serial transaction file is processed from beginning to end by the validation program. The sum of the transaction records relating to each batch should match the batch total. If any validation error is detected, either by differences in batch totals or through the character of field checks described earlier, the offending batch is rejected to be checked and re-submitted. Rejected batches are reported on a computer printout.

Figure 17.3. *Arrangement of serial transaction file, with batch totals*

Validation during updating

Checks can be made in the manner described earlier, on transactions for deleted or new records, or on data which is inconsistent with the relevant record on the master file. These controls can be used in conjunction with proper clerical procedures to ensure that as far as possible, the information stored on the master files is accurate.

File controls

In addition to controlling the accuracy of data entering the system it is essential to check both that the data is complete and that all relevant data is processed. This can be done through the use of file controls on the transaction file. Following the validation of the batches of transactions, correct batches are written to another file to be sorted and used for updating the relevant master file. During validation, the validation program accumulates totals for all the correct batches. These can be used during the update run to ensure that the whole transaction file is processed.

Validation in on-line systems

On-line systems, as described in the Chapter on Processing Methods, tend to be interactive and transactions are processed immediately against the master files at the data entry stage. The main controls which can be introduced to such systems include:

❑ the character, field and record validation checks described earlier. Error messages are displayed on the screen at the time data is entered and require immediate correction at that time;

❑ visual verification. At the end of each transaction entry, the operator is given the opportunity to scan the data on the screen and to re-enter any incorrect entries detected. This usually takes the form of a message at the bottom of the screen which is phrased in a way such as "Verify (yes or no)";

❑ the use of well-trained data entry operators. They should have sufficient knowledge of the data being entered and the application it serves, to respond to error messages and make corrections to data accordingly.

Data security

The controls used have several main functions:

❑ to prevent loss of files by software or procedural errors, or by physical hazards;

❑ to protect data from accidental or deliberate disclosure to unauthorised individuals or groups;

❑ to protect the data from accidental or deliberate corruption or modification. This is known as maintaining *data integrity*;

❑ to protect the rights of individuals and organisations to restrict access to information which relates to them and is of a private nature, to those entitled or authorised to receive it. This is known as *data privacy*.

Security against data loss

The loss of *master files* can be an extremely serious occurrence for any organisation so properly organised security procedures need to be employed. Among commercial organisations that have lost the major part of their information store, a large percentage subsequently go out of business. The main causes of data loss are as follow:

❑ environmental hazards such as fire, flood and other natural accidents;

❑ mechanical problems, for example the danger of disk or tape damage caused by a drive unit malfunction;

❑ software errors resulting from programming error;

❑ human error. A wrong file may be loaded, the wrong program version used, a tape or disk mislaid, or physical damage caused to tape or disk;

❑ malicious damage. It is not unknown for staff to intentionally damage storage media or to misuse programs at a terminal.

The standard solution to such problems is to take regular copies of master files and to store the copies in a separate secure location. It is also necessary to maintain a record of transactions affecting a file since the last copy was taken, so that if necessary they can be used to reconstruct the latest version of the file.

Magnetic tape file security

When a tape master file is updated by a tape transaction file the physical nature of the medium makes it necessary for a new tape file to be produced. As Figure 17.4 illustrates, the updating procedure provides a built-in security system referred to as the Grandparent, Parent and Child (*generation*) system.

In the first run, Master File 1 is updated by the transactions file

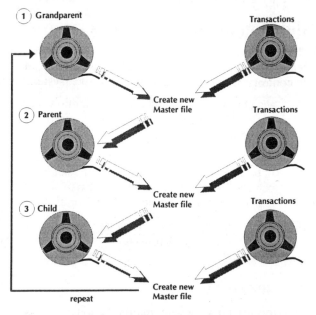

Figure 17.4. *Generation security system for tape files*

to produce Master File 2 as its Child. Master File 1 is the Parent. Should the Child file be damaged and the data lost, it can be re-created from the Parent master file and the relevant transactions. At the end of the second run, Master File 1 becomes the Grandparent, Master File 2 becomes the Parent and Master File 3, the Child. Each generation provides security for subsequent files. The number of generations used will depend on the policy of the organisation. Three generations are usually regarded as providing sufficient security and the oldest files are re-used by being overwritten as each cycle of generations is completed.

Internal header labels

Internal header labels are designed to deal with two major areas of concern:

- [ ] It is important that the correct file is used in a file processing operation to ensure correct results. Thus, the *subject* of the file and the *version* must be identifiable. For example, it is no good producing monthly payslips using information from a payroll master file three months out of date.

- [ ] A tape file must be protected against accidental erasure. This may occur because tapes are re-usable and when a file is no longer required it can be overwritten by new information.

To ensure that the correct file is used for any particular job, a tape file usually has an internal header label. The label appears at the beginning of the tape and identifies it. The identifying information in the label is usually recorded under program control or by a data encoding device.

A tape header label usually contains the following items of information:

- [ ] file name e.g. Payroll, Stock, Sales;
- [ ] date created;
- [ ] purge date - the date after which the tape is no longer required and may be re-used.

The label is checked by the program, before the file is processed, to ensure that the correct tape is being used.

File protection ring

A device called a file protection ring can be used to prevent accidental erasure. When tapes are stored off-line, the rings are not fitted. To write to a tape, the ring must first be fitted to the centre of the reel. A tape can be read by the computer whether or not a ring is fitted. The simple rule to remember is 'no ring, no write'.

Magnetic disk file security

Security back-ups

Disk files can be treated in the same way as tape files in that the updating procedure may produce a new master file leaving the original file intact. On the other hand, if the file is updated *in-situ* (which in so doing overwrites the existing data), then it will be necessary to take regular back-up copies as processing proceeds. The frequency with which copies are taken will depend on the volume of transactions affecting the master file. If the latest version of the master file is corrupted or lost, then it can be re-created using the previous back-up together with the transaction data received since the back-up.

Transaction logging

The systems flowchart in Figure 17.5 illustrates the transaction logging procedure.

Figure 17.5. *Backup and transaction logging*

In an on-line system, transactions may enter the system from a number of terminals in different locations, thus making it difficult to re-enter transactions for the re-creation of a damaged master file. One solution is to log all the transactions onto a serial transaction file at the same time as the master file is updated. Thus, the re-creation process can be carried out without the need for keying in the transactions again.

Access controls

Unauthorised access to a system may: provide vital information to competitors; result in the deliberate or accidental corruption of data; allow fraudulent changes to be made to data; result in loss of privacy for individuals or organisations. To avoid such hasards an information system should be protected *physically*, by *administrative procedures* and *software*. To detect any unauthorised access or changes to the information system:

☐   users should require *authorisation* (with different levels of authority depending on the purpose of access);

☐   the computer should *log* all successful and attempted accesses;

☐   users should be *identifiable* and their identity *authenticated;*

☐   the files should be capable of being *audited;*

☐   the actions of *programmers* should be carefully controlled to prevent fraud through changes to software.

Physical protection

These include the use of security staff, mechanical devices, such as locks and keys and electronic alarm/identification systems.

Computer systems with terminals at remote sites present a weak link in any system and they must be properly protected and here software plays an important protection role. Disk and tape libraries also need to be protected, otherwise it would be possible for a thief to take file media to another centre with compatible hardware and software. A variety of methods may be used to *identify* and possibly *authenticate* a system user. They include:

☐   Identity cards. Provided that they cannot be copied and have a photograph, they can be effective and cheap. The addition of a magnetic strip which contains encoded personal details including a *personal identification number* (PIN), which the holder has to key in, allows the user to be checked by machine. This method is used to allow access to service tills outside banks. Of course, the user of the card may not be the authorised holder, possession of the PIN being the only additional requirement; the following methods allow authentication as well as identification.

☐ Personal physical characteristics. Voice recognition or fingerprint comparison provide effective, if expensive, methods of identification and authentication.

Such methods are only effective if the supporting administrative procedures are properly followed.

Software protection

Ideally, before a user is given access to a system, the log-in procedures should check for: *authorisation*; *identification*; *authentication*.

Authorisation is usually provided by an account code, which must be keyed in response to a computer prompt; similar prompts may appear for a user-id *(identification)* and a password *(authentication)*.

Further control can be exerted with *fixed terminal identifiers*, whereby each terminal and its location is physically identifiable by the controlling computer, thus preventing access from additional unauthorised locations. Such controls can also be used to restrict particular terminals to particular forms and levels of access.

Password controls

Access to files can be controlled at different levels by a series of passwords, which have to be keyed into the terminal in response to a series of questions displayed on the screen. For example, a clerk in a Personnel Department may be given authority to display information regarding an employee's career record but only the Personnel Manager is authorised to change the information held on file.

Passwords should be carefully chosen, kept secure (memorised and not divulged) and changed frequently. Using people's names, for example, may allow entry by trial and error. Characters should not be echoed on screen as the password is entered.

Handshaking is a technique which requires more than a simple password and may be used between two computers or a computer and a user, as a means of access control. In the latter case, the user would be given a pseudo-random number by the computer and the expected response would be a transform, of that random number. The transform may be to multiply the first and last digits of the number and add the product to a value equal to the day of the month plus 1. Provided the transform is kept secret, handshaking provides more security than simple passwords.

One-time passwords. The computer will only accept a password for *one access occasion*; subsequently, it will expect the user to provide a different password for each additional access, in a pre-defined sequence. Provided the password list and their expected sequence list are kept separate, then possession of one list only will not be of any assistance. The number of attempts at logging-on should be controlled, so, for example, after three unsuccessful attempts, the user should be locked out and a record kept of the time and nature of the attempt.

Authorisation tables

These are held with the relevant files and detail the kinds of access permitted by particular users or groups of users - read only, read and write or delete. Control may also be exerted at a record or field level.

Data encryption

If data signals being transmitted along the telecommunication links are not properly protected, *hackers* can pick up the signals and display them on their own machines. To prevent such intrusion, data encryption methods are used to protect important financial, legal and other confidential information during transmission from one centre to another. Encryption scrambles the data to make it unintelligible during transmission. As the power and speed of computers has increased, so the breaking of codes has been made easier.

Code designers have produced methods of encryption which are currently unbreakable in any reasonable time period, even by the largest and most powerful computers available. An example of such an elaborate coding system is illustrated by the operation of the Electronic Funds Transfer (EFT) system. This is used by banks and other financial institutions to transfer vast sums of money so these transmissions are protected by the latest data encryption techniques. The Data Encryption Standard (DES) was approved by the American National Bureau of Standards in 1977, but as costs of powerful computers have fallen and come within the reach of criminal organisation, EFT makes use of the DES standard, plus additional encryption techniques.

Security to maintain data integrity

Data integrity refers to the accuracy and consistency of the information stored and is thus covered by the security methods outlined above. A major threat to data integrity comes from a variety of computer viruses.

Computer viruses

A computer virus is program code designed to create nuisance for users, or more seriously, to effect varying degrees of damage to files stored on magnetic media. Generally, the code

❏ is introduced through portable media, such as floppy disks, particularly those storing pirated or shareware programs; files downloaded from *bulletin boards* on the Internet may be infected and uncontrolled use of these services is likely to result in the receipt of viruses;

❏ transfers itself from the infected medium into the computer's main memory as soon as the medium is accessed;

❏ transfers from memory onto any integral storage device, such as a hard disk and commonly conceals itself in the boot sector (and sometimes in the partition sector where it is less likely to be traced), from where it can readily infect any other media placed on line in that computer system, whether it be stand-alone or networked. Naturally, any write-protected media cannot be infected.

Some virus codes are merely a nuisance, whilst others are developed specifically to destroy, or make inaccessible, whole filing systems. They pose a serious threat to any computer-based information system, but a number of measures can be taken to minimise the risk:

❏ only use proprietary software from a reliable source;

❏ write-protect disks being used for reading purposes only;

❏ use virus detection software, although this is only effective in respect of viruses using known storage and proliferation techniques;

❏ use diskless workstations on networks;

❑   control access to portable media and forbid employees to use their own media on the organisation's computer system.

Security to maintain privacy of data

The rights of individuals and organisations concerning their confidential records are similarly protected by the security controls outlined earlier. In addition, legislation by parliament (the Data Protection Act- see Chapter 31) attempts to exert some control by requiring persons or organisations holding personal information on computer files to register with the Data Protection Registrar. Some countries have 'Freedom of Information Acts' which allow the individual to see any personal information stored in their own files, except where national security is thought to be threatened. It is generally accepted that the Data Protection Act falls far short of complete freedom of information.

Exercises

1. Distinguish between *verification* and *validation*.
2. Using batch order processing as an example:
    (a)   suggest four *data collection controls* to control the accuracy of data entering the system;
    (b)   suggest three *validation checks* which could be applied to customer order details;
    (c)   indicate any *file processing controls* which could be employed.
3. Draw a *system flowchart* to illustrate the batch processing of customer orders and the updating of stock, order and customer files.
4. With the use of an example, describe the *generation system* of security for tape files.
5. What is transaction logging?
6. With the aid of an example organisation, describe two methods to prevent *unauthorised access* to data.
7. What is data encryption and why is it important? Give and example to illustrate your answer.
8. (a)   What is a computer virus?
    (b)   Suggest two measures which an organisation can take to minimise the risk of damage from computer viruses.

Chapter 30

Health and safety

Although a computer is not inherently dangerous, users should be aware of a number of potential risks to their safety and general health. Most employers have obligations (under Section 2 of the Health and Safety at Work Act, 1974) to protect the health, safety and welfare of their employees, by ensuring safe equipment, work systems and working environment. This legislative protection applies to work with a computer *workstation* (a visual display unit and its associated equipment and furniture), as it does to other work. In 1993, specific legislation was introduced to implement European Directive 90/270/EEC, "on the minimum safety and health requirements for work with display screen equipment".

This section examines the potential hazards of using a computer workstation and the steps that can be taken to avoid them. The 1993 legislation recognises that good work organisation and job design, and the application of established *ergonomic* principles, can largely avoid the hazards to health and safety.

Ergonomics

Ergonomics is the "study of efficiency of workers and working arrangements" (Oxford English Dictionary). Although a separate science in its own right, certain aspects of ergonomics are being applied increasingly to the design of:

❑ furniture associated with office computer systems;

❑ computer equipment for person/machine interfacing, for example, screen displays and keyboards;

❑ office and workstation layout.

It is generally recognised that, if workstation facilities and the working environment are inadequate, computer users will tend to be inefficient and may suffer from general fatigue and boredom. The increased emphasis on ergonomic design has come about because of the large increase in the number of computer users. The term *user* includes not only computer specialists, but also non-specialist users, such as data entry operators, clerks, accountants and managers.

Hazards to operator health and efficiency

In designing a suitable workstation, the designer needs to be aware of a number of potential hazards, which are described in the following paragraphs.

Visual fatigue

Various symptoms may indicate the onset of visual fatigue: sore eyes; hazy vision; difficulty in focusing when switching vision between near and distant objects; aching behind the eyes. Certain workstation features and user behaviour can contribute to visual fatigue. The screen display and the positioning of documents that are being transcribed, typically contribute to this fatigue. More specifically, the fatigue may be caused by one or more of the following.

☐   screen glare;

☐   poor character-definition on screen;

☐   excessive periods of screen viewing and consequent short distance focusing;

☐   screen flicker;

☐   screen reflection;

☐   insufficient or excessive ambient (surrounding) lighting;

☐   frequent, excessive eye movement when switching between screen and document.

Bodily fatigue

Tense and aching muscles or inflamed nerves, generally in the shoulders, neck, back, wrists or hands may result from:

☐   adopting a poor seating posture;

☐   bending frequently to reach various parts of the workstation;

☐   using a keyboard which is not at a comfortable height. *Repetitive strain injury* (RSI), or *carpal tunnel syndrome*, is now recognised as a disabling condition, which can result from intensive keyboard work. Products are available to support wrists and help users to avoid the injury. The nerves which lie down the edge of the hand can also become inflamed and painful, a condition known as *ulnar neuritis*.

☐   holding the head at an awkward angle to view the screen or a document.

Other hazards to health and safety

The proper design and positioning of a workstation can help prevent a number of potential hazards, generally relating to the use of equipment. The hazards may include:

☐   *electric shock.* A person may receive a live electric shock, from faulty equipment (such as incorrect earthing of the power supply), and from incorrect use of equipment (such as the removal of the machine's casing, without first isolating the machine from mains power). This form of electric shock will persist until the person breaks contact with the machine, or else the power is cut. Clearly, this hazard is life threatening, and although this is the primary concern, it will probably also cause damage to the machine.

☐   *static electric shock.* This is caused by the sudden discharge through any conducting material of static electricity, which may have built up in the body. The equipment earths the static electricity which the person has accumulated. A person may build up static electricity by walking on a nylon carpet. Sometimes, static electricity accumulates on the computer screen and a shock may be received when it is touched (the person acts as the earth). If the screen is cleaned with special anti-static wipes, this problem should be avoided. Static electric shock is momentary and, whilst in exceptional circumstances it may injure someone, it is more likely to damage the equipment and, possibly, the stored data.

❑   *injury from impact*. For example, someone may bump against the sharp corner of a desk, be injured by dropping equipment when attempting to move it or be cut by sharp edges on equipment;

❑   *muscular or spinal strain*. Lifting heavy equipment may cause strained or torn muscles, or spinal injuries such as a 'slipped' disc;

❑   *burns, cuts or poisoning caused by equipment breakdown*. These injuries may result from fire or overheating of equipment.

Analysis of workstation requirements

There is no single standard for workstation design. The type of equipment and its layout will depend on, amongst other things, who is going to use it and how it is going to be used. Therefore, before choosing an appropriate workstation design, information should be gathered on the following topics.

Users

The physical characteristics and abilities of potential users should, if possible, be identified. User features may include: gender; physical or mental handicap; age range; height; build. Obviously, it may not be possible to identify personally all members of a user group, in which case, information may be more generalised. Questions to ask may be as follow.

❑   Does the user group include males only, females only or both?

❑   What is the age range?

❑   Are there any handicapped users and if so, what are the handicaps?

❑   Are the physical characteristics of users similar or highly varied?

In addition to identifying the features of current users, it is important to allow for possible changes. For example, there may be no wheelchair users at present, but business policy may result in their inclusion in the future.

Existing workstations

If there are workstations already in use within the organisation, then it is useful to determine if there are any good features to include, or bad features to avoid, in any new workstations. The general physical state of the old workstations should be determined. Questions to pose may include: "Have screen displays lost some clarity or steadiness?", "Is the seating still clean and serviceable?", "Are keyboards still fully operable?"

The opinions of users should also yield useful information on the suitability of the existing workstations concerning, for example, seating comfort, positioning of equipment and reliability of hardware.

The location of the workstation

The size of the room in which the workstation is to be located and the layout of existing furniture may place constraints on any design features.

Workstation usage

The various kinds of work to be carried out at a workstation may involve:

- [ ] data entry involving transcription from source documents;
- [ ] use of large reference manuals;
- [ ] storage of file media;
- [ ] customer enquiries which involve customers viewing the screen display;
- [ ] side-by-side working with another member of staff;
- [ ] use of a mouse which requires a flat surface area for its movement;
- [ ] some activities which do not involve the use of a computer. There may be no other available work areas in the office, so sufficient space should be available at each workstation.

It is also important to know how often particular activities are likely to be carried out and how long they will last.

Designing an appropriate workstation

Work surface

Height. A user should have thigh clearance amounting to at least 180mm, measured from the front surface of the seat, to the underside of the work surface. Obviously, this measurement can be obtained if the chair is adjustable in height and the work surface height does not require seat adjustment below its minimum height. The minimum clearance may be insufficient for someone to sit cross-legged, a position which he or she may wish to adopt for short periods, so some extra thigh clearance may be desirable.

Typical heights of manufactured workstations are either 710mm for fixed or between 520mm and 750mm when adjustable. The standard 710mm which manufacturers use for a fixed height desk is based on the ideal writing height for an average male and does not take account of keyboard thickness.

Area. The work surface area required obviously depends on the nature of the work being carried out at the workstation. If transcription work is to be carried out, a *document holder* can be attached to one corner of the mobile workstation. Where more space is available, users may prefer that the document holder is positioned between the keyboard and the screen to reduce the amount of eye movement when alternately viewing the screen and the document. As with all computer equipment, a *matt surface* is desirable to avoid screen reflection and eye strain.

Chair

Where a fixed height desk of, say, 710mm is bought, then it is important that the chair's height is *adjustable* and that a footrest is available for persons of small stature. This is necessary for a comfortable keying height. At the same time, support is provided for the feet (if they are not supported, blood circulation in the legs may be impaired as pressure is exerted by the edge of the seat on the back lower thighs). The footrest should allow the thighs to be slightly raised above the front edge of the chair, thus avoiding 'pins and needles' in the legs and feet. An adjustable chair should be variable in height from 340mm to 520mm. Invariably, manufacturers produce workstation chairs which are adjustable for height and back, particularly lower back, support.

Screen display

In workstation design, the screen display has to be judged for its *quality* and its *position* in relation to the operator. Screen quality is measured for the clarity and steadiness of the images it displays. A high *resolution* screen is generally desirable, even for word processing work, but is of paramount importance if it is used for detailed design work. Several precautions can be taken to minimise eye strain if a poorer quality display is being used:

☐ appropriate lighting; this is examined in the next subsection;

☐ comparisons can be made with other screen displays (the clarity may deteriorate with age) and any deterioration reported;

☐ the use of a higher resolution screen, appropriate to the application and colour where graphical work is involved;

☐ the correct adjustment of contrast and brightness controls. Filters can cut glare and improve character definition by preventing screen reflection from inappropriate lighting. However, their quality is highly variable and a good quality screen should avoid the problem of glare.

There are two major concerns regarding the *positioning* of the screen. First, there is an optimum viewing range. Second, its location should be aimed at minimising excessive head and eye movement. The distance between the user's eyes and the screen should, ideally, fall somewhere between 450mm and 500mm and the design should try to achieve a viewing distance within this range. However, eye strain is more likely to result from repeated re-focusing for lengthy periods, whilst attention is switched from the screen to a document on the desk top. This can be avoided by attempting to position documents approximately the same distance away as the screen. A document holder can be useful in achieving this aim, even if it is positioned to one side and thus requires some head movement to view the document. Some head movement helps to keep the neck and shoulder muscle loosened and avoids stiffness and aching in those areas. A user should try to look away from the screen occasionally, perhaps to the other side of the office, to avoid eye strain which stems from constant focusing at one distance.

Lighting

Natural light falling through office windows may, at times, be adequate for healthy and efficient working but there will be many occasions when it is either too dark or too bright. It is generally necessary to supplement the natural light with artificial lighting and control the entry of bright sunshine with window blinds. The following points provide some basic guidelines as to the artificial lighting requirements for a workstation;

☐ attempt to avoid glare. This can result if there is insufficient lighting and the screen's brightness contrasts sharply with the ambient level of brightness;

☐ reflection on screen can make it difficult to see the displayed characters and cause eye strain. The use of window blinds and non-reflective work surfaces and equipment can help.

Cabling

Cabling is needed to power individual systems, connect the component parts of system unit, printer, keyboard and screen and for communications purposes when separate systems are networked. Loose cable trailing beneath desks or across the floor can result in injury to staff who trip over it. If, in the process, hardware is pulled from a desk onto the floor, it is likely to be damaged and may result in loss of data and temporary loss of system use. Cabling should be channelled through conduit or specially designed channels in the workstation. Cable 'bridge' conduit is specially designed to channel cable safely across floor areas.

Office layout

If the designer has the luxury of starting from 'scratch', then the simplest approach to designing the layout is to make a scale drawing of the office on which the location of equipment and furniture can then be marked. Designated work positions should also be indicated. Numerous drawing and computer aided design packages make experimentation easy. Libraries of standard symbols (representing office equipment and furniture) are available, which the designer can select and locate on screen. The designer has to take into account a number of constraints which will dictate the location of some furniture and equipment. Fixed items should be placed on the drawing first so that those with fewer constraints can be tried in different locations until an optimum layout is achieved. Ideally, the designer should present two or three alternatives for consideration by management and office staff, whose opinions ought to be paramount. A number of factors should be taken into account when choosing the location of workstations:

❑ staff should not be obliged to work in areas which are subject to extremes of temperature, for example, next to radiators or near a frequently used door which creates a draught each time it is opened;

❑ computer equipment should not be placed next to a radiator as overheating may cause the system to malfunction;

❑ computer screens should be protected from direct sun-light which causes screen reflection and glare;

❑ there should be sufficient space for staff to move around the office without moving equipment or furniture;

❑ workstations should have sufficient space to allow routine maintenance and cleaning to be carried out;

❑ there should always be easy access to fire fighting equipment and fire exits should be kept clear.

Exercises

1. What is meant by the term *ergonomics* and why is it important for the computing industry?

2. Identify two items of equipment which can be used to reduce the health risks for data entry operators and others who use computer systems intensively.

3. Draw a scale plan for a room layout which needs to accommodate 4 computer workstations and their users. Assume that the room is 7 × 5 metres, has a ceiling height of 3 metres, one exit door and that one of 7 metre walls has continuous window along its length. 2 × 2 metre radiators are fitted to the same wall.

Chapter 31

Privacy, fraud and copyright

Confidentiality is important for the protection of personal privacy and in the case of organisations, commercial advantage. For example, informing a competitor organisation about your employer's product development plans may be seriously damaging. Even if you have not signed a confidentiality agreement, you could be disciplined or dismissed from your job. Breaking confidence for monetary gain would be a prosecutable offence. The following paragraphs detail the legislation which exists to deter computer crime and protect personal privacy.

Computer Misuse Act (1990)

The Act identifies three categories of offence: (i) unauthorised access to computer material; (ii) unauthorised access with intent to commit or facilitate commission of further offences; (iii) unauthorised modification of computer material.

The Act deals with the general crime of 'hacking'. The first category of offence deals with unauthorised access to a computer system, its programs and data. An offence is committed if a person performs any computer function with the <u>intent</u> of securing unauthorised access to any program or data held in any computer. The second category covers the offence of persistent hacking. The third category covers the alteration of data to which a hacker has gained access. These crimes are punishable by prison sentences.

Computer fraud and protection measures

Computer fraud is invariably committed for financial gain, but unlike some forms of fraud, the perpetrator(s) will make considerable efforts to prevent discovery of any loss by the victim. The rewards for such efforts may be complete freedom from prosecution, or at least a delay in discovery of the fraud and a consequent chance of escape. Unless proper controls and checks are implemented, computer systems are particularly vulnerable to fraudulent activity, because much of the time processing and its results are hidden. The following section examines some methods for committing fraud and the measures which can be taken to foil them. To extract money from a financial accounting system requires its diversion into fictitious, but accessible accounts. To avoid detection, appropriate adjustments must be made to ensure that the accounts still balance. Sometimes, fraudulent activity may involve the misappropriation of goods rather than cash. Frequently, the collusion of several people is necessary to effect a fraud, because responsibility for different stages of the processing cycle is likely to be shared. Some common methods of fraud are given below.

Bogus data entry. This may involve entering additional, unauthorised data, modifying valid data or preventing its entry altogether. Such activity may take place during the data preparation or data entry stages.

Bogus output. Output may be destroyed or altered to prevent discovery of fraudulent data entry or processing.

Alteration of files. For example, an employee may alter his salary grading in the payroll file or adjust the amount owing in a colluding customers account.

Program patching. This method requires access to program coding and a detailed knowledge of the functioning of the program in question, as well as the necessary programming skill. By introducing additional code, in the form of a conditional subroutine, certain circumstances determined by the perpetrator can trigger entry to the subroutine, which may, for example, channel funds to a fictitious account.

Suspense accounts. Rejected and unreconciled transactions tend to be allocated to suspense accounts until they can be dealt with; fraud may be effected by directing such transactions to the account of someone colluding in the crime. Transactions can be tampered with at the input stage to ensure their rejection and allocation to the suspense/personal account.

An organisation can minimise the risk of computer fraud by:

Controlling access to computer hardware; in centralised systems with a limited number of specialist staff access can be readily controlled. On the other hand, if power is concentrated in the hands of few staff, then the opportunities for undetected fraud are increased. Distributed systems or centralised systems with remote access, for example through the Internet, may increase the number of locations where fraud can be perpetrated;

Auditing of data and procedures; until hard copy is produced the contents of files remain invisible and a number of auditing techniques can be used to detect fraudulent entries or changes.

Monitoring of the programming function; program patching can be controlled by division of the programming task, so that an individual programmer does not have complete responsibility for one application program. Unauthorised alterations to existing software can be detected by auditing utilities which compare the object code of an operational program with an original and authorised copy.

Data Protection Acts (1984 and 1998)

The Data Protection Act of 1984 states that a business or other organisation which holds personal information on their computer system must register with the Data Protection Registrar, the body that administers the act. The registration process requires identification of the classes of data held and the purposes for which they are to be used. For example, a business may hold personal data which includes information on lifestyle and income which it uses to target its marketing campaigns. A new UK Data Protection Act, passed in 1998 and which came into force on 1 March 2000, specifically concerns the processing of personal data on the Internet. The main provisions of each Act are given in the following sections.

Data Protection Act (1984)

Since the 1960s, there has been growing public concern about the threat that computers pose to personal privacy. Most countries, including the UK, have introduced legislation to safeguard the privacy of the individual. The Younger Report of 1972 identified ten principles which were intended as guidelines to computer users in the private sector. A Government White Paper was published in 1975 in response to the Younger Report, but no legislation followed. The Lindop Report of 1978 was followed by a White Paper in 1982 and this resulted in the 1984 Data Protection Act. Apart from public pressure concerning the protection of personal privacy, a major incentive for the Government to introduce the Act stemmed from the need to ratify the Council of Europe Data Protection Convention. In the absence of this ratification, firms within the UK could have been considerably disadvantaged in trading terms through the Conventions provision to allow participating countries to refuse the transfer of personal information to non-participating countries. The principles detailed in the Younger Report formed the foundation for future reports and the Data Protection Act. They are listed below.

❑ Information should be regarded as being held for a specific purpose and should not be used, without appropriate authorisation, for other purposes.

❑ Access to information should be confined to those authorised to have it for the purpose for which it was supplied.

❑ The amount of information collected and held should be the minimum necessary for the achievement of a specified purpose.

❑ In computerised systems which handle information for statistical purposes, adequate provision should be made in their design for separating identities from the rest of the data.

❑ There should be arrangements whereby a subject could be told about the information held concerning him or her.

❑ The level of security to be achieved by a system should be specified in advance by the user and should include precautions against the deliberate abuse or misuse of information.

❑ A monitoring system should be provided to detect violation of the security system.

❑ In the design of information systems, periods should be specified beyond which information should not be retained.

❑ Data held should be accurate. There should be machinery for the correction of inaccuracy and updating of information.

❑ Care should be taken in coding value judgements.

The White Paper which followed the Younger Report identified certain features of computerised information systems which could be a threat to personal privacy:

❑ The facility for storing vast quantities of data.

❑ The speed and power of computers make it possible for data to be retrieved quickly and easily from many access points;

❑ Data can be rapidly transferred between interconnected systems.

❑ Computers allow data to be combined in ways which might otherwise be impracticable.

❑ Data is often transferred in a form not directly intelligible.

The 1984 Data Protection Act sets boundaries for the gathering and use of personal data. It requires all holders of computerised personal files to register with a Registrar appointed by the Home Secretary. The holder of personal data is required to keep to both the general terms of the Act, and to the specific purposes declared in the application for registration.

Terminology

The Act uses a number of terms which require some explanation:

☐ Data. Information held in a form which can be processed automatically. By this definition, manual information systems are not covered by the Act.

☐ Personal data. That which relates to a living individual who is identifiable from the information, including any which is based on fact or opinion.

☐ Data subject. The living individual who is the subject of the data.

☐ Data user. A person who processes or intends to process the data concerning a data subject.

Implications

The requirements of the Act may result in an organisation having to pay more attention to the question of security against unauthorised access than would otherwise be the case; appropriate education and training of employees are also needed to ensure that they are aware of their responsibilities and are fully conversant with their roles in the security systems. The Act also provides the right of a data subject (with some exceptions) to obtain access to information concerning him or her. Normally, a data user must provide such information free of charge or for a nominal charge of around £10. From the individuals point of view, the Act can be said to have a number of weaknesses:

☐ Penalties for infringement of the rules are thought to be weak and ineffective.

☐ There are a number of exemptions from the Act. Some holders do not need to register and there are exceptions to the right of access to ones own file. There are also limits to confidentiality.

The Registrar is appointed by the Home Secretary and cannot therefore, be wholly independent.

Data Protection Act (1998)

"An Act to make new provision for the regulation of the processing of information relating to individuals, including the obtaining, holding, use or disclosure of such information." [16th July 1998 Data Protection Act]. The Act defines 'data' as information which is automatically processed, or is gathered with that intention, or is held in a structured filing system which is not automatically controlled. In other words, the Act covers manual filing systems which were not covered in the 1984 Act. The Act also refers to:

☐ the "data controller" as the person or persons who determine the purposes to which the personal data is put and the manner in which it is processed;

☐ the "data processor", meaning any person (other than an employee of the data controller) who processes the personal data;

The terms "data subject" and "personal data" retain the same meanings as stated in the 1984 Act. The 1998 Act additionally refers to "sensitive personal data", meaning personal information relating to racial or ethnic origin, political opinions, religious or similar beliefs, trade union membership, physical and mental health, sexual life, offences or alleged offences and court proceedings for such offences. There are a number of exemptions to registration, for example, when the data is held for national security, crime prevention or detection and certain tax purposes.

Copyright, Designs and Patents Act 1988

A computer program can now obtain the status of literary work and as such, retains protection for 50 years from the first publishing date. Computer software is now covered by the Copyright Designs and Patents Act 1988 and infringements include:

❑   the pirating of copyright protected software;

❑   the running of pirated software, in that a copy is created in memory;

❑   transmitting software over telecommunications links, thereby producing a copy.

The major software producers have funded an organisation called FAST (Federation Against Software Theft) which successfully lobbied for the inclusion of computer software into the above-mentioned Act. The law also covers material published on the World Wide Web, including images and materials used as part of a Web site's design. For example, you would be committing an offence if you copied images of products from a manufacturer's on-line brochure. Technically, an offence is also committed if you place a link in your own Web site to another site which contains copyright material, without the copyright holder's permission.

It is wise to assume that material is copyright protected unless there is a statement to the contrary. In the UK, copyright is created by the mere act of publication, although it is usual to include a notice of copyright ownership. You should make it standard practice to acknowledge the sources of information you include in your assignments, even though they are not to be made available to the public. If you produce material for publication, even through a web site, you must obtain permission from copyright holders for any material you include, such as published directories, extracts from reports or pictures taken, for example, from another web site or scanned from a manufacturer's catalogue.

✍️Exercises

1.   A DIY retailer is launching a new e-commerce service to provide on-line shopping to its customers. The directors are concerned about the new service's vulnerability to crime.

   (a)   Give two examples of crime which may damage the company.

   (b)   Describe a legislative deterrent which may help to combat the threat.

   (c)   Describe any measures the company can take to protect themselves from electronic crime.

   (d)   The DIY company aims to gather marketing information from customers through the Web site. Identify the company's obligations under the Data Protection Acts (1984 and 1998).

   3.   Identify aspects of the DIY company's operations which will require careful attention to the Copyright, Designs and Patents Act (1988).

Assignments

5.1. Weaving a Web

Your County Council is developing a Web site to attract businesses to the area and also wishes to encourage people to move there. A number of Web pages will feature case studies of various organisations, designed to demonstrate the variety of employment opportunities and to attract employers to the County. You are part of a team gathering the data for these Web pages and you particular tasks are as follows.

1. Research organisations in your County (or elsewhere if necessary) and choose six, two for each of the following: *industrial*; *public service*; *commercial service*.

    One organisation in each pair should be significantly different in size from the other. For example, your two service organisations could be a bank and a firm of solicitors.

    (a) Create a table showing the six organisations classified as indicated.

    (b) Include a brief description of the main purposes of each organisation.

    (c) List the types of information each organisation uses as part of its primary purpose. Briefly explain how each type of information is used by the organisation and the forms in which it may be held (verbal, documentart or electronic).

    (d) Using the examples of the types of information you identified in (c), show how the size of an organisation can affect the types of information it holds.

2. Using the sample organisations chosen in 1. as illustrative examples:

    (a) Explain why organisations are necessary and the reasons for their formation.

    (b) Identify characteristics which are common to all organisations.

3. Select one of the organisations with which you are particularly familiar, or are able to research sufficiently to carry out the following tasks.

    (a) Draw and annotate an organisation chart, showing its functional and management structure.

    (b) Draw up a suitable table listing the main internal and external functions and the activities which are carried out within of the internal functions.

    (c) Draw an information or data flow diagram, identifying the main internal and external functions and the primary information flows which take place between them.

    (d) Choose two directly related internal functions, and explain how the information flows between them are 'triggered' by particular events. Briefly describe the activities which are necessary to initiate, handle and receive each information flow between the two functions. Also identify any documents used as part of the process.

5.2. It isn't just about money

This assignment (which could usefully be undertaken as a team project) requires some research into the functional areas of a large clearing bank (or another type of large organisation with which you are familiar) to determine the data handling systems the bank is likely to use. For example, customer services comprise a number of different, but related systems:

> on-line telephone banking (touch tone or voice processing);
>
> account statement maintenance and production;
>
> charges calculation;
>
> personal insurance;
>
> mortgage services.

Some of these services can be provided by home visits from a personal account manager, who will make use of a notebook computer for the provision of information and completion of application forms.

1. Produce a table (using a word processor's table facility) of the systems you identify and for *each system*, indicate, with reasons, which processing method (*batch* or *transaction*) it would use. Use an example system to explain the batch and transaction processing methods and place the explanations beneath the table of systems already described.

2. Using several bank system examples, explain what is meant by a *single user* and a *multi-user* system.

3. Define the terms *centralised* and *distributed processing* and suggest reasons why modern banks favour a measure of distributed processing. Use the systems you have identified to support your suggestions.

4. Explain the function and general operation of the following types of data handling system and identify the applications of these systems in the clearing bank organisation: *bookings, payroll, ordering, invoicing, stock control, personal records*.

5. Using suitable examples from the bank's systems, explain the operation of the *system life cycle*.

Unit 6

Communications technology

Chapters

Unit 6 Outcomes and assessment criteria

Outcomes	Assessment criteria To achieve each outcome a student must demonstrate the ability to:
1. Understand the main elements in a **data communication system**	<ul><li>describe signals occurring in a data communications link</li><li>demonstrate the effect on signals on a transmission system</li><li>discuss the need to modulate signals to enable transmission</li><li>identify characteristics of data communications systems</li><li>define commonly used data communications terms</li><li>describe common error checking protocols</li><li>identify different transmission media and comment on the advantages and disadvantages of each.</li></ul>
2. Describe **hardware** and **software** used in data communications.	<ul><li>identify equipment necessary for data communications</li><li>describe basic tasks performed by communications software</li><li>list essential functions of communications software</li><li>define the terminology used in establishing a communication link</li><li>describe file transfer protocols.</li></ul>
3. Describe **computer networks** and specify interconnection devices.	<ul><li>explain the concept of networking</li><li>define different types of networks and explain their uses</li><li>discuss different network topologies</li><li>explain different network interconnection devices</li><li>discuss the OSI seven layer model in relation to interconnection devices.</li></ul>
4. Demonstrate an ability to **search, access and retrieve remote information**.	<ul><li>use search engines to retrieve general information on specific subjects</li><li>store web pages.</li></ul>
5. Demonstrate an ability to **create information** that can be accessed remotely.	<ul><li>compose a web page</li><li>describe web structures and concept of linking pages and sites.</li></ul>
6. Design an **appropriate ICT solution** to a given business context.	<ul><li>describe the effect of the PC on LAN developments</li><li>understand the main attributes of ICT and how to decide on the most appropriate system in a given business context.</li></ul>

Chapter 32

Data communications

Telecommunications and data communications

The word *telecommunications* can be applied to any system capable of transmitting text, sounds, graphical images or indeed, data of any kind, in electronic form. The signals may travel along wires or they may be radio signals, which require no wires, but can travel through the atmosphere and space. The combination of computer and telecommunications technologies has profoundly affected the way computer systems and other communication devices are used.

To a computer, text, sounds and graphical images all constitute data, which it represents digitally, using the *binary* coding system. Although not all transmissions of digital data involve general-purpose computers, they are usually generated and controlled by digital computer technology. Data generated by a computer is already in digital form, but other data (the term is used in its broadest sense), such as sounds of human speech, or a photograph, need to be digitally encoded before transmission over a digital network. The term *data communications* can be applied to systems that combine the use of telecommunications and computer technologies.

Digital networks and user devices

Figure 32.1 illustrates the relationship between users and the various digital networks for computer, telephone, cellular mobile phone, radio and television transmissions.

The white circular band contains examples of the devices we use to switch information between the analogue forms we require into the digital forms needed by the networks. The analogue forms include, for example, pictures on television screens, text on a printout, pressure readings on a gauge, words spoken into a microphone, movement of a joystick, pictures received by a television camera, numbers displayed in a spreadsheet, spoken directions from a car's global positioning system

Figure 32.1. *Digital networks and user devices*

(GPS) and temperature readings taken by a sensor. Some user devices, such as televisions, radios and cameras are still manufactured for use in analogue communications, but to use digital networks devices must use digital technology. It is anticipated that within the next few years any remaining analogue networks in the UK, notably for televison and radio, will be wholly digital.

Signalling

In this section we examine the principles of signalling between network devices.

To transmit data electronically between two devices requires the use of a signalling method which is 'understood' by both the transmitter and receiver and is supported by the communication link (the *medium*) which connects them. There are two types of signal which can be transmitted along a medium, analogue and digital. Computer data is represented in *digital* form, so where the telecommunications systems support it, data is moved between remote computer systems as digitised signals. Although digital communications are now the norm, there are still some parts of our communications networks which are designed for analogue communication. The Public Switched Telephone Network (PSTN) is now primarily digital, but connections to it from most homes and small business premises are still analogue. For this reason, and because the principles of digital signalling are better understood with a foundation knowledge of analogue signalling, we briefly explain its principles here.

Analogue signals

Analogue comes from the word analogous, meaning similar. Thus, an analogue signal varies continuously in the same way as the information it represents. An analogue signal can vary in its amplitude and/or frequency.

Before we consider the transmission of computer data, it is helpful to look at the analogue representation of sound, which the telephone network was initially designed to carry. Figure 32.2 represents a simple sound sequence and shows a *sine* wave form with two characteristics, *amplitude* and *frequency*.

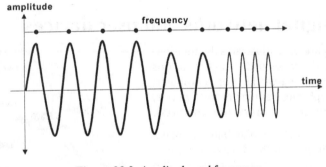

Figure 32.2. *Amplitude and frequency*

Amplitude determines loudness, or volume and frequency determines pitch. *Pitch* is commonly referred to in terms of high and low notes. Increasing frequency raises the pitch of a sound, whereas reducing it lowers the pitch. In the Figure, the amplitude and thereby the volume, begins at one level and is then reduced. Towards the end, the frequency and thereby the pitch, is increased. Frequency is measured according to the number of times a wave form is repeated per second, expressed as Herz (Hz) or cycles per second.

The PSTN was originally designed for voice transmission, using analogue electrical signals. to represent what is spoken and heard at each end of a link. A telephone mouthpiece contains a diaphragm, which vibrates when struck by sound waves. These vibrations are converted into electrical signals which have a direct relationship to what is said. When the signals arrive at the earpiece on the receiving telephone, its diaphragm converts the impulses back into sound.

Electrical analogue signalling is subject to distortion from magnetic fields emanating from, for example, nearby electricity cabling. Unless the distortion is severe, the parties will still be able to communicate satisfactorily. Many radio stations still transmit using analogue signalling (because few of us have digital radios) and we are all familiar with the crackles and whistles which come from signal distortion.

Modems and analogue circuits

Signal distortion caused by line noise (interference) is one reason why computer data cannot be carried over analogue telephone circuits in the same way as the human voice. Distortion could easily prevent communicating computers from reliably distinguishing between 1's and 0's, the patterns of which are crucial to accurate transmission of data. It is the job of a device called a *modem* to convert the computer's 1's and 0's to an analogue form resembling that of speech signals.

Amplitude modulation

A binary sequence could be represented by *modulating* the amplitude of the wave, as shown in Figure 32.3.

Figure 32.3. *Amplitude modulation*

Amplitude modulation (AM) signals can easily be corrupted by interference on the line and is not generally used for the transmission of computer data.

Frequency modulation

Frequency modulation uses one frequency for binary 1 and another frequency for binary 0, as shown in Figure 32.4.

Figure 32.4. *Frequency modulation*

Frequency modulation is also known as *frequency-shift keying* (FSK). Modem transmission rates are measured in bits per second (bps) and FSK is still used for low speed transmissions up to 300 bps. Another modulation technique, TCM (Trellis Coded Modulation), which is mathematically complex and beyond the scope of this text, is used for today's high speed modems. TCM is a CCITT (see later) standard for modem communications.

Frequency bandwidth

The analogue sections of the telephone network are designed to carry voice signals ranging in frequency from 300 to 3000 Hz. This is known as the bandwidth. Referring back to Figure 32.2 of the sound wave, this means any sounds which are pitched outside of this range are lost. This is not a problem because, although the loss of some frequencies will alter the normal sound of a person's voice it is still perfectly intelligible to the listener. There is a problem in respect of digital signals, for which the analogue telephone network was not designed. For reasons which we do not need to explore here, digital signals generate frequencies outside of this range, including a frequency of 0Hz. If a digital signal is applied directly to an analogue line, the sine waves which represent the binary digits will be severely *attenuated* (weakened) and be so distorted as to be unrecognisable by the receiving device.

To overcome this problem, a *modem* (modulator-demodulator) is used to modulate the digital signal into an analogue form which will survive intact from transmitter to receiver. A modem acts as the interface between a computer and the analogue telephone connection to which it is attached. The modem for the transmitter device modulates the digital signal into the corresponding analogue form for transmission along the telephone line and the modem at the receiver device carries out the reverse operation. As Figure 32.5 shows, modems are capable of both functions, so that two way communications are supported.

Figure 32.5. *Modems in a data communications link*

Digital communications

Where the network and user devices are wholly digital, analogue wave forms are not used. Instead, the communications medium carries two discrete (separate, distinct from one another) signals which correspond to the binary values of 1 and 0. For example, voltages of +12 volts and −12 volts may represent logical 0 and logical 1, respectively. Figure 32.6 illustrates the 'square wave' of a digital signal.

Figure 32.6. *Discrete signals for representing binary data*

Optical fibre, which is now widely used for digital communications, uses pulses of light rather than electricity to represent binary data. The information given in the next section applies to data communications generally, regardless of whether the transmission medium is analogue or digital.

Data communication modes

Direction of transmission

Communications media can be classified according to direction of transmission:

    ❑ *Simplex* mode allows communication in one direction only (Figure 32.7).

Figure 32.7. *Simplex transmission*

The mode would appear to be suitable where no interactivity is required, for example, information displayed on an electronic motorway sign or an airport's flight arrivals and departures display. In practice, a *reverse channel* is always necessary to allow the receiving device to request the re-transmission of lost data (see Error Detection).

❑ *Half-duplex* (Figure 32.8) supports communications in both directions, but not at the same time; in other words there is only a single channel and the direction is switched after completion of transmission in the other direction. The mode is only suited to low volume data transmissions where an immediate response is not required. For example, a shop may upload its daily order requirements to a central warehouse at the end of the day and receive confirmation of deliveries during the night. As with simplex, a reverse channel is needed to allow error control messages to be transmitted from receiver to transmitter during data transmission. A reverse channel is

Figure 32.8. *Half-duplex transmission*

used purely for data transmission control and does not provide simultaneous two-way communication (see duplex).

❑ *Duplex* (Figure 32.9) mode allows communication in both directions at the same time, as there are two channels permanently available. In interactive systems, where two

Figure 32.9. *Duplex transmission*

way communication is continuously required, such as for telephone conversations, on-line enquiries and Internet shopping transactions, duplex is the only suitable mode.

Devices differ in the ways they communicate or talk with each other. The next section examines the principles of *serial* communications, which for practical and economic reasons are used in all remote communication systems. *Parallel* transmission, briefly described first, is only feasible for short distances such as for the connection between a computer and a locally attached printer.

Parallel transmission

As the term *parallel transmission* suggests and Figure 32.10 illustrates, data bits are transmitted in groups.

Figure 32.10. *Parallel transmission*

This is obviously quicker than sending the bits one after another (serially), but it is only practicable over short distances. Communication between a computer and its nearby peripherals can be carried out using parallel transmission, which is particularly important where high-speed devices, such as disk or tape units, are concerned. Microcomputer systems often use parallel transmission to communicate with a nearby printer.

Serial transmission

As Figure 32.11 shows, serial transmission sends the binary signals one after another in a serial fashion and is the only practicable method for communication over long distances.

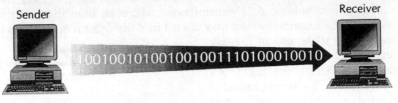

Figure 32.11. *Serial transmission*

The principle problems with serial transmission concern the identification of the individual bits which make up a data stream and the division of bit groupings into words. A *word* is a given number of bits used as a standard unit. For example, a character within a data stream may comprise, say 7 or 8 bits, depending on the coding system in use. A commonly used coding system is ASCII, which uses 7 bits per character, plus a *parity* bit for error checking (see later). There are two techniques for achieving this separation of bits and words:

- ❑ asynchronous transmission;
- ❑ synchronous transmission.

Asynchronous serial transmission

When a sending device transmits characters at irregular intervals, as does for example, a keyboard device, it is said to be transmitting *asynchronously*.

Although the characters are not sent at regular intervals, the bits within each character must be sent at regularly timed intervals. An example of asynchronous character format is shown in Figure 32.12. It can be seen that the line has two electrical states, representing 1 and 0.

To allow the receiver to identify individual characters, the transmitter signals the beginning of a character with a *start* bit and the end with a *stop* bit. In the Figure, the character comprises 7 data bits. The Figure also shows the use of a parity bit which was a simple but primitive method of detecting errors caused by noise on the transmission line. To provide an introduction to the topic of transmission error control, single bit parity checking is described in the next section. However, it should be noted that

Figure 32.12. *Asynchronous character format*

the sophisticated error detection and correction controls provided by high speed modems make the use of the single parity bit unnecessary. Figure 32.13 shows the current format of an asynchronous character.

Figure 32.13. *Asynchronous character format without parity bit*

When no data is being transmitted the line is in its *idle* state, a condition maintained by a logical 1 output from the transmitter. This is known as the *mark* level.

When it is ready to send a character, the transmitter outputs a logical 0 signal, which drops the signal to *space*. Sensing this state, the receiver starts its clock after one *bit time* (for example, on a line operating at 9600 bits per second, one bit time is 1/9600^{ths} of a second) and counts off and samples the regularly timed bits that form a character. Even if the receiver's clock is not exactly in time with that of the transmitter, the bit-time is sufficient to allow each bit to be sampled and identified. If the receiver is out of synchronisation by no more than 5% then the system should still operate effectively.

When a stop bit is reached and the line returns to the mark level, the receiver switches back to its listening state. Although the transmission of individual bits requires fairly closely matched time control by transmitter and receiver, the presence of start and stop bits for each character permits the time interval between characters to be irregular, or asynchronous.

Modem frequency spectrum

A modem which uses frequency modulation (see Frequency Shift Keying or FSK earlier) will use different one frequency for logical 0 (space) and logical 1 (mark). For example, an early modem standard, CCITT (see Standards Authorities later) V21, used the following frequencies to provide full duplex, asynchronous transmission at 300 bps.

Modem operation		Space (logical 0)	Mark (logical 1)
Originate transmission	Transmit frequency	1180 Hz	980 Hz
Originate transmission	Receive frequency	1850 Hz	1650 Hz
Answer	Transmit frequency	1850 Hz	1650 Hz
Answer	Receive frequency	1180 Hz	980 Hz

Parity bit

The ASCII code (Chapter 11) is a useful 7-bit code for plain text transmission, but its error control facilities are primitive. An additional bit, known as the *parity bit* (in the left-most or most significant bit position), is attached to each character and can be used to detect *single bit* errors which may occur during data transfer.

There are two types of parity, odd and even, though it is of little significance which is used. If odd parity is used, the parity bit is set to binary 1 or 0, such that there is an odd number of binary 1s in the group. Conversely, even parity requires that there is an even number of binary 1s in the group. Examples of these two forms of parity are provided in Table 32.1 on the next page.

7-bit characters	using odd parity	using even parity
1 0 0 1 0 1 0	**0** 1 0 0 1 0 1 0	**1** 1 0 0 1 0 1 0
0 1 0 1 1 0 1	**1** 0 1 0 1 1 0 1	**0** 0 1 0 1 1 0 1

Table 32.1. *Odd and even parity checking*

The parity bit is shown in bold. If even parity is being used and the receiving device identifies the grouping 10010100 then the presence of an odd number of binary 1s indicates an error in transmission. Provided that the number of bits corrupted is odd, all transmission errors will be detected. However, an even number of bits in error will not affect the parity condition and thus will not be revealed.

Asynchronous modem settings

Figure 32.14 shows the Connection tab for modem settings in Windows 98, with each character comprising 8 data bits and one stop bit. Because the modem uses its own error controls, a parity bit is not required.

Figure 32.14. *Asynchronous modem settings*

Baud rate, bandwidth and data compression

The term *baud rate* refers to the line speed operating between two modems. For example, a 28,800 baud connection can transfer 28,800 bits per second (bps). The term *bandwidth* was used earlier in relation to the signal frequency range supported by an analogue circuit, but the term is also used in respect of digital communications, measured in bps. For example, a modem operating at 56 Kbits has twice the bandwidth of one operating at 28 Kbits. Bandwidth is important for modern communications because of the increased use of networks for the transmission of multimedia images. By using data compression, a modem can transfer a given amount of data with fewer bits, thus improving the rate of data throughput. Typically, a modem can receive data through the COM port (a PC's RS232 modem interface) at around four times the rate of the actual line. So, for example, using a connect speed of 28,800 baud, a modem could accept data from the COM port at 115,200 bps (4 × 28,800). Figure 32.15 shows the COM port set at this speed.

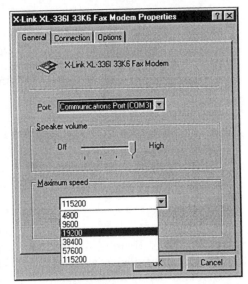

Figure 32.15. *Serial port settings*

Figure 32.16 illustrates this relationship between line and modem speeds. The fastest modems will operate at 56 K (56 × 1024) bits per second and with data compression can achieve much higher effective data transfer rates (throughput). However, to achieve this maximum speed, the receiving modem must be able to operate at the same speed and use the same compression *protocols* (rules) to uncompress the data.

Figure 32.16. *Data compression allowing modem to handle more data through serial port*

As part of the data compression process, a modem will also strip out the start and stop bits which are still attached to each character for transmission through the COM port to the modem. This massively reduces the wasted transmission time which would otherwise be taken up by start and stop bits for each character. In earlier systems, these transmission overheads significantly reduced data throughput. For example, an early 2400 baud modem could transfer only 240 characters per second (cps), because each character required a minimum of 10 bits (1 start bit, 1 stop bit and 8 data bits). Without the start and stop bits, the rate would be 300 cps.

Although the technological advances in modems have permitted a radical increase in asynchronous data transmission performance, the sending PC is still having to attach start and stop bits to each character and there are circumstances when *synchronous* transmission provides a more efficient alternative.

V.90 Modem standard

Figure 32.17 illustrates a V.90 modem to ISP connection (the role of the router is described in Chapter 33).

Figure 32.17. *Internet connection using a V.90 modem*

This most recent standard for analogue modems enables connection to the Internet at speeds of up to 56 Kbps (V.90 modems are labelled as such, but the theoretical maximum speed is 54 Kbps, because of technical restrictions). Previous modem standards were developed on the assumption that analogue modems would be used at each end of a link, and that the analogue/digital conversion processes at either end would limit the connect speed to 33.6 Kbps.

In fact, most computers are communicating via the Internet, using Internet Service Providers (ISP) who have wholly digital connections to the PSTN. Thus, analogue/digital conversions are only being carried out at one end of the link, for the analogue connection between the Internet user's computer and the local digital exchange on the PSTN.

When a V.90 modem user accesses information on the Internet, the ISP's computer (provided it handles the V.90 standard) encodes it digitally for transmission to the users' PC, rather than using the modulation signalling techniques of analogue modems. This enables downstream transmission (from ISP to user's PC) at 56 Kbps. The higher speed allows the retrieval of complex Web pages incorporating images, sound and video sequences without excessive delays. Upstream (modem to ISP) transmissions are limited to 33.6Kbps, which for keystroke and mouse commands entered by the user, is perfectly adequate. The technical reason for the lower speed is that the V.90 modem uses the conventional V.34 modulation techniques for upstream transmission.

Pulse Code Modulation (PCM)

PCM has long been used for the digitisation of audio signals in particular (music CD recording) and samples an analogue wave form 8000 times per second. Figure 32.18 illustrates this process with each vertical line representing a sampling point.

Figure 32.18. *PCM signal sampling*

Each sample point is encoded as a separate signal. For the journey from ISP to the user's local PSTN exchange, the data travels at 64 Kbps, but is then slowed to 54 Kbps when it is converted to the analogue waveform needed for the local connection to the user's PC. The user's V.90 modem can accept the PCM signals and convert them to the digital form required by the computer.

All connections via analogue modems are subject to variations in line conditions and the connect speed will frequently be below the modem's maximum speed. ISDN connections provide a quicker and more reliable service and are described later.

Synchronous serial transmission

The start and stop bits used in asynchronous transmission are wasteful, as they do not contain information. With higher speed devices or *buffered* (memory for the accumulation of data before it is transmitted) low-speed devices, data can be transmitted in more efficient, timed, or *synchronous* blocks. Figure 32.19 illustrates the technique.

Figure 32.19. *Synchronous character format*

Most modems can operate synchronously or asynchronously, as required. In synchronous transmission, a data stream may be very long, so it is vital that the bit timing between transmitter and receiver is synchronised and that individual characters are separated. This can be achieved by using an additional transmission path to copy the transmitter's timings to the receiver. Alternatively, timing signals can be embedded within the data stream. These timing signals, referred to as SYN characters are placed at the beginning of each data block and at intervals within the block. If timing is lost, the receiver can re-time its bit groupings from the last received SYN character. Like the start and stop bits used in asynchronous transmission, SYN characters constitute an overhead and have to be stripped out by the receiver. Some computer terminals are designed for high speed data transmission and use synchronous transmission, but many others use asynchronous transmission. The data in a stream may consist of discrete text characters, coded in a character code such as ASCII, or it may be pure binary. Examples of pure binary data are found in graphic images, executable machine-code programs and numbers in floating point (Chapter 5) form. For character data streams, the allocation of a particular bit pattern to act, for example as a SYN character is not difficult. Obviously, for pure binary data, the binary patterns within the data block are not predictable and cannot, therefore, include embedded and unique SYN characters. HDLC (High-Level Data Link Control) is an example of a transmission protocol which is designed to overcome this problem.

HDLC frame structure

Each data block occupies a *frame* or *packet* which may vary in size, typically up to 4 Kb. An important standard for synchronous communications uses the HDLC frame structure, illustrated in Figure 32.19.

| Flag | Address | Control | Data | CRC | CRC | Flag |

Figure 32.19. *HDLC frame structure*

The frame components are explained below.

❑ The *flag* fields mark the limits of the frame with the binary sequence 01111110. To ensure that this sequence always appears at the start of each frame and nowhere else, the transmitter inserts additional zeros if the reserved flag sequence happens to occur within the data area. This is know as *bit stuffing* or *zero insertion*. The receiver strips out (*unstuffs*) these extra zeros as part of the frame unpacking process. If a communication protocol uses a fixed frame size, bit stuffing may be used to extend frames which are shorter than the required length. A detailed description of bit stuffing is beyond the scope of this text.

❑ The *address* field occupies one or more bytes (1 byte = 8 bits) and contains the address of the destination device, or sometimes of the sending device. For example, when a central server wishes to communicate with an attached workstation, it will add the workstation's address to the frame. If the workstations only communicate with the central server and never directly with one another, then a transmitting workstation need only add its own address to the frame.

❑ The *control* field also occupies one or more bytes and identifies the type of frame. Apart from containing user data, some special frames may have a Supervisory control function, perhaps to control the flow of data across the network. The field also contains a sequence number to ensure that frames are not lost in transmission.

❑ The *data* field has no particular format and is simply the collection of bits which form the particular user data.

❑   The CRC (Cyclic Redundancy Check - see Error Controls) fields contain the result of an arithmetic calculation carried out on all the bits enclosed within the flag fields. The receiver carries out the same calculation and if it obtains the same result, it is almost certain that the contents of the frame have not been corrupted. If a CRC error is found, the frame is discarded and the transmitter has to send it again.

Communication standards

Standards authorities

The data communications industry has always had to deal with problems of *incompatible* standards. Standards have to do with all aspects of a communications system, including, for example, *hardware devices*, *encoding* of data and forms of *signals*. At first, the only computer systems available for use in data communications were mainframes and later, minicomputers. These computer systems were produced by a small number of very large manufacturers, the most important being IBM; they also produced communications devices that worked with their computers. In competition with one another, each manufacturer set the standards for use with its equipment. These *closed* systems prevented a customer from using equipment, produced by different manufacturers, in the same data communications system.

The huge expansion in the uses of data communications, both nationally and internationally has been made possible through the adoption of some common standards. Common standards lead to *open* systems, which allow users to use components from more than one manufacturer.

A number of bodies are concerned with the establishment of international standards and these are listed below. Frequently, a standard arises initially from the work of a particular manufacturer, and then, often because of the importance of the manufacturer, it is included in the recommendations of the standards authorities.

❑   CCITT. This is an acronym for Comité Consultatif Internationale de Télégraphie et Téléphonie an organisation that has its headquarters in Geneva, Switzerland. It is part of the United Nations International Telecommunications Union (ITU). The CCITT makes recommendations on most aspects of data communications, for example, modems (see earlier), networks and facsimile transmission or FAX and publishes them every four years. These recommendations usually obtain world-wide acceptance. CCITT's 'V' series of standards cover equipment used on telephone lines and its X series relate to digital packet transmission standards. Some examples of these standards are mentioned later in this chapter.

❑   ANSI is the acronym for American National Standards Institute. ANSI has long maintained a strong influence on standards in the computer and data communications industries. It is formed from industrial and business groups and is a member of the International Standards Organisation (ISO). Examples of its influence can be found in the fields of computer hardware and programming languages. For example, by conforming to ANSI standards, the FORTRAN, COBOL and C languages enable the production of computer software, which is largely *portable*. In other words, because each language is more or less universal, a program written in, for example, COBOL can be readily translated for use on any make of computer. In the area of microcomputer hardware, the ANSI standards define the SCSI (an acronym for Small Computer System Interface) parallel interface, for the connection of peripherals, such as disk drives and printers. The institute is also responsible for the ANSI.SYS *device driver*, a program that provides facilities for greater control of a computer console (screen and keyboard), than is possible with the MS-DOS operating system.

❑ IEEE is the acronym for the Institute of Electrical and Electronic Engineers. The organisation has set numerous standards for various aspects of telecommunications and computing. Notably, the IEEE has defined standards for local area network (LAN) protocols.

❑ The ISO (International Standards Organisation), has its headquarters in Geneva, Switzerland and is responsible for the definition of the Open Systems Interconnection (OSI) model. This model aims to ensure that any computer terminal is able to connect to any network and communicate with any other terminal, whether it is connected to the same or any other linked network. The OSI model is examined in greater detail in the section on Communications Protocols.

Communication protocols

We begin by looking at the protocols which are used for modem communications, typically between a home or small business user and an Internet Service Provider's server. Sending and receiving computers must use the same modem protocols and settings if they are to communicate reliably. Protocols are, essentially, sets of rules about how the two devices are to communicate. So, for example, if a modem is set to use 8 data bits, no parity bit and 1 stop bit (see earlier), the other modem will not be able to interpret the data unless it uses the same settings.

Also, both modems must operate at the same speed. This is why, for example, when connecting to the Internet, the connect speed may vary, up to the maximum of the user's modem. The connect speed depends on the modem speed at the Internet Service Provider's site, when the dial-up connection is made. For communication between two devices, the protocol must establish as a minimum:

❑ the data transmission rate (measured in bits per second). If the devices have different maximum transmission rates, the rate is dictated by the slower of the two.

❑ whether both devices may transmit to each other simultaneously (in *full-duplex* mode) or one direction at a time (in *half-duplex* mode). In the latter case, the protocol must also allow determination of which device currently has *control of the communications link*.

❑ whether *synchronous* (data is sent in a stream with sender and receiver synchronised to identify when one character ends and another starts) or *asynchronous* (characters are sent at irregularly timed intervals, with start and stop bits to separate characters) transmission is to be used.

A protocol may also specify the form of *handshaking*, the method of data *flow control* and mechanisms for *error control* and *data compression*.

Handshaking, flow control

Handshaking means that communicating devices must have a common method of determining their presence and readiness to communicate. Although the details vary, a handshake can be illustrated simply by the following example. Suppose that device A wishes to communicate with device B. Device A signals "Hello Device B, are you there?", to which device B replies, "Yes, I am here A.". Finally, device A responds "I see that you are there B." The handshake should also define when each device has finished sending or receiving a message.

A flow control mechanism is needed to ensure that data transmission flows smoothly, that the communications channel is not overloaded and that the transmitting device does not send data more quickly than the receiver can handle.

All modern modems include hardware to do this, but if both modems do not support hardware flow control, then software (XON/OFF) must be used. When the receiving device's buffer is full, it sends an XOFF signal to the sending device, which then pauses transmission. Once the receiving device has cleared space in its buffer and is ready to receive again, it sends an XON signal to the sending device.

Error control and data compression

Although digital signals are infinitely more stable than their analogue equivalent, errors will occur and the communicating devices must have a means of detecting and re-transmitting them correctly. For transmission over analogue links (which are the norm for local connections to the public telephone network) error detection and correction is even more important and all modem error protocols are built in to the hardware. Data compression (see earlier) reduces the volume of data, allowing its speedier transmission.

Protocols can be implemented by software or hardware. Typically, dedicated network devices such as modems use hardware implementation, but general-purpose computers which have not been designed for connection to a particular network may have to set up transmission protocols through the communications software. Figure 32.14, earlier in this chapter, shows the protocol settings in Windows 98 for a dial-up connection to the Internet. The settings for eight data bits, no parity bit and 1 stop bit are standard for PC to modem communication. Other options, such as the use of 1.5 or 2 stop bits and varying numbers of data bits relate to largely obsolete terminal devices.

Example protocols

TCP/IP

TCP/IP (Transmission Control Protocol/Internet Protocol) is the standard for communication between Internet host computers and is probably the most well known. It is actually a suite of several protocols. The importance of the Internet for network communications means that all modern operating systems provide support for TCP/IP, including those PC and Macintosh computer systems and network operating systems such as Novell Netware. Unix, as the standard operating system for most Internet host computers, has the TCP/IP protocol built in.

SMTP

SMTP stands for Simple Mail Transfer Protocol and is the standard for e-mail transmissions between servers and between clients (user e-mail software) and servers on the Internet.

UDP

UDP or User Datagram Protocol is used for the broadcast of data over IP (Internet Protocol) networks but unlike TCP, does not require that a connection is first established between sender and receiver (point to point). In other words, the data is transmitted without any guarantee that it will reach its destination. For this reason, UDP is referred to as a *connectionless* protocol; TCP is a *connection-orientated* protocol, which means that the link between devices must be established before communication can begin. Ethernet local area networks also operate on a connectionless, broadcast principle.

X.25

This is a CCITT protocol for packet switching networks. X.25 Packet Switched networks allow remote devices to communicate with each other across high speed digital links without the expense of individual leased lines. Packet Switching is a technique whereby the network routes individual packets of data between different destinations based on addressing within each packet.

FTP

File Transfer Protocol (FTP) allows large amounts of information to be transferred between two computers very conveniently. FTP originated with the UNIX operating system and was used to transfer files of all types between remote computer systems. A popular application of FTP is for the uploading and downloading of Web site pages.

ASCII

This is only appropriate for *text* files, which contain no control characters. Thus it cannot be used to transfer files produced with a word processor, spreadsheet or graphics package. Neither can it transfer command (COM) or executable (EXE) files, or files in compressed (ZIP, for example) form. Apart from this, the protocol is not good at controlling errors.

Xmodem

This is a file-transfer protocol used for asynchronous communications. It is commonly used in communications packages. Its ability to find and correct errors makes it suitable for the transfer of files which must retain their integrity, such as program files.

Zmodem

This is one of the most advanced protocols, being much faster than Xmodem. Its error correction controls are absolutely reliable.

CCITT V42bis

This protocol includes a *data compression* (through encoding, data is reduced in volume) technique and error detection and correction. Both the sending and receiving modem must possess the error correction facility.

Error detection

Block check characters (BCC)

The idea of even and odd parity bits for each character is introduced earlier in this chapter and is shown to be inadequate for the detection of even numbers of bit errors. Block check characters (BCCs) aim to conquer this problem by checking the parity of blocks of characters within a data transmission stream. BCCs may carry out *longitudinal* or *cyclic* redundancy checks.

Longitudinal redundancy checking (LRC)

By reference to Table 32.2, the principles of LRC can be explained as follows. Each BCC consists of a group of parity bits which carry out LRC. However, each LRC bit is a parity check on the corresponding bits in all the characters in a block. Thus, the first parity bit in the BCC relates to the bits which occupy the first position in each character in the block, the second parity bit in the BCC relates to the second position bits in each character in the block and so on. LRC ensures that multiple errors, whether even or odd, are likely to be discovered, so at the receiver end of the transmission, the parity of individual characters and blocks of characters is checked.

		7	6	5	4	3	2	1	0
		0	1	0	0	1	0	1	1
		0	1	0	0	1	1	1	0
		1	1	0	0	1	1	1	1
		1	1	0	1	0	1	0	0
		1	1	0	1	0	1	0	0
VRC (bit-7) on		1	1	0	1	0	1	1	1
each character		0	1	0	0	0	0	0	1
		1	1	0	0	1	0	0	1
		1	1	0	1	0	1	0	0
		1	1	0	0	0	1	0	1
		0	1	0	1	0	0	1	1
		1	1	0	1	0	1	1	1
	BCC to check LRC parity (per block)								

Table 32.2. *Vertical (VRC) and longitudinal redundancy checks (LRC)*

Cyclic redundancy checking (CRC)

The BCCs described previously treat a data block as a set of characters, whereas cyclic redundancy checking (CRC) uses a BCC which views each data block as a continuous *stream* of bits.

Firstly, the data block is regarded as one large binary number. That number is divided by another agreed binary number, the quotient is discarded and the remainder (sometimes referred to as a *checksum*) is attached to the data block as a BCC. Upon receipt of the data block, the receiver repeats the calculation used to generate the BCC and compares the result with the BCC attached by the transmitter; any difference between them indicates some corruption of the block. CRC is easy to implement in hardware and detects a very large proportion of all potential errors. CRC is also used by a number of file transfer protocols, including Zmodem (see earlier).

Hamming code, which is beyond the scope of this text, is capable of detecting and correcting transmission errors. Codes which allow the receiver to both detect and correct errors are known as *forward error-correcting codes* (FECs). The majority of data transmission systems do not use FECs and favour the use of powerful CRC techniques to detect errors, even though the receiver then has to request re-transmission of the incorrect data. The alternatives for requesting re-transmission are described in the next section.

Error correction

Echoplex (echo checking)

Echoplex was used in asynchronous communications, for low speed, *dumb* (no processing power of its own) terminals connected to a remote host computer. When a character is transmitted (in other words, when a key is pressed) the host device immediately sends it back to be displayed on the dumb terminal's screen. If the displayed character does not match the character selected from the keyboard, the operator should detect this; the host device can be advised, by the terminal operator, to ignore the incorrect character, by the sending of an agreed *control* character. Clearly, the method is slow and crude. A character could have been received correctly by the host device and an error could corrupt it on its way back. The operator has no way of knowing how and at what point an error occurred. Another disadvantage is that error correction is manual; in an interactive system, the user needs to rely on automatic error control and correction.

Automatic repeat request (ARQ)

When a receiver detects an error it must tell the sending device to re-transmit the erroneous data; this is known as *automatic repeat request* (ARQ). The technique is most appropriate to the handling of data streams, that is, synchronous communications, in conjunction with cyclic redundancy checking (CRC - see earlier). ARQ can take one of three forms:

Stop and wait ARQ or ACK and NAK. With this form the receiver acknowledges every block of data, with ACK if it detects no error and NAK if an error is detected. The sending device cannot send the next block until an acknowledgement is received. Any NAK block is re-transmitted repeatedly, if necessary, until an ACK is received.

Go-back N ARQ. With this form, a block is only acknowledged if an error is detected. The sending device can continue transmitting without waiting for an acknowledgement. When a NAK is received, the block in which the error occurred is identified and that block, plus any transmitted since (N blocks), must be re-transmitted.

Selective-repeat ARQ. This is the most sophisticated form of ARQ, in that blocks transmitted since the erroneous block (correct ones are not acknowledged), do not have to be sent again. Thus the sender only re-transmits the identified block and then continues from where it left off, when the NAK was received.

Transmission media

Cables of various types, radio and light waves can be used to carry the data between communicating devices. Each such medium has particular qualities which make it suitable for a particular task. For example, the mobile phone network, by definition, cannot rely entirely on physical cabling and uses radio communications for transmissions to and from mobile phones. The following sections describe the major transmission media.

Physical cabling

Unshielded twisted-pair (UTP) cable

UTP cable is formed from strands of wire twisted in pairs. It predates any other method and is still extensively used for standard telephone or telex terminals. Each twisted pair can carry a single telephone call between two people or two machines. Although twisted-pair cable is generally used for analogue signal transmission, it can be used successfully for digital transmission. Variation in the lengths of wire within pairs can result in signals being received out of phase (mis-timed), but this can be overcome by the frequent use of *repeaters*. The repeaters refresh the signal as it passes to maintain its consistency. Although transmission rates permitted by such cable are lower than for some other media, including co-axial and optical fibre, they are acceptable for many computer applications.

Its low cost and ease of installation make it a popular choice for local area networks and for the analogue connections to the PSTN.

Coaxial cable

Coaxial cable is resistant to the transmission interference which can corrupt data transmitted via twisted-pairs cable. It thus provides a fast, relatively interference-free transmission medium. Its construction consists of a central conductor core which is surrounded by a layer of insulating material. The insulating layer is covered by a conducting shield, which is itself protected by another insulating layer. During network installation, the cable can be cut and connections made, without affecting its transmission quality. The quality of cable can vary and some low quality cable is unsuitable for data transmission over long distances. On the other hand, high quality cable can be quite rigid and difficult to install in local networks, where space is limited. Despite this difficulty, it is an extremely popular choice for LANs.

Optical fibre cable

Optical fibre cable consists of thousands of clear glass fibre strands which transmit light or infra-red rays instead of electrical signals. The data is transmitted by a light-emitting diode (two-state signals) or injection-laser diode. Bandwidth is measured in gigabits per second and repeaters are only required after around 60 miles (copper cable requires repeaters every 3 or 4 miles). The other end of the cable has a detector which converts the light pulses into electrical pulses suitable for the attached device. Optical fibre cable is slightly more expensive than electrical cable, is used widely in WANs, but is also finding increasing use in LANs, particular for network backbones.

Public switched telephone network (pstn)

The *pstn* is the main telecommunications network for the United Kingdom. It was originally designed for voice transmission, using analogue electrical signals; these electrical signals represent what is spoken and heard at each end of a link. A telephone mouthpiece contains a diaphragm, which vibrates when struck by sound waves. The vibrations are converted into electrical impulses and are sent over the network to the earpiece on the receiving telephone; a diaphragm in the earpiece converts the impulses back into sound.

Much of the pstn is now digital, in particular the national trunk network and call switching exchanges; the analogue connections are mainly confined to the pstn's local links to homes and businesses. Digital voice transmission uses coded patterns of digital impulses, which are similar to those used to represent computer data. To transmit computer data over analogue sections of the pstn, requires use of a *modem* (see earlier).

Types of telecommunications lines

Dedicated lines

These can be leased from British Telecom and provide a permanent connection for devices in a network. They provide high transmission rates and are relatively error-free. They are only cost-effective for high volume data transmission, or when a permanent link is vital to the users. Charging is by a flat rate rather than when calls are made.

Dial-up or switched lines

These are cheaper, but support lower transmission rates than leased lines. They are more cost effective than leased lines for low-volume work and allow the operator to choose the destination of transmissions.

Switched digital network systems

Public switched data network (psdn)

The psdn, owned by British Telecom (BT) is a *packet switching* (see later) service. Modems are not required and transmission performance is better than that achievable over the partially analogue pstn. The service conforms to the CCITT (see Standards Authorities) standard known as the X.25 protocol and for this reason is often referred to as the X.25 network. A major benefit of using this CCITT standard is that the network can be used for international communications. The protocol is steadily being replaced by ATM (see later).

Circuit switching

In any network, setting up a connection between two devices may involve circuit switching. For example, if a network is busy a connection may be established through a series of switches, from one circuit to another, over an alternative route. Thus the actual distance the signals travel may be greatly in excess of the geographical distance between the two points. Charges, whether the connection is for voice or data, will be made according to the geographical distance between the devices (local, medium, long distance), rather than the distance the signals actually have to travel through the various switches.

Packet switching

The main components of a packet switching network are: high speed data lines; packet switching exchanges (PSEs); packet assembler/disassembler (PAD); packet terminal. With the use of a specialised computer, called a *packet terminal*, a customer can create the packets and connect directly to the network through a dedicated dataline.

If the customer is not using a packet terminal, a dial-up connection is used and the data has to go through a *packet assembler /disassembler* (PAD). This device converts data to and from the networks protocol as it enters and leaves the network.

Figure 32.20 illustrates these features.

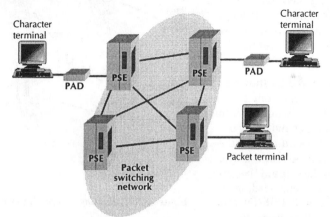

Figure 32.20. *Packet switching network*

The principles of packet switching are as follow. Messages are divided into data packets, which are then directed through the network to their destination under computer control. Besides a *message* portion, each packet contains data concerning:

❑   the destination address;

❑   the source identification;

❑   the sequence of the packet in the complete message;

❑   the detection and control of transmission errors.

The progress of a packet is monitored and controlled by *packet switching exchanges* (PSE) located at each *node* in the network. A node is a junction of network lines, which could be a computer or a computer terminal or other device.

As a packet arrives at a node, the exchange checks the addressing instructions and unless it corresponds to its present location, forwards it on the most appropriate route. Each node has an *input queue*, into which all arriving packets are entered (even those which are addressed to the node itself) and a number of *output queues* (to allow for the possibility of network congestion).

The route may be determined by one of a number of *routing strategies*:

❑   *hot potato*. The packet is sent as quickly as possible to the shortest output queue; such packets are not unduly delayed, although they may not be transmitted on the most direct route;

❑   *pre-determined routing*. With this method, the routing details are included in the packet itself, each switching exchange forwarding the packet according to the embedded instructions;

❑   *directory routing*. Each switching exchange has a copy of a routing table to which it refers before forwarding each packet. The appropriate output queue is determined from the table and the packet destination.

Network traffic information is continually transmitted between the various nodes, so that each switching computer has information to allow, for example, the avoidance of congested routes. Figure 32.21 illustrates how a network structure provides alternative routes by which a packet may reach its destination.

If a network is structured as shown in Figure 32.21, a packet sent from terminal T(2) to terminal T(6), would go into the input queue of packet switching exchange PSE (a). Depending on the routing strategy and network traffic conditions, the packet could be directed to an output queue leading to any of the other PSEs. If PSE (e) was inoperative, the alternative routes would be cut drastically; in fact the

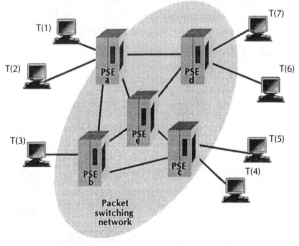

Figure 32.21. *Routing in a packet switching network*

packet would either have to go through PSEs (b), (c) and (d), in that sequence, or direct from PSE (a) to PSE (d). Packet switching allows packets relating to a single message, to be transmitted on different routes. This may be necessary, either because of the breakdown of some routes, or because of variations in traffic conditions over different routes.

Packet switching versus circuit switching

Packet switching networks maximise use of network connections and provide a cheaper, more reliable and efficient, though slightly slower, alternative. Circuit switched connections are ideal for the transmission of data in real-time, when the delays inherent in a packet switching network would not be acceptable.

Message switching

As the name suggests, this type of network deals with identifiable and complete messages, in contrast to a packet switched system where the destination user nodes are responsible for re-assembling their packets into complete messages upon receipt. A number of points can be made when comparing and contrasting packet switching and message switching networks:

- both use a store and forward principle; each node in the network has storage facilities for the accumulation of data prior to its onward transmission and the intelligence to examine the destination data before forwarding it;

- packet switching networks treat data transparently. Individual packets generally do not contain complete messages and the network does not recognise connections between packets, except from identification of their destination. The destination user nodes are left with the responsibility of re-assembling individual packets into complete messages;

- the store and forward facilities in message switching networks need to be much larger than those for packet switching systems, because complete messages must be accumulated at each point of transfer in the network;

- message switching requires increased processing time at intervening nodes while messages are accumulated before onward transmission;

- message switching provides users with greater confidence that messages will be transmitted and received in complete form.

X.25 protocol

As already mentioned, the psdn uses a packet switching protocol, known as X.25. The CCITT (see Standards Authorities) provide the X.25 protocol for interfacing terminals with a psdn. The protocol provides users with the following facilities.

- Division of a message into packets.

- Error checking and re-transmission of any packet effected by an error.

- An addressing format that allows international transmission.

- The PSEs control the transmission of packets through the network.

Integrated services digital network (ISDN)

Many forms of data, including text, voice and video images, can be digitised and an Integrated Services Digital Network (ISDN) is designed to allow the *integrated* transmission of these various data forms over the same network. An Integrated Services Digital Network exists in various forms in different countries, although the ultimate aim is to achieve an international system. It is defined as a wholly *digital* system, with end-to-end digital connections and digital exchanges throughout. ISDN has become achievable because the telephone network has become largely digital. The public telephone network is, by far, the largest communications network, so once it is fully digitised, every business and home user will have access to ISDN services. British Telecom's ISDN began with a pilot scheme in 1985, which was extended in 1986 and has continued to develop since. The network provides three types of access:

- ❑ *single-line* IDA (integrated digital access). The user gains access with *Network Terminating Equipment* (NTE);

- ❑ *line adapter module* (LAMs). A LAM allows two terminals to simultaneously share the same, two-wire, connection; this could provide a cheap method of communicating with a remote computer system;

- ❑ *multi-line* IDA, which provides 30 independent channels, each being capable of transmitting voice or data.

ADSL (Asynchronous Digital Subscriber Line)

ADSL is a relatively new service, similar to ISDN, which operates over standard telephone lines and provides Internet access at around 10 times the speed of a conventional modem. As with ISDN, simultaneous voice communication is also provided. Transmissions are separated at the telephone exchange to channel the voice calls through the standard public switched telephone network and the computer transmissions through fibre optic connection to the user's Internet Service Provider.

Multiplexed network services

Kilostream

An alternative to packet switching is to use *multiplexing*. The Kilostream service uses this technique for data transmission. The service provides a high speed direct link between two points. Data can pass in both directions at the same time; this is known as *full duplex* mode. The main link can transmit data at a rate of 2048 megabits per second (Mbits/s); this allows a number of low speed terminals to be connected to the high speed link through separate low speed links, each transmitting at either 128 kilobits per second (Kb/s) or 64 Kb/s. The signals from each terminal can then be merged for transmission along the high speed link, using a technique known as *time division multiplexing* (TDM).

The process of multiplexing is carried out by a *terminal multiplexer*. At the receiving end of the link, the signals are separated out for transmission along low speed lines connected to their respective terminals. The terminal multiplexer at each end of the link can carry out the functions of multiplexing (combining signals) and demultiplexing (separating the signals). This is obviously necessary for full duplex operation.

Multiplexers fall into two broad categories according to the methods used to combine signals and separate them:

❑ *Time Division Multiplexing (TDM)*, as the term suggests, provides a *time slice* on the higher-speed line for each terminal. The multiplexer has a number of registers, one per low-speed channel. Each register can store one character. The multiplexer scans each register in sequence, emptying the contents into a continuous stream of data to be transmitted. A multiplexer will send a null character whenever it finds an empty slot. TDM is used for digital networks. Figure 32.22 illustrates the time division multiplexing of signals from three terminals to a remote mainframe computer.

Figure 32.22. *Multiplexed link*

❑ *Frequency Division Multiplexing (FDM)* differentiates between the data signals sent from different devices by using a different *frequency range* for each. This can be likened to tuning a radio or television to receive particular programmes. So that any given radio programme does not interfere with the transmissions of another (although, they sometimes do), it is assigned a frequency that is not too close to the other assigned frequencies. In the same way, when a data transmission channel is multiplexed to accommodate signals from separate devices, some space must be left between the frequency ranges to avoid confusion of signals. Spaces between the different frequency ranges are know as *guard bands*. FDM relates to analogue signalling.

Megastream

This service is similar to Kilostream, except that no terminal multiplexing equipment is provided. Data can be transmitted at 2.048, 8, 34 or 140 Mbits/s. A user can choose to use the high speed circuit directly or multiplex the circuit, such that a number of low speed channels are made available across the link. Each separate lower speed channel can then be used to carry data or some may be left for the transmission of digitised speech.

Satstream

This digital data service provides customers with a small dish aerial to allow radio transmission of data, through a communications satellite. Customers are thus able to connect with networks in Western Europe.

ATM (Asynchronous Transfer Mode) and virtual networking

ATM evolved partially from the X.25 protocol and offers high bandwidth, packet switching and multiplexing support. ATM's bandwidth can handle data, video and voice transmissions through a single communication link. Its support for TCP/IP and other protocols allows ATM to handle a variety of traffic and services across network backbones, WANs (including the Internet), LANS and desktop computer connections. ATM makes maximum use of the available bandwidth by using virtual networking. This means that different logical networks can be created over the same physical network. For example, if the departments of an organisation are located in different parts of the country and are not connected to the same network segment, they can still be given access to the same set of network resources through a virtual network. Virtual network management software is needed to allow the administrator to view the physical network topology and create the logical views required by the organisation. Graphical user interface (GUI) software allows the administrator to use drag and drop functions to move network nodes and create the desired logical structure.

Optical communications and WDM

The high bandwidth of optical fibre (see earlier) makes it suitable for multiplexing. WDM (Wavelength Division Multiplexing) modulates signals to create several channels within the light spectrum and is the digital equivalent of FDM (frequency division multiplexing) used with analogue transmissions on coaxial cable. Even greater bandwidth can be obtained with D(Dense)WDM. It is protocol independent and can carry, for example, IP (Internet Protocol), ATM (Asynchronous Transfer Mode) and Ethernet traffic at rates between 100 megabits/sec and 2.5 gigabits/sec.

Connecting to a remote mainframe

In organisations with mainframe computers, it is often desirable for staff with microcomputers on their desks to be able to communicate with the mainframe via those systems. With non-IBM systems, where the host computer uses asynchronous transmission, the connection can be made via the RS232C (this refers to a standard used in most serial communications) serial transmission port, located at the back of the microcomputers system casing. However, the most common mainframe systems, IBM and ICL in particular, use synchronous communications, so special terminal emulation cards are required.

Thus, microcomputer workstations can be converted to mainframe terminals using a technique called emulation. A terminal emulation card is fitted into one of the expansion slots in the microcomputers system casing. If there are a number of terminals to be connected, the microcomputer is then connected, via a coaxial cable, to a terminal cluster controller. The controller is linked to a front-end processor (usually a minicomputer, dedicated to handling incoming and outgoing communications for the mainframe), which is itself connected to the mainframe computer. In this way, a microcomputer can, for example, be converted into an emulation of an IBM 3270 terminal.

The advantage of using a microcomputer as a mainframe terminal is that it can also be used on a stand-alone basis for local processing tasks, such as word processing or spreadsheet work. The terminal emulation package ensures that the mainframe responds in the same way as it would to a dedicated terminal. Security mechanisms, such as passwords, prevent users of emulated terminals from carrying out processes which are forbidden to users of dedicated terminals. However, the microcomputer's facility for local storage and processing can present serious security problems for the mainframes data and various mechanisms have to be included to prevent unauthorised updates. Where emulated terminals are to be linked to a mainframe via a wide area network, adapter cards are available which combine the terminal emulation with the gateway software, to access the intervening network.

Wireless networks

Television and radio broadcasting

When a television studio broadcasts a programme, the signals are carried to television receivers through a network of transmitters; radio programmes are broadcast from a studio in a similar fashion. An out-of-date term for a radio is a wireless; thus the transmissions in these broadcast networks are all carried out without the use of wires, that is, as *radio waves*. Radio waves vary in *frequency* and different frequency bands are used for different kinds of broadcasting. It is beyond the scope of this text to go into detail concerning these frequency bands, but the abbreviations VHF (very high frequency) and UHF (ultra-high frequency) should be familiar. The term *broadcast* is used because the radio wave signals can be received by any number of receivers within the broadcast area. The geographical area which can be reached by a broadcasting station depends on which method is used, namely:

- ❑ *cable* connections; this is an exception here as it clearly involves the use of wire or cable;

- ❑ *terrestrial* transmitters;

- ❑ *communications satellites*.

A broadcasting company may use a combination of cable, terrestrial and satellite transmitters to distribute its programmes. For example, the American company WTBS, in Atlanta, Georgia uses satellite to transmit low-cost sports and entertainment programmes to cable systems across the USA. Cable broadcasting, as the term indicates, uses physical cabling and is only economic over a limited area, such as a large city. However, in combination with satellite broadcasting, cable television plays an important role. Although terrestrial transmitters allow a much larger broadcast area than cable, satellites are essential to modern television broadcasting. Within the UK, pictures and monophonic sound are transmitted as analogue signals. The BBC has developed and transmits, NICAM stereo sound and digital aerial services, using digital encoding techniques.

Television broadcasting allows the transmission of *moving pictures*, *sound* and *data* to television receivers within the area served by a broadcasting station. Database services provided by television are *one-way* only, to television receivers and are collectively known as *Teletext* (see Network services). The BBC teletext service is known as Ceefax. To access these services a television receiver must have a Teletext *decoder*.

Microwave transmissions and communications satellites

Microwaves are super-high frequency (SHF) radio waves and can be used where transmitter and receiver are not in sight of one another. The communication path must be relatively obstruction-free. Microwaves can also be transmitted, through earth transmitters, to communications satellites; microwaves can penetrate cloud. Earth stations must be no more than 25-30 miles apart, because humidity in the atmosphere interferes with microwave signals. Each station in a communication path acts as a *repeater* station. Obviously, it is impractical to build sufficient repeater stations to deal with all transmissions, so communications satellites are essential. Once a satellite has received a signal, it amplifies it and sends it back to earth. Satellite communications are now fairly common and provide a cheaper and better trans-ocean transmission medium than undersea cable. Apart from television broadcasting, satellites form an essential part of the international telephone network. Voice and data messages are digitally transmitted as packets (see Packet Switching). There are three basic types of satellite:

❑ GEO (geosynchronous earth orbit). A GEO satellite remains fixed above a given point on the earth's surface. This means that a terrestrial station, once set to point at the satellite, does not require further adjustment. It is the most expensive to build and launch, but its powerful transmitters mean that few are needed to maintain global coverage. It also has an orbital life in excess of 12 years. A weakness of GEO satellite communication is *latency*, or propagation delay. A transmission passed via a GEO satellite from one terrestrial station to another takes more than two tenths of a second, which may make it unsuitable for use in high speed networks, but suitable for television broadcasting, mobile communications and global positioning services (GPS).

❑ MEO (medium earth orbit). A MEO satellite moves relative to a point on the earth's surface. This means that ground-based stations must have tracking equipment to maintain contact with a MEO. Global coverage requires the use of more MEOs than is the case for GEOs, but they are cheaper to build and launch and the transmission delay is insignificant. Its orbital life is between 6 and 12 years.

❑ LEO (low earth orbit). A LEO satellite moves quickly relative to a point on the earth's surface and many are needed to provide global coverage. LEOs are the cheapest to build and launch, provide the greatest bandwidth and suffer from virtually no transmission delay. However, a LEO satellite may have a lifespan of only 5 years.

Applications of satellite communication

Undersea cabling used to be the only way of connecting telephone networks on different continents but satellite communication provides a much cheaper alternative. Satellites also make it feasible and cost effective to extend networks to geographically remote and poorer countries which do not have established telecommunications systems. Satellite communications have been used in television broadcasting for over thirty years by traditional aerial delivery networks and cable networks. The bandwidth available through satellite communications allows the transmission of hundreds of television channels. Today, Direct Broadcast Satellite (DBS) allows television networks to transmit direct to individual users. A DBS satellite is geosynchronous and can transmit up to 150 channels, using digital signals to provide high quality reception to consumers.

Satellite communications allow ship to shore communications, linking a ship to a land-based receiver/transmitter anywhere in the world; aircraft use a similar service. A satellite phone can be used, even in the most remote parts of the world for voice and data communications; Inmarsat, for example, provides for ISDN communication. Global positioning services (GPS) can be used by ships, aircraft and land vehicles to determine their precise geographical position. Multiple geosynchronous satellites triangulate their signals to produce geographical coordinates.

Weather forecasting involves reporting, predicting, and studying the weather, including temperature, moisture, barometric pressure, and wind speed and direction. Satellites are vital for the rapid collection and transmission of meteorological data from the many terrestrial and atmospheric sources which contribute to more accurate weather forecasting.

Cellular telephone networks

These networks use *cellular radio* communications, which operate in the UHF (ultra-high frequency) band. Local *base stations* allow cellphone (hand-held or vehicle-based) users to access the pstn. Each base station covers a *cell site*, an area within which it can pick up cellphone signals. Within the UHF band, signals can penetrate buildings and other barriers, but a user must be within a few miles of a transmitter, particularly in urban areas, where the largest numbers of users tend to be found. Thus, a base station in a rural area, serving fewer users, can cover a larger cell site than is possible in an urban area. Computers are used to allow links to be maintained even while the caller is moving from one transmission area to another. Thus, when a base station receives a signal from a cellphone, it monitors the strength of the signal continuously to determine if it is still the most suitable base station to handle the transmission. Obviously, if the user is driving while making a call, a different base station may be handling the call at different points on the journey. The only effect of these changes is a brief (about one-fifth of a second) interruption to the call as the switch is made to a different base station. Major cellular radio operators in the UK are Orange, Cellnet and Vodaphone.

New generation mobile phones

Apart from voice transmission, mobile phones can be used to transmit text messages and those that support Internet Protocol (IP) or the newer WAP (Wireless Application Protocol - see later) can be used to access Internet services, albeit very slowly. The delivery of Internet services through mobile networks is hampered by the mobile phone itself, with its slow processor, poor battery life, mono display and awkward keypad, as well as by limited bandwidth.

The development of broadband mobile networks and more sophisticated phones is vital if the full potential of the Internet's multimedia content is to be made as accessible through a mobile phone as it is through a PC. In the meantime, services are largely text-based and perfectly adequate for the viewing of such information as travel, weather, sport results, share prices and the delivery of bank, ticket and message services.

New generation mobile phones are making use of larger flip-up screens with touch-sensitive input and handwriting recognition as additions to the usual keypad.

WAP and WML (Wireless Markup Language)

Although mobile phones have been able to access Web pages coded in HTML for some time, a WAP-enabled mobile can use its WAP browser to access pages coded in WML, a language specially designed to take account of the limitations of mobile networks and phones. Access to the Internet must be provided through a *gateway* which supports the WAP protocol. All the major cellular networks provide WAP gateways to allow their users to access Internet data services and as the market expands it is likely that conventional Internet Service Providers (ISPs) will provide a similar service.

Once cellular networks are able to provide the bandwidth (see UMTS later) presently available to PC users, full Java-enabled HTML content will be easily accessible to mobile phone users and the need for WAP and WML is likely to be reduced.

Use of satellites in cellular networks

In common with other communication networks, digital signalling has largely replaced analogue signalling. Each cell in a network provides a number of communication channels. In the case of analogue signalling each channel occupies a separate frequency band (frequency division multiplexing or FDM). Digital networks divide the cells into channels by time slot (time division multiplexing). When a network is busy, all the channels in a particular cell may be occupied, preventing other callers from using that cell. Satellites which are operating within a different bandwidth to the cell are able, when they have free bandwidth, to provide extra channel space for overloaded terrestrial cells. Digital cellular networks provide better performance (analogue networks can be subject to cross call interference) and more channels.

GSM and UMTS

GSM (Global System for Mobile communications) is the European standard for digital mobile communications and is the most widely used digital standard in the world today. Mobile phones which use the GSM standard are equipped with a SIM (Subscriber Information Card) which is a *smart* card for storing the phone number, personal security key and other information necessary for handset operation. The SIM provides levels of security which were not possible with first generation, analogue handsets, as well as the facility to make calls from any country which supports the GSM standard. The SIM can also be used to store personal phone numbers, signal missed calls, notify receipt of voice mail, text messages and so on. GSM also allows notebook and palmtop computers to be communicate with GSM handsets.

Users of analogue phones are vulnerable to eavesdropping, but GSM networks use encryption algorithms to scramble the digitised voice signals before transmission between the handset and the GSM transmitter site. The information stored in the SIM card enables the voice signals to be decrypted so that the user hears what the connected caller actually says.

Like the ISDN (see earlier) standard, GSM allows information to be transmitted in different forms through a single network. Thus, GSM provides integrated voice, data, fax and text message services, as well as services such as call forwarding, speed dialling (popular numbers can each be assigned to a single key press) and the selected blocking or receipt of calls, for example, based on location or time. GSM is regarded as second generation wireless technology.

UMTS (Universal Mobile Telecommunications System) is the planned third generation standard for mobile communications, with increased bandwidth (up to 2 Mbps). As a *broadband* network, UMTS is designed to carry multimedia (voice, data, pictures and video) information, a facility which is not feasible with the bandwidth of current GSM standards. Although a WAP phone can be used to access the Internet for e-mail, only WAP sites can be visited and these are largely text-based.

UMTS will be supported by all fixed, wireless and satellite networks, making it possible for the mobile phone to be used as the primary user device for communicating with computer-based systems of all kinds. A competing standard being developed in the USA and with similar aims, is called 'BlueTooth'.

Inter-networking components

The term inter-networking is used to describe the formation of integrated systems, through the connection of separate networks, locally and remotely. This enables organisations to construct organisation-wide information and communications systems, even if sections of it are a few or thousands of miles apart. This section looks at the devices used to make connections between local area networks (LANs) and between LANs and wide area networks. In general, these devices deal with the:

❑ connection of networks operating on different protocols;

❑ connection of LANs to LANs;

☐ connection of LANs to WANs;

☐ connection of networks of different architecture, cabling and protocol;

☐ routing of packets (see packet switching earlier) along the most efficient path;

☐ conversion between different packet formats, protocols and transmission speeds.

Computer networking is a relatively new industry and terminology is not entirely standardised. For this reason, definitions of terms, such as bridge, router and gateway can vary from one manufacturer's specification to another. Some devices, for example, combine the features of bridges and routers and are referred to as bridge/routers. Bearing this in mind, the following definitions are generally accepted.

Repeaters

Repeaters allow the effective length of a LAN cable to be increased. For example, the maximum length of an Ethernet segment is restricted because of signal loss and distortion which occurs as a data packet travels along the cable. A repeater re-strengthens, that is, *re-amplifies* the signal and resets its timing, so that the effective length of the segment can be increased (see Figure 32.23).

It is also used to enable a signal to travel to another segment of a network. A repeater can normally con-

Figure 32.23. *Repeaters connecting segments*

nect any kind of cable medium: thick or thin Ethernet, twisted pair or optical fibre. In relation to the Open Systems Inter-connection (OSI) model, referred to at the end of this chapter, a repeater works at the Physical level and only needs to know how to interact with the physical transmission medium.

Bridge

A bridge is used to connect two LANs of the same type, that is, two IBM token ring or two Ethernet LANs. This is known as *local inter-networking*. Packets crossing such a link are *forwarded* by the bridge device. Some bridges are *protocol transparent* and the otherwise similar networks can be using different protocols, for example, IPX (Novell) or IP (Internet Protocol). They can also be used to divide large networks into smaller segments. Segmenting large networks can improve administrative control and the performance of the separate segments. In the latter case, the bridge can be configured such that only data which needs to cross the bridge actually does. For example, if there are two segments, one for the Sales department and the other for Accounts, the data traffic for each function will be isolated within the respective segments, except when data needs to travel between the two. This improves the performance of each segment and thus the effectiveness of the whole network. A bridge operates at the Data Link Layer in the OSI model.

Hubs and switches

A hub has multiple ports to allow devices (or other network segments) to share a common connection point to the LAN cable. Some hubs are passive and simply pass packets between the devices and the network cable, but others provide device status information which allows, for example, a technician to identify a faulty device and disconnect it without affecting the operation of the remainder of the network. A hub contains devices called *switches* which forward packets from one segment to another.

Gateway or router

A gateway, or router, is used to connect two LANs of different (they do not have to be) type ; thus, for example, an Ethernet LAN can be connected to a Token Ring LAN, or the connection may be Ethernet to Ethernet. The LANs may be remotely connected through, for example, a packet switching WAN, with a gateway at each LAN's entry point to the WAN.

The term *router* is used to signify that the device is more intelligent than a bridge, in that it makes decisions about the route a data packet (by reference to its destination address) should follow to reach its destination; in this way, packets can be made to take the most efficient path. It may determine an alternative route for a packet, in the event of, for example, congestion or breakdown on a particular link. Networks may have different architectures and protocols.

A LAN using IPX (Novell) protocol can use a gateway to allow users access to, for example, a remote IBM network, which uses SNA protocol, through the Kilostream packet (X.25 protocol) switching network. In the OSI model (see later), a router operates at the Network Layer level.

Multiplexer

A multiplexer allows a number of low-speed devices to share a high-speed line, as illustrated in Figure 32.24.

Figure 32.24. *Multiplexers to allow several terminals to use a single link*

The messages from several low-speed lines are combined into one high-speed channel and then separated out at the other end by a demultiplexer. In two-way transmissions, both these functions are carried out in one unit at each end of the higher speed channel. Multiplexers send data from multiple sources along a single, high speed, communications link by dividing it into different channels, allocated as time slots. A brief time slot it given to each of a succession of terminals in which to send a block of data. The transmission rate of each terminal is relatively slow and limited by the speed of its human operator, so the high speed link can easily accommodate the transmissions of many terminals. The multiplexed link's capacity is known as its *bandwidth* (the rate at which data can be sent, measured in bits per second). The process of dividing this bandwidth into many channels is known as *time division multiplexing* (TDM - see earlier).

Concentrator

A concentrator is a type of multiplexer which greatly increases data throughput by increasing the number of low-speed channels and instead of transmitting a null character, empties the contents of the next full register. The data from each low-speed device is identified by extra identification bits and this constitutes an overhead.

Front-end-processors (FEP)

A front-end-processor is the most sophisticated type of device for communications control and is usually a minicomputer held at the site of a mainframe host computer. Its main task is to handle all the communications traffic, leaving the mainframe free to concentrate on other processing tasks. Its main tasks include:

❑ parity checking;

❑ stripping of overhead characters from serial transmission, such as start-stop bits and SYN characters (refers to synchronous transmission - see earlier);

❑ conversion from serial to parallel transmission and vice versa;

❑ network control;

❑ network accounting;

❑ character conversion.

Communications software

Various programs are available to provide users with different ways of communicating with remote computer systems. The following examples are used to illustrate typical communication services on the Internet:

❑ Internet Explorer, a Web browser (see Chapter 34).

❑ Hyperterminal, for logging in to Telnet BBS (Bulletin Board Services).

❑ Cute FTP (File Transfer Protocol) for transferring files to or from an FTP server.

❑ Microsoft Outlook for e-mail and newsgroups.

Hyperterminal

This Windows 9x program allows connection to any remote computer, to which the user has authorised access. The program includes a dialler so connection can be made directly to another computer, but more usually the connection is indirect via an Internet Service Provider (ISP). Hyperterminal can be used as a Telnet client and thereby access Telnet BBS (Bulletin Board Services). A BBS site may offer a variety of services, including for example, various files for downloading, e-mail facilities, a discussion forum, or simply an information service. *Telnet* is designed to allow remote terminals to operate in the same way as those which are locally attached and has been in use since before the introduction of the World Wide Web. One such Telnet site is illustrated in Figure 32.25.

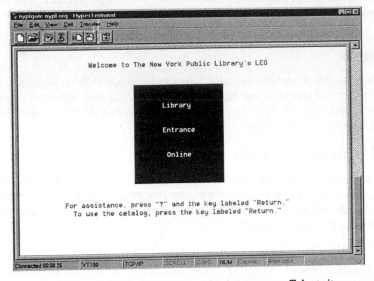

Figure 32.25. *Hyperterminal used to connect to a Telnet site*

Notice that the status bar at the bottom of the screen identifies the terminal type as VT100, which provides basic text facilities. The Hyperterminal package terminal settings were set to AutoDetect before the connection was made and the Telnet site changed that setting to VT100. Other terminal types are shown in the Settings tab in Figure 32.26. Some operating systems, including VAX and Unix, provide a built-in Telnet *client* and do not require the use of an additional package.

Many users access Telnet services via a Web browser which automatically *calls* the Telnet client into action, as illustrated in Figure 32.27. The New York Library web site in the Figure has a hyperlink "Leo via Telnet" which launches the Telnet client as shown. Many Telnet sites allow visitors to sign in as "guest".

Hyperterminal can also be used for sending or receiving text and binary files. Apart from plain text files without any formatting all other

Figure 32.26. *Terminal types available with Hyperterminal*

file types must be transferred in binary format, using one of the protocols available in Hyperterminal. Figure 32.28 shows the drop-down list of protocols for sending binary files.

Normally, the communications software on the receiving computer needs to be set to receive the file using an agreed protocol.

Figure 32.27. *Launching a Telnet session from a Web site link*

With the facility to transfer almost any type of file as an e-mail attachment, the use of Hyperterminal for these purposes is extremely limited. In addition, a much more widely used protocol, File Transfer Protocol or FTP is the standard for most remote file transfers.

All Internet ISPs support the protocol and for Web site maintenance, an FTP package is an essential piece of software. To make a Web site available to the world, its pages must be uploaded to an Internet server and for mainte-

Figure 32.28. *Protocols for sending binary files*

nance pages will need to be downloaded, modified and uploaded again. An FTP package such as CuteFTP is designed to communicate with the FTP server which hosts Web sites. Figure 32.29 shows an FTP package being used to upload pages to a Web site. The left panel shows the directory structure of the local machine and the right panel shows the relevant part of the directory structure on the Web server. The bottom panel shows the pages queued for uploading.

Figure 32.29. *FTP software uploading Web pages tp the Web server*

The OSI (open systems interconnection) model

Many computer devices are now designed for use in networked systems. Manufacturers are now tending to conform to standard protocols that make their equipment compatible with a variety of user networks. *Closed* networks, that are restricted to one manufacturer's equipment and standards, are not attractive to the user, because it restricts the choice of equipment which can be used. The aim of standardisation is to achieve more open systems which allow users to select from a wider range of manufacturers' products. A Reference Model for Open Systems Interconnection (OSI) has been under development by the International Standards Organisation (ISO) since 1977. Other standards, including SNA (IBM's System Network Architecture) and Ethernet, are largely incompatible with one another. Certain standards in the OSI model have been set by manufacturers as their commercial products have gained in popularity.

The OSI reference model for communications protocol identifies a hierarchy of seven layers. The layers and their functions are briefly described in the following paragraphs.

Application layer

This is the highest layer in that it is closest to the user. It supports the transfer of information between end-users, applications programs and devices. Several types of protocol exist in this layer, including those for specific applications and those for more generalised applications, such as accounting, directory services, network management, entry control and user identification. The applications layer hides the physical network from the user, presenting a user-orientated view instead. For example, the user need not know that several physical computers are involved when accessing a database.

Presentation layer

This layer covers standards on how data is presented to the end-user devices. The aim is to ensure that different devices, which may be using data in different formats, can communicate with one another. The presentation layer can, for example, handle conversions between ASCII and EBCDIC character codes. It may also carry out encryption to ensure data security during transmission over vulnerable telecommunication links. The presentation layer also attempts to deal with conversions between terminals which use different line and screen lengths and different character sets.

Session layer

The session layer is concerned with the exchange of information between different applications and users; it is the users' interface into the network. When a user requests a particular service from the network, the session layer handles the dialogue.

Transport layer

The data transmission system on any network will have its own peculiarities and the function of the transport layer is to mask out any undesirable features which may prevent a high quality transmission for the network. For example, a message may have to be divided into packets or frames of a particular size before it is passed over to the network layer for routing though the network. The transport layer also ensures message delivery and provides acknowledgements.

Network layer

The function of the network layer is to perform the routing of information around the network and also to connect one network to another. The software can also carry out accounting functions to enable the network owner to charge users.

Data link layer

The physical data transmission media used in a network are subject to interference which can corrupt data and other signals. The data link layer handles data transmission errors and thus improves the quality of the network. The techniques used, for example, for the receipt and acknowledgement of data by a receiver device, are determined by the data link layer. The CCITT V42bis protocol, with its error detection and correction facilities falls into this level.

Physical layer

The physical layer provides the means to connect the physical medium and is concerned with the transmission of binary data within the communication channel, such as determining what signal state represents a binary 1. Standards are set regarding the mechanical, electrical and procedural aspects of interface devices. For example, standards are set for the number of pins a network connector should have and the function and position of each pin. The RS232 and V24 protocols are within this level.

The purpose of layering

Layering allows the separation of system components into the physical and a range of logical levels and makes them independent of one another. This separation facilitates the development and production of platform (different hardware and operating systems) components which can communicate with one another. For example, by using a common language to write network card drivers, the same network card can then handle different network protocols, say IPX (Novell) and TCP/IP (Internet Protocol).

Exercises

1. Give two examples of information which are commonly transmitted in digital form, but are presented to users in analogue form.

2. (a) Distinguish between the amplitude and frequency of a sine wave signal and sketch a diagram showing how each could be used to represent binary data.

    (b) Briefly explain the concept of frequency bandwidth and the role of the modem in the transmission fo computer data over analogue sections of the PSTN.

3. Why is a duplex connection the favoured option for most data communications applications?

4. Suggest organisations and applications which would be likely to use:

    (i) leased lines

    (ii) dial-up connections.

    to access external networks. Justify your choice in each case, indicating how the link would be used.

5. Distinguish between asynchronous and synchronous serial transmission and suggest circumstances when each may be appropriate.

6. Why does data compression require a distinction to be made between baud rate and the rate of data throughput?

7. What main characteristic distinguishes the V.90 modem standard from its predecessors?

8. With the use of a simple sketch, illustrate the technique of pulse code modulation (PCM).

9. Briefly explain the concepts of *handshaking* and *flow control* and state why they are a necessary part of data communications.

10. Identify two methods of error checking.

11. Identify three types of cabling used in data communications.

12. Briefly explain the principles of packet switching.

13. Distinguish between packet and message switching.

14. What is meant by time division multiplexing (TDM)?

15. What major advantage will the new UMTS standard for mobile communications provide over the existing GSM standard?

16. Briefly identify the role of the following internetworking components: *repeater*, *bridge*, *router*, *hub*, *front-end processor*.

17. State the primary purpose of each of the following communications software products: *HyperTerminal*; *Cute FTP*; *Microsoft Outlook*.

18. (a) What is the main pupose of the OSI model?

    (b) List the 7 layers is contains.

Chapter 33

Computer networks

Networking computer systems has the effect of decentralising computer processing and improving communications within and between organisations and between organisations and individuals. Some computer networks use dedicated intelligent terminals or microcomputer systems to permit some independent processing power at sites remote from the *host* computer, to which they are connected. Other networks distribute even more processing power by linking microcomputer, minicomputer, mainframe and supercomputer systems. They are sometimes referred to as *distributed processing* systems. Networks can be configured to suit almost any application, from the provision of a world-wide airline reservation system to home banking. *Nodes* (connection points in the network) may only be a few feet apart and limited to a single building, or they may be several thousand miles apart.

Local and wide area networks

Computer networks can be classified according to their geographical spread. A network confined to, say, one building, with microcomputer workstations distributed in different rooms, is known as a *local area network* (LAN). One particular type, known as a ring network can extend over a diameter of around five miles. A computer network distributed nationally or even internationally makes use of telephone and sometimes, satellite links, and is referred to as a *wide area network* (WAN). In large organisations with several branches, it is common practice to maintain a LAN at each branch for local processing requirements and to link each LAN into a WAN covering the whole organisation. In this way, branches of an organisation can have control over their own processing and yet have access to the organisation's main database at headquarters. In addition, inter-branch communication is possible.

Network architecture

The architecture of any network includes definition of: its *components*, both hardware and software, identified by *name* and *function*; the ways the components are connected and communicate with one another. The architecture of wide area networks (WANs) is described in Chapter 32 and the following primarily relates to local area networks (LANs). However, the section on Network Topologies does relate, in part, to WANs.

LAN architecture

It is important that the components are combined in such a way that the LAN can be: *extended*. The LAN must be capable of providing for new users and new equipment, as the need arises; *upgraded* to take advantage of new technologies which can improve network performance; *connected* to other LANs, both local and remote and Wide Area Networks.

LAN architecture comprises hardware and software, both for the control of the LAN communications and as an interface between the LAN and its users. In order that all components are compatible and operate as a coherent system, it is important that they conform to agreed standards (Chapter 32). This means that LAN producers have to take account of generally agreed standards for equipment linking and data communications, so that as new products come onto the market, the user is not left with a system which cannot take advantage of them. Unfortunately, a number of different standards exist and this means that the decision on which type of LAN to purchase is not always straightforward.

Hardware components

Figure 33.1 shows a simple *client-server* LAN and identifies the main hardware components: *workstation*; *file server*; *printer server*; network *cabling*. The way in which they are connected defines its general *topology* or physical shape.

Figure 33.1. *Main components of a local area network*

LAN Workstation

A *workstation* gives a user access to a LAN and its facilities. A workstation comprises a *microcomputer* with a *network card*, which fits into an *expansion slot* inside its system casing. The network card enables workstations to communicate across the network, and with the *file server* (see later). The card converts computer-generated data into a form suitable for transmission over the LAN and as such is an *interface* (Chapter). The card is operated with a network card *driver*.

Servers

The general function of servers is to allocate shared resources to other nodes on the network. There are a number of different types of server, classed according to the resources they control.

File server

The file server is usually a specially configured microcomputer, with a network card, more memory and disk storage, as well as a more powerful processor than is needed for a workstation. It has to control access to shared storage, directories and files. In addition, it controls the exchange of files between network users. Most network software provides *multiple device* support. This means that file servers can support several disks, allowing file storage capacity on the LAN to be increased beyond that of the file server's integral hard disk. A LAN can also consist of several file servers; indeed except for the smallest of networks, this is normally the case.

Print server

A print server (there may be several) accepts and queues jobs from workstations; the user may be informed when printing is complete. The print server may also provide certain print management functions, for example, to attach priorities to different print jobs so that certain jobs are printed before others, no matter what their positions in the queue. A print server will be configured to:

❑   support the use of particular printers;

❑   service particular printer *queues*; users with the right to use a particular print queue can then place their jobs in that queue.

Communications server

If a LAN is to have access to external networks or databases, a communications server is required. Generally, the communications server can establish a temporary link with remote computers or users on other networks (see Remote Inter-networking).

Network topologies

Computer networks can be categorised according to their physical shape or topology. Each terminal in a network is known as a *node*. If a central computer controls the network it is known as the *host* computer. The topology of a network is the *arrangement* of the nodes and the ways they are interconnected. The communication system within a network is known as the *subnet*. Data can be transmitted around the subnet either on a *point-to-point* basis or through a *broadcast* channel. If point-to-point transmission is used, the data passes through each device in the network. Thus, if two devices wish to communicate, they must do it indirectly, via any intervening devices. Each device must have the facility to store the entire message and forward it when the output channel is free. If a broadcast channel is used, a common communication channel is shared by all devices in the network. This means that any message sent by a device is received by all devices. The message contains the address of the device intended to receive it, so that the other devices can ignore it. There are a number of recognised network topologies and some of the most common are described below.

Star network

A star topology means that each node is connected, by separate connections to a computer at the centre, known as the *hub*. Figure 33.2 shows a LAN in a star topology. It is also a popular topology for a WAN. In this structure, all messages pass through the host (probably a mainframe or minicomputer) computer, which interconnects the different devices on the network. So, in this topology the host computer at the hub has a *message switching* function. Messages are transmitted point-to-point. The topology is particularly useful for intercommunications between pairs of users on the network (via the host). The network may consist of numerous computer systems (the nodes), connected to a larger host computer which switches data and programs between them.

Figure 33.2. *Star topology*

The star computer network is by far the most popular for WANs, because most large organisations start with a central computer at the head office, from which branch computer facilities are provided through the telephone network. The main aim is to provide computer communication between the branches and head office. Most other network topologies aim to provide communication between all devices on a network. The star topology can also be used for a LAN.

The *advantages* of a star network topology are as follow:

❑ It is suitable for WANs where organisations rely on a central computer for the bulk of processing tasks, perhaps limiting the nodes to their local processing needs and the validation of data, prior to transmission to the central computer;

- Centralised control of message switching allows a high degree of security control;

- Each spoke in the star is independent of the rest and a fault in a link or device in one spoke, can be identified by the computer at the hub;

- The data transmission speeds used can vary from one *spoke* (a link from the hub to a node) to another. This is important if some spokes transmit using high speed devices, such as disk, whilst others transmit from low speed keyboard devices. The method of transmission may also vary. For example, one node may only require access to the network at the end of each day, in which case a *dial-up* connection may be sufficient. A dial-up connection uses the public telephone network and the user only pays for the time taken for transmission. Alternatively, other nodes may require the link for most of the working day, in which case a permanent *leased line* is appropriate. Leased lines provide a more reliable transmission medium and also allow higher speeds of data transmission.

The main *disadvantages* inherent in star networks are as follow:

- The network is vulnerable to hub failures which affect all users. As a distributed processing system, some processing is still possible at the nodes but inter-node communication is lost when the host computer fails;

- For a WAN, the control of communications in the network requires expensive technology at the hub, probably a mini or mainframe computer. Complex operating and communications software is needed to control the network.

Ring network

The ring topology is specifically designed for use with a LAN and is not suitable for a WAN. A ring network connects all the nodes in a ring, as illustrated in Figure 33.3. The *Cambridge Ring*, developed at Cambridge University, has no host computer and none of the nodes need have overall control of access to the network. In practice, a monitoring station is used for the control of data transmission in the network. Messages in a ring network flow in one direction, from node to node.

Figure 33.3. *Ring topology*

The ring consists of a series of repeaters, which are joined by the physical transmission medium (twisted pair, co-axial, or fibre-optic cable). The choice of medium depends on the distances to be covered and the desired transmission rates. Fibre-optic cable allows the greatest distances to be covered and the highest transmission rates. Repeaters are used to regenerate messages as they pass around the network. The use of repeaters allows a ring network to cover larger distances than is possible for other topologies. In fact, recent developments using fibre optic cable allow a ring with a range of about 100 kilometres, which makes it a *metropolitan area network* (MAN). The user devices are connected to the repeaters. A message from one node, addressed to another, is passed continually around the ring until the receiving node flags that it is ready to accept it. Acceptance of a message is determined by its *destination address*, which is examined by each node it passes. If the destination address matches the node's own address, the node takes the message; otherwise, the node repeater regenerates the signal to be passed to the next node in the ring. Data is transmitted in mini-packets of about 40 bits and contains the address of the sending node, the address of the destination node and some control bits. A variation on the Cambridge ring is the IBM ring, which uses a different protocol to allow better control of message flow on the network; the two protocols, *empty slot* and *token passing* are described in Network Access Protocols. The ring network presents advantages:

❑ There is no dependence on a central host computer as data transmission around the network is supported by all the devices in the ring. Each node device has sufficient intelligence to control the transmission of data from and to its own node;

❑ Very high transmission rates are possible; 10 megabits/sec is typical;

❑ Routing between devices is relatively simple because messages normally travel in one direction only around the ring;

❑ The transmission facility is shared equally amongst the users.

The main disadvantages are as follow:

❑ The system depends on the reliability of the whole ring and the repeaters, although it can be designed to bypass any failed node;

❑ It may be difficult to extend the length of the ring because the physical installation of any new cable must ensure that the ring topology is preserved.

Star/ring network - IBM token ring

The *IBM Token Ring* Network is a star-based topology, with a hub or *multiple access unit* (MAU) to which all the workstations are connected. The movement of data is, however in a *logical ring*. All signals between workstations are through the MAU. The star/ring structure has a major advantage over the basic ring. If one workstation breaks down, or the connection with the MAU is broken, other workstations are not affected (except that they cannot communicate with the damaged workstation). Failure of the MAU will prevent operation of the network. The Cambridge ring structure, described earlier, is prone to complete failure if one workstation fails (the continuous ring is broken).

Bus network

The bus network topology is illustrated in the Figure 33.4. With a bus topology, the workstations are connected to a main cable (known as the *bus* or trunk), along which data travels. The ends of a bus are not connected, so that data has to travel in both directions to reach the various nodes on the network. The bus topology makes the addition of new

Figure 33.4. *Bus topology*

devices straightforward, either by attachment to the existing cable or to cable which can be added at either end. The main bus standard is known as *Ethernet*. The term *station* tends to be used rather than node for this type of network. The communications subnet uses a *broadcast* channel, so all attached stations can hear every transmission. As is the case in the ring network, there is no host computer and all stations have equal priority in using the network to transmit. The maximum length of a single bus *segment* is 500 metres and 100 stations can be attached to it. Segments can be specially linked to form larger configurations, up to a maximum of about 12 kilometres. Transmission speeds of 10 megabits/second are obtainable.

The bus network provides certain benefits:

❑ If a node malfunctions, it simply stops communicating; it doesn't prevent the rest of the network from working;

❑ The attachment of devices is straightforward and the cable can be extended, if necessary; additional *segments* can be linked to extend the network.

The main drawback is that:

❑ If a part of the Ethernet cabling develops a fault, the whole network (assuming it consists of a single segment) fails.

Mesh network

The nodes of a mesh network are fully interconnected. The mesh topology is not found in LANs, but is typical of the public switched telephone network (pstn) and WANs. Its complexity requires the use of switching techniques to route data through the network.

Network cabling - the transmission medium

In order to share resources on a network, servers, workstations and other devices must be connected; although wireless radio media are possible, most LANs use physical cabling, which acts as the *transmission medium*. The physical layout of the cabling should conform to one of the basic *topologies*: star, ring or bus. The type of cable used depends on the chosen topology and the rules governing the transmission of data through the cable (the *protocol*). The cabling standards of Ethernet and Token Ring, described below, are also LAN protocols.

Ethernet cabling

Ethernet is one the two most widely accepted standards (the other is Token Ring) for specifying how data is placed on and retrieved from a LAN. An Ethernet-equivalent standard is IEEE 802.3 (see Chapter), which also uses Ethernet cable, but packets data slightly differently for transmission through the cable. Ethernet cable falls into three main categories:

❑ *Thick Ethernet* coaxial cable, with a diameter of 10mm has a solid copper core conductor. A single network segment can be 500 metres and supports the attachment of 100 devices. The cabling conforms to the IEEE 802.3 Type 10Base5 standard. The transmission rate is 10 megabits (1,000,000 bits) per second (Mb/s).

❑ *Thin Ethernet*, which is 10 millimetres in diameter, has a core of stranded cable. The maximum length of cable which can be used in a single network segment is around 180 metres and the maximum number of workstations is around 30. The cabling conforms to the IEEE 802.3 Type 10Base2 standard. The cable supports a maximum transmission rate of 2 Mb/s.

❑ *10BaseT* Standard Ethernet. The T stands for *twisted pair*. This cable is much cheaper than the thick Ethernet cabling, but provides the same transmission rate of 10 Mb/s; being the same as most telephone cabling, it is easier to install.

Token ring cabling

Used in *IBM token ring* networks use twisted pair cabling, either two pairs or four, depending on data transmission requirements. A single IBM Token Ring network will support up to 260 network devices at rates of 4 Mb/s or 16 Mb/s. Up to eight rings can be connected using *bridges*.

Fibre-optic cabling and FDDI

Cable of this type is available for use with any of the network types, but provides greater *bandwidth* and permits transmission over greater distances, without the use of *repeaters*. Fibre Distributed Data Interface (FDDI) is a fibre optic standard with bandwidth of over a Gigabit (1024^3) per second. FDDI is also a token ring standard, but operates with two counter rotating rings and workstations may be attached to one or both rings. FDDI is used widely for network backbones. A *backbone* is the part of a network which carries the main traffic and connects, for example, the LANs in different departments of an organisation.

Cable bandwidth

Digital bandwidth is measured in bits per second and indicates the volume of data which can be transmitted over a communications link in a fixed time. Bandwidth is important because is determines the practicability of using remote communications for modern user applications. High bandwidth is not a crucial consideration for users who wish to exchange the occasional text email, but it is fundamental to the success of businesses with more complex and high volume communication needs. For example, a multi-sited organisation may need use its communications links to the Internet for the transmission of complex documents containing high quality images, voice communications and video conferencing. To meet these requirements the organisation would need dedicated, high speed links from each site to a 'backbone' (a major communications link) in the Internet In summary, bandwidth can be:

❑ Baseband. In a baseband network, a transmitting device uses the whole bandwidth (frequency range), so only one signal can be carried at any one time. This means that, for a brief moment, a transmitting device has exclusive use of the transmission medium. In general, broadband networks are suitable for networks which only transmit data signals.

❑ Broadband. Broadband networks provide a number of frequency bands or channels within the total bandwidth (*frequency division multiplexing*) and thus allow simultaneous use by different devices on the network. Generally, one channel is dedicated to the user workstations, leaving others free for transmitting video pictures for the security system, voice communication, television pictures and so on.

Cable-device connection

A number of different devices are used to make the connection between network devices, such as workstations and servers, and the transmission medium. The particular components used will depend on the type of network (for example, Ethernet or Token Ring); even for the same type of network, there are a range of connection alternatives. This paragraph only details the main categories of connection component, which are:

❑ *network card* (adapter), which is the *interface* for linking a network device to all other resources on the network; this is fitted into an expansion slot inside each workstation and other network devices. A device attaching to a Token ring network needs a different type of network card, from one attaching to an Ethernet network. A notebook or portable computer can be connected using its PCMCIA (Personal Computer Memory Card International Association) slot and a special network adapter;

❑ *Ethernet transceiver*; this device implements the CSMA/CD access protocol (see Access protocols). It is external from the network device and is connected to the network card and the Ethernet network cable. Although most network cards already contain a transceiver chip, *thick* Ethernet connections need an external transceiver. Thin Ethernet connections simply use the transceiver chip on the network card;

❏ *BNC connector*. Figure 33.5 illustrates its appearance; this is one of several types of connector used for *thin* Ethernet cable. There are BNC male and female connectors for linking sections of cable and T connectors for attaching devices to the cable. *Thick* Ethernet cabling uses a stronger screw coupling for cable connections (N-series connectors);

Figure 33.5. *BNC "T" connector*

❏ *Terminator*; this is an electrical resistor which must be attached to each end of an Ethernet network segment (see Bus Topology);

❏ *Multiple Access Unit* (MAU). This is the central component of a star/ring topology and is used in the IBM Token Ring network (see Star/Ring Network).

Connecting and extending LANs

Although there are limitations to the range of a LAN and the number of devices which can be attached, imposed by the performance ability of the network transmission medium, networks can be connected to one another and extended. LANs set up separately can be connected permanently, or data transmission between them can be restricted, for special user or system requirements. The devices used in this area of LAN architecture are described in Chapter 32.

Software components

Apart from physical components identified in the previous section, various types of software are also needed and these are described the the following sections.

Network operating system

A network operating system typically includes functional components to set-up, monitor and administer:

❏ The *directory* and *file* system on the server; directories are used to organise the storage of programs and data held on the file server's hard drive(s). Some directories are for the storage of the network operating system; others contain application programs and some directory space is allocated for the storage of user's data. Chapter provides an example of a file server's directory structure; each directory is labelled to identify the nature of the files it contains.

❏ *User login* and activity. A user must be identified by the network operating system before being given access to the network. The supervisor *creates* users and assigns a user-id to each. A user may also be assigned to a *user-group*, for example, Sales or Marketing. To access a network, a user must login at a workstation, which will require the entry of a *user-id* and possibly, a *password*. The precise conditions can be set by the network supervisor; certain time periods can be set when users are not allowed to log into the network; the time restrictions can be applied to all users, specific groups or individuals. The resources available to any given user can also be controlled through the login procedure.

❏ *User access* to applications and data files. Typically, users are assigned *rights*, sometimes as individuals, but more usually as members of a group. These rights relate to directories and files; in other words, the rights determine whether, for example, a user is allowed to delete or copy files in a particular directory. Access rights to *network executables*, that is application programs, only allow the programs to be run.

❏ *Network printing*; users can be given access to a shared printer, through a print *queue*; each queue is controlled by a printer server, which directs the jobs to a network printer under its control.

❏ *Electronic messaging*; this is a LAN version of electronic mail and provides a mailbox facility for inter-user communication.

❏ *Network backup*. This task, although important to users, because it may prevent the loss of important work, or network facilities, is a task carried out on a regular basis by the network supervisor.

All these tasks are the responsibility of the *network supervisor* or *administrator* who has special rights of access, not available to others. Usually, these tasks are carried out through a system console; any computer on the network can be used for this purpose, but, usually it will be secure in a separate location. Although printing, electronic messaging, applications and limited file management are available to users, their rights should not extend to the amendment of these facilities.

Workstation operating system

Each workstation has its own local operating system, such as MS-DOS or Windows95 to control processing; once an application is retrieved from the file server, the workstation must be able to run it.

Network connection software

The network connection software must be loaded into the workstation RAM (usually from the its integral hard drive, during start-up), before the workstation can be logged onto the network. This software remains in the workstation RAM as long as it is logged onto the network. A program which remains resident like this is referred to as a TSR (terminate and stay resident) program. There are usually several components to the connection software, each having a separate function. Two major functional components are the:

❏ *Communication protocol*. This is the set of rules for transmitting data through the network; it ensures that devices can successfully communicate with one another by using the same language. Example protocols are: IPX (Novell Netware); TCP/IP (Internet); SNA (IBM).

❏ *LAN driver*, which controls the network card fixed inside the workstation. LAN drivers which conform to the ODI (Open Data-link Interface) standard can accept data from the network in any of the standard communication protocols, listed in the previous paragraph. This means that workstations of different operating system types (MS-DOS, Macintosh, UNIX etc.) can be attached to the same LAN and share its resources.

Network access protocols

Empty slot technique

This system is appropriate for networks in the shape of rings or loops, where messages are passed point-to-point in one direction. One or more empty   *slots* or *packets* circulate continuously around the ring. When a device has information to transmit, it loads it into the slot, which carries it to its destination. At the time of loading, the destination address is placed in the slot and a full-empty flag is set to full. As the slot is passed from one repeater to another, no attempt will be made to load the slot as long as the flag is set to full. When the slot reaches the destination device, the devices repeater reads the information without clearing the slot. Before passing it on, the repeater sets a received message flag in the slot. When the slot again reaches the sending device, the flag is set to empty. The destination device can check that the message was received by checking the received flag. If the message was not successfully received, perhaps because the destination device was not listening, the sender device can check the acknowledgement flag and re-transmit in the next slot.

Token passing technique

This technique is also used for ring networks. An imaginary *token* is passed continuously around the ring. The token is recognised as such by the devices, as a unique character sequence. If a device is waiting to transmit, it catches the token and with it, the authority to send data. As long as one device has the token, no other device can send data. A receiving device acknowledges the receipt of a message by inverting a 1-bit field. Token Ring employs this method.

Carrier sense multiple access (CSMA)

CSMA is used on broadcast systems such as the bus network. Each device is theoretically free to transmit data to any other device at any time. Before attempting to transmit, a device's network card polls the network path to ensure that the destination device is free to receive data and that the communications channel is free. A device wishing to transmit must wait until both conditions exist. Generally such delay will be no more than a few millionths of a second.

❑ CSMA *Collision Detection* (CSMA-CD). Because of the possibility of collision through simultaneous transmission, a collision detection mechanism is used. When collision does occur, the devices involved cease transmission and try again some time later. In order to avoid the same collision, each device involved is made to wait a different time. If a number of retries prove unsuccessful, an error will be reported to the user. Ethernet (IEEE 802.3 Standard) networks (see Network Cabling) use a form of CSMA/CD.

❑ CSMA *Collision Avoidance* (CSMA-CA). This strategy attempts to improve on that of CSMA-CD, which allows a device to place a packet onto the network path as soon as its network card detects it as being free. In the time between the test (measured in fractions of a microsecond) and the placing of the packet onto the path, another device's network card may have detected the path as free and be about to place another packet onto it. CSMA-CA seeks to remedy this problem by requiring a device's network card to test the path *twice*, once to see if the path is free and a second time, after alerting the device that it may use the network, but before the packet is placed onto the path.

Benefits of computer networks

The general benefits are:

❑ sharing of appropriate *software*, *hardware resources* and common *data*;

❑ sharing of *processing* activity;

❑ *connectivity*; this is a very broad term used to categorise facilities and devices which support connection and communication between otherwise incompatible systems or devices. For example, a *terminal emulation* card, which enables a microcomputer to communicate with a remote IBM host computer, falls into this category;

❑ accessible services for *security*, *user support* and *system maintenance*.

Sharing hardware and software

In a LAN, particularly, there are opportunities to share hardware and software. This is because resources tend to be distributed over a small area; it is reasonable to ask users to share a printing resource if the printers serving them are within the same room, or perhaps in an adjacent room. It could be argued that the rapid fall in hardware costs has, to a certain extent, reduced the need for sharing peripherals, such as hard disk drives and printers. Although the prices of hard drives have fallen, the heavy demands of modern software and the increasing number of applications, ensures matching increases in demand for on-line storage. It is now common for microcomputer systems, even at the cheaper end of the market, to have their own hard disk storage with capacities measured in gigabytes (1024^3 bytes). Although printers are becoming much cheaper, increasing numbers of users are demanding the high quality output (and sometimes colour) provided by top quality printers; printers at the top of the quality range are still relatively expensive. In summary, a number of factors concerning computer usage, storage and printing confirm that resource sharing remains a major purpose of a LAN.

❑ Applications. The range of computer applications and the number of users is continually increasing.

❑ Software packages. The increasing sophistication of software means that large amounts of disk space are needed for each package. Network versions of a package are cheaper (per user) than those for stand-alone systems.

❑ Storage technologies. Optical storage and high performance hard drives are capable of storing thousands of megabytes (gigabytes or gb) and are still relatively expensive. Individual users, each with their own hard disk-based microcomputer, are unlikely to make use of the several hundred megabytes available on each machine. A shared, large volume, hard or optical drive can satisfy the storage needs of all users.

❑ Printers. Most users require only occasional use of a printer, so there is little point in providing one for each. This is particularly the case for colour printers. A laser printer can produce the high quality output demanded by many applications and it operates at speeds which allow sharing to take place, without unreasonable delay for users.

❑ Other devices, such as scanners and plotters are relatively expensive and are likely to be used only occasionally.

Sharing data

A major benefit of all types of network concerns the sharing of data, frequently from centralised databases. This purpose is made particularly clear by the expansion of *Internet*, the world-wide network described in Chapter 34. Data can also be regarded as a resource, so sharing it can bring similar benefits to those available from sharing hardware. For example, a common data store supports the use of a *database* system, which itself reduces the need for data duplication. Traditional computer processing methods require that each application has its own files and this results in the duplication of many data items and the updating process. For example, in a retail business both the stock control and purchasing departments make use of commodity details such as Stock Codes, Descriptions and Prices; if separate files are maintained by each department, a change in, for example, the Price of a commodity requires more than one input.

Limiting access to shared storage

The sharing of data files presents some problems which need to be tackled. Firstly, access to some data may have to be restricted to particular users. Although the aim of networks is to provide computer access to as many users as possible, procedural and software controls can be built in to limit entry to the system, or to particular files or processes. Network software allows the network administrator to vary the rights of users, according to the kinds of access they require to particular applications or files.

Another problem with sharing files is that several users may attempt to update the same data at the same time. This can lead to corruption of data. To combat this problem, network software usually provides a facility for locking individual records while they are being updated. Thus, if a particular record is being altered, it is locked and made inaccessible by any other user until the updating process is complete.

Sharing processing activity

Host computer with intelligent terminals

A host computer with intelligent terminals allows processing to be carried out at remote sites; as such it comes under the heading of WAN. The distribution of processing work may be very limited, such that the majority is processed by a central computer. For example, terminals connected to a remote host computer often have their own processing power, file storage and printing facilities. Usually, before being transmitted to the host computer for the updating of files, *transaction* data will require some *validation* and other accuracy checks and this can be done at the terminal. Microcomputers equipped with suitable software are often used to *emulate* mainframe intelligent terminals, with the added advantage of being useable as stand-alone systems, when not communicating with the mainframe.

Alternatively, the work may be equally shared amongst a number of powerful computer systems, which then merge the results of their separate efforts.

Client-server network

A *client-server* LAN aims to exploit the full processing power of each computer in the network, including the *file server* and the user workstations or *clients*. This is effected by dividing the processing tasks between a client and a server. The client, a microcomputer in its own right (as opposed to the *dumb* terminal found in older mainframe systems) provides the user with a completely separate facility for running applications. The file server which could be a microcomputer, minicomputer, or mainframe, enhances the client component by providing additional services.

These services are traditionally offered by minicomputer and mainframe systems operating a *time-sharing* operating system; they include shared file management, data sharing between users, network administration and security. The major benefit of a client-server network is that the power of the client and server machines is used jointly to carry out the processing of an application. Interactive activities, for example, construction of a spreadsheet or the word processing of a report, are carried out by the client machine; having logged onto the network, the user can load the required applications software from the file server.

Backup and file sharing security, relating to the application, can be handled by the server. Printing tasks can also be queued and handled as a shared printer becomes available. This task is handled by one or more *print servers*, which can be dedicated devices, or microcomputers assigned to the task. Except for small LANs, most operate on the client-server principle.

Peer-to-peer network

With a peer-to-peer configuration, it is not necessary to have a file server; instead all the workstations on the network contribute to the control of the network. Thus, any workstation can supply or use resources of others, as required. Unfortunately, this has the effect of slowing performance; in addition it means that files are not held centrally and this complicates file management. *Novell Personal Netware* and *LANtastic 6.0* are popular examples of peer-to-peer networking products.

The peer-to-peer approach is highly suitable for very small networks, but both the products mentioned allow the system to be developed to introduce some file server control. Facilities are also included to allow users to share resources in groups; the name of another peer-to-peer networking product illustrates this feature: *Windows for Workgroups*; up to 10 users can be networked.

Exercises

1. Identify the main *components* of a LAN and briefly explain the function of each.
2. Identify one advantage and one disadvantage of each of the following network topologies: *star*; *ring*; *bus*.
3. How does the *IBM Token Ring* network overcome a weakness of the basic ring topology?
4. Name the main *Ethernet cable standards*, and the performance specification of each.
5. (i) Differentiate between *baseband* and *broadband* networks.
   (ii) Suggest, by reference to applications, why broadband networks will become increasingly important.
7. Identify four functions of a *network operating system*.
8. What is meant by a workstation's *local operating system*?
9. In the context of network connection software, briefly describe the functions of the:
   (i) *communication protocol*;
   (ii) *LAN driver*.
10. Outline the operation of the following network access protocols:
    (i)   *empty slot*;
    (ii) *token passing*;
    (iii) *CSMA/CA*.
11. A major benefit of a network is its facilities for *resource sharing*. Identify the particular resources which can be shared and the benefits such sharing brings for an organisation and its users.
12. Distinguish between a *client-server* and *peer-to-peer* network operating system.

Chapter 34

The Internet

The Internet is a world-wide network composed of thousands of smaller regional networks scattered throughout the globe. A common set of communication protocols enables every computer connected to the Internet to interchange information with every other computer so connected. Every day it connects millions of users in dozens of countries. Over the last 25 years, the Internet has grown to include government and educational institutions, and, more recently, commercial organisations that trade over the Internet.

No single person or organisation owns the Internet. There are companies which help manage different parts of the networks which tie everything together, but there is no single governing body which controls what happens on the Internet. The networks within different countries are funded and managed locally according to local policies.The Internet began in early 1969 under the experimental project ARPAnet. ARPA (Advanced Research Projects Agency, later known as the Defence Advanced Research Projects Agency) wanted to demonstrate the feasibility of building computer networks over a wide area such that the loss of a number of hosts on that network did not disrupt it. So ARPA initially interconnected four computers and linked them with Internet Protocol (IP), and the Internet grew from there. In the 70s and 80s US universities began to link with DARPAnet so that it could be used for academic research and in 1991 the U.S. government lifted its ban on commercial use of the Internet. The considerable business opportunities provided by the Internet ensure that it will continue to grow.

Today the Internet is a huge collection of different, intercommunicating networks funded by commercial, government and educational organisations. It has developed to handle larger volumes of data, software has become more powerful and user-friendly, and the types of services available have grown. The Internet now links more than 150 countries. All types of computers make up the hardware connected on the Internet. They vary from PCs, Macintoshes and UNIX workstations to minicomputers, mainframes and supercomputers. Anyone who wants to have access to the enormous amount of information available regionally or around the world can use the Internet. They can access electronic libraries, receive periodicals, exchange ideas, read the news, post questions with newsgroups, examine the weather (from reports or satellite photos), obtain the latest stock market prices and currency exchange rates, and access public government information on trade, laws, research and other subjects. It is likely that in the very near future, every school will be connected to the Internet, an Internet connection in your house will be no more unusual than a telephone line and, if you run a business, the Internet will be a vital tool (see E-commerce in Chapter 27, Data handling systems).

Connecting to the Internet

Figure 34.2 shows a PC connected to the Internet via a remote service provider which is itself a LAN (Local Area Network). The PC connects to the service provider using a modem and the telephone system. The service provider is directly connected to the Internet by means of a *router,* a computer which provides the link to special data transmission lines required to access the Internet. A large organisation might have its own direct link to the Internet, but many private users rely on commercial service providers for the connection, for which they must pay a subscription. Some service providers do not charge a subscription but generate revenue from advertising and a percentage of telephone call charges received from subscribers who take advantage of the telephone help lines they run for their clients.

Figure 34.2. *PC connected to a server for access to the Internet*

Uses of the Internet

The Internet is essentially a tool for transferring information between computers. This can be achieved in numerous ways and for various purposes. For example, *E-mail* is a convenient, quick and cheap alternative to the postal system for business and personal correspondence; *File Transfer Protocol (FTP)* allows large amounts of information to be transferred between two computers very conveniently; *Usenet,* the world-wide collection of interest groups, or *Newsgroups*, allows groups of people with similar interests to exchange views and information. Another important use of the Internet is the remote control of computer systems via *Telnet*. The *World-Wide Web* provides a uniform means of accessing and transferring information in the form of hypermedia documents. Accessing these documents does not require any particular machine or operating system. These and other Internet services are discussed in the following sections. A rapidly expanding application of the Internet is e-commerce, or on-line trading, between businesses and between businesses and consumers; this topic is examined at the end of this chapter. Note that programs used on the Internet can be classified as being either *server* or *client*. Server programs operate at Internet sites where the particular Internet service being used is provided; the program which is used to access a site, on a home PC for example, is the client program. For instance, a Web server at a Web site processes requests made by client programs called Web *browsers*.

The World-Wide Web

Abbreviated to the Web and WWW, this is the fastest growing Internet service. Though the World-Wide Web is mostly used on the Internet, the two terms do not mean the same thing. The Web refers to a world-wide collection of knowledge, while the Internet refers to the physical side of the global network, an enormous collection of cables and computers. The World-Wide Web uses the Internet for the transmission of hypermedia documents between computer users connected to the Internet. As with the Internet, nobody actually owns the World-Wide Web. People are responsible for the documents they author and make available publicly on the Web.

Via the Internet, hundreds of thousands of people around the world are making information available from their homes, schools, colleges and workplaces. The aim of WWW is to make all on-line knowledge part of one interconnected web of documents and services.

The World-Wide Web began in March 1989, when Tim Berners-Lee of the European Particle Physics Laboratory (known as CERN, a collective of European high-energy physics researchers) proposed the project as a means of distributing research results and ideas effectively throughout the organisation. The initial project proposal outlined a simple system of using networked hypertext to transmit to members of the high-energy physics community. By the end of 1990, the first piece of Web software had been introduced on a NeXT machine. It had the capability to view and transmit hypertext documents to other people on the Internet, and came with the capability to edit hypertext documents on the screen. Since then many people throughout the world have contributed their time writing Web software and documents, or telling others about the Web.

The World-Wide Web is officially described as a wide-area hypermedia information retrieval initiative aiming to give universal access to a large universe of documents. What the World-Wide Web (WWW, W3) project has done is provide users on computer networks with a consistent means to access a variety of media in a simplified fashion. With the aid of a popular software interface to the Web, called a *browser* (described later), the WWW has changed the way people view and create information. The first true global hypermedia network, it is revolutionising many elements of society, including commerce, politics, and literature.

Hypertext and hypermedia

The operation of the Web relies mainly on *hypertext* as its means of interacting with users. Hypertext is basically the same as ordinary text - it can be stored, read, searched, or edited -with an important exception: hypertext contains links to other places within the same document or to other documents. A Web browser indicates text links by the use of colour or by underlining. For example, Figure 34.3 shows part of a document called Writing Java Programs which contains three underlying links to other documents, the second one being The Anatomy of a Java Application.

Figure 34.3. *Three linked hypermedia documents*

This latter document in turn contains a link to a third document called The Hello World Applet. The first document would be retrieved from the WWW using a browser and the user, by pointing and clicking with a mouse on a link, will cause the browser to retrieve the appropriate document automatically, no matter where it is located.

Hypermedia is hypertext with a difference - hypermedia documents contain links not only to other pieces of text, but also to other forms of media, namely sounds, images, and movies. Images themselves can be selected to link to sounds or documents. Hypermedia simply combines hypertext and multimedia.

Figure 34.4 shows a browser displaying a hypermedia document with three buttons which, when clicked with a mouse, would demonstrate sound, graphics and video files.

Figure 34.4. *A hypermedia document being displayed by a Netscape browser*

The appearance of a hypermedia document when it is displayed by a browser is determined partly by the browser which provides a certain amount of control over such things as text fonts and colours, but mainly by the language used to encode the document. This language is *Hyper-Text Mark-up Language* (HTML). HTML is described in more detail in a later section of this chapter.

Web browsers

These are graphical interface client programs to help users to navigate through the Web, to transmit and to receive information from other users or information providers. By using a browser, the user does not have to know the format and location of the information: he or she simply jumps from site to site by clicking on hypertext links. Examples of commercially available browsers are Netscape's *Navigator*, Microsoft's *Explorer* (Figure 34.5)

Although there are many different ways to represent a document on the screen, it is often called a *page*. Usually, those responsible for creating a given collection of interrelated documents also create a special document which is intended to be viewed first - one that contains introductory information and/or a master menu of documents within that collection. This type of document is called a *home page* and is generally associated with a particular site, person, or named collection. The example document has underlined hypertext phrases. These phrases are hyperlinks (or links) - typically, clicking on one of them with a mouse will cause another document to appear on the screen, which may hold more images and hyperlinks to other places. There is no single way to represent text which is linked to other things - some browsers underline, others use special colours, and many give the user a variety of options. Images which are part of the document and are displayed within the page are called *inline images*.

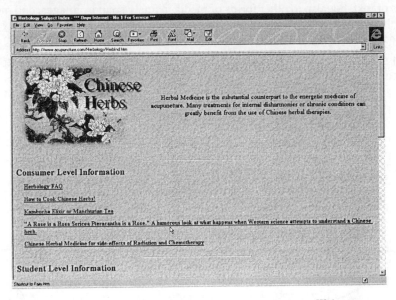

Figure 34.5. *Microsoft's Explorer browser displaying a Web page*

There is usually a toolbar at the top or bottom of the screen. This contains buttons which perform frequently used operations. For example, a set of navigation buttons is provided because a user might go to many different pages by selecting links in hypertext and there needs to be some method of retracing one's steps and reviewing the documents that have been explored.

How the Web works

Web software is designed around a distributed client-server architecture. A Web client (called a Web browser if it is intended for interactive use) is a program which can send requests for documents to any Web server. A Web server is a program which, upon receipt of a request, sends the document requested (or an error message if appropriate) back to the requesting client.

Using a distributed architecture means that a client program may be running on a completely separate machine from that of the server, possibly in another room or even in another country. Because the task of document storage is left to the server and the task of document presentation is left to the client, each program can concentrate on those duties and progress independently of each other. Since servers usually operate only when documents are requested, they put a minimal amount of workload on the computers on which they run. Here is an example of how the process works:

1.   Running a Web client program, such as a browser, the user selects a hyperlink in a piece of hypertext connecting to another document - Java Programming for example.

2.   The Web client uses the address associated with that hyperlink to connect to the

Web server at a specified network address and asks for the document associated with Java Programming.

3. The server responds by sending the text and any other media within that text (pictures, sounds, or video clips) to the client, which the client then renders for presentation on the user's screen.

The World-Wide Web is composed of thousands of these virtual transactions taking place per hour throughout the world, creating a web of information flow. Web servers are now beginning to include encryption and client authentication abilities, allowing them to send and receive secure data and be more selective as to which clients receive information. This allows freer communications among Web users and ensures that sensitive data is kept private. In the near future, it will be harder to compromise the security of commercial servers and educational servers which want to keep information local.

The language which Web clients and servers use to communicate with each other is called the *HyperText Transfer Protocol* (HTTP). All Web clients and servers must be able to 'speak' HTTP in order to send and receive hypermedia documents. For this reason, Web servers are often called HTTP servers.

HTML - The Hypertext Markup Language

The standard language the Web uses for creating and recognising hypermedia documents is the Hypertext Mark-up Language (HTML). An important characteristic of HTML is its ease of use. Web documents are typically written in HTML and are usually named with the suffix *.html* or *.htm*. HTML documents are nothing more than standard 7-bit ASCII files with formatting codes which contain information about layout (text styles, document titles, paragraphs, lists) and hyperlinks. One of the major attractions of using HTML is that every WWW browser can 'understand' it, no matter what machine the browser is being run on. This means that Web page developers do not need to worry about producing different versions for different computer platforms. HTML is discussed in more detail in Chapter 35 Introduction to HTML.

Uniform Resource Locators

The World-Wide Web uses what are called Uniform Resource Locators (URLs) to represent hypermedia links and links to network services within HTML documents. It is possible to represent nearly any file or service on the Internet with a URL. The first part of the URL (before the two slashes) specifies the method of access. The second is typically the address of the computer which the data or service is located on. Further parts may specify the names of files, the port to connect to, or the text to search for in a database. A URL is always a single unbroken line with no spaces.

Sites which run World-Wide Web servers are typically named with a "www" at the beginning of the network address.

Here are some examples of URLs:

```
http://www.nc.edu/nw/book.html
```

Connects to an HTTP server and retrieves an HTML document called 'book.html' in a directory called 'nw'

```
file://www.nc.edu/sound.au
```

Retrieves a sound file called 'sound.au' and plays it.

```
file://www.abc.com/picture.gif
```

Retrieves a picture and displays it, either in a separate program or within a hypermedia document.

    file://www.bcd.org/dd/

Displays the contents of directory 'dd'.

    ftp://www.wer.uk.co/pub/file.txt

Opens an FTP connection to www.uk.co and retrieves a text file.

    gopher://www.hcc.hawaii.edu

Connects to the Gopher at www.hcc.hawaii.edu.

    telnet://www.nc.edu:1234

Telnets to www.nc.edu at port 1234.

    news:alt.hypertext

Reads the latest Usenet news by connecting to a news host and returns the articles in the "alt.hypertext" newsgroup in hypermedia format.

Most Web browsers allow the user to specify a URL and connect to that document or service. When selecting hypertext in an HTML document, the user is actually sending a request to open a URL. In this way, hyperlinks can be made not only to other texts and media, but also to other network services.

Intranets and Extranets

An intranet is a private Internet which uses Internet software and the TCP/IP protocols. Its appearance is that of the Web and the familiar browser is its user interface. 'Out of the box' Web servers provide a convenient and relatively cheap method of developing internal network requirements and many organisations have built intranets as part of their overall Internet strategy. Employees are usually familiar with the Web and require little training to access the resources they need on the company intranet.

Web tools, such as HTML editors, are relatively cheap and application development only becomes expensive when large and complex databases are needed, as in the case of an on-line store's product database.

An intranet may be developed on private corporate LANs or WANs but organisations frequently wish to provide appropriate and limited access to clients and suppliers and develop an outward facing extension for those purposes.

Exercises

1. Distinguish between the *Internet* and the *World Wide Web*.
2. (i) What is the purpose of a *browser*?
   (ii) Give two examples of the use of *hyperlinks*.
   (iii) Distinguish between *hypertext* and *hypermedia*.
   (iv) Distinguish between and *Intranet* and and *Extranet*.
3. Give a well-known example of a *URL* (Uniform Resource Locator).

Chapter 35

Introduction to HTML

Hypertext Markup Language (HTML) is a *page description language* for specifying the layout and appearance of a Web page. When a browser retrieves an HTML document, it uses this specification to display the Web page in the required form. In terms of displaying information contained in an HTML file, a browser performs much the same function as a wordprocessor which uses its own form of page description language to display a page of text containing a variety of styles, fonts and other forms of formatting. As such, web pages designed using HTML exclusively simply allow a browser to present information comprising some combination of text, images, video and sound.

This chapter presents the basic information required for the creation of simple HTML documents. It is not intended to be a comprehensive HTML reference text - that would require a complete book to itself - but as a starting point for the creation of web pages. Detailed information on HTML, style sheets and other related subjects can be found at the World Wide Web Consortium site at www.w3.org.

By working through this chapter and trying the examples you will become familiar with enough HTML syntax to be able to create your own basic web pages.

Note that all of the screenshots of web pages were created using of Microsoft's Internet Explorer 5; other versions of Internet Explorer or other browsers may render web pages differently to some degree.

An HTML editor such as Allaire's "Homesite" is ideal for experimenting with HTML. There are many versions of this type of editor and they usually provide powerful facilities for creating and editing HTML and they allow you to view the resulting web page immediately. However, since HTML documents are simply text documents, the minimum software you need to try the examples in this chapter is a a word processor, such as Word for Windows or a simple text editor such as Notepad, and a recent Web browser such as Internet Explorer 5. Create the HTML document in the word processor and save it as a .htm document. Then load the document into the browser using File|Open on the menu bar to view it as a web page.

HTML tags

An HTML document consists of nested *tags*. A tag starts with `<tagname>` and ends with `</tagname>`, with the data that the tag controls being placed between the two. For instance, the level 1 heading tag has the form

     `<H1>`Heading`</H1>`

This tag, often used for the main title of a web page, would cause the word 'Heading' to be displayed in a large font.

Most tags have *attributes* that change the effect they have on the information included within them. These attributes vary according considerably. For example, whereas some attributes of the IMAGE tag specify the location and size of the image to be displayed, the BODY tag includes attributes which affect the background colour and the left and right margins of the complete web page.

A typical HTML document looks something like that shown in Listing 35.1:

Listing 35.1

```
<HTML>
<HEAD>
        <TITLE>A basic HTML document</TITLE>
</HEAD>

<BODY>

{Information to be displayed}

</BODY>
</HTML>
```

There are four major tags in this document:

`<HTML>...</HTML>`. This is the single most important tag to remember when creating a web page. It identifies the document as containing HTML and it encloses all other tags and web page information in the document.

`<HEAD>...</HEAD>`. This tag contains additional information about your web page and is used in conjunction with other tags appearing within it. These include the TITLE tag described next.

`<TITLE>...</TITLE>`. This tag specifies the title of the web page and must appear in the HEAD tag described above. It is used by browsers for their title bars and search engines may also use it.

`<BODY>...</BODY>`. This tag contains the actual contents of the the HTML document that will be displayed by the browser. It also has a number of attributes that affect the appearance of web pages.

In the next sections we will introduce a range of some of the most generally useful tags with examples of their uses. The examples will progressively develop a small web site comprising a number of linked pages.

Heading and paragraph text <h1>, <h2>, <p>

Listing 35.2 illustrates the use of headings and paragraph tags.

The <h1>...</h1>, <h2>...</h2>, <h3>...</h3> etc tags apply predefined styles to the enclosed text. In the example, the title of the web page, "Aikido - the Way of Harmony", is enclosed in a heading 1 tag and the subtitle "What is Aikido" is enclosed by a heading 2 tag.

The main text is enclosed by <p>...</p> paragraph tags which cause the enclosed text to start on a new line. The HTML document displayed by a browser is shown in Figure 35.2.

Listing 35.2

```
<HTML>
<HEAD>
         <TITLE>AIKIDO</TITLE>
</HEAD>
<BODY>
<h1>AIKIDO - the Way of Harmony</h1>
<h2>What is Aikido?</h1>
<p>A martial art designed solely for self-defence, traditional Aikido is
essentially non-violent and non-competitive.</p>
<p>Aikido is based on full and natural body movement, exercising practi-
cally every limb and joint of the body. Flexibility, muscle tone, stamina
and co-ordination are all developed, and consequently it is an excellent
way of restoring and preserving a healthy body.</p>
<p>Aikido classes often combine practical and effective self-defence
techniques with other disciplines for health and inner vitality. The re-
sult is a form of physical training that educates your body and makes it
stronger and healthier,  teaches you
how to remain relaxed and in control
when under stress, and shows you how
to defend yourself effectively using
as little violence as possible.</p>

</BODY>
</HTML>
```

Bold face and Italics < *b* >, < *i* >

The following lines added to the end of Listing 35.1 (before </BODY>) illustrate the use of the <b> tag to make text appear bold.

The bold face, <b>...<b> tag, make the words "Morihei Ueshiba" appear emphasised as shown on the right.

Italics are applied in the same way using the italics tag, <i>...</i>:

AIKIDO - the Way of Harmony

What is Aikido?

A martial art designed solely for *self-defence*, traditional Aikido is essentially non-violent and non-competitive.

Aikido is based on full and natural body movement, exercising practically every limb and joint of the body. Flexibility, muscle tone, stamina and co-ordination are all developed, and consequently it is an excellent way of restoring and preserving a healthy body.

Aikido classes often combine practical and effective self-defence techniques with other disciplines for health and inner vitality. The result is a form of physical training which educates your body and makes it stronger and healthier, teaches you how to remain relaxed and in control when under stress, and trains you to defend yourself effectively using as little violence as possible.

Figure 35.2. *Listing 35.2 displayed by browser*

```
<h2>Morihei Ueshiba - the Founder of Aikido</H2>
<p>Aikido was created by <b>Morihei Ueshiba</b>, born in 1883 in Ja-
pan. He wanted Aikido to be a basis for both physical and spiritual
development.</p>
```

Bold face tag

The <i> tag causes the enclosed text to appear in italics. Notice the <br> tag that inserts a blank line between the two sentences.

Morihei Ueshiba - the Founder of Aikido

Aikido was created by **Morihei Ueshiba**, born in 1883 in Japan. He wanted Aikido to be a basis for both physical and spiritual development.

Lists < ul >, < ol >, < li >

To create a bulleted list, put <li> at the beginning of each bullet point and enclose the set of bullet points in <ul>...</ul>, the unordered list tag as shown in the next HTML code fragment.

```
<p>
<i>"I want considerate people to listen to the voice of Aikido.<br>
    It is not for correcting others; it is for correcting your own
    mind".</i>
</p>
```

italics tag

```
<h2>Benefits of Aikido</h2>
<p>Some of the benefits of practising Aikido are listed below:
<ul>
  <li>Provides complete defence against physical attack.
  <li>Improves stamina, speed of reaction, flexibility, fitness and
      health.
  <li>Calms the mind and increases confidence.
  <li>Promotes mental, emotional and physical stability.
  <li>Promotes a more relaxed attitude, being at ease with oneself and
      others.
</ul>
```

Unordered list tags

The Example HTML document to date is shown in Figure 35.3.

To create a numbered list, use <ol>...</ol> instead of <ul>...</ul>. The <li> items are automatically numbered.

Style Sheets < LINK >, < STYLE >

Though Figure 35.2 looks OK, we could greatly improve its appearance by changing the default attributes of certain tags. For example, we could change the colour of the text or use a different font or change the font size. There are many ways to achieve this; here we describe the use of an external style sheet linked by the <LINK> tag in the Head of the HTML document.

AIKIDO - the Way of Harmony

What is Aikido?

A martial art designed solely for self-defence, traditional Aikido is essentially non-violent and non-competitive.

Aikido is based on full and natural body movement, exercising practically every limb and joint of the body. Flexibility, muscle tone, stamina and co-ordination are all developed, and consequently it is an excellent way of restoring and preserving a healthy body.

Aikido classes often combine practical and effective self-defence techniques with other disciplines for health and inner vitality. The result is a form of physical training which educates your body and makes it stronger and healthier, teaches you how to remain relaxed and in control when under stress, and trains you to defend yourself effectively using as little violence as possible.

Morihei Ueshiba - the Founder of Aikido

Aikido was created by **Morihei Ueshiba**, born in 1883 in Japan. He wanted Aikido to be a basis for both physical and spiritual development.

That he meant Aikido to be much more than a method of self-defence is conveyed in his words:

"I want considerate people to listen to the voice of Aikido. It is not for correcting others; it is for correcting your own mind".

Benefits of Aikido

Some of the benefits of practising Aikido are listed below:

- Provides complete defence against physical attack.
- Improves stamina, speed of reaction, flexibility, fitness and health.
- Calms the mind and increases confidence.
- Promotes mental, emotional and physical stability.
- Promotes a more relaxed attitude, being at ease with oneself and others.

Figure 35.3. *The web page to date.*

The LINK tag shown on the right tells the browser to load the style sheet called "HTMLBasics.css" before displaying the web page.

The style sheet is the text file shown in the next HTML code fragment.

```
<HTML>
<HEAD>
 <TITLE>AIKIDO</TITLE>
 <LINK REL=STYLESHEET HREF=HTMLBasics.css
  TYPE=text/css>
</HEAD>

<BODY>
<h1>AIKIDO - the Way of Harmony</h1>
```

Style sheet tag

```
<STYLE>
{};
h1 {font-family:Arial, sans-serif; font-size:13pt;
    text-align:center;color:Red}
h2 {font-family:Arial, sans-serif; font-size:11pt; color:Red}
p  {font-family:Arial, sans-serif; font-size:10pt;
    text-align:justify; margin-left:0.5in; margin-right:0.5in}
li {font-family:Arial, sans-serif; font-size:9pt;
    margin-left:0.3in}
i  {font-family:Arial, sans-serif; font-size:9pt}

</STYLE>
```

Style sheet

The <STYLE>...</STYLE> tag encloses all of the style definitions for the text formatting tags used in the above style sheet. Each item inside the curly brackets defines an attribute of the relevant tag. The attribute name and value are separated by a colon; the different attributes are separated by a semi-colon. The effect of the style sheet is shown in Figure 35.4.

AIKIDO - the Way of Harmony

What Is Aikido?

A martial art designed solely for self-defence, traditional Aikido is essentially non-violent and non-competitive.

Aikido is based on full and natural body movement, exercising practically every limb and joint of the body. Flexibility, muscle tone, stamina and co-ordination are all developed, and consequently it is an excellent way of restoring and preserving a healthy body.

Aikido classes often combine practical and effective self-defence techniques with other disciplines for health and inner vitality. The result is a form of physical training which educates your body and makes it stronger and healthier, teaches you how to remain relaxed and in control when under stress, and trains you to defend yourself effectively using as little violence as possible.

Morihei Ueshiba - the Founder of Aikido

Aikido was created by **Morihei Ueshiba**, born in 1883 in Japan. He wanted Aikido to be a basis for both physical and spiritual development. That he meant Aikido to be much more than a method of self-defence is conveyed in his words:

"I want considerate people to listen to the voice of Aikido.
It is not for correcting others; it is for correcting your own mind."

Benefits of Aikido

Some of the benefits of practising Aikido are listed below:

- Provides complete defense against physical attack
- Improves stamina, speed of reaction, flexibility, fitness and health
- Calms the mind and increases confidence
- Promotes mental, emotional and physical stability
- Promotes a more relaxed attitude, being at ease with oneself and others

Figure 35.4. *Effect of using the style sheet.*

Notice how the character of the web page has completely changed. Furthermore, the same style sheet could be used for other web pages; this provides a very convenient method of making the separate pages of a web site have a consistent look, and it also means that to change the appearance of the whole web site you need only change the style sheet.

The tag attributes used in the style sheet are described in the following section along with a number of other useful attributes that can be used.

Style sheet tag attributes

Many of the attributes described here can be defined in a number of different ways.

color: You can use this attribute to set the colour of displayed text. You can used a named colour such as red, black, green, blue etc, or specify the colour as a six-digit hexadecimal value such as #ff33cc. The first two digits - in this example ff - represent the red component of the colour, the next two digits represent the green component and the final two digits represent the blue component.

font-family: This defines a prioritised list of fonts to be used by the tag. You can name a group of fonts for the browser to use. The first font named will be used if it is on the web page visitor's local system; otherwise the next font named is used, and so on. You can also specify a generic family which is a more general category of font. The browser will attempt to find any font in this generic family. Generic font families include:

- ❏ sans-serif (eg Arial)
- ❏ serif (eg Times New Roman)
- ❏ monospace (eg Courier)
- ❏ fantasy (eg Ransom)
- ❏ cursive (eg Comic sans)

font-size: This enables you to set the size of a font for an HTML element in a number of different ways. In our example we have used point size, eg font-size:10pt, to specify the size.

font-style: You can use this attribute to apply italics to a font, eg font-style: italic.

font-weight: You can use this attribute to apply bold to a font, eg font-weight: bold.

line-height: You can use this attribute to adjust the vertical space occupied by a line of text. For example, if your font size is 10pt, you could set line-height to 14pt which allows a 2pt space above and below the line.

margin-left, **margin-right**: You can use these attributes to set the left and right margins of text. In our example we used margin-left:0.5in and `margin-right:0.5in` which set the left and right text margins to half an inch.

text-align: You can use this attribute to left align, right align or fully justify a block of text: text-align:left, text-align:right, text-align:justify.

Images < img >

The <img> tag allows you to embed graphical content in your web pages. Although we consider only static images here, the <img> tag can also be used for video clips and VRML (virtual Reality Modelling Language) files.

Listing 35.3 places a map image to the right of a block of text.

The screenshot in Figure 35.5 shows Listing 35.3 displayed by a browser.

Some of the attributes of the <img> tag, including those used in the example above, are described below.

align: specifies the alignment of the graphic with respect to text. Four of the values for this attribute are **top** - the image appears above the text; **bottom** - the image appears below the text; **left** - the image is to the left of the text; **right** - the image is to the right of the text.

alt: allows you to provide a text message that appears when the mouse is over an image.

border: allows you to specify the thickness in pixels of a frame around the image.

Listing 35.3

```
<HTML>
<HEAD>
      <TITLE>Map</TITLE>
        <LINK REL=STYLESHEET HREF=HTMLBasics.css TYPE=text/css>
</HEAD>

<BODY>

<h1>How to find us</h1>
<p>
<img src="images/map.gif" align=right height=300 width=200 hspace=20
 border=1>
Leave the A1 for the A689 at junction 60. Follow the A689 to Bishop
Auckland. After three miles there is a r/bout at the Eden Arms Hotel. Con-
tinue towards Bishop Auckland on the A689. After another three miles
there is another r/bout. Take the 3rd exit to Coundon and Leeholme. After
about 200 yds turn right. On the left are terraced houses (Osborne ter-
race) opposite allotments.  Go about 300 yds up the bank. The Koteikan
Aikido Centre is on the left, enclosed in a wooden fence and opposite a
bungalow.
</p>
</BODY>
</HTML>
```

height: used with the **width** attribute to specify the dimensions in pixels of the image to be displayed. Even if the image is not the size specified, the browser stretches or contracts the image to fit the dimensions specified.

src: used to specify the location of the image file. Example 2 displays the graphics file named "map.gif", located in the folder, "images". Two graphics file formats are commonly used for web page images - *gif* and *jpg*. Generally speaking, jpg files are used for photographic quality images; gifs are used when a limited palette of colours (256) is sufficient to display the graphic.

hspace: specifies the horizontal space between the left and right borders of the image and any text around it.

How to find us

Leave the A1 for the A689 at junction 61. Follow the A689 to Bishop Auckland. After three miles there is a r/bout at the Eden Arms Hotel. Continue towards Bishop Auckland on the A689. After another three miles there is another r/bout. Take the 3rd exit to Coundon and Leeholme. After about 200 yds turn right. On the left are terraced houses (Osborne terrace) opposite allotments. Go about 300 yds up the bank. The Koteikan Aikido Centre is on the left, enclosed in a wooden fence and opposite a bungalow.

Figure 35.5. *Listing 35.3 displayed*

vspace: specifies the horizontal space between the top and bottom borders of the image and any text around it.

width: used with the **height** attribute to specify the dimensions in pixels of the image to be displayed. Even if the image is not the size specified, the browser stretches or contracts the image to fit the dimensions specified.

The Class attribute for tags

The Class attribute allows you to specify alternative forms of tags in style sheets. For example, as shown below, you can define alternative forms of the <p> tag by adding some lines to the style sheet we created earlier:

```
<STYLE>
{};
h1 {font-family:arial, sans-serif;
    font-size:13pt; text-align:center;color:Red}
h2 {font-family:arial,sans-serif;
    font-size:11pt;color:Red;}
p  {font-family:arial,sans-serif;font-size:10pt;
    text-align:justify;margin-left:0.5in;
    margin-right:0.5in}
p.tblHead{margin-left:0in;margin-right:0in;
         font-weight:bold}
p.tblBody {margin-left:0in; margin-right:0in;}
li{font-family:arial,sans-serif; font-size:9pt;
    margin-left:0.3in}
i {font-family:arial, sans-serif; font-size:9pt;}
</STYLE>
```

style sheet class attribute for tags

The first additional style sheet definition, p.tblHead, defines a variation of the <p> tag in which the left and right margins are set to zero and the font-weight attribute is set to bold. These settings override the previous values for the <p> tag attributes; the other attributes of the <p> tag remain the same. The second additional definition simply resets the left and right margins. To apply these new values, the <p> tag needs to include the class attribute: <p class = tblHead> or <p class = tblBody>.

This style sheet feature provides the means to add unlimited combinations of text formatting attributes to HTML pages. We illustrate the use of the class attribute in the next section which deals with HTML tables.

Tables < table >, < tr >, < td >

Tables are used very frequently for web pages. They provide a good degree of control over the placement of HTML elements. In Listing 35.4, we use a table to display a course calendar in two columns:

Listing 35.4

```
<HTML>
<HEAD>
        <TITLE>Courses</TITLE>
        <LINK REL=STYLESHEET HREF=HTMLBasics.css TYPE=text/css>
</HEAD>
<BODY>
<h1>KAA Course Calendar - 2001</h1>
<table width=80% align=center border=10>
<tr bgcolor=DarkGray>         <td><p class=tblHead>Month</p></td>
     <td><p class=tblHead>Details</p></td></tr>
     <tr><td><p class=tblBody>January</p></td>
     <td><p class=tblBody>8th and 9th, Birkenhead</p></td></tr>
     <tr><td><p class=tblBody>March</p></td>
     <td><p class=tblBody>11th - 13th, Fort William</p></td></tr>
     <tr><td><p class=tblBody>April</p></td>
     <td><p  class=tblBody>Easter  School:11th  -  16th,  Birken-
head</p></td></tr>
     <tr><td><p class=tblBody>June</p></td>
     <td><p class=tblBody>17th and 18th, Holland</p></td></tr>
     <tr><td><p class=tblBody>August</p></td>
     <td><p  class=tblBody>Summer  school:  5th  -  11th,  Birken-
head</p></td></tr>
     <tr>    <td><p class=tblBody>November</p></td>
     <td><p class=tblBody>10th - 12th, Durham</p></td></tr>
</table>
</BODY>
</HTML>
```

The complete table is enclosed by the <table>...</table> tag. Within this tag are <tr>...</tr> (table row) tags for each row in the table, and within each of these are two <td>...</td> (table data) tags for the two columns in each row. The information to be displayed in a table is always enclosed by <td>...</td> tags. Figure 35.6 shows the HTML code as displayed by the browser.

KAA Course Calendar - 2001

Month	Details
January	8th and 9th, Birkenhead
March	11th - 13th, Fort William
April	Easter School:11th - 16th, Birkenhead
June	17th and 18th, Holland
August	Summer school: 5th - 11th, Birkenhead
November	10th - 12th, Durham

Figure 35.6. *Table displayed by browser*

Before we go on to discuss table tag attributes, notice that we have used the class attribute for the <p> tags as described in the previous section. The table headings have the class name tblHead and the rest of the table elements have the class name tblBody. You can see how the class styles alter the characteristics of the previously defined <p> tag.

< table >

The <table> tag is used to affect the appearance of the complete table. Some of its eighteen or so attributes are described below.

align: the align attribute allows you to position a table horizontally on the page. Values used with align include:

❏ left - table is positioned at the left margin of the page;

❏ center - table is centred , as in Listing 35.4;

❏ right - table is positioned at the right of the page.

bgcolor: sets the background colour of the cells in the table. Colours can be specified by name, eg Blue, or by hex value, e.g. #ffcc99.

border: allows you to set the width of the border around each cell in the table. Setting border=0 displays the table without a border. In Listing 35.4, the border is set at border=10.

height: sets the height of the table in pixels or as a percentage of the browser window. Used in conjunction with the width attribute, it can be used to specify the exact size of a table or its size relative to that of the browser window. In Listing 35.4, the width of the table has been set to 80% of the width of the browser window. This setting leaves a 10% left and right margin.

width: sets the width of the table in pixels or as a percentage of the browser window. Used in conjunction with the height attribute, it can be used to specify the exact size of a table or its size relative to that of the browser window.

< tr >

This tag specifies the appearance of a single row of a table. Its attributes include:

align:controls the horizontal alignment of text within the row cells. Values used with align are

❏ left - text is positioned at the left margin of the cells

❏ center - text is centred within the cells

❏ right - text is positioned at the right of the cells

❏ justify - text is justified to both left and right margins of the cells

bgcolor: sets the background colour of the cells in the row. Colours can be specified by name, eg Blue, or by hex value, eg #ffcc99.

< td >

This tag specifies the characteristics of individual cells in a table. Because cells defined by the <td> tag can also contain images, one or more tables are frequently used as the framework for complete web pages.

<td> attributes include:

align:controls the horizontal alignment of text within a cell. Values used with align are

❑ left - text is positioned at the left margin of the cell

❑ center - text is centred

❑ right - text is positioned at the right of the cell

❑ justify - text is justified to both left and right margins

bgcolor: sets the background colour of a cell. Colours can be specified by name, eg Blue, or by hex value, eg #ffcc99.

colspan and rowspan: specify that more than one column or row is to be spanned by the cell. In the table on the right, for cell 1 colspan=2, for cell 2 rowspan=2 and for cell 5 colspan=3.

cell 1	cell 2	
	cell 3	cell 4
cell5		

```
<table width="300" border="2">
<tr>
    <td rowspan="2">cell 1</td>
    <td colspan="2">cell 2</td>
</tr>
<tr>
    <td>cell 3</td>
    <td>cell 4</td>
</tr>
<tr>
    <td colspan="3">cell 5</td>
</tr>
</table>
```

colspan and rowspan tag attributes

The code that generated the table is shown below.

valign: controls the vertical alignment of cell text. It includes the values:

❑ top - cell text is aligned with the top of the cell

❑ middle - cell text is positioned in the middle

❑ bottom - cell text is aligned with the bottom

In the table on the right, cell 1 is top aligned, cell 2 is middle aligned and cell 3 is bottom aligned:

cell 1		
	cell 2	
		cell 3
cell 4	cell 5	cell 6

The HTML code is shown in the following HTML fragment..

```
<table border=1>
<tr>
    <td height=100 align="center" valign="top">cell 1</td>
    <td height=100 align="center" valign="middle">cell 2</td>
    <td height=100 align="center" valign="bottom">cell 3</td>
</tr>
<tr>
    <td>cell 4</td>
    <td>cell 5</td>
    <td>cell 6</td>
</tr>
</table>
```

table valign attribute

Hypertext links < a >

Hypertext links represent one of the most important concepts upon which the World Wide Web is based. They are often indicated by underlined text and by the mouse pointer changing to a hand when it is over a link. Clicking the link causes either a jump to another part of the document or a new document to replace the current one shown by the browser. The <a>, or *anchor*, tag is used to specify hypertext links to other parts of the same document, to other documents at the same web site and to documents that are located at other sites.

Listing 35.5 shows an HTML page that incorporates a variety of different types of links. Figure 35.7 shows the page displayed by a browser.

Linking to other parts of the same document

The name attribute of the <a> tag is used to identify particular locations in a web page. In Listing 35.5, the top of the page is identified by

```
<a name=top></a>
```

To establish a link to this part of the page we use an <a> tag such as

```
<a href=#top>Top of page</a>
```

The href attribute in this case indicates that a hypertext jump to location "top" is required if the text "Top of page" is clicked by the user. The # symbol indicates a reference to a position within a document. Further down the page in Listing 35.5 is a link to another part of the document:

```
<a href="#KAA">KAA</a>
```

This time clicking on the link causes a forward jump to

```
<a name=KAA></a>
```

Links to documents located at the same site

When the requirement is link to another document at the same site, the href attribute is given the value of the path and filename of the relevant document.

In Listing 35.5 there are two links to the document "aikido.htm". The first one is the text link

```
 <a href="aikido.htm" target="_self">Aikido</a>.
```

This causes "aikido.htm" to replace the page shown in the current browser window when the user clicks the word "Aikido". Because no filing system path is specified the location of the document is assumed to be the same as the current document being displayed by the browser.

If you want to link to a particular point on this new page, use the # option as described in the previous section. For example, you could use

```
<a href = "aikido.htm#founder" target=_self>The founder of Aikido</a>
```

to link to the location indicated by <a name-founder></a> in the target document.

The second link to this document is an image:

```
<a href="aikido.htm" target="_self">
<img src="images/aiki.jpg" align=right  border=0 alt="About Aikido">
</a>
```

"Aikido.htm" is loaded into the browser when the user clicks the source image referenced in the <img> tag.

Listing 35.5

```
<HTML>
<HEAD>
            <TITLE>Home page</TITLE>
            <LINK REL=STYLESHEET HREF= HTMLBasics.css TYPE=text/css>
</HEAD>

<BODY>
<a name=top></a>
<h1>Koteikan Aikido Centre</h1>
<p><i><center>24 Windsor Terrace, Leeholme, Bishop Auckland. Co.
Durham. DL14 8HZ</center></i>
<p> Originaly a methodist Chapel, the centre is located in the small
village of Leeholme, just a few miles from Bishop Auckland and
Spennymoor. In addition to regular classes in Aikido the centre
offers professional acupuncture treatment. There is a permanently
matted area for
<a href="aikido.htm" target="_self">Aikido</a>
and a separate treatment room for health therapies.
<p>The Koteikan Aikido Centre is affiliated to the
<a href="#KAA">KAA</a></p>
<p><b>Practice times:</b>
<a href="aikido.htm" target="_self">
<img src="images/aiki.jpg" align=right border=0 alt="About Aikido">
</a>
Monday 7-9pm, Wednesday 7-9pm, Sunday 10-12am</p>
<p><b>Enquiries:</b>Ring Nick Waites on (01388) 605710</p>
<p><b>Email:</b>
<a href="mailto:nick@infortex.com">nick@infortex.com</a>
</p>
<a name=KAA></a>
<h1>Komyokan Aikido Association</h1>
<p>Founded in 1999 by Terry Ezra, the KAA is dedicated to integrating
the profound philosophy of Aikido into daily practice.</p>
<p>Ezra Sensei feels that there is a need to make Aikido truly a Way
of Harmony, in both the physical and the spiritual sense.
Consequently, KAA practice is conducted in a spirit of honesty and
integrity, and attempts to make the deeper aspects of Aikido a day-
to-day reality. </p><p> Training follows a methodical system based on
sound principles in which relaxation and sensitivity are key
elements. </p>
<p>The KAA is open to everyone, regardless of age, gender and racial
or religious orientation.</p>
<p>Please click
<a href="http://www.aikido.co.uk" target="_blank">here</a>
to go to the KAA website
</p>
<p><a href="#top">Top of page</a></p>
</BODY>
</HTML>
```

Link to doc
at same site

Email

Link to doc
at different
site

Koteikan Aikido Centre

24 Windsor Terrace, Leeholme, Bishop Auckland. Co. Durham. DL14 8HZ

Originally a Methodist chapel, the centre is located in the small village of Leeholme, just a few miles from Bishop Auckland and Spennymoor. In addition to regular classes in Aikido the centre offers professional acupuncture treatment. There is a permanently matted practice hall for Aikido and a separate treatment room for health therapies.

The Koteikan Aikido Centre is affiliated to the KAA.

Practice times: _Monday 7-9pm, Wednesday 7-9pm, Sunday 10-12am

EnquiriesRing Nick Waites on (01388) 605710

Email: nick@infortex.com

Komyokan Aikido Association

Founded in 1999 by Terry Ezra, the KAA is dedicated to integrating the profound philosophy of Aikido into daily practice.

Ezra Sensei feels that there is a need to make Aikido truly a Way of Harmony, in both the spiritual and physical sense. Consequently, KAA practice is conducted in a spirit of honesty and integrity, and attempts to make the deeper aspects of Aikido a day-to-day reality.

Training follows a methodical system based on sound principles in which relaxation and sensitivity are key elements.

The KAA is open to everyone, regardless of age, gender and racial or religious orientation.

Please click here to go to the KAA website

Top of page

Figure 35.7. *Using hypertext links*

Links to documents located at other sites

When the target document of a link is located at a different site from the current document, the URL of the target document is provided as the value for the href attribute. In our example the link

```
<a href="http://www.aikido.co.uk" target="_blank">here</a>
```

links to the *index page* of the site with domain name www.aikido.co.uk when the word "here" is clicked by the user. The attribute target=_blank specifies that the index page of the www.aikido.co.uk site is to be shown in a new browser window rather than in the current window displaying the current document.

Note that the *index page* of a site is usually called "index.htm" or "index.html" and is by default the page that is automatically loaded into a browser when a site is visited.

Email links

Another use of a link is to provide the user with the facility to send an email. In Listing 35.5, the <a> link

```
<a href="mailto:nick@infortex.com">nick@infortex.com</a>
```

causes the browser to launch the default email software so that an email can be created and posted. Figure 35.8 shows an example of a user composing an email after having clicked the email link.

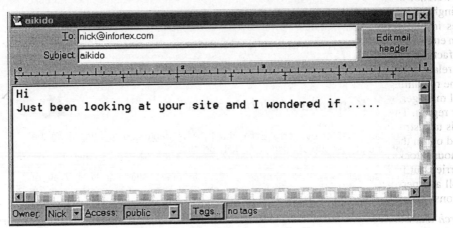

Figure 35.8. *Example of an email editor*

Assignments

6.1. Data communications

This assignment requires reference to the Pilcon Polymer Case Study, given below.

Pilcon Polymers

Pilcon Polymers is a manufacturer of plastic containers of all kinds. Its Head Office, factory and main warehouse are in Peterlee, County Durham, but it also has distribution warehouses in Leeds, Birmingham, Milan and Cologne also The company also has regional office and wholesale outlet facilities in Glasgow, Leeds, Belfast, Swansea and Birmingham. Across the whole organisation, Pilcon employ 450 people, of whom 350 are in administrative, marketing, sales or clerical roles. The manufacturing processes are highly automated, so the factory only employs 50 people, whose main tasks relate to machine minding and maintenance. 25 staff are employed in warehouse operations and the remaining 25 research, design and develop new products. The UK centres each have a regional manager, who is responsible for the marketing, wholesale and distribution operations in his or her region. The Milan and Cologne centres have a warehouse and distribution manager who responds to instructions from Head Office in Peterlee. Physical stock control operations need to be carried out in the Milan and Cologne warehouses, but the records of stocks held of the continental warehouse stocks issues and receipts are all held by Head Office. Marketing and sales operations are all carried out from the UK, so the Milan and Cologne centres do not employ staff in these roles. Payroll and personnel management are functions handled by the Peterlee Head Office. The main functions carried out in Peterlee are:

research and development (R&D); *product design and manufacture*; *product testing* and *quality control*; *sales* and *marketing*; *personnel*; *payroll*; *financial accounting* (sales, purchasing and so on); *stock control*; *sales order processing*.

The UK centres also take regional responsibility for these functions, except for R&D, product design and manufacture, product testing and quality control. Management information produced by these regional functions is regularly transmitted to Head Office, to allow assessment of regional efficiency and profitability, as well as a corporate view of performance to be obtained. Each month, the warehouses in Milan and Cologne need to transmit their orders to replenish stocks; these order may involve several hundred different stock items. Goods are transported by rail and road. There may also be a need for an emergency order to be transmitted (the goods can then be flown out). Peterlee also wish to send information to Milan and Cologne, but the communications do not need be interactive (both ways at the same time). Local area networks are installed in all the United Kingdom offices and are linked across communications networks.

The following Tasks concern the investigation of various aspects of data communications and networks, in the context of that case study. Present the information you gather, in the process of the following activities, in a word processed report.

Tasks

1. Use a suitable package to draw a block diagram showing the various data communications and network links between the regional and continental centres of the business. Include the title 'Pilcon Polymers – Communications' and a company logo of your own design.

2. Describe *simplex*, *half duplex* and duplex modes of communication and explain which modes are appropriate for the circumstances outlined in the case study.

3. State, with reasons, whether serial or parallel communications would be employed between the offices and warehouses of Pilcon Polymers.

4. Synchronous and asynchronous communications are also used in data communications systems. Explain the difference between these two forms and, by reference to the various needs of Pilcon Polymers, argue when each might be most appropriate.

5. Annotate the diagram prepared in Task 1, to illustrate your explanation of these technical terms. You should use vector drawing tools. Embed the image as an object within the report document.

6. The criteria of transmission speed and data integrity (uncorrupted - without error) are vital to the usefulness of data communications. With reference to Pilcon and using example circumstances, explain why this is so. Also explain the role of modems and protocol parameters (flow control, stop bits, parity and other error checking techniques) in achieving speed and integrity.

7. Apart from data transfer, Pilcon want to make use of various network services. These include: electronic mail; video and teleconferencing; file transfer; bulletin board services (BBSs); databases, electronic data interchange (EDI); integrated services digital network (ISDN). Briefly explain the function of each of these services. Identify those services, which you judge could be of use to Pilcon Polymers, and develop your explanations with example applications.

6.2. Networks and applications

Tasks

1. Use *vector* graphics drawing tools and bit map *clip art*, to produce a simple guide to network topologies. The guide should include text to annotate the graphics. The final product should fold into a multi-page, A5, booklet (short edge across the top) and include a title page.

2. This Task requires a team approach to research and report on computer networks. It also requires the *merging* of separate document files of a consistent format and the use of *presentational graphics* software to summarise main points in your investigation. A team could have four members, one being the team leader responsible for the co-ordination and integration of the work of individual team members. The terms of reference for the investigation are:

   types of networks, with examples. Also describe the features of each and organisational types for which they are appropriate;

   network *components* and *topologies*, together with examples of network products, their topologies and the *protocols* they support; network and PC magazines are a good source;

   benefits of the various types of network and the applications each has for particular organisations.

   The team could focus on a particular organisational type, such as an airline, a bank, DIY store, college and highlight the important role of the Internet and the services which provide such benefit for many organisations.

   The assignment should provide opportunities for practising a variety of resrach methods and sources, team discussions and the development of team building qualities.

6.3 HTML

This assignment is to create a small personal website consisting of at least two separate web pages. For example, you could have a Home Page that provides information about yourself and your interests and another page providing more information about one of those interests.

Your pages should contain at least one of each of the following elements:

A link to another page on your site
A link to a site at a different location
A table
An image link

Use a style sheet to format the text on your pages.

Index

C

P

T